D1200619

Richard A. Denholm
Robert G. Underhill
Mary P. Dolciani

EDITORIAL ADVISERS

Andrew M. Gleason

Albert E. Meder, Jr.

Elementary Algebra

New Edition

Part 1

HOUGHTON MIFFLIN COMPANY / BOSTON

Atlanta Dallas Geneva, Ill. Hopewell, N.J. Palo Alto Toronto

ABOUT THE AUTHORS

Richard A. Denholm, Supervisor, Office of Teacher Education and Lecturer, Department of Mathematics, University of California at Irvine. Dr. Denholm has also served as Director of Curriculum for grades K-12, Orange County, California, and prior to that was Coordinator of Mathematics and Physical Science Instruction. In addition to his extensive authorship experience in mathematics texts and professional journals, he has made active contributions to the fields of mathematics curriculum planning, teacher preparation, and criteria reference testing.

Robert G. Underhill, Associate Professor and Coordinator of Mathematics Education, Department of Curriculum and Instruction, University of Houston. Dr. Underhill has had extensive teaching experience in high school and university mathematics and teacher education. He has authored teacher-education books and audio-visual materials. In addition, he has contributed to professional journals and has been a speaker and presider at professional conferences.

Mary P. Dolciani, Professor of Mathematics, Hunter College, City University of New York. Dr. Dolciani has been a director and teacher in numerous National Science Foundation and New York State Education Department institutes for mathematics teachers. She is also Visiting Secondary School Lecturer for the Mathematical Association of America and a member of the United States Commission on Mathematical Instruction.

ABOUT THE EDITORIAL ADVISERS

Andrew M. Gleason, Hollis Professor of Mathematics and Natural Philosophy, Harvard University.

Albert E. Meder, Jr., Dean and Vice Provost and Professor of Mathematics, Emeritus, Rutgers, The State University of New Jersey.

Printed in the United States of America
ISBN: 0-395-24030-1

Contents

LIST OF SYMBOLS

Symbol	Meaning	Page
$=$	equals (is equal to)	5
$\{\ \}$	the set of	30
$\ldots$	and so on	30
$\emptyset$	the empty set	30
$^{-}2$	negative two	34
$^{+}2$	positive two	34
π	pi	40
$<$	is less than	41
$>$	is greater than	41
(a,b)	ordered pair	47
$a:b$	ratio of a to b	68
%	percent	74
$\leftrightarrow$	is the same as	78
$\leq$	is less than or equal to	143
$\geq$	is greater than or equal to	143
$f(x)$	the value of the function f for x	175
$\neq$	does not equal	221
-3	the opposite of three	240
$\stackrel{?}{=}$	does it equal?	243
$\lvert x \rvert$	absolute value of x	261
P(e)	probability of event e	288
a^n	a to the nth power	346
$\sim$	is similar to	404
Δ	triangle	404
$\overline{PQ}$	line segment PQ	405
$\angle$	angle	405

LIST OF METRIC SYMBOLS

m	meter
mm	millimeter
cm	centimeter
km	kilometer
g	gram
kg	kilogram
°C	degrees Celsius
m^2	square meter

ABOUT THE CHAPTER OPENERS

There are two photographs at the beginning of each chapter. These pictures show some of the changes in a career or process which have taken place in the past century. Many of these changes are the result of developments in mathematics and technology.

Left: Pilots of 1913-model airplane. This photo was taken just ten years after the Wright Brothers' flight.

Right: Pilot of modern jet.

1 Working with Integers

Numerical Expressions, Equations, Variables

1-1 *Numerical Expressions*

OBJECTIVE

Simplify expressions like $\frac{10 + 8}{9}$ and $5^2 - 10$.

A numerical expression may be very simple, like 15, or more complicated, like $\frac{10}{2 + 3}$. We may simplify an expression by doing the indicated operations.

EXAMPLE 1 Expression ► $\underbrace{10 + 6} + 3$

Add (twice). ► $16 \quad + 3 = \mathbf{19}$

EXAMPLE 2 Expression ► $\frac{27 - 7}{2}$

Subtract. Then divide. ► $\frac{20}{2} = \mathbf{10}$

EXAMPLE 3 Expression ► $14 - 3^2$

Square. Then subtract. ► $14 - 9 = \mathbf{5}$

EXAMPLE 4 Expression ► $\frac{2 + (4 \times 2)}{5}$

Multiply. ► $\frac{2 + 8}{5}$

Add. ► $\frac{10}{5}$

Divide. ► 2

Different expressions may name the same number. Each of these expressions names the number **3**.

EXAMPLE 5 $\frac{27}{5 + 4} = \frac{27}{9} = \mathbf{3}$ $\qquad \frac{3 \times 3 \times 3}{3^2} = \frac{27}{9} = \mathbf{3}$

$(10 \times 10) - 97 = 100 - 97 = \mathbf{3}$

Match to tell how to simplify.

1. $7 + 0$

2. $(5 \times 6) - 10$

3. $\frac{10}{2}$

4. $3^2 - 5$

5. $4 \times (3 + 6)$

A. Multiply 5 and 6. Subtract 10. The result is 20.

B. Square 3. Subtract 5. The result is 4.

C. Add 7 and 0. The result is 7.

D. Add 3 and 6. Multiply by 4. The result is 36.

E. Divide 10 by 2. The result is 5.

Tell how to simplify.

Sample: $\frac{3 + 7}{5}$ *What you say:* Add 3 and 7; the sum is 10. Divide 10 by 5. The simplified form is 2.

6. $4 + 8 + 7$	**7.** 4^2	**8.** $\frac{15}{5}$
9. $46 - 9$	**10.** 17×0	**11.** $\frac{32}{8}$
12. $48 \div 6$	**13.** 0×9	**14.** $\frac{23}{1}$

Written EXERCISES

Simplify.

A

1. $3 + (6 \times 7)$	**2.** $4 \times (8 + 2)$	**3.** $(4 \times 6) - 7$
4. $4 \times 2 \times 9$	**5.** 19×0	**6.** $25 - (2 \times 8)$
7. $100 \div 5$	**8.** 1×37	**9.** 5^2
10. $50 + 50 + 50$	**11.** $23 \div 1$	**12.** $3^2 + 1$
13. $\frac{45}{15}$	**14.** $67 \div 67$	**15.** $4 \times 4 \times 4$

B

16. $10^2 + 6$	**17.** $3^2 + 5^2$	**18.** $426 \div 18$
19. $\frac{14 + 11}{5}$	**20.** $\frac{50}{6 + 19}$	**21.** 1×7^2
22. $17 - 17$	**23.** $4 - \frac{6}{2}$	**24.** $\frac{48 + 12}{2^2 + 6}$

Complete to name the given number.

Sample: $5 \left\{ \begin{array}{l} 5 \times \underline{\ ?\ } \\ 10 \div \underline{\ ?\ } \\ 17 - \underline{\ ?\ } \end{array} \right.$ *Solution:* $5 \left\{ \begin{array}{l} 5 \times 1 \\ 10 \div 2 \\ 17 - 12 \end{array} \right.$

25. $40 \left\{ \begin{array}{l} 1 \times 5 \times \underline{\ ?\ } \\ 10 + \underline{\ ?\ } + 10 \\ 2 \times 4 \times \underline{\ ?\ } \end{array} \right.$

26. $64 \left\{ \begin{array}{l} 7^2 + \underline{\ ?\ } \\ 4 \times 4 \times \underline{\ ?\ } \\ 50 + \underline{\ ?\ } + 3^2 \end{array} \right.$

27. $18 \left\{ \begin{array}{l} 3 \times 3 \times \underline{\ ?\ } \\ 72 \div \underline{\ ?\ } \\ 30 - \underline{\ ?\ } \end{array} \right.$

28. $100 \left\{ \begin{array}{l} 10 \times \underline{\ ?\ } \\ \underline{\ ?\ } \div 1 \\ 5 \times 5 \times \underline{\ ?\ } \end{array} \right.$

29. $1 \left\{ \begin{array}{l} 15 \div \underline{\ ?\ } \\ 1 \times 1 \times \underline{\ ?\ } \\ 0 + \underline{\ ?\ } \end{array} \right.$

30. $75 \left\{ \begin{array}{l} \underline{\ ?\ } + 75 \\ 5^2 \times \underline{\ ?\ } \\ 75 \times \underline{\ ?\ } \end{array} \right.$

C **31.** $9 \left\{ \begin{array}{l} \dfrac{36}{?} \\ \dfrac{50 + ?}{7} \end{array} \right.$

32. $96 \left\{ \begin{array}{l} 4^2 \times (5 + \underline{\ ?\ }) \\ (\underline{\ ?\ } - 3^2) + 0 \end{array} \right.$

33. $15 \left\{ \begin{array}{l} \dfrac{?}{3} \\ 3 + \underline{\ ?\ } + 3^2 \end{array} \right.$

34. $38 \left\{ \begin{array}{l} \underline{\ ?\ } + 1^2 \\ 5^2 + (\underline{\ ?\ } + 3) \end{array} \right.$

Christine Ladd-Franklin 1847–1930

Christine Ladd-Franklin received a degree from Vassar in 1869. Several of her articles on mathematics appeared in the *Educational Times* of Great Britain while she was teaching secondary school science. She attended Johns Hopkins University and later expanded her work in mathematics and logic to include the theory of color vision. At the age of 79 she wrote an article for the National Academy of Sciences on the "blue arcs" visual phenomenon, the origin of which is still not clearly understood.

1-2 *Expressions and Equations*

OBJECTIVES

Identify a statement as either true or false; $4 + 0 = 2 \times 2$ is true.

$18 - 6 = \frac{6}{2}$ is false.

Complete equations like $4 + 8 = 6 \times$ _?_ to make true statements.

A number sentence that consists of two expressions joined by the "is equal to" symbol, **=**, is called an equation.

$$14 \times 3 = 6 \times 7$$

is equal to

$$15 + \underline{\ ?\ } = \frac{60}{3}$$

is equal to

An equation with no information missing makes a statement that is either true or false. The statement is true if both expressions name the same number. Otherwise it is false. If information is missing, the equation is neither true nor false.

True: $4 + 4 + 11 = 20 - 1$

$$19 = 19$$

same number

$$\frac{8 + 7}{3} = 2^2 + 1$$

$$5 = 5$$

same number

False: $15 + 7 = 12 \times 2$

$$22 = 24$$

not the same

$$\frac{15 - 3}{4} = 0 + 0$$

$$3 = 0$$

not the same

How can we make $18 - \underline{\ ?\ } = 4 + 9$ into a true statement? If we replace _?_ with 5, each expression names **13.** Then the statement is true.

$$18 - \underline{\ ?\ } = 4 + 9 \quad \blacktriangleright \quad 18 - 5 = 4 + 9$$

$$13 = 13$$

EXERCISES

Tell why the statement is true or false.

Sample: $8 + 10 = 9 \times 2$ *What you say:* True. Both $10 + 8$ and 9×2 name 18.

1. $2 + 2 = 4 \times 2$
2. $4 \times 4 \times 1 = 8 \times 3$
3. $10 - 7 = 3 + 0$
4. $8 \times 0 = 1 \times 8$
5. $10 \times 10 = 100$
6. $48 - 8 = 30 + 5$
7. $15 - 6 = 3 \times 3$
8. $\frac{15}{1} = \frac{15}{5}$
9. $\frac{6}{2} + 4 = 4 + 3$

Match expressions that name the same number.

10. $6 \times 7 \times 0$
11. $20 \div 5$
12. $\frac{12 + 6}{9}$
13. $6 + 7 + 0$
14. $10 + \frac{6}{3}$

A. 2^2
B. 13
C. $8 + 2^2$
D. $15 \times 0 \times 12$
E. $0 + 1 + 1$

Written
EXERCISES

Show whether each statement is true or false.

Sample: $4 \times 9 = 25 + 11$ *Solution:* $4 \times 9 = 36$ and $25 + 11 = 36$; True

Sample: $18 + 7 = 14 + 10$ *Solution:* $18 + 7 = 25$ and $14 + 10 = 24$; False

A

1. $12 + 6 = 6 \times 3$
2. $43 + 15 = 8 + 50$
3. $3 \times 4 \times 5 = 100 - 30$
4. $468 = 400 + 6 + 8$
5. $\frac{75}{3} = 10 + 10 + 10$
6. $1 \times 1 \times 0 = 1 + 1 + 0$
7. $9 \times 5 = 36 + 9$
8. $\frac{17}{17} = 7 - 5$
9. $\frac{16}{8} = \frac{18}{6}$
10. $4^2 = 1 + 3 + 5 + 7$

11. $10 + 3^2 = 4^2 + 8$

12. $2.5 \times 8 = 5 + 4$

13. $\frac{3 \times 6}{6 \times 3} = \frac{9 \times 2}{2 \times 9}$

14. $\frac{81}{9} + 11 = \frac{100}{5} + 0$

15. $\frac{80}{5} = 4 \times 4 \times 2$

16. $\frac{4 + 10}{7} = \frac{10 + 10}{4}$

B

Complete to make a true statement.

Sample: $35 + 4 = 6^2 + \underline{?}$ *Solution:* $35 + 4 = 6^2 + 3$

17. $13 + 9 + 3 = 5 \times \underline{?}$

18. $3^2 = 1 + 3 + \underline{?}$

19. $\underline{?} \times 18 \times 1 = 9 \times 4$

20. $\frac{4 + 5 + 6}{3} = \underline{?} + 0$

21. $9^2 + \underline{?} = 101$

22. $6^2 = 11 + \underline{?}$

23. $145 + 35 = \underline{?} \times 90$

24. $\frac{48 + 204}{12} = \underline{?}$

25. $\frac{429}{3} + 7 = 5 \times 5 \times \underline{?}$

26. $\frac{1 + 4 + 5}{?} = 1$

27. $73 - \underline{?} = \frac{24 + 14}{2}$

28. $5^2 - \underline{?} = 5 + 3^2$

29. $\underline{?} + 52 = 10^2 \times 1$

30. $(9 \times 2) - 8 = \frac{80}{?}$

31. $16 - \underline{?} = 3 \times 7 \times 0$

32. $1^2 + 2^2 + 3^2 = \frac{?}{5}$

C

Make a true statement. Use the same whole number to complete both expressions.

33. $4 + 6 + \underline{?} = 6 \times \underline{?}$

34. $8 + 8 + \underline{?} = 3 \times \underline{?}$

35. $2 \times \underline{?} = 2 + \underline{?}$

36. $15 - \underline{?} = \frac{50}{?}$

37. $\underline{?} \times 2^2 \times 2 = 21 + \underline{?}$

38. $10 + 5^2 + \underline{?} = 6^2 \times \underline{?}$

39. $2 + 3 + \underline{?} = \frac{50}{?}$

40. $\frac{17 - ?}{5} = 5 - \underline{?}$

41. $\frac{? \times 6}{12} = \frac{?}{2}$

42. $3 + \underline{?} = \frac{13 + ?}{2}$

43. $\frac{9 - ?}{4} = 3 - \underline{?}$

44. $\underline{?} + 3 = \frac{3 \times ?}{2}$

1-3 *Expressions and Variables*

OBJECTIVE
Find the values of expressions that contain variables, using given replacements.

In algebra, letters are used to represent numbers that are not known. A letter used in this way is called a **variable.**

$4 + n$	$6 + k + 12$	$m^2 + 7$
variable (n)	variable (k)	variable (m)

The value of an expression that contains one or more variables depends on the numbers used as replacements for the variables. Look at the examples:

Expression	*Replacement*	*Value*
$m - 6$	Let $m = 10$.	When $m = 10$, $m - 6 = 10 - 6$ $= \mathbf{4}$
$2 \times b \times b$	Let $b = 5$.	When $b = 5$, $2 \times b \times b = 2 \times 5 \times 5$ $= \mathbf{50}$
$r + s + 6$	Let $r = 4$ and $s = 12$.	When $r = 4$ and $s = 12$, $r + s + 6 = 4 + 12 + 6$ $= \mathbf{22}$
$36 \div a^2$	Let $a = 3$.	When $a = 3$, $36 \div a^2 = 36 \div 3^2$ $= 36 \div 9$ $= \mathbf{4}$

EXERCISES

Name the variables.

Sample: $\frac{t}{4} + b$ *What you say:* The variables are t and b.

1. $m + 15$ **2.** w^2 **3.** $2 \times (t + n)$

4. $t \times 3 \times 5$ **5.** $12 - y$ **6.** $2 \times (c + a)$

7. $b + b + 0$ **8.** $40 + d^2$ **9.** $x + y + w$

Find the value.

Sample: $3 + q + r$, when $q = 6$ and $r = 20$

Solution: $3 + q + r = 3 + 6 + 20 = \mathbf{29}$

A

1. $6 + t + 18$, when $t = 12$

2. e^2, when $e = 5$

3. $3 \times 7 \times a$, when $a = 4$

4. a^2, when $a = 8$

5. $42 \div h$, when $h = 6$

6. $20 + r^2$, when $r = 3$

7. $13 - m$, when $m = 10$

8. $3 \times (a + 5)$, when $a = 9$

9. $x + 0$, when $x = 7$

10. $\frac{6 + k}{3}$, when $k = 15$

11. $\frac{15}{y}$, when $y = 5$

12. $d + d + d + d$, when $d = 20$

13. $\frac{26}{b}$, when $b = 2$

14. $\frac{40}{s + 3}$, when $s = 7$

Find the value. Use $a = 5$, $n = 7$, $t = 10$, and $m = 3$.

B

15. $\frac{a + n}{6}$

16. $3 \times (n + m)$

17. $a^2 + t$

18. $a^2 \times m^2$

19. $n^2 + m$

20. $\frac{n + a}{m}$

21. $t^2 + a^2$

22. $t \times n \times a$

C

23. $\frac{a^2 + n^2 + 1}{a^2}$

24. $m \times (a + n)$

25. $\frac{t^2}{n + m}$

26. $(t + m) \times a^2$

27. $a^2 \times a^2$

28. $\frac{a + t}{m} + n$

Use at least two of the variables listed to write an expression having the value given. Use $m = 1$, $y = 2$, $w = 5$, and $z = 4$.

Sample: 10

Solution: $\frac{w \times z}{y}$, or $w + z + m$ (Other answers are possible.)

29. 8 **30.** 25 **31.** 28

32. 2 **33.** 9 **34.** 12

1-4 *Special Equations: Formulas*

OBJECTIVE

Replace variables in a formula with given values.

Formulas can help us to solve problems when we know the replacements for variables. Look at these examples:

Formula	*Find the value of*	*Value*
$A = l \times w$	A, when $l = 5$ $w = 7$	$A = l \times w$ $= 5 \times 7 = \mathbf{35}$
$r = \frac{d}{t}$	r, when $d = 48$ $t = 4$	$r = \frac{d}{t}$ $= \frac{48}{4} = \mathbf{12}$
$s = \frac{1}{2} \times a \times t^2$	s, when $a = 6$ $t = 5$	$s = \frac{1}{2} \times a \times t^2$ $= \frac{1}{2} \times 6 \times 5^2 = \mathbf{75}$

EXERCISES

Complete.

Sample: $V = 10 \times h$
When $h = 7$, $V =$ _?_

What you say: Replace h with 7.
When $h = 7$,
$V = 10 \times 7 = 70$.

1. $D = 4 \times s$
When $s = 10$,
$D =$ _?_

2. $s = a \times 8$
When $a = 32$,
$s =$ _?_

3. $T = \frac{s}{3}$
When $s = 27$,
$T =$ _?_

4. $V = b \times 30$
When $b = 6$,
$V =$ _?_

5. $P = 6 \times l$
When $l = 9$,
$P =$ _?_

6. $A = b - 14$
When $b = 34$,
$A =$ _?_

Written EXERCISES

Complete.

Sample: $A = s \times s$
When $s = 15$,
$A = \underline{\ ?\ }$

Solution: $A = s \times s$
$= 15 \times 15 = 225$

A

1. $A = m + m$
When $m = 46$,
$A = \underline{\ ?\ }$

2. $T = 6 \times a$
When $a = 135$,
$T = \underline{\ ?\ }$

3. $A = \frac{1}{2} \times b \times h$
When $b = 16$
and $h = 4$,
$A = \underline{\ ?\ }$

4. $V = e \times e \times e$
When $e = 14$,
$V = \underline{\ ?\ }$

5. $s = 16 \times t \times t$
When $t = 25$,
$s = \underline{\ ?\ }$

6. $P = I \times E$
When $I = 10$
and $E = 1$,
$P = \underline{\ ?\ }$

7. $d = r \times 6$
When $r = 45$,
$d = \underline{\ ?\ }$

8. $A = l \times w$
When $l = 18$
and $w = 40$,
$A = \underline{\ ?\ }$

9. $I = \frac{E}{R}$
When $E = 48$
and $R = 6$,
$I = \underline{\ ?\ }$

10. $A = s \times s$
When $s = 24$,
$A = \underline{\ ?\ }$

11. $V = B \times h$
When $B = 74$
and $h = 15$,
$V = \underline{\ ?\ }$

12. $A = s^2$
When $s = 13$,
$A = \underline{\ ?\ }$

B

13. $S = \frac{1}{2} \times a \times t^2$
When $a = 32$
and $t = 5$,
$S = \underline{\ ?\ }$

14. $V = l^2 \times l$
When $l = 12$,
$V = \underline{\ ?\ }$

15. $V = l^2 \times h$
When $l = 20$
and $h = 1$,
$V = \underline{\ ?\ }$

16. $V = l \times w \times h$
When $l = 5$,
$w = 7$,
and $h = 12$,
$V = \underline{\ ?\ }$

17. $A = (B + b) \times h$
When $B = 7$,
$b = 9$,
and $h = 16$,
$A = \underline{\ ?\ }$

18. $B = 3L + W$
When $L = 9$
and $W = 10$,
$B = \underline{\ ?\ }$

19. $C = s^2 \times l$
When $s = 3$
and $l = 17$,
$C = \underline{\ ?\ }$

20. $A = \frac{22}{7} \times r^2$
When $r = 7$,
$A = \underline{\ ?\ }$

21. $t = l^2 + e^2$
When $l = 5$
and $e = 10$,
$t = \underline{\ ?\ }$

C

22. $a = \dfrac{v^2}{R + r}$

When $v = 16$,
$R = 8$,
and $r = 0$
$a = \underline{\ ?\ }$

23. $k = \dfrac{m \times v^2}{2}$

When $m = 9$
and $v = 4$,
$k = \underline{\ ?\ }$

24. $G = \dfrac{3 + r^2}{m \times v}$

When $r = 9$,
$m = 3$,
and $v = 14$
$G = \underline{\ ?\ }$

Problems

Complete. Use the given formula and dimensions.

1. $A = l \times w$

$A = \underline{\ ?\ }$

$w = 12$

$l = 17$

2. $A = \dfrac{1}{2} \times b \times h$

$A = \underline{\ ?\ }$

$h = 20$

$b = 10$

3. $V = l \times w \times h$

$V = \underline{\ ?\ }$

$h = 5$

$w = 3$

$l = 4$

4. $V = l \times l^2$

$V = \underline{\ ?\ }$

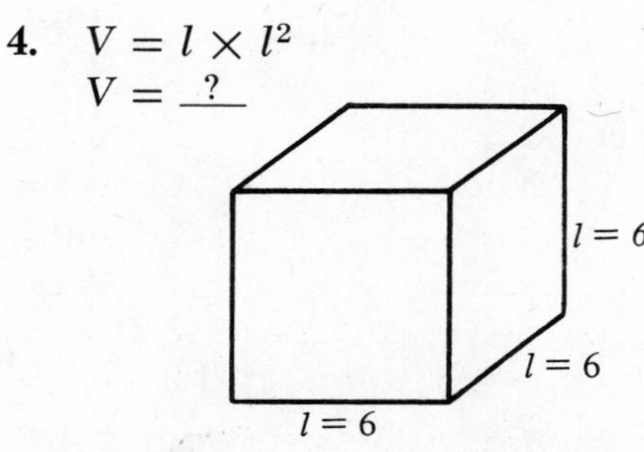

5. $A = \dfrac{1}{2} \times (B + b) \times h$

$A = \underline{\ ?\ }$

$b = 4$

$h = 3$

$B = 6$

6. $A = \dfrac{22}{7} \times r^2$

$A = \underline{\ ?\ }$

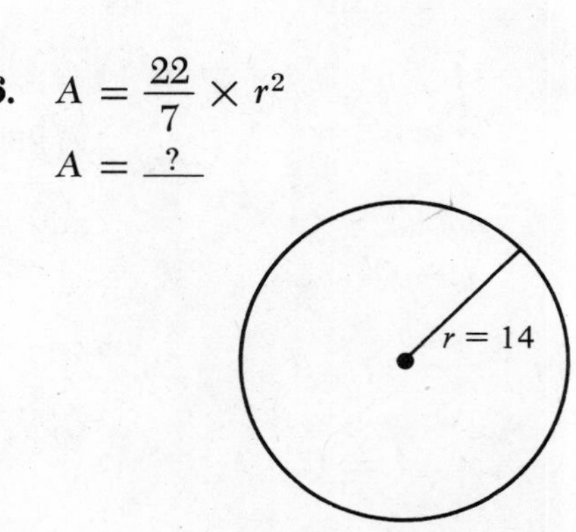

SELF-TEST 1

Be sure that you understand these terms and symbols.

simplify (p. 2) $\quad$ = (p. 5)
equation (p. 5) $\quad$ variable (p. 8)

Simplify: **Section 1-1, p. 2**

1. $2 \times (3 + 4)$
2. $\dfrac{24}{2^2 \times 3}$

True or false? **Section 1-2, p. 5**

3. $10 - 6 = 2 \times 3$
4. $14 - \dfrac{8}{2} = 2 \times 5$

Complete to make a true statement. **Section 1-3, p. 8**

5. $5^2 = \underline{\ ?\ } + 17$
6. $\dfrac{2 \times 8}{?} = 4$

Find the value. **Section 1-4, p. 10**

7. $A = l \times 5$
   when $l = 4$,
   $A = \underline{\ ?\ }$
8. $V = l^2 \times h$
   When $l = 2$,
   and $h = 3$, $V = \underline{\ ?\ }$

Check your answers with those printed at the back of the book.

calculator corner

How can an arctic scientist go from one experiment site to another? You can find out by using your calculator. Begin with the number of hours in one half-day. Multiply by the number of degrees in two right angles. Divide by the number of months in a year. Multiply by the number of centimeters in a meter. Add the number of grams in 0.455 kilograms. Multiply by the number of huskies in the scientist's kennel (25). To see the answer, turn your calculator upside down.

Writing and Solving Equations

1-5 *Using Symbols for Words*

OBJECTIVE
State expressions and equations in words and in mathematical symbols.

Expressions and equations can be stated in words or in mathematical symbols.

EXAMPLE 1 Symbols: $20 - 4$
Words: The difference between twenty and four

EXAMPLE 2 Symbols: $5 + 8$
Words: The sum of five and eight

EXAMPLE 3 Symbols: $5 + 8$ $=$ 13
Words: The sum of five and eight / is equal to / thirteen.

When a variable is included, it can be referred to simply as "some number."

EXAMPLE 4 Symbols: $t - 2$
Words: The difference of some number and two

EXAMPLE 5 Symbols: $\frac{20}{n}$ $=$ 5
Words: The quotient of twenty and some number (or twenty divided by some number) / is equal to / five.

EXERCISES

Give the meaning in words.

Sample: 8×6 *What you say:* The product of six and eight

1. $10 - 7$ **2.** $\frac{24}{6}$ **3.** $6 - 5$

4. $6 + 12$ **5.** $18 \div 3$ **6.** 12×9

Written EXERCISES

Write the meaning in words.

Sample 1: $7 + 9$ *Solution:* The sum of seven and nine

Sample 2: $n \times 15$ *Solution:* The product of some number and fifteen

A

1. $6 + 9$
2. $s + 10$
3. $16 \div k$
4. $20 - 7$
5. $m - 6$
6. $4 \times a$
7. 5×8
8. $4 + t$
9. $r \times 10$
10. $\frac{18}{2}$
11. $25 - w$
12. $\frac{45}{n}$

Write the meaning in words.

Sample: $6 \times r = 42$ *Solution:* The product of six and some number is equal to forty-two.

13. $10 + x = 42$
14. $27 = m + 13$
15. $35 - t = 19$
16. $64 = w - 26$
17. $37 + a = 95$
18. $48 = 3 \times b$
19. $\frac{45}{9} = k$
20. $\frac{40}{b} = 5$

B

21. $t - 68 = 14$
22. $t = 111 \times 3$
23. $39 = n + 10$
24. $s \times 41 = 246$
25. $75 = 92 - y$
26. $300 = z \times 25$

Write an equation. Use a variable.

Sample: The sum of nineteen and some number is equal to thirty-seven. *Solution:* $19 + b = 37$

27. The sum of some number and sixteen is equal to seventeen.
28. The product of zero and some number is equal to zero.
29. Thirty-six is equal to the product of six and some number.
30. The difference of some number and seven is equal to seventy-three.
31. Some number divided by fifteen is equal to ten.
32. Twelve is equal to ninety-six divided by some number.
33. The sum of zero and some number is equal to twelve.

C

34. The product of six and some number is equal to the sum of nine and ten.

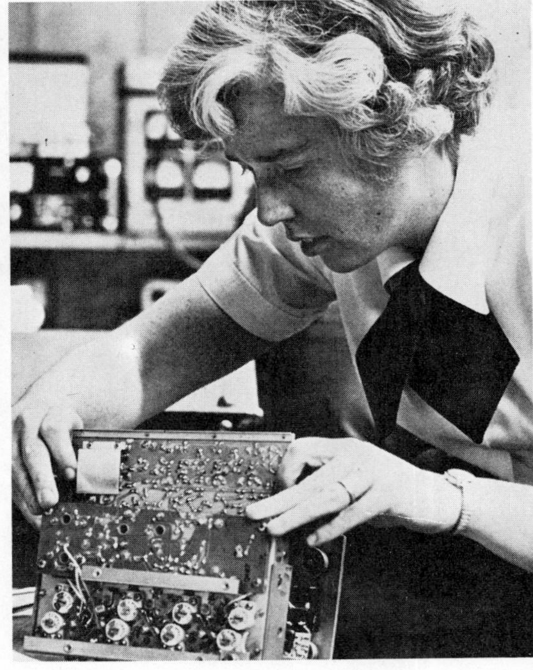

career capsule

Maintenance Electrician

Maintenance electricians keep electrical equipment in good working order. They detect and repair defects *before* equipment breaks down. They install wire and conduit (tubes which enclose electrical wire). Often they must make mathematical calculations. In emergencies, they advise management whether or not hazards require that equipment be shut down. Maintenance electricians who work in small plants and office buildings generally maintain all types of electrical equipment. Others may specialize.

Maintenance electricians need a background in algebra, basic science, electricity, and blueprint reading. They must have good color vision, good health, manual dexterity, and mechanical aptitude.

1-6 *Solving Equations: Addition and Subtraction*

OBJECTIVE

Solve equations like $x + 3 = 18$ and $15 = y - 3$.

The equation $4 + 8 = 6 + 6$ makes a true statement because the **left member,** $4 + 8$, names the same number as the **right member,** $6 + 6$. An equation may be thought of as a balanced scale. The left member "balances" (or names the same number as) the right member.

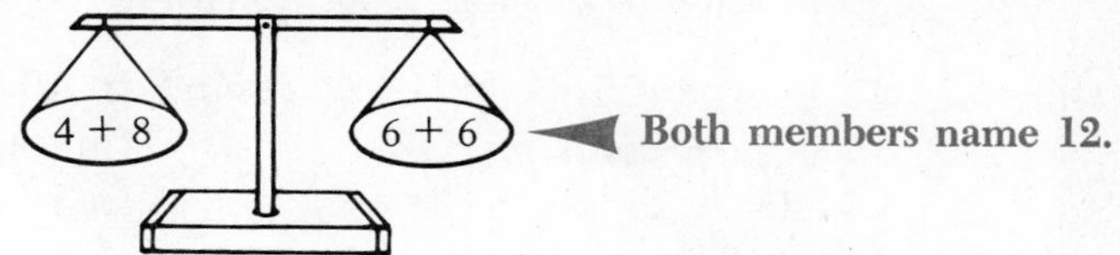

Both members name 12.

We solve an equation such as $x + 3 = 18$ by finding a replacement for the variable so that the left member and the right member name the same number.

Equation:	$x + 3$	$=$	18
Think:	The sum of what number and 3	is equal to	18?
Solution:	Since $15 + 3 = 18$, $x = 15$.		

Both members name 18.

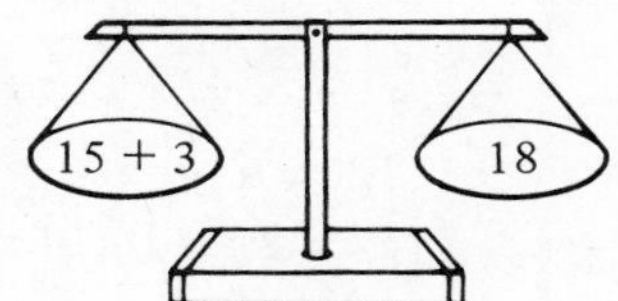

EXAMPLE 1

Equation:	$46 + b$	$=$	48
Think:	46 plus what number	is equal to	48?
Solution:	Since $46 + 2 = 48$, $b = 2$.		

EXAMPLE 2

Equation:	15	$=$	20	$-$	t
Think:	15	equals	20	minus	what number?
Solution:	Since $15 = 20 - 5$, $t = 5$.				

EXAMPLE 3

Equation:	$9 + 4$	$=$	K	$+$	3
Think:	The sum of 9 and 4	equals	what number	plus	3?
Solution:	Since $9 + 4 = 13$, and $10 + 3 = 13$, $K = 10$				

Match the equation with the question it suggests.

1. $14 + m = 20$
2. $20 - m = 10$
3. $20 = m - 10$
4. $m = 20 + 10$

A. What number subtracted from 20 equals 10?
B. What number is equal to the sum of 20 and 10?
C. 14 added to what number equals 20?
D. 20 equals the difference of what number and 10?

Use the true statement to solve each equation.

Sample: $15 + 10 = 25$
$15 + n = 25,\ n = \underline{\ ?\ }$
$s + 10 = 25,\ s = \underline{\ ?\ }$
$15 + 10 = m,\ m = \underline{\ ?\ }$

What you say: In $15 + n = 25,\ n = 10$
In $s + 10 = 25,\ s = 15$
In $15 + 10 = m,\ m = 25$

5. $16 - 7 = 9$
$16 - b = 9,\ b = \underline{\ ?\ }$
$16 - 7 = k,\ k = \underline{\ ?\ }$
$t - 7 = 9,\ t = \underline{\ ?\ }$

6. $13 = 18 - 5$
$b = 18 - 5,\ b = \underline{\ ?\ }$
$13 = 18 - s,\ s = \underline{\ ?\ }$
$13 = w - 5,\ w = \underline{\ ?\ }$

7. $12 - 3 = 9$
$12 - b = 9,\ b = \underline{\ ?\ }$
$12 - 3 = k,\ k = \underline{\ ?\ }$
$t - 3 = 9,\ t = \underline{\ ?\ }$

8. $3 = 8 - 5$
$b = 8 - 5,\ b = \underline{\ ?\ }$
$3 = 8 - s,\ s = \underline{\ ?\ }$
$3 = w - 5,\ w = \underline{\ ?\ }$

9. $12 = 2 + 10$
$x = 2 + 10,\ x = \underline{\ ?\ }$
$12 = 2 + z,\ z = \underline{\ ?\ }$
$12 = h + 10,\ h = \underline{\ ?\ }$

10. $18 = 74 - 56$
$18 = a - 56,\ a = \underline{\ ?\ }$
$x = 74 - 56,\ x = \underline{\ ?\ }$
$18 = 74 - d,\ d = \underline{\ ?\ }$

A

Solve.

Sample: $15 + a = 22$ *Solution:* Since $15 + 7 = 22,\ a = 7$.

1. $n + 7 = 19$
2. $k - 5 = 13$
3. $m - 6 = 30$
4. $m + 10 = 45$
5. $18 - x = 12$
6. $20 = 25 - y$
7. $12 + t = 20$
8. $14 - r = 10$
9. $t = 10 + 20 + 30$
10. $6 + w = 20$
11. $16 = 20 - x$
12. $h + 2 = 36$
13. $19 = 7 + b$
14. $50 = s - 25$
15. $50 - 10 = m$
16. $34 = 24 + e$
17. $35 = 36 - z$
18. $3 + 8 = t$

Sample: $h + 7 = 12 + 14$ *Solution:* $h + 7 = 12 + 14$
$h + 7 = 26$
Since $19 + 7 = 26$,
$h = 19$.

B

19. $n + 4 = 9 + 3$ **20.** $m - 3 = 16 - 4$
21. $10 - 7 = 1 + d$ **22.** $t + 7 = 10 + 8$
23. $c - 2 = 12 - 9$ **24.** $18 - h = 5 + 10$
25. $10 + b = 9 + 7$ **26.** $12 + 3 = y + 2$
27. $75 + 25 = 150 - q$ **28.** $15 + k = 17 + 12$
29. $n - 3 = 15 - 9$ **30.** $23 - h = 7 + 10$

Sample: $t - 10 = 47 + 4 + 9$ *Solution:* $t - 10 = 47 + 4 + 9$
$t - 10 = 60$
$t = 70$

C

31. $4 + s = 2 + 8 + 9$ **32.** $15 = k + 4 + 0 + 8$
33. $18 + 0 = t - 11$ **34.** $m - 2 = 10 + 3 + 7$
35. $n + 0 = 46 - 37$ **36.** $6 + 8 - 7 = 15 - y$

consumer notes *Nutrition*

Consumers must make important decisions when shopping for food. You must choose the foods which will give you the most food value for your money. Good nutrition is basic to good health.

Here's one way to tell if you are eating the right kind of food. You can use an encyclopedia, an almanac, or a cookbook to look up the recommended daily dietary allowances (RDA) established by nutritionists. The allowances vary according to age, height, weight and other factors. Look up *your* RDA for the following: protein, calcium, iron, vitamin A, thiamine, riboflavin, niacin, and ascorbic acid. The same information source should list the percentages of the RDA supplied by certain foods. Try to remember everything you ate yesterday. Use the charts to see if you met your nutritional needs. Now plan a menu for tomorrow.

1-7 *Solving Equations: Multiplication and Division*

OBJECTIVE

Solve equations like $4 \times m = 28$ and $\frac{30}{b} = 5$.

To solve the equation $4 \times m = 28$, we can use the idea of balancing a scale:

Think: The product of 4 and what number equals **28?**

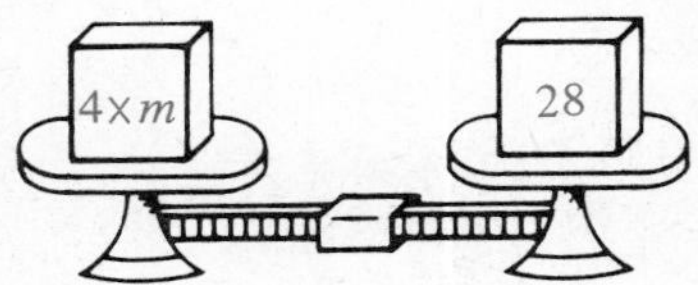

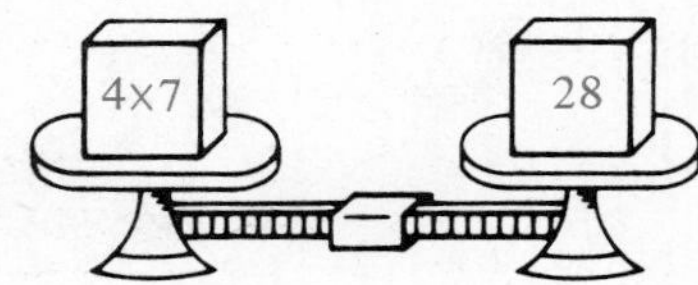

Solution: When $m = \mathbf{7}$, the scale balances.

EXAMPLE 1 Equation: $m \times 7 = 35$

Question: The product of what number and 7 equals **35?**

Solution: Since $5 \times 7 = 35$, $m = \mathbf{5}$.

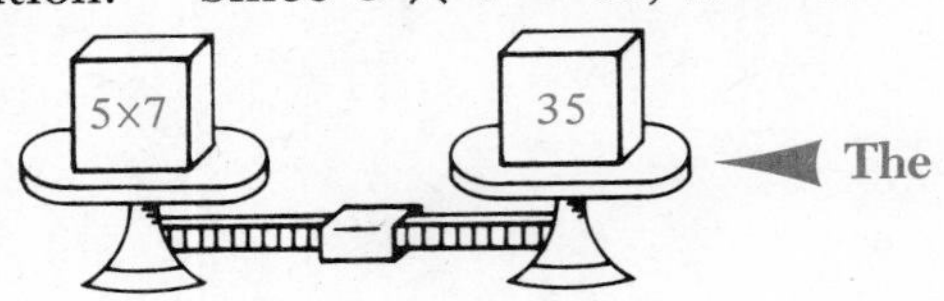

The scale is balanced.

EXAMPLE 2 Equation: $\frac{18}{t} = 3$

Question: 18 divided by what number equals 3?

Solution: Since $\frac{18}{6} = 3$, $t = 6$.

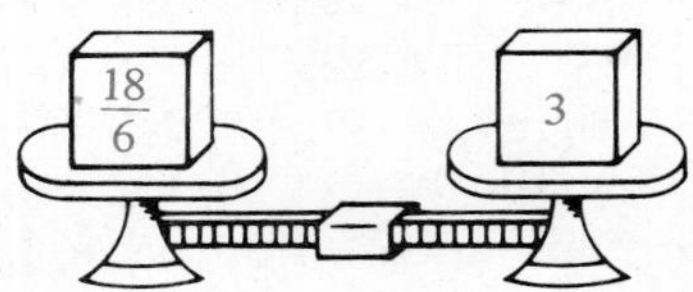

EXAMPLE 3 Equation: $m + 6 = 18 - 5$

Question: What number plus six equals 18 minus 5?

Solution: Since $18 - 5 = 13$, and $7 + 6 = 13$, $m = 7$.

Match.

1. $42 \div 6 = k$
2. $n \times 7 = 42$
3. $\frac{42}{m} = 7$
4. $42 \times 7 = t$
5. $\frac{r}{7} = 42$

A. The product of 42 and 7 equals what number?
B. 42 divided by 6 equals what number?
C. The product of what number and 7 equals 42?
D. 42 divided by what number equals 7?
E. What number divided by 7 equals 42?

Answer.

Sample: 24 divided by what number equals 8?
What you say: 24 divided by 3 equals 8.

6. The product of 4 and what number equals 20?
7. 40 is equal to the product of 5 and what number?
8. 10 is equal to 20 divided by what number?
9. What number divided by 7 equals 5?
10. The product of 7 and what number equals 49?

Written EXERCISES

A

Write an equation.

Sample: The product of what number and 9 equals 36?
Solution: $n \times 9 = 36$

1. The product of 6 and what number equals 30?
2. What number divided by 2 equals 7?
3. 8 equals 32 divided by what number?
4. The product of what number and 50 equals 100?
5. 42 equals the product of 6 and what number?

Use the true statement to solve each equation.

Sample: $\frac{20}{2} = 10$; $\frac{c}{2} = 10$, $c = \underline{\ ?\ }$ *Solution:* $c = 20$

$\frac{20}{b} = 10$, $b = \underline{\ ?\ }$ $b = 2$

$\frac{20}{2} = a$, $a = \underline{\ ?\ }$ $a = 10$

6. $3 \times 7 = 21$
$3 \times t = 21,\ t = \underline{\ ?\ }$
$s \times 7 = 21,\ s = \underline{\ ?\ }$
$3 \times 7 = r,\ r = \underline{\ ?\ }$

7. $5 \times 12 = 60$
$5 \times n = 60,\ n = \underline{\ ?\ }$
$x \times 12 = 60,\ x = \underline{\ ?\ }$
$5 \times 12 = z,\ z = \underline{\ ?\ }$

8. $9 \times 8 = 72$
$m \times 8 = 72,\ m = \underline{\ ?\ }$
$9 \times 8 = q,\ q = \underline{\ ?\ }$
$9 \times n = 72,\ n = \underline{\ ?\ }$

9. $42 = 7 \times 6$
$42 = c \times 6,\ c = \underline{\ ?\ }$
$42 = 7 \times h,\ h = \underline{\ ?\ }$
$d = 7 \times 6,\ d = \underline{\ ?\ }$

10. $\frac{57}{3} = 19$
$\frac{57}{x} = 19,\ x = \underline{\ ?\ }$
$\frac{w}{3} = 19,\ w = \underline{\ ?\ }$
$\frac{57}{3} = z,\ z = \underline{\ ?\ }$

11. $17 = \frac{153}{9}$
$a = \frac{153}{9},\ a = \underline{\ ?\ }$
$17 = \frac{n}{9},\ n = \underline{\ ?\ }$
$17 = \frac{153}{k},\ k = \underline{\ ?\ }$

Solve.

Sample: $\frac{m}{3} = 9$ *Solution:* Since $\frac{27}{3} = 9$, $m = 27$.

B

12. $t \times 5 = 40$
13. $\frac{r}{2} = 25$
14. $4 = \frac{28}{x}$
15. $6 \times n = 30$
16. $16 = k \times 1$
17. $3 = \frac{z}{8}$
18. $\frac{24}{m} = 2$
19. $30 = 3 \times w$
20. $y = \frac{45}{3}$

Sample: $14 \times 2 = 7 \times k$ *Solution:* $14 \times 2 = 7 \times k$
$28 = 7 \times k$
Since $28 = 7 \times 4$, $k = 4$.

C

21. $6 \times b = 4 \times 24$
22. $3 \times 15 = 9 \times y$
23. $\frac{20}{1} = \frac{80}{z}$
24. $n \times 4 = \frac{40}{5}$
25. $6 \times 10 = m \times 3$
26. $b \times 3 = \frac{63}{7}$
27. $\frac{x}{4} = 11$
28. $3 + 9 = \frac{36}{c}$
29. $4 \times k = \frac{60}{15}$

1-8 *Equations and Exponents*

OBJECTIVE
Find a solution of an equation like $y^2 = 100$ or $n^3 = 125$.

We can use an exponent to shorten a multiplication expression when the same factor is used more than once.

10 used as a factor twice

$10 \times 10 = 10^2$ ◄ 10 squared
$10^2 = 100$

5 used as a factor three times

$5 \times 5 \times 5 = 5^3$ ◄ 5 cubed
$5^3 = 125$

We can find a solution of an equation when the variable has an exponent:

EXAMPLE 1 Equation: $s^2 = 49$

Question: What number used as a factor twice equals 49?
$s \times s = 49$

Solution: Since $7 \times 7 = 49$, $s = 7$.

EXAMPLE 2 Equation: $m^3 = 64$

Question: What number used as a factor three times equals 64?
$m \times m \times m = 64$

Solution: Since $4 \times 4 \times 4 = 64$, $m = 4$.

EXERCISES

Complete.

Sample: When t is 10, the value of t^2 is _?_.

What you say: When t is 10, the value of t^2 is 10 times 10 or 100.

Sample: When m is 2, the value of m^3 is _?_.

What you say: When m is 2 the value of m^3 is 2 times 2 times 2 or 8.

1. When n is 4, the value of n^2 is _?_.
2. When b is 6, the value of b^2 is _?_.
3. When k is 3, the value of k^3 is _?_.
4. When x is 1, the value of x^2 is _?_.
5. When s is 1, the value of s^3 is _?_.

Complete.

Sample 1: $3^2 = \underline{?}$ *What you say:* Three squared equals nine.

Sample 2: $2^3 = \underline{?}$ *What you say:* Two cubed equals eight.

6. $5^2 = \underline{?}$ **7.** $10^3 = \underline{?}$ **8.** $1^3 = \underline{?}$

9. $8^2 = \underline{?}$ **10.** $6^2 = \underline{?}$ **11.** $7^2 = \underline{?}$

Written EXERCISES A

Copy and complete the table of squares.

1.

n	n^2
1	1
2	4
3	9
4	?
5	?
6	?
7	?
8	?
9	?
10	?

2.

n	n^2
11	121
12	144
13	?
14	?
15	?
16	?
17	?
18	?
19	?
20	?

3.

n	n^2
21	441
22	?
23	?
24	?
25	?
26	?
27	?
28	?
29	?
30	?

Copy and complete the table of cubes.

4.

n	n^3
1	1
2	8
3	?
4	?
5	?

5.

n	n^3
6	216
7	?
8	?
9	?
10	?

6.

n	n^3
11	1331
12	?
13	?
14	?
15	?

Complete. Use the tables of squares and cubes from Exercises 1–6.

Sample: $7^3 = \underline{?} \times \underline{?} \times \underline{?}$
$7^3 = \underline{?}$

Solution: $7^3 = 7 \times 7 \times 7$
$7^3 = 343$

7. $10^3 = \underline{?} \times \underline{?} \times \underline{?}$
$10^3 = \underline{?}$

8. $\underline{?} \times \underline{?} = 25^2$
$\underline{?} = 25^2$

9. $15^3 = \underline{?} \times \underline{?} \times \underline{?}$
$15^3 = \underline{?}$

10. $6^3 = \underline{?} \times \underline{?} \times \underline{?}$
$6^3 = \underline{?}$

11. $\underline{\ ?\ } \times \underline{\ ?\ } = 28^2$
$\underline{\ ?\ } = 28^2$

12. $12^2 = \underline{\ ?\ } \times \underline{\ ?\ }$
$12^2 = \underline{\ ?\ }$

13. $19^2 = \underline{\ ?\ } \times \underline{\ ?\ }$
$19^2 = \underline{\ ?\ }$

14. $1^3 = \underline{\ ?\ } \times \underline{\ ?\ } \times \underline{\ ?\ }$
$1^3 = \underline{\ ?\ }$

15. $4^3 = \underline{\ ?\ } \times \underline{\ ?\ } \times \underline{\ ?\ }$
$4^3 = \underline{\ ?\ }$

Find a solution. Use the tables of squares and cubes.

Sample: $r^2 = 289$ *Solution:* Since $17 \times 17 = 289$, $r = 17$.

B

16. $y^2 = 81$
17. $a^3 = 125$
18. $m^2 = 324$
19. $m^2 = 400$
20. $r^3 = 1000$
21. $k^2 = 576$
22. $b^2 = 625$
23. $1728 = z^3$
24. $q^2 = 841$
25. $h^2 = 64$
26. $196 = x^2$
27. $v^3 = 729$
28. $900 = w^2$
29. $p^3 = 2744$
30. $c^2 = 529$

Find a solution.

C

31. $r^2 = 20 + 5$
32. $a^2 = 5^2 + 11$
33. $m^3 = 0 + 8^2$

SELF-TEST 2

Be sure that you understand the term *exponent* (p. 23).

1. Write the meaning of $3 \times y = 21$ in words. **Section 1-5, p. 14**
2. Write an equation for the sentence "The sum of some number and twelve is equal to forty-eight." **Section 1-6, p. 17**

Solve. **Section 1-7, p. 20**

3. $2 + n = 26$
4. $20 - k = 3 + 6$
5. $3 \times s = 33$
6. $\frac{15}{t} = 5$

Find a solution. **Section 1-8, p. 23**

7. $x^2 = 16$
8. $a^3 = 27$

Check your answers with those printed at the back of the book.

chapter summary

1. An **expression** can be **simplified** by carrying out the indicated operations.
2. An **equation** consists of two expressions joined by the equality symbol (=). The expressions are called the **left member** and the **right member.** The statement made by an equation is **true** when the left member and the right member name the **same number.**
3. A letter used to represent an unknown number is called a **variable.**
4. To **solve** an equation that contains a variable, we find a number to replace the variable so that a **true** statement results.

chapter test

Simplify.

1. $\frac{3 \times 8}{6}$ **2.** $7^2 + 1$ **3.** $4 \times 4 \times 4$ **4.** $6 \times 19 \times 0$

True or False?

5. $15 + 6 = 3 \times 7$ **6.** $\frac{10}{10} = 5 - 3$ **7.** $\frac{6}{3} + 0 = \frac{6}{3} \times 0$

Name the value. Let $b = 5$, $t = 3$, and $m = 10$.

8. $b + 4$ **9.** $b + t + 2$ **10.** $m^2 + 35$

11. $t \times b$ **12.** $6 + t^2$ **13.** $\frac{75}{t}$

Write the equation in symbols.

14. The sum of twenty and sixteen equals thirty-six.

15. The product of six and some number is equal to twenty-four.

Solve each equation.

16. $6 + t = 15$ **17.** $14 - k = 8$ **18.** $\frac{20}{s} = 5$

19. $w \times 8 = 80$ **20.** $40 = n + 30$ **21.** $12 = m - 3$

22. $6 = \frac{36}{b}$ **23.** $34 = c \times 2$

Find the value.

24. 4^2 **25.** 3^3 **26.** 5^2 **27.** 10^3

challenge topics

Cutting Up

A. Duplicate this figure three times on squared paper.
   1. Cut one shape into **two** congruent pieces.
   2. Cut one shape into **three** congruent pieces.
   3. Cut one shape into **four** congruent pieces. Then try to put the four pieces back together to form the original shape.

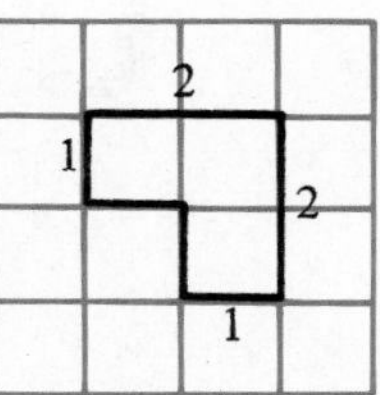

B. Duplicate figures I and II on squared paper.

I
2
8

II
12
$1\frac{1}{3}$

Cut shape II into two congruent pieces that will exactly cover shape I.

review of skills

Complete. Use $<$, $>$, or $=$.

1. $909 \underline{\ ?\ } 990$
2. $2\frac{1}{2} \underline{\ ?\ } \frac{5}{2}$
3. $0 \underline{\ ?\ } 0.1$
4. $1\frac{1}{2} \underline{\ ?\ } 4$
5. $5\frac{1}{2} \underline{\ ?\ } 5\frac{1}{4}$
6. $4.50 \underline{\ ?\ } 4.8$

Express in words.

Sample: 2.35 *Solution:* Two and thirty-five hundredths.

7. 0.47
8. 5.08
9. 3.125
10. 10.3
11. 0.01
12. 136.1

Express as a decimal.

Sample: one and twenty-three hundredths *Solution:* 1.23

13. ten and sixty-five hundredths
14. five tenths
15. five hundredths
16. seven and sixteen thousandths

Add or subtract.

17. $\begin{array}{r} 425 \\ 816 \\ \underline{102} \end{array}$

18. $\begin{array}{r} 6.04 \\ 2.15 \\ \underline{17.33} \end{array}$

19. $\begin{array}{r} 5\frac{7}{10} \\ \underline{6\frac{1}{10}} \end{array}$

20. $\begin{array}{r} \$106.25 \\ 35.00 \\ \underline{19.37} \end{array}$

21. $\begin{array}{r} 396 \\ \underline{-127} \end{array}$

22. $\begin{array}{r} 861.23 \\ \underline{-104.08} \end{array}$

23. $\begin{array}{r} 9\frac{7}{8} \\ \underline{-2\frac{1}{8}} \end{array}$

24. $\begin{array}{r} \$643.85 \\ \underline{-62.79} \end{array}$

Multiply or divide.

25. 146×35
26. 9.2×8
27. $\frac{3}{5} \times \frac{1}{2}$
28. 275×1000
29. 2.5×7.1
30. $2\frac{7}{8} \times \frac{1}{3}$
31. $27\overline{)216}$
32. $23 \div 4.6$
33. $\frac{2}{3} \div 2$
34. $\frac{184}{46}$
35. $230 \div 4.6$
36. $\frac{5}{8} \div \frac{7}{8}$

Left: Linotype operator, 1919.

Right: Operator using video display terminal, part of computer typesetting system.

2 Positive and Negative Numbers

Whole Numbers and Integers

2-1 *The Whole Numbers*

OBJECTIVES

Complete patterns of consecutive whole numbers.

Name the coordinate of a point on the number line.

The whole numbers are the numbers 0, 1, 2, 3, 4, 5, and so on. The set of whole numbers can be written:

{0, 1, 2, 3, 4, 5, 6, 7, 8, 9, 10, 11, . . .}

{ } means "the set of"

The three dots show that the set goes on and on.

Whole numbers are pictured here in consecutive order on the number line.

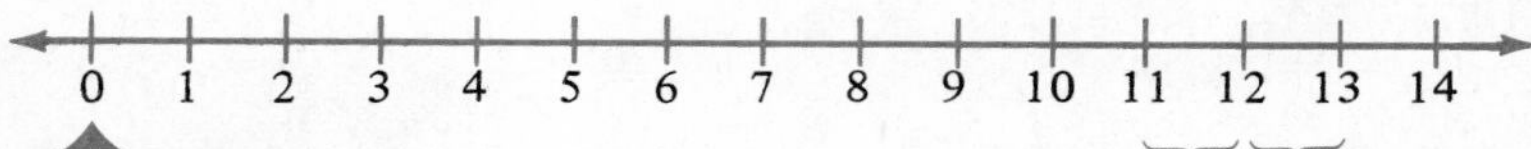

0 is the first whole number. The point marked 0 is called the origin.

Note that the marks are equally spaced.

The number line can help us understand ideas about whole numbers.

EXAMPLE 1 The set of whole numbers greater than 5 is {6, 7, 8, 9, 10, . . .}.

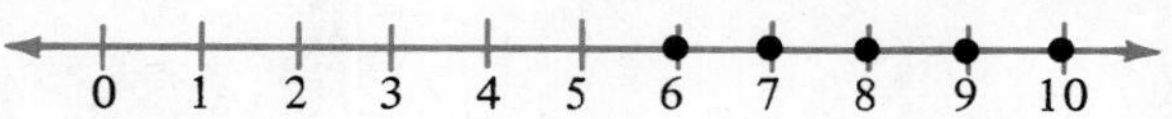

EXAMPLE 2 The set of whole numbers between 2 and 6 is {3, 4, 5}.

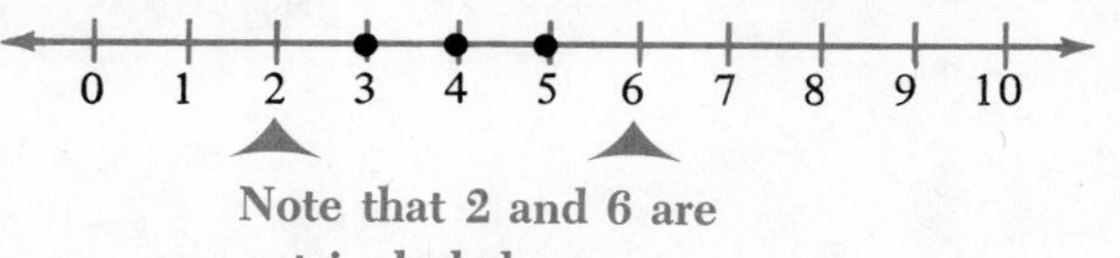

Note that 2 and 6 are not included.

EXAMPLE 3 The set of whole numbers between 6 and 7 has no members. Such a set is called the empty set. The symbol for the empty set is **∅**.

The number matched with a point on the line is called the **coordinate** of that point. Sometimes letters as well as numbers are used to name the points.

EXAMPLE 4

R (0), *B* (1), *S* (2), *M* (3), *K* (5)

0 1 2 3 4 5 6 7

The coordinate of point *S* is 2.

EXAMPLE 5

M (0), *Q* (3), *A* (6)

0 1 2 3 4 5 6 7 8 9

The point half the distance from point *M* to point *A* is point *Q*. Its coordinate is 3.

Name the set of whole numbers described. Look at the number line if you need help.

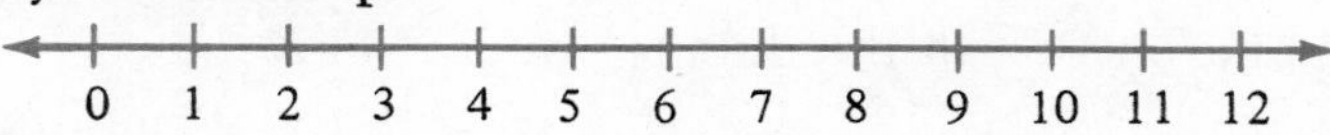

Sample: Between 3 and 9 *What you say:* The set 4, 5, 6, 7, 8

1. Between 1 and 6

2. Less than 1

3. Between 2 and 9

4. Greater than 6

5. Between 0 and 5

6. Greater than 5

7. Less than 3

8. Less than 0

Complete the whole number pattern.

Sample: 33, 34, __?__, __?__, __?__, 38 *What you say:* 33, 34, 35, 36, 37, 38.

9. 67, 68, __?__, __?__, __?__, __?__, 73

10. 495, 496, __?__, __?__, __?__, __?__, 501

11. 96, 97, 98, __?__, __?__, __?__, __?__

12. 997, 998, 999, __?__, __?__, __?__, __?__

13. __?__, __?__, __?__, 302, __?__, 304, 305

14. __?__, __?__, __?__, __?__, 5002, 5003, 5004

Written EXERCISES

Name the coordinate.

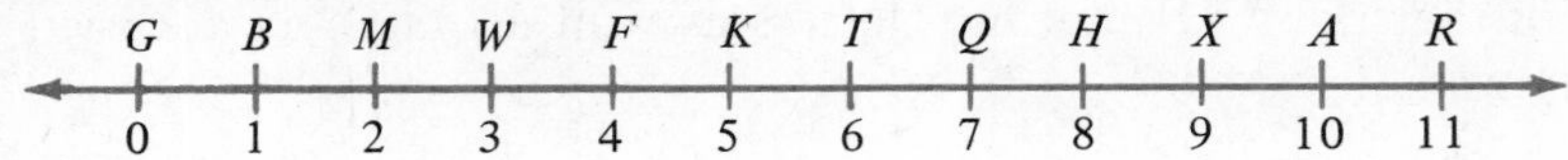

Sample: W *Solution:* 3

A

1. *H*
2. *G*
3. *Q*
4. *X*
5. *F*
6. A
7. *B*
8. *K*
9. *M*
10. The point between *W* and *K*.
11. The point between *H* and *T*.
12. The point between *K* and *Q*.
13. The point between *X* and *Q*.
14. The point half the distance from *W* to *K*.
15. The point half the distance from *G* to *F*.
16. The point half the distance from *M* to *H*.

B

17. The point one-third the distance from *B* to *F*.
18. The point one-third the distance from *H* to *R*.
19. The point one-fourth the distance from *G* to *F*.
20. The point one-fourth the distance from *B* to *X*.

Name the set of whole numbers described.

Sample: Between 7 and 11 *Solution:* {8, 9, 10}

21. Between 0 and 2
22. Less than 0
23. Between 5 and 8
24. Between 999 and 1001
25. Less than 6
26. Between 9998 and 10,001
27. Less than 9
28. Between 0 and 1

Describe the numbers listed.

Sample: 9, 10, 11, 12 and 13 *Solution:* Whole numbers between 8 and 14

C

29. 3, 4, 5, and 6
30. 0, 1, 2, 3, and 4
31. 10, 11, and 12
32. 0, 1, 2, 3, 4, 5, 6, 7, and 8
33. 7, 8, 9, 10, 11, . . .
34. 0, 1, 2, 3, 4, . . .
35. 21, 22, 23, 24, . . .
36. 1000, 1001, 1002, 1003, . . .

Find the average.

Sample: 5, 6 and 7 *Solution:* $\frac{5 + 6 + 7}{3} = 6$

37. 2, 3, and 4

38. 53, 54, and 55

39. 7, 8, and 9

40. 99, 100, and 101

41. 12, 13, and 14

42. 405, 406, and 407

43. What pattern do you see in Exercises 37–42? Explain.

44. Name two consecutive whole numbers whose sum is 15.

45. Name two consecutive whole numbers whose sum is 27.

46. Name two consecutive whole numbers whose product is 12.

47. Name three consecutive whole numbers whose sum is 30.

consumer notes *Electricity*

Do you turn off the radio when you're not listening to it? If you do, you are saving electricity. Electricity usage is measured in kilowatt-hours (KWH) by an electric meter. To read a meter, note the position of the pointer on each of the four dials. If the pointer is between numbers, read the smaller number. This meter reads 4726 KWH.

Find the electric meter in your house or apartment. Make readings at 9 A.M., 1 P.M., 6 P.M., and 10 P.M. Calculate the amount of electricity used during each period. Over which of these periods was the most electricity used? Have your family think of and use ways of saving electricity. After a week make another set of readings. Do you notice a difference?

2-2 *The Integers*

OBJECTIVES

Read symbols for positive and negative integers.

Name the opposite of an integer.

Complete patterns of consecutive integers.

When the number line shows points on both sides of zero, positive numbers name points to the **right** of 0. Negative numbers name points to the **left** of 0.

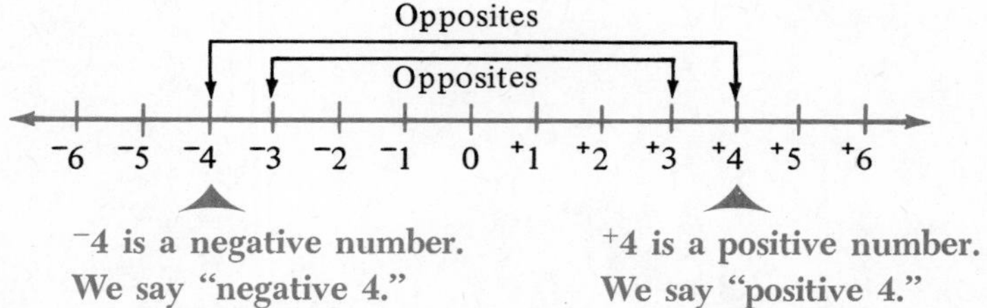

$^-4$ is a negative number.
We say "negative 4."

$^+4$ is a positive number.
We say "positive 4."

Each positive number can be matched with a negative number that is its opposite. **Zero** is its own opposite.

Opposites ► $^+5$ and $^-5$
► $^-17$ and $^+17$
► 0 and 0

The whole numbers (including zero) and their opposites are called the integers.

$$\{\text{the integers}\} = \{\ldots {}^-4, {}^-3, {}^-2, {}^-1, 0, {}^+1, {}^+2, {}^+3, {}^+4, \ldots\}$$

The number line can be used as a model for ideas about integers.

EXAMPLE 1 $^-3$ $^-2$ $^-1$ 0 $^+1$ $^+2$ $^+3$

The set of integers between $^-3$ and $^+2$ is $\{^-2, ^-1, 0, ^+1\}$.

EXAMPLE 2 *A* at $^-4$, *M* at $^-2$, *B* at $^-1$, *K* at $^+1$; $^-4$ $^-3$ $^-2$ $^-1$ 0 $^+1$ $^+2$ $^+3$ $^+4$

The coordinate of point *B* is $^-1$.

EXAMPLE 3

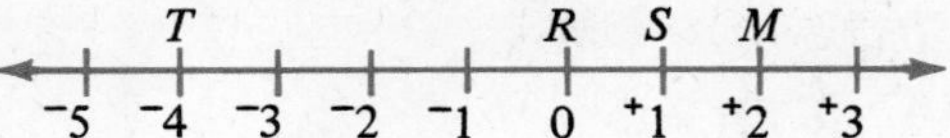

The point half the distance from point *R* to point *M* is point S. Its coordinate is $^{+}1$.

Oral EXERCISES

Read the symbol.

Sample: $^{-}6$ *What you say:* Negative six

Sample: $^{+}3$ *What you say:* Positive three

1. $^{-}8$	**2.** $^{+}15$	**3.** $^{-}19$
4. $^{-}10$	**5.** $^{+}3$	**6.** $^{+}12$
7. $^{+}7$	**8.** $^{-}75$	**9.** $^{-}12$

Name the opposite.

Sample: $^{+}20$ *What you say:* The opposite of $^{+}20$ is $^{-}20$.

10. $^{+}5$	**11.** $^{-}21$	**12.** $^{+}11$
13. $^{+}1$	**14.** 0	**15.** $^{+}100$

Written EXERCISES

A

Name the coordinate.

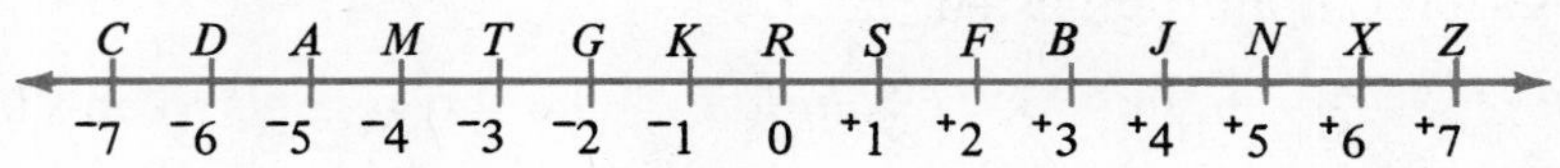

Sample: *G* *Solution:* $^{-}2$

1. *J*	**2.** *B*	**3.** Z
4. *D*	**5.** *R*	**6.** *M*
7. C	**8.** *K*	**9.** S

10. The point between *D* and *M*.

11. The point between *N* and Z.

12. The point between *A* and *T*.

13. The point between *K* and S.

14. The point half the distance between S and *B*.

15. The point half the distance between *R* and *M*.

Complete the pattern.

Sample: $^{-}8, ^{-}7, ^{-}6,$?, ?, ?

Solution: $^{-}8, ^{-}7, ^{-}6, ^{-}5, ^{-}4, ^{-}3$

16. $^{-}15, ^{-}14, ^{-}13,$?, ?, ?

17. ?, ?, $^{-}1, 0, ^{+}1,$?, ?

18. $^{-}4, ^{-}3,$?, ?, ?, $^{+}1$

19. $^{-}2,$?, ?, ?, ?, $^{+}3, ^{+}4$

20. $^{-}1, 0, ^{+}1,$?, ?, ?

21. $^{-}5, ^{-}4, ^{-}3,$?, ?, ?

22. $^{-}3, ^{-}2,$?, ?, ?, $^{+}2$

23. $^{-}2, ^{-}1,$?, ?, ?, $^{+}3$

Name the set of integers described.

Sample: Between $^{-}6$ and $^{-}2$ *Solution:* $\{^{-}5, ^{-}4, ^{-}3\}$

B

24. Between $^{-}7$ and $^{-}4$

25. Between $^{+}1$ and $^{-}6$

26. Between $^{-}2$ and $^{+}2$

27. The positive integers

28. Between $^{-}1$ and $^{+}5$

29. The negative integers

30. Between $^{-}1$ and $^{+}10$

31. Between $^{-}1$ and $^{+}1$

32. Between $^{-}5$ and $^{+}5$

33. The integer that is neither positive nor negative

Describe the integers listed.

Sample: $^{-}5, ^{-}4,$ and $^{-}3$ *Solution:* The integers between $^{-}6$ and $^{-}2$

34. $^{+}5, ^{+}6, ^{+}7,$ and $^{+}8$

35. $^{-}2, ^{-}1,$ and 0

36. $^{+}1, ^{+}2,$ and $^{+}3$

37. $^{-}1, 0,$ and $^{+}1$

The number-line graph of a number is described. Tell whether the number is positive or negative.

C

38. Four units to the left of the graph of $^{+}1$

39. Two units to the right of the graph of $^{-}5$

40. Five units to the left of the graph of $^{+}4$

41. Three units to the right of the graph of $^{-}2$

42. Two units to the left of the graph of $^{-}2$

2-3 *Graphing Integers on the Number Line*

OBJECTIVES

Graph a set of integers on the number line.

Name a set of integers by stating a rule or listing the members.

We can graph a set of integers on the number line. We put a dot at each point that corresponds to an integer to be graphed.

EXAMPLE 1 $\{-1, 0, {}^{+}1, {}^{+}2\}$ ◀ This set is named by listing the members.

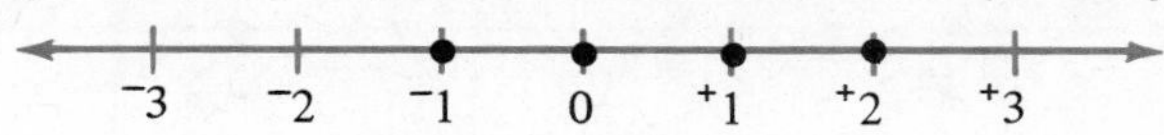

EXAMPLE 2 {the integers between $^{+}2$ and $^{-}3$} ◀ This set is named by stating a rule, or description.

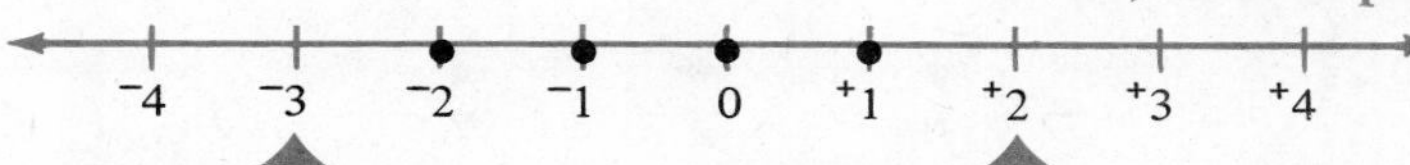

Note that $^{+}2$ and $^{-}3$ are *not* included in the graph.

EXAMPLE 3 {the integers between $^{+}1$ and $^{-}3$, *inclusive*}

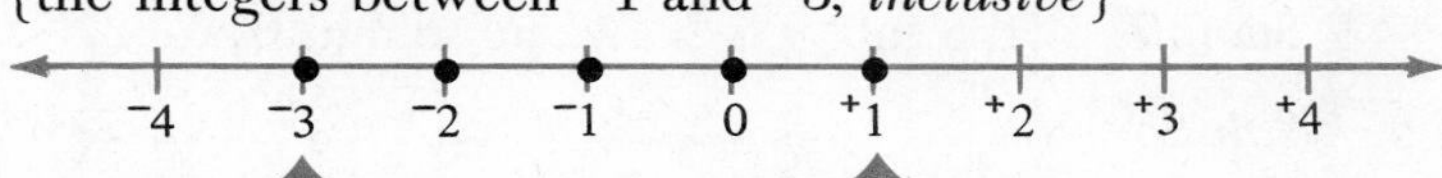

Note that $^{+}1$ and $^{-}3$ *are* included in the graph.

Match.

1. {the integers between $^{-}1$ and $^{+}3$} **A.**
2. {the positive integers less than $^{+}4$} **B.**
3. $\{{}^{-}1, 0, {}^{+}1\}$ **C.**
4. {the integers between $^{-}3$ and 0, inclusive} **D.**
5. $\{0, {}^{+}2\}$ **E.**

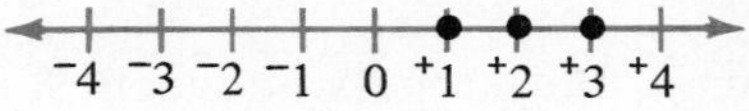

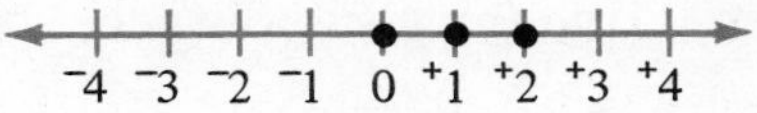

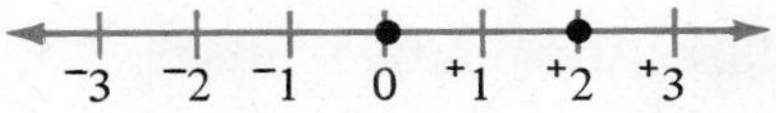

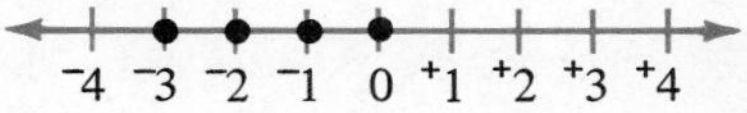

Written EXERCISES

Name the set graphed. List the members.

Sample: 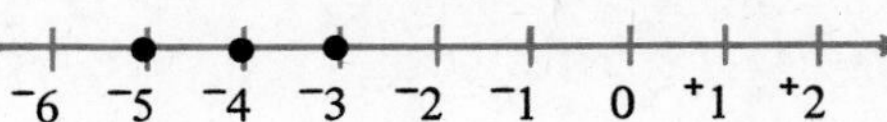

Solution: $\{^-5, ^-4, ^-3\}$

A

1. 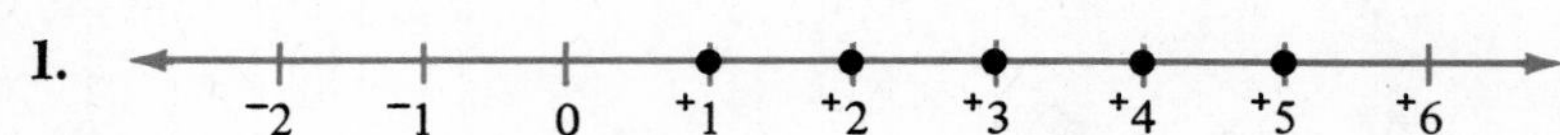

2. 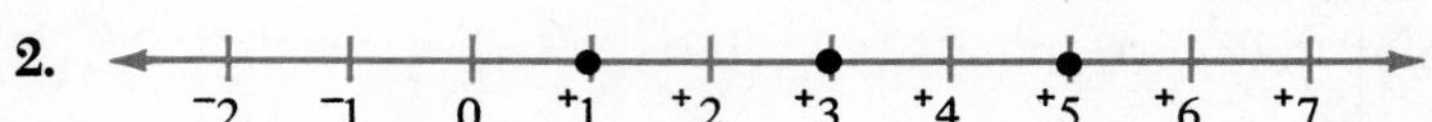

3. $^-4$ $^-3$ $^-2$ $^-1$ 0 $^+1$ $^+2$ $^+3$ $^+4$ $^+5$

4. $^-4$ $^-3$ $^-2$ $^-1$ 0 $^+1$ $^+2$ $^+3$ $^+4$

5. $^-7$ $^-6$ $^-5$ $^-4$ $^-3$ $^-2$ $^-1$ 0 $^+1$ $^+2$

Graph the set of numbers on the number line.

Sample: {the integers between $^-6$ and 0}

Solution: 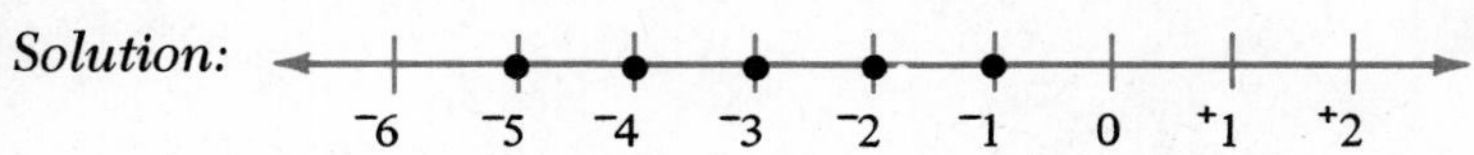

6. $\{^-9, ^-7, ^-5, ^-3\}$
7. {the integers between $^-5$ and $^+5$}
8. $\{^-1, 0, ^+1, ^+2, ^+3\}$
9. {the integers between $^-4$ and $^+2$, inclusive}
10. {the integers between $^-3$ and 0}
11. {the integers between $^-1$ and $^+4$, inclusive}

B

12. {the negative integers greater than $^-3$}
13. {the positive integers between $^-1$ and $^+8$}
14. {the negative integers greater than $^-7$}
15. {the integers between $^-1$ and $^+1$}
16. {the positive integers less than $^+5$}
17. {$^-5$, $^-2$, and their opposites}

Name each set with a rule.

Sample: $\{^-9, ^-8, ^-7, ^-6\}$ *Solution:* {the integers between $^-10$ and $^-5$}

18. $\{0, ^+1, ^+2, ^+3\}$
19. $\{^+100, ^+101, ^+102, \ldots\}$
20. $\{^+1, ^+2, 0, ^-1, ^-2\}$
21. $\{^+10, ^+11, ^+12, ^+13\}$
22. $\{^-5, ^-6, ^-7, ^-8\}$
23. $\{\ldots, ^-3, ^-2, ^-1, 0\}$
24. $\{0\}$
25. $\{^-4, ^-3, ^-2, ^-1\}$
26. $\emptyset$
27. $\{^-9, ^-8, ^+8, ^+9\}$
28. $\{^+1, ^+2, ^-1, ^-2\}$
29. $\{0, ^+2, ^+4, ^+6\}$
30. $\{^-1, ^-2, ^-3, ^-4, \ldots\}$
31. $\{^+5, ^+6, ^+7, ^+8, ^+9, \ldots\}$

SELF-TEST 1

Be sure that you understand these terms and symbols.

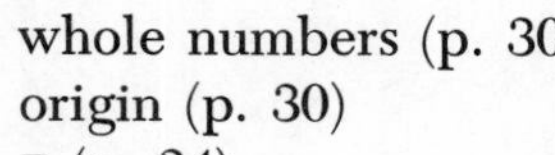

whole numbers (p. 30)	{ } (p. 30)	. . . (p. 30)
origin (p. 30)	Ø (p. 30)	coordinate (p. 31)
$^-$ (p. 34)	$^+$ (p. 34)	integers (p. 34)

1. Name the whole numbers between 793 and 798. **Section 2-1 p. 30**

2. Name the coordinates of *V*, *S*, *Q*, *P*, and *W*.

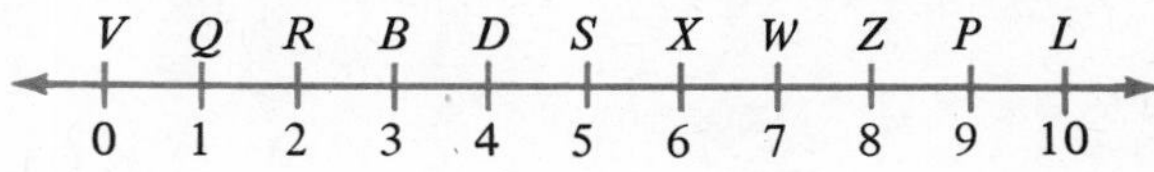

3. Name coordinates of *A*, *G*, *J*, *Y*, and *C*, and their opposites. **Section 2-2 p. 34**

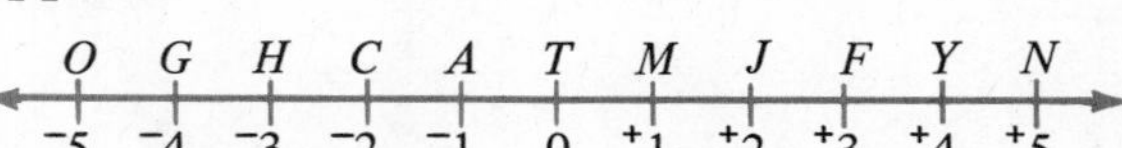

4. Complete the pattern. $^-11, ^-10, ^-9,$ _?_, _?_, _?_.

5. Graph the set on the number line and list the members. {the integers between $^-2$ and $^+3$} **Section 2-3 p. 37**

6. Name $\{^+3, ^+4, ^+5, ^+6\}$ with a rule.

Check your answers with those printed at the back of the book.

Graphs of Numbers and of Pairs of Integers

2-4 *Numbers on the Number Line*

OBJECTIVES

Assign numbers written as fractions and decimals to points on the number line.

Use the symbols > and < to compare numbers.

Arrange positive and negative numbers in order.

Every point on the number line can be matched with a number. Here are some examples.

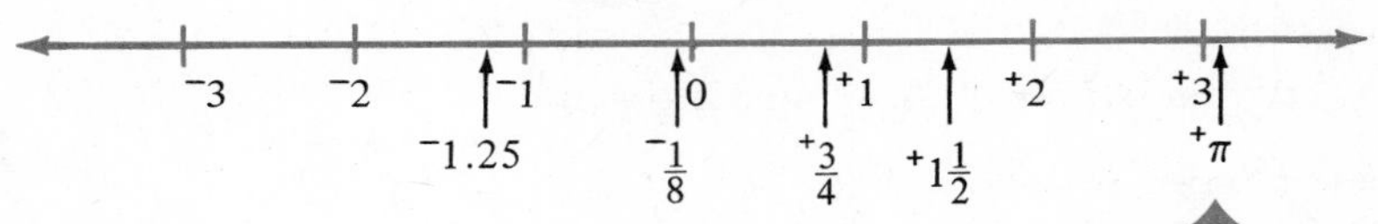

The value of $^{+}\pi$ is about $3\frac{1}{7}$.

Every number is the coordinate of a point on the number line. This is why we can speak of "a number on the number line." For example, we say that every number on the number line has an opposite.

$\frac{^{+}1}{2}$ and $\frac{^{-}1}{2}$

Opposites $^{-}0.25$ and $^{+}0.25$

$\frac{^{+}\pi}{2}$ and $\frac{^{-}\pi}{2}$

The number line can help us compare numbers. Let's agree to speak of the position of a number on the number line when we mean the position of its graph.

The graph of $^{-}1$ is to the left of the graph of $^{+}1$. ► $^{-}1$ is to the left of $^{+}1$.

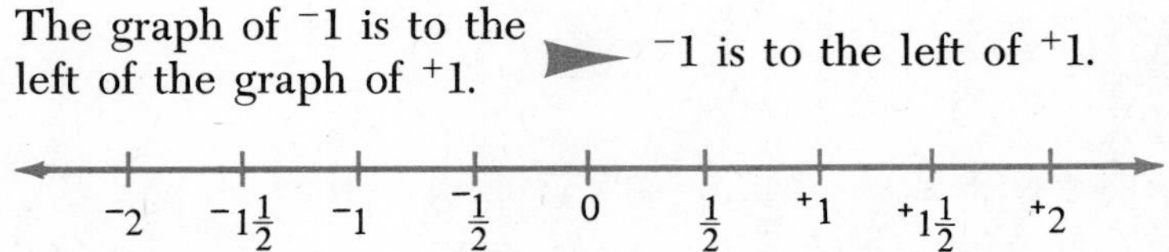

EXAMPLE 1 Compare $^{-}1$ and $\frac{^{+}1}{2}$.

$^{-}1$ is to the left of $\frac{^{+}1}{2}$ ➤ $^{-}1$ is less than $\frac{^{+}1}{2}$

We write $^{-}1 < \frac{^{+}1}{2}$.

is less than

EXAMPLE 2 Compare 0 and $^{-}2$.

0 is to the right of $^{-}2$ ➤ 0 is greater than $^{-}2$

We write $0 > {}^{-}2$.

is greater than

Give the meaning.

Sample: $\frac{^{-}2}{3}$ *What you say:* Negative two-thirds

Sample: $^{+}0.35$ *What you say:* Positive thirty-five hundredths

1. $\frac{^{-}1}{4}$ **2.** $\frac{^{+}2}{5}$ **3.** $^{+}3.8$ **4.** $^{+}1\frac{3}{4}$

5. $\frac{^{-}7}{8}$ **6.** $\frac{^{+}9}{10}$ **7.** $^{-}4.7$ **8.** $^{-}2\frac{1}{2}$

Name the opposite.

Sample: $\frac{^{+}5}{8}$ *What you say:* The opposite of $\frac{^{+}5}{8}$ is $\frac{^{-}5}{8}$.

9. $\frac{^{+}3}{4}$ **10.** $\frac{^{-}1}{3}$ **11.** $^{+}2\frac{3}{5}$ **12.** $^{-}6.25$

13. $\frac{^{+}1}{8}$ **14.** $\frac{^{-}7}{10}$ **15.** $^{-}1\frac{1}{10}$ **16.** $^{+}1.5$

Read the sentence. Tell whether it is true or false.

17. $^{-}2 > {}^{+}1$ **18.** $\frac{^{+}2}{3} < {}^{+}1$ **19.** $^{+}1\frac{1}{2} < {}^{+}2$ **20.** $\frac{^{-}1}{3} > {}^{-}3$

Written EXERCISES

Name the coordinate of each point.

A TR SK M N X P Z

$^{-}3$ $^{-}2$ $^{-}1$ 0 $^{+}1$ $^{+}2$ $^{+}3$

Sample: M *Solution:* $^{+}\frac{1}{4}$

A

1. R	**2.** X	**3.** Z
4. K	**5.** T	**6.** A
7. S	**8.** P	**9.** N

Complete. Use **left** or **right** and $<$ or $>$.

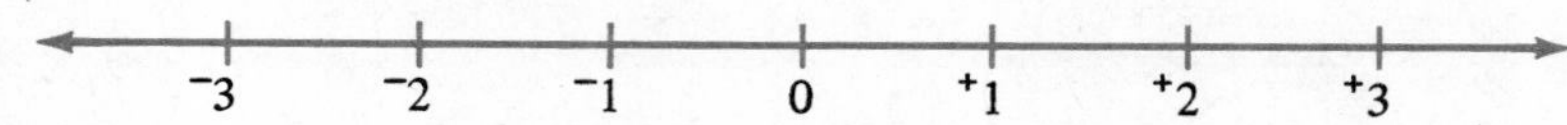

Sample: $^{-}2$ is to the __?__ of $^{+}1$, so $^{-}2$ __?__ $^{+}1$.

Sample: $^{-}2$ is to the **left** of $^{+}1$, so $^{-}2 < {}^{+}1$.

10. $^{+}1$ is to the __?__ of $^{-}1$, so $^{+}1$ __?__ $^{-}1$.

11. $^{-}3$ is to the __?__ of $^{+}3$, so $^{-}3$ __?__ $^{+}3$.

12. $^{+}\frac{2}{3}$ is to the __?__ of 0, so $^{+}\frac{2}{3}$ __?__ 0.

13. $^{-}\frac{2}{3}$ is to the __?__ of 0, so $^{-}\frac{2}{3}$ __?__ 0.

14. $^{-}2$ is to the __?__ of $^{+}\frac{1}{3}$, so $^{-}2$ __?__ $^{+}\frac{1}{3}$.

15. $^{-}1\frac{2}{3}$ is to the __?__ of $^{-}\frac{2}{3}$, so $^{-}1\frac{2}{3}$ __?__ $^{-}\frac{2}{3}$.

16. $^{-}3$ is to the __?__ of $^{-}\frac{1}{3}$, so $^{-}3$ __?__ $^{-}\frac{1}{3}$.

Arrange in order, least to greatest. Use the number line if needed.

Sample: $^{-}6$, $^{+}7$, $^{-}3\frac{1}{2}$, 0, $^{+}\frac{3}{4}$ *Solution:* $^{-}6$, $^{-}3\frac{1}{2}$, 0, $^{+}\frac{3}{4}$, $^{+}7$

17. 0, $^{-}5$, $^{-}7$, $^{+}2$, $^{+}8$

18. 0, $^{-}\frac{1}{2}$, $^{-}\frac{9}{10}$, $^{+}\frac{1}{2}$, $^{+}\frac{9}{10}$

19. $^{-}2$, $^{-}6$, $^{+}1$, 0, $^{-}3$

20. $^{+}5$, $^{-}3$, $^{-}\frac{1}{10}$, $^{-}10$, 0

21. $^-1\frac{1}{2}, {}^+1, {}^+5, {}^-6, 0$

22. $^-3\frac{3}{4}, {}^-3, {}^-3\frac{1}{2}, {}^-3\frac{1}{4}, {}^-4$

23. $^-3, {}^-5, {}^-7, {}^-1, {}^-4$

24. $^-1, {}^+1, {}^+2\frac{1}{2}, {}^-2\frac{1}{2}, 0$

25. $\frac{^-2}{3}, \frac{^+1}{2}, {}^-1\frac{1}{2}, \frac{^+4}{5}$

26. $^+1.5, {}^+2.0, 0, {}^-3.7, {}^-0.5$ B

27. $^+5, \frac{^-3}{4}, {}^-75, 0, {}^+1$

28. $^-3.4, {}^+3.4, {}^-3.3, {}^+3.3, {}^+1, {}^-1$

Draw a number line. Locate each point as accurately as you can.

Sample: $\frac{^-4}{5}, {}^+1\frac{1}{3}, {}^-1\frac{1}{2}, {}^+\pi$

Solution:

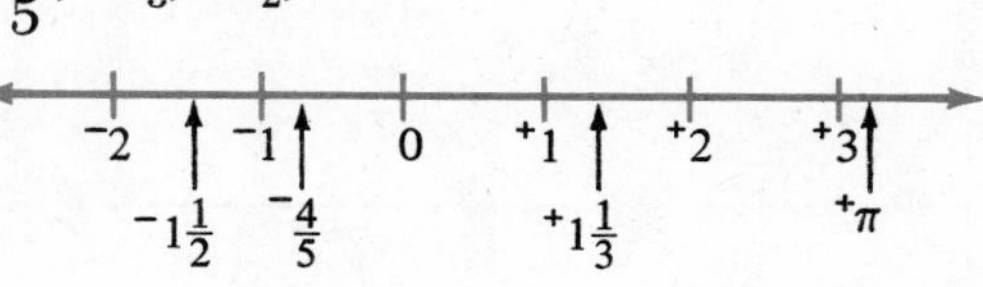

29. $\frac{^+2}{5}, {}^+1\frac{3}{5}, {}^-1\frac{2}{5}, {}^-4\frac{1}{2}$

30. $^-2\frac{1}{3}, \frac{^+5}{6}, {}^+1\frac{2}{3}, \frac{^-1}{6}$

31. $\frac{^-1}{2}, \frac{^+1}{2}, {}^-1\frac{3}{4}, {}^+1\frac{3}{4}$

32. $^-1\frac{5}{8}, \frac{^-3}{8}, \frac{^+7}{8}, {}^+2\frac{1}{8}$

33. $\frac{^+6}{10}, {}^+1\frac{6}{10}, \frac{^-6}{10}, {}^-1\frac{6}{10}$

34. $\frac{^+7}{10}, \frac{^+3}{10}, \frac{^+9}{10}, \frac{^-5}{10}, \frac{^-1}{10}$

35. $^-1.5, {}^+1.9, {}^+0.3, {}^-0.7$

36. $^-0.5, {}^-5.0, {}^-0.05, {}^+5.0, {}^+0.5$ C

37. $0, {}^-2.5, {}^+3.5, {}^+2.5$

38. $^-\pi, {}^-3, {}^+\pi, {}^+3, {}^-1, {}^+1$

Complete. Use $<$ or $>$.

39. $\frac{^+3}{4}$ __?__ $\frac{^+1}{2}$

40. $^-4.5$ __?__ $^+4.8$

41. $^-1\frac{1}{2}$ __?__ $^+1\frac{1}{4}$

42. $^+3.7$ __?__ $^-3.9$

Time out

A horse trader sold a horse that had four shoes and six nails in each shoe. The price was set in this way: the buyer was to pay 1¢ for the first nail, 2¢ for the second, 4¢ for the third, and so on, doubling the amount for each nail until all were paid for. What was the price of the horse?

2-5 *More about Graphing Numbers*

OBJECTIVE

Graph sets of numbers on the number line.

A set such as {the numbers greater than $^{+}2$}, contains infinitely many members. Notice how the graph of such a set is drawn.

EXAMPLE 1 {the numbers greater than $^{+}2$}

The arrow shows that the set continues on and on.

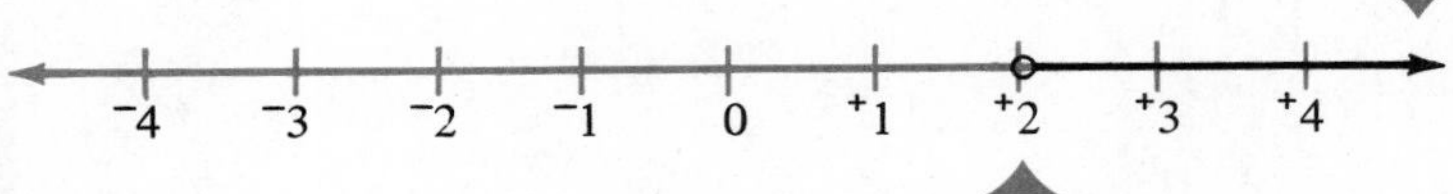

The hollow dot shows that $^{+}2$ is not included.

EXAMPLE 2 {the numbers between $^{+}1$ and $^{-}3$}

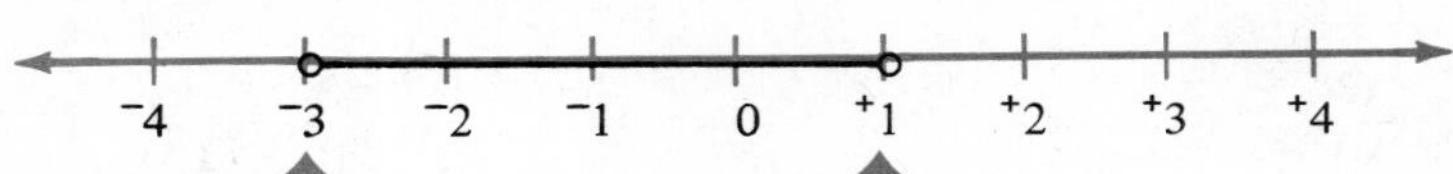

The hollow dots show that $^{-}3$ and $^{+}1$ are not included.

The graph of a set such as {the numbers between $^{-}2$ and $^{+}1$, inclusive} is just a little different.

EXAMPLE 3 {the numbers between $^{-}2$ and $^{+}1$, inclusive.}

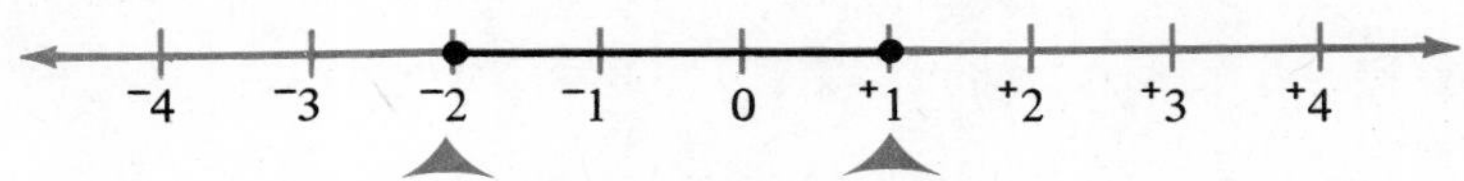

The solid dots show that $^{-}2$ and $^{+}1$ are included.

EXAMPLE 4 {$^{+}1$ and the numbers less than $^{+}1$}

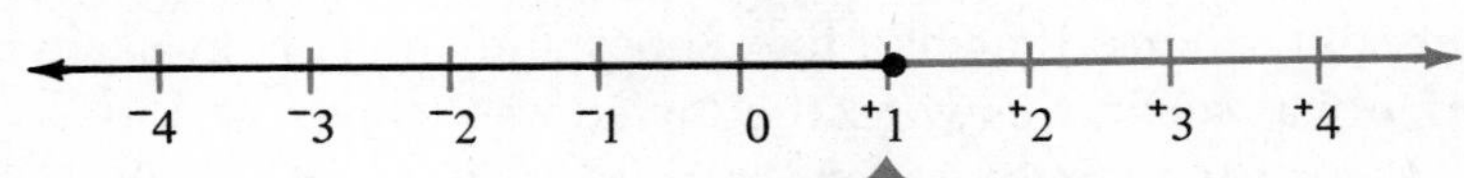

The solid dot shows that $^{+}1$ is included.

Match each set with its graph below.

1. {the numbers less than $^{-}1$}
2. {the numbers between $^{-}1$ and $^{+}2$}
3. {$^{+}3$ and the numbers greater than $^{+}3$}
4. {the numbers between $^{-}1$ and $^{+}2$, inclusive}
5. {the numbers greater than 0}

A.
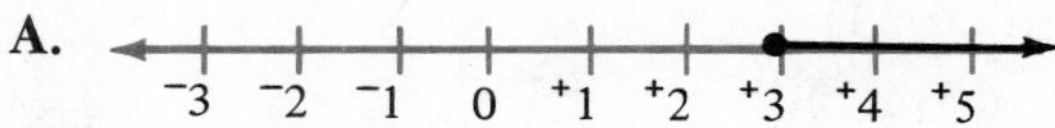

B.
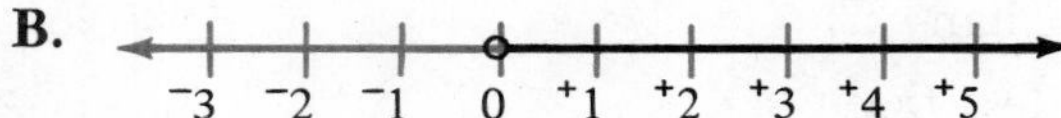

C.

$^{-}3$ $^{-}2$ $^{-}1$ 0 $^{+}1$ $^{+}2$ $^{+}3$ $^{+}4$ $^{+}5$

D.

$^{-}3$ $^{-}2$ $^{-}1$ 0 $^{+}1$ $^{+}2$ $^{+}3$ $^{+}4$ $^{+}5$

E.

$^{-}3$ $^{-}2$ $^{-}1$ 0 $^{+}1$ $^{+}2$ $^{+}3$ $^{+}4$ $^{+}5$

Written EXERCISES

Graph.

Sample 1: {the numbers between $^{+}2$ and 0}

Solution:

$^{-}2$ $^{-}1$ 0 $^{+}1$ $^{+}2$ $^{+}3$ $^{+}4$

Sample 2: {the numbers between $^{+}1$ and $^{+}4$, inclusive}

Solution:

$^{-}2$ $^{-}1$ 0 $^{+}1$ $^{+}2$ $^{+}3$ $^{+}4$

A

1. {the numbers between $^{-}2$ and $^{-}1$}
2. {the numbers between $^{-}1$ and $^{+}2$, inclusive}
3. {the numbers between 0 and $^{+}3$}
4. {the numbers between $^{-}3$ and 0, inclusive}
5. {the numbers between $^{+}2$ and $^{-}2$}
6. {the numbers between $^{-}2$ and $^{+}2$, inclusive}
7. {the numbers between $^{-}1$ and $^{+}4$}
8. {the numbers between $^{-}4$ and $^{-}2$, inclusive}

Graph.

Sample 1: {the numbers greater than $^{+}1$}

Solution:

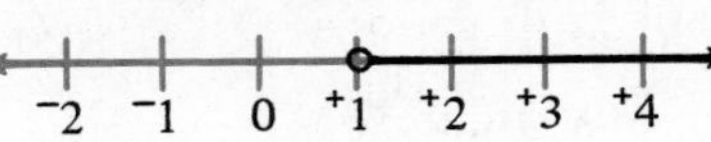

Sample 2: {the numbers less than $^{-}2$}

Solution:

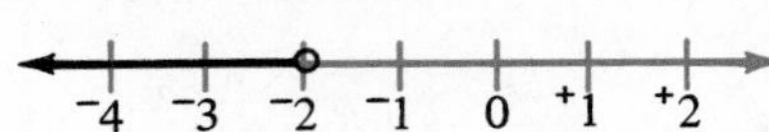

9. {the numbers greater than $^{+}4$}

10. {the numbers less than $^{+}5$}

11. {the numbers greater than $^{-}2$}

12. {$^{-}4$ and the numbers less than $^{-}4$}

13. {the numbers greater than 0}

14. {the numbers less than $^{-}1$}

15. {$^{-}3$ and the numbers greater than $^{-}3$}

16. {0 and the numbers less than 0}

Graph.

Sample: {the numbers between $^{-}3$ and $^{+}1$, including $^{+}1$}

Solution:

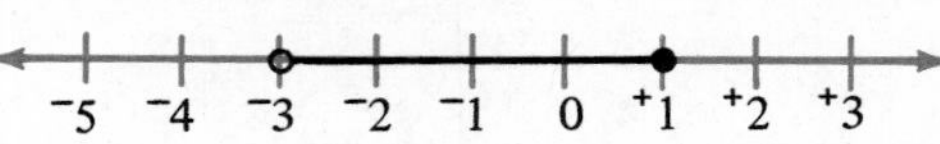

17. {the numbers between $^{-}2$ and $^{+}2$, including $^{+}2$}

18. {$^{-}3$ and the numbers between $^{-}3$ and 0}

19. {the numbers between $^{-}3$ and $^{+}2$, including $^{-}3$}

20. {$^{-}1$ and the numbers between $^{-}1$ and $^{+}1$}

B **21.** {the numbers between $^{-}2$ and $^{+}1\frac{1}{4}$}

22. {the numbers between $^{-}1$ and $^{+}2\frac{1}{2}$}

23. {the numbers between $^{-}1\frac{1}{2}$ and $^{+}3\frac{1}{2}$, inclusive}

24. {the numbers between $^{-}4\frac{1}{3}$ and $^{+}3$, inclusive}

25. {$^{+}2\frac{3}{4}$ and the numbers between 0 and $^{+}2\frac{3}{4}$}

26. {$^{-}1\frac{1}{2}$ and the numbers between $^{-}1\frac{1}{2}$ and $^{+}4$}

27. {the numbers between $^{-}3.5$ and $^{+}3.5$}

28. {the numbers between $^{-}\pi$ and $^{+}\pi$}

29. {$\frac{^{-}2}{3}$ and the numbers between $\frac{^{-}2}{3}$ and 0}

2-6 *Graphing Pairs of Integers*

OBJECTIVES

Use coordinate axes to graph ordered pairs of integers.

Name number pairs as coordinates of points in the plane.

Two perpendicular number lines called coordinate axes may be used to graph an ordered pair of numbers, such as ($^+2$, $^-3$). The numbers in the pair are called coordinates.

($^+2$, $^-3$)

first coordinate second coordinate

To graph ($^+2$, $^-3$), begin at the point (0, 0) where the number lines intersect. This point is called the origin. Count **two** units to the **right,** then **three** units **down.**

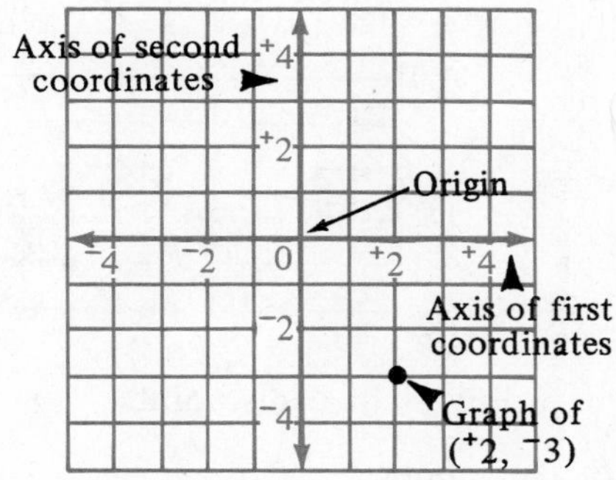

EXAMPLE 1 Graph the ordered pairs:
($^+4$, $^+1$) ($^-2$, $^+3$)
($^+3$, 0) ($^-2$, $^-4$)

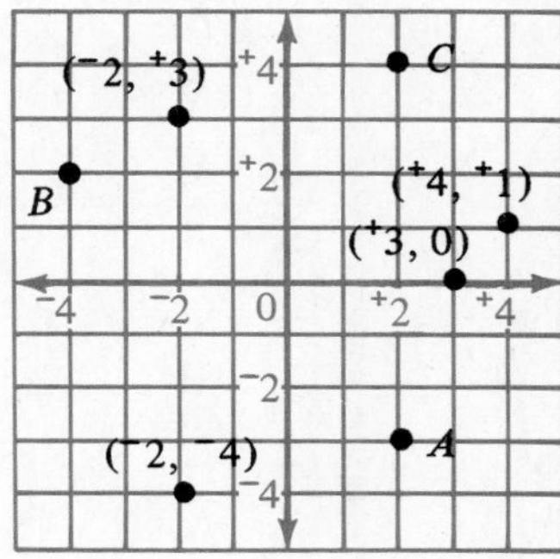

EXAMPLE 2 Name the ordered pair for each lettered point.
A, ($^+2$, $^-3$)
B, ($^-4$, $^+2$)
C, ($^+2$, $^+4$)

EXERCISES

Tell how to locate the graph.

Sample: $(^+3, ^-4)$: __?__ units to the right, __?__ units down.
What you say: **Three** units to the **right, four** units **down.**

1. $(^+1, ^+5)$: __?__ unit to the right, __?__ units up.
2. $(^+2, ^+4)$: __?__ units to the right, __?__ units up.
3. $(^-3, ^+1)$: __?__ units to the left, __?__ units up.
4. $(^-5, ^+2)$: __?__ units to the left, __?__ units up.
5. $(^-2, ^-7)$: __?__ units to the left, __?__ units down.
6. $(0, ^-5)$: __?__ units to left or right, __?__ units down.

Written

EXERCISES

Match the ordered pair with the letter that names its graph.

A

1. $(^+4, ^+2)$
2. $(^-1, ^-2)$
3. $(^-1, ^+2)$
4. $(^+2, ^-4)$
5. $(^-4, ^+2)$

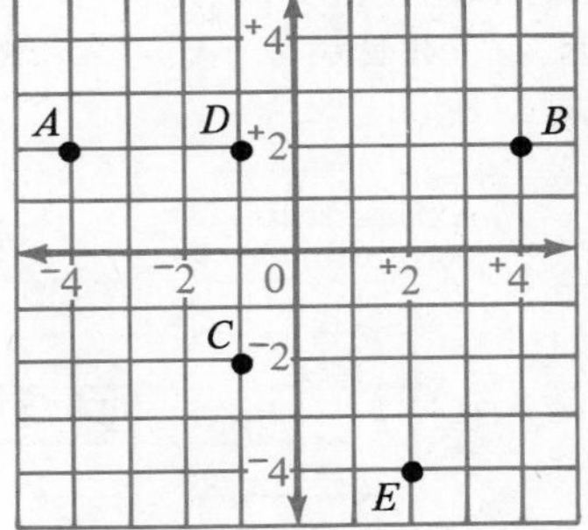

Name the coordinates of each point.

Sample: *R* *Solution:* $(^+5, ^-2)$

6. *P*
7. *N*
8. *M*
9. *T*
10. *Q*
11. *W*
12. *L*
13. *K*
14. *B*
15. *H*

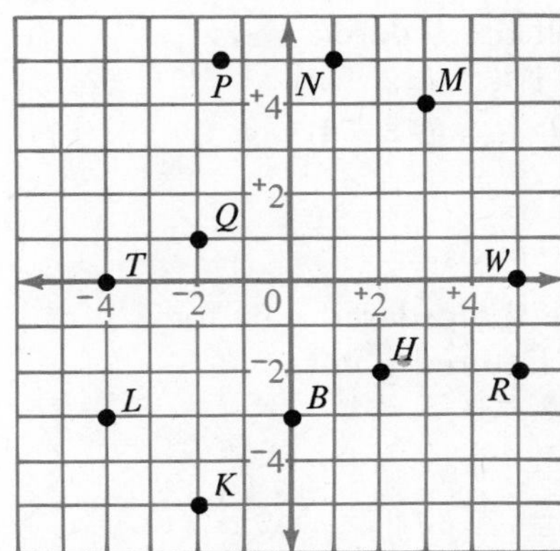

Draw axes and graph.

Sample: $(^-2, ^+3)$ *Solution:*

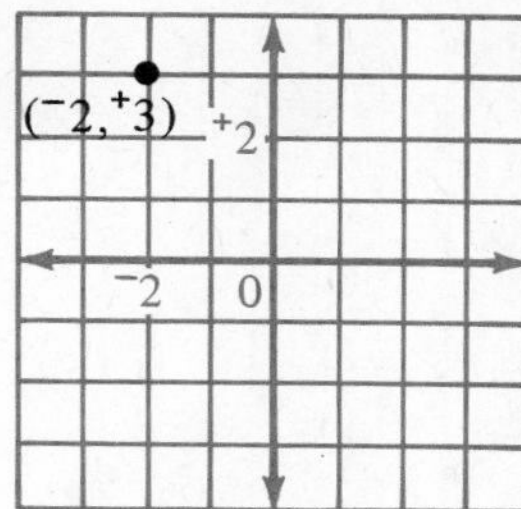

16. $(^+1, ^+3)$ **17.** $(0, 0)$

18. $(^+1, ^-5)$ **19.** $(0, ^-3)$

20. $(^-2, ^+3)$ **21.** $(0, ^+6)$

22. $(^-4, ^-4)$ **23.** $(^+4, 0)$

24. $(^-8, ^+2)$ **25.** $(^-7, 0)$

Name the coordinates.

Sample: 8 units right, 2 units down *Solution:* $(^+8, ^-2)$

26. 1 unit right, 5 units down

27. 2 units right, 0 units up or down

28. 5 units left, 1 unit down

29. 8 units left, 5 units up

30. 3 units right, 2 units down

31. 0 units left or right, 6 units up

32. 4 units right, 1 unit up

33. 0 units left or right, 6 units down

B

Name the points. Describe the pattern.

Sample:

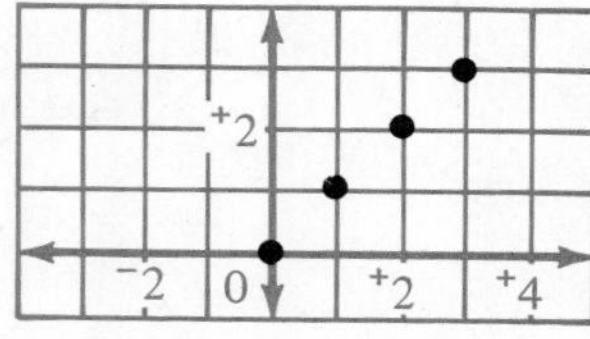

Solution: $(0, 0)$, $(^+1, ^+1)$, $(^+2, ^+2)$ and $(^+3, ^+3)$

The first and second coordinates are the same positive number.

34.

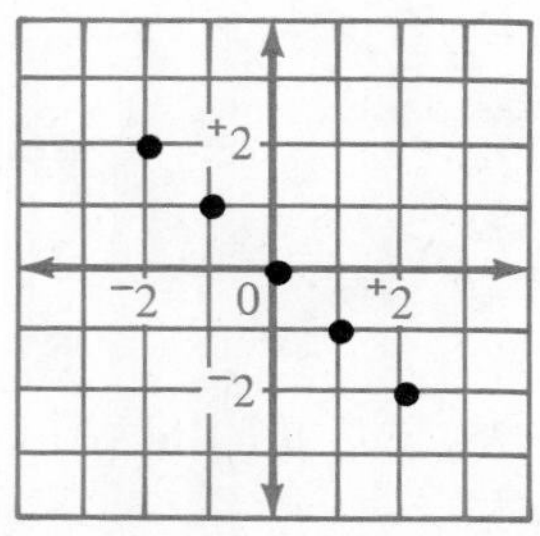

35.

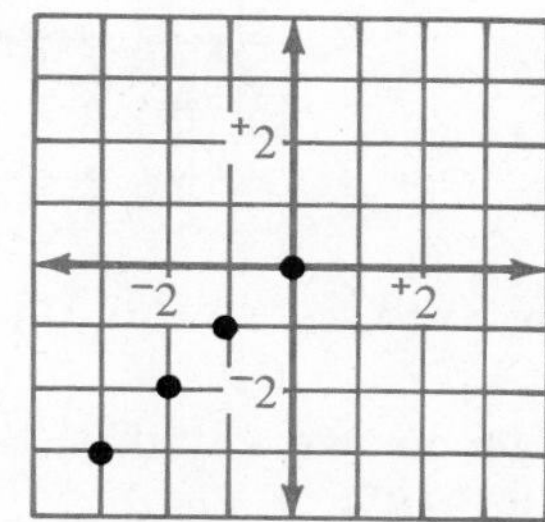

Name the points. Describe the pattern.

36.

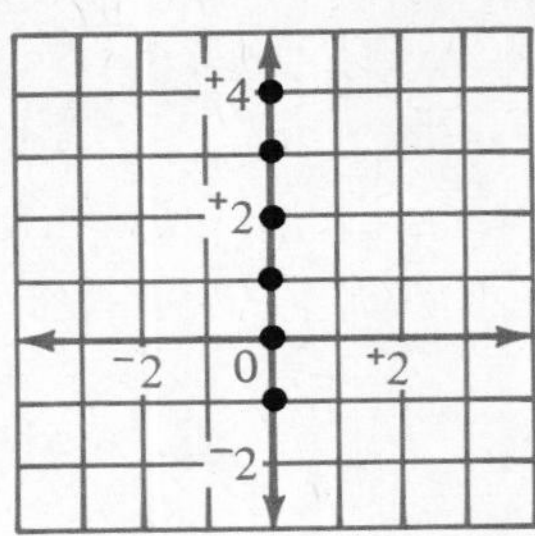

37.

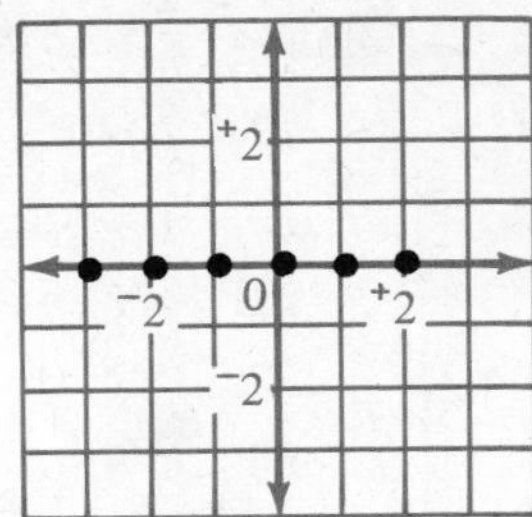

SELF-TEST 2

Be sure that you understand these terms and symbols.

$<$ (p. 41)	$>$ (p. 41)	hollow dot (p. 44)
coordinate axes (p. 47)	ordered pair (p. 47)	origin (p. 47)

Section 2-4 p. 40

1. Name the coordinates of *A*, *V*, *J*, *L* and *T*.

2. Complete using $<$ or $>$. $\frac{^-3}{4}$? $\frac{^-1}{4}$

3. Arrange $^-2\frac{3}{4}$, $^-5$, $\frac{^+9}{10}$, $^+1$, $\frac{^+1}{2}$ in order from least to the greatest.

Section 2-5 p. 44

4. Graph {the numbers between $^-2$ and $^+3$}.

Section 2-6 p. 47

5. Name the coordinates of *P*, *Q*, *Z*, and *T*.

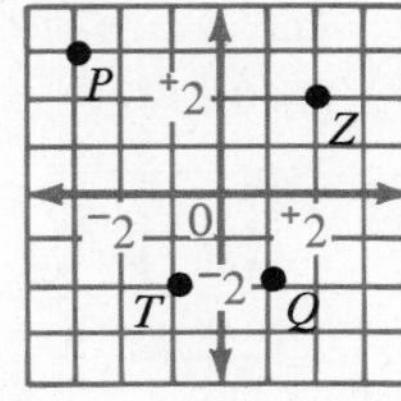

6. Draw axes and graph $(^-3, ^+2)$.

Check your answers with those printed at the back of the book.

chapter summary

1. The set of **whole numbers** is written: {0, 1, 2, 3, 4, 5, . . .}.
2. The set of **integers** includes both positive and negative numbers. Positive numbers are indicated by small raised plus signs ($^+$). Negative numbers are indicated by small raised minus signs ($^-$).
3. The set of integers includes 0, the positive whole numbers, and their **opposites.** The set of integers is written:

   $$\{\ldots {}^-3, {}^-2, {}^-1, 0, {}^+1, {}^+2, {}^+3, \ldots\}.$$

   Zero is neither positive nor negative.
4. Integers may be matched with equally spaced points on the number line. An integer is the coordinate of the point with which it is matched. The point is marked with a dot to show the **graph** of the number.
5. Every point on the number line can be matched with a positive number, a negative number, or zero. Every number has an opposite. Zero is its own opposite.
6. The symbol $>$ means **is greater than** and the symbol $<$ means **is less than.** These symbols are used to compare numbers.
7. Positive and negative numbers can be graphed on the number line.
8. An ordered number pair can be graphed on a plane, using coordinate axes consisting of two perpendicular number lines.

calculator corner

The decimal form of $6\frac{2}{3}$ or $\frac{20}{3}$ is a repeating decimal, $6.\overline{6}$, larger than any calculator display can show. You can use this decimal to tell if your calculator rounds when it performs division. Divide 20 by 3. If the display shows 6.666 . . . . 7, your calculator rounds. If the display shows 6.666 . . . , your calculator "truncates" or merely cuts off any digits not displayed.

chapter test

Name the coordinate.

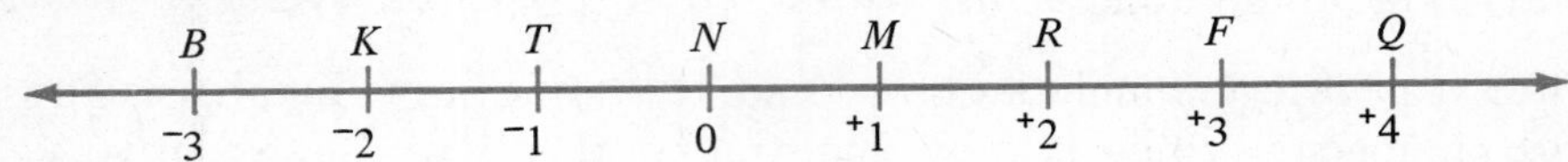

1. B 2. R 3. Q
4. M 5. K 6. The point half the distance from T to M
7. T 8. F 9. The point half the distance from K to N

Name the opposite.

10. $^+6$ **11.** $^-8$ **12.** 0 **13.** $^+\frac{3}{4}$

14. $^-18$ **15.** $^+10$ **16.** $^-\frac{1}{2}$ **17.** $^+1.5$

Complete the pattern.

18. $^-4, ^-3, ^-2,$? , ? , ? , $^+2$ **19.** ? , ? , $^-3, ^-2, ^-1,$?

20. $^-1, 0,$? , ? , ? , ? , $^+5$ **21.** $^-26, ^-25,$? , ? , ? , $^-21$

Graph. Use the number line.

22. The integers between $^+1$ and $^-3$.

23. The integers between 0 and $^+4$, inclusive.

24. The numbers greater than $^-1$.

25. The numbers between $^-2$ and $^+2$.

Complete. Use $<$ or $>$.

26. $^+5$? $^+2$ **27.** $^+3$? $^-1$ **28.** 0 ? $^-10$

29. 0 ? $^+4$ **30.** $^-5$? $^-2$ **31.** $^-4$? $^-7\frac{1}{2}$

Draw axes and graph.

32. $(^-3, ^+3), (^-2, ^+4), (^+5, ^+4), (^+4, ^-2)$, and $(^+1, ^+3)$.

33. $(^-1, ^-6), (0, ^+3), (0, ^-3), (^+5, 0)$, and $(^-5, 0)$.

challenge topics

Sugar Cubes

Each one of eight sugar cubes is 1 centimeter on an edge. The eight cubes can be arranged in several different ways to form three-dimensional shapes. One way is shown here.

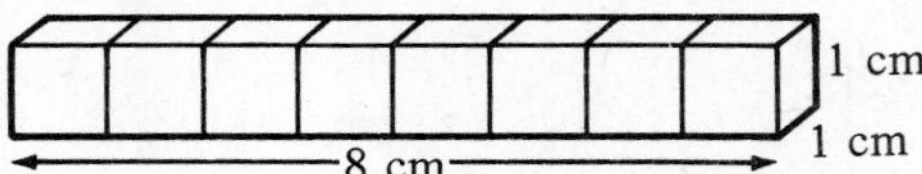

How many faces of cubes could be shown in this shape? Imagine covering the shape with graph paper that is divided into centimeter squares. Make a diagram of the graph paper needed to cover the shape. Count the number of squares in your diagram. The number of square centimeters is the surface area of the shape. Draw sketches of a cube and other shapes you can make with the eight sugar cubes. Make a diagram of the graph paper needed to cover each shape. Copy the chart below and use it to record your findings. List the shapes in order from least to greatest, according to the surface area.

Sketch Of Shape	*Surface Area*	*Faces Showing*

Do you notice any similarities in your completed chart? Explain them. Which shape is listed first? Which is listed second? Do you notice any physical similarities between the two shapes? Which shape is listed last? Is this shape different from those listed first? How? Make a statement about relationships between shapes and surface areas.

review of skills

Complete.

1. $2 \times \underline{\ ?\ } = 18$
2. $\underline{\ ?\ } \times 5 = 35$
3. $7 \times \underline{\ ?\ } = 28$
4. $4 \times \underline{\ ?\ } = 32$
5. $\frac{8}{1} = \underline{\ ?\ }$
6. $9 \times \underline{\ ?\ } = 45$
7. $\underline{\ ?\ } \times 7 = 28$
8. $\frac{?}{2} = 4$
9. $\underline{\ ?\ } = \frac{4}{1}$

Name the place value of the underlined digit.

Sample: $34\underline{8}.25$ *Solution:* 8 is in the ones place.

10. $2.\underline{9}3$
11. $\underline{6}39.1$
12. $31.89\underline{5}$
13. $45.0\underline{7}$
14. $0.004\underline{2}$
15. $5.\underline{0}$
16. $5.\underline{7}2$
17. $1.23\underline{3}$
18. $0.000\underline{1}$

Simplify.

Sample: $(2 \times 9) + 1$ *Solution:* $(2 \times 9) + 1 = 18 + 1 = 19$

19. $(2 \times 5) + 3$
20. $(5 \times 4) + 1$
21. $3 + (4 \times 4)$
22. $(4 \times 6) + 1$
23. $(2 \times 7) + 1$
24. $(9 \times 2) + 1$
25. $(2 \times 2) + 2$
26. $3 \times (1 + 1)$
27. $1 \times (1 + 1)$

Divide. Write the quotient as a decimal.

28. $5\overline{)2}$
29. $2\overline{)5}$
30. $5\overline{)4}$
31. $5\overline{)3}$
32. $4\overline{)3}$
33. $8\overline{)4}$
34. $8\overline{)7}$
35. $4\overline{)1}$
36. $8\overline{)5}$

Left: Actors producing sound effects for 1925 radio program "Rip Van Winkle."

Right: Television sound engineer.

3 Factors and Multiples; Decimals and the Metric System

3-1 *Multiples and Common Multiples*

OBJECTIVES

Name the multiples of a number.

Name the common multiples and the least common multiple of two numbers.

From now on, we will not use $^+$ signs for positive numbers. For example, $^+1$ will be written 1.

The **counting numbers** are the numbers 1, 2, 3, 4, 5, 6, 7, and so on. The **multiples** of a whole number are found by multiplying the number by the counting numbers. That is, to find the multiples of 3, we replace n in $3 \times n$ with counting numbers. (Remember 0 is *not* a counting number.)

Replace n with counting numbers.

EXAMPLE 1

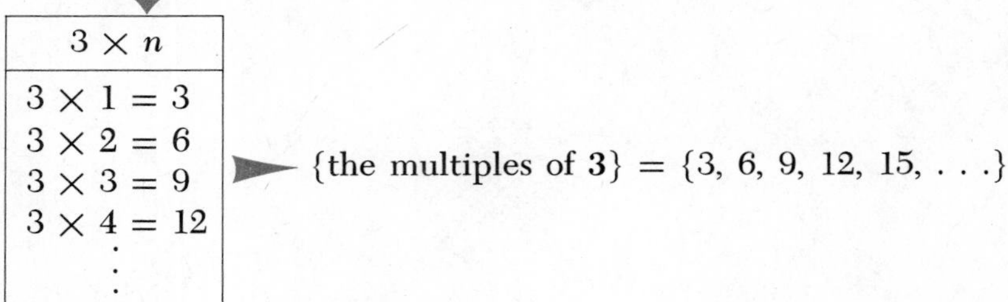

3 × n
3 × 1 = 3
3 × 2 = 6
3 × 3 = 9
3 × 4 = 12
{the multiples of 3} = {3, 6, 9, 12, 15, . . .}

To find the multiples of 5 we replace n in $5 \times n$ with counting numbers.

EXAMPLE 2

$5 \times n$
$5 \times 1 = 5$
$5 \times 2 = 10$
$5 \times 3 = 15$
$5 \times 4 = 20$
⋮

{the multiples of **5**} = {5, 10, 15, 20, 25, . . .}

The set of common multiples of 3 and 5 is {15, 30, 45, 60, . . .}. The **least common multiple** (LCM) of 3 and 5 is **15.**

Oral EXERCISES

Complete.

Sample: {the multiples of 10} = {10, 20, 30, _?_, _?_, _?_, . . .}
What you say: The set 10, 20, 30, 40, 50, 60, and so on.

1. {the multiples of 2} = {2, 4, 6, _?_, _?_, _?_, _?_, . . .}
2. {the multiples of 6} = {6, 12, 18, _?_, _?_, _?_, _?_, . . .}
3. {the multiples of 4} = {4, 8, 12, _?_, _?_, _?_, _?_, . . .}
4. {the multiples of 100} = {100, 200, 300, _?_, _?_, _?_, _?_, . . .}

Complete. Use 2, 3, 4, or 5.

Sample: 12 is divisible by _?_, _?_, and _?_.
12 is a multiple of _?_, _?_, and _?_.
What you say: 12 is divisible by 2, 3, and 4.
12 is a multiple of 2, 3, and 4.

5. 10 is divisible by _?_ and _?_.
   10 is a multiple of _?_ and _?_.
6. 15 is divisible by _?_ and _?_.
   15 is a multiple of _?_ and _?_.
7. 30 is divisible by _?_, _?_ and _?_.
   30 is a multiple of _?_, _?_ and _?_.

Written EXERCISES

Solve each equation. Then write the set of multiples.

Sample:
$1 \times 7 = s$
$2 \times 7 = b$
$3 \times 7 = n$
$4 \times 7 = y$
{the multiples of 7} = _?_

Solution:
$s = 7$
$b = 14$
$n = 21$
$y = 28$
{7, 14, 21, 28, . . .}

A

1. $1 \times 9 = a$
   $2 \times 9 = h$
   $3 \times 9 = m$
   $4 \times 9 = w$
   {the multiples of 9} = _?_

2. $1 \times 12 = c$
   $2 \times 12 = k$
   $3 \times 12 = x$
   $4 \times 12 = s$
   {the multiples of 12} = _?_

3. $1 \times 4 = t$
   $2 \times 4 = r$
   $3 \times 4 = p$
   $4 \times 4 = n$
   {the multiples of 4} = _?_

4. $1 \times 8 = f$
   $2 \times 8 = z$
   $3 \times 8 = y$
   $4 \times 8 = n$
   {the multiples of 8} = _?_

Complete the table.

	Numbers	*Sets of Multiples*	*Common Multiples*	*LCM*
5.	3 2	{3, 6, 9, 12, 15, 18, . . .} {2, 4, 6, 8, 10, 12, . . .}	{6, 12, 18, . . .}	?
6.	4 5	? ?	?	?
7.	3 4	? ?	?	?
8.	6 10	? ?	?	?

Name the least common multiple (LCM).

Sample 1: 4 and 8 *Solution:* 8
Sample 2: 4 and 9 *Solution:* 36

9. 3 and 5 **10.** 2 and 5 **11.** 3 and 4
12. 3 and 6 **13.** 12 and 4 **14.** 4 and 6
15. 5 and 10 **16.** 2 and 10 **17.** 8 and 16

B **18.** 5 and 8 **19.** 6 and 9 **20.** 10 and 15
21. 12 and 15 **22.** 7 and 9 **23.** 15 and 20
24. 7 and 8 **25.** 5 and 11 **26.** 9 and 10

Complete. Name the greatest multiple of 10 that makes the statement true.

Sample: $\underline{\ ?\ } < 48$ *Solution:* $40 < 48$

27. $\underline{\ ?\ } < 14$ **28.** $\underline{\ ?\ } < 21$ **29.** $\underline{\ ?\ } < 47$
30. $\underline{\ ?\ } < 86$ **31.** $\underline{\ ?\ } < 29$ **32.** $\underline{\ ?\ } < 31$
33. $\underline{\ ?\ } < 43$ **34.** $\underline{\ ?\ } < 125$ **35.** $\underline{\ ?\ } < 279$

Complete. Name the greatest multiple of 8 that makes the statement true.

Sample: $\underline{\ ?\ } < 63$ *Solution:* $56 < 63$

C **36.** $\underline{\ ?\ } < 75$ **37.** $\underline{\ ?\ } < 100$ **38.** $\underline{\ ?\ } < 130$
39. $\underline{\ ?\ } < 86$ **40.** $\underline{\ ?\ } < 203$ **41.** $\underline{\ ?\ } < 148$

3-2 *Common Factors*

> **OBJECTIVES**
> **Name the whole number factors of a number.**
> **Name the common factors and the greatest common factor of two numbers.**

We can use either multiplication or division to find the whole number factors of a number.

$8 = \mathbf{8} \times \mathbf{1}$ $\qquad$ $8 \div \mathbf{1} = \mathbf{8}$

$8 = \mathbf{2} \times \mathbf{4}$ $\qquad$ $8 \div \mathbf{2} = \mathbf{4}$

factors of 8 $\qquad$ factors of 8

The set of factors of 8 is $\{1, 2, 4, 8\}$.

$20 = \mathbf{1} \times \mathbf{20}$ $\qquad$ $20 \div \mathbf{1} = \mathbf{20}$

$20 = \mathbf{2} \times \mathbf{10}$ $\qquad$ $20 \div \mathbf{2} = \mathbf{10}$

$20 = \mathbf{4} \times \mathbf{5}$ $\qquad$ $20 \div \mathbf{4} = \mathbf{5}$

The set of factors of 20 is $\{1, 2, 4, 5, 10, 20\}$. We can use a diagram to show the common factors of 8 and 20.

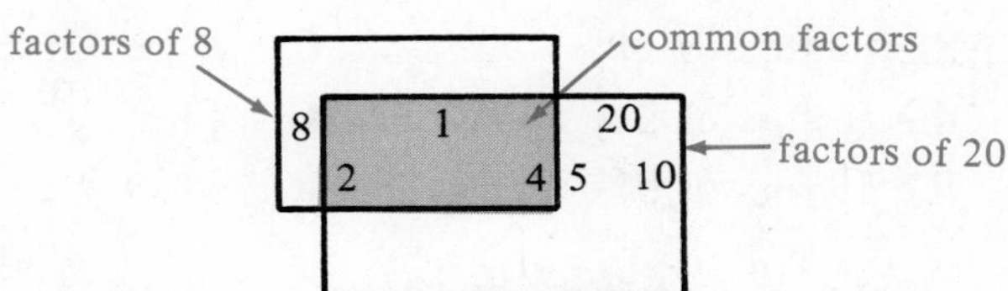

The set of common factors of 8 and 20 is $\{1, 2, 4\}$. The greatest common factor (GCF) of 8 and 20 is 4.

EXAMPLE 1 Factors of 6: $\{\mathbf{1}, \mathbf{2}, \mathbf{3}, \mathbf{6}\}$ Factors of 18: $\{\mathbf{1}, \mathbf{2}, \mathbf{3}, \mathbf{6}, 9, 18\}$
Common factors of 6 and 18: $\{1, 2, 3, 6\}$
The GCF of 6 and 18 is 6.

EXAMPLE 2 Factors of 7: $\{\mathbf{1}, 7\}$ Factors of 9: $\{\mathbf{1}, 3, 9\}$
Common factor of 7 and 9: $\{1\}$
The GCF of 7 and 9 is 1.

EXERCISES

Name the common factors and the GCF.

Sample:

Numbers	*Factors*
6 15	{1, 2, 3, 6} {1, 3, 5, 15}

What you say:
The common factors are 1 and 3. The GCF is 3.

1.

Numbers	*Factors*
3 5	{1, 3} {1, 5}

2.

Numbers	*Sets of Factors*
12 20	{1, 2, 3, 4, 6, 12} {1, 2, 4, 5, 10, 20}

3.

Numbers	*Factors*
7 8	{1, 7} {1, 2, 4, 8}

4.

Numbers	*Factors*
9 6	{1, 3, 9} {1, 2, 3, 6}

Written
EXERCISES

A

Match.

1. {the factors of 18} **A.** {1, 11}
2. {the factors of 21} **B.** {1, 3, 9}
3. {the factors of 11} **C.** {1, 2, 11, 22}
4. {the factors of 22} **D.** {1, 2, 3, 6, 9, 18}
5. {the factors of 9} **E.** {1, 3, 7, 21}

Replace the variable in each equation. Then list the factors.

Sample 1: $1 \times r = 8$
$2 \times s = 8$
{the factors of 8} = ___?___

Solution: $1 \times 8 = 8$
$2 \times 4 = 8$
{the factors of 8} = {1, 2, 4, 8}

Sample 2: $\frac{10}{1} = W$

$\frac{10}{2} = Z$

{the factors of 10} = ___?___

Solution: $\frac{10}{1} = 10$

$\frac{10}{2} = 5$

{the factors of 10} = {1, 2, 5, 10}

6. $1 \times a = 16$
$2 \times b = 16$
$4 \times c = 16$
{the factors of 16} = ___?___

7. $1 \times V = 35$
$5 \times W = 35$
{the factors of 35} = ___?___

8. $\frac{6}{1} = m$

$\frac{6}{2} = n$

{the factors of 6} = ___?___

9. $\frac{17}{1} = k$

{the factors of k} = ___?___

List the numbers in each set.

Sample: {the factors of 27} *Solution:* 1, 3, 9, 27

10. {the factors of 4}
11. {the factors of 26}
12. {the factors of 24}
13. {the factors of 14}
14. {the factors of 30}
15. {the factors of 13}
16. {the factors of 15}
17. {the factors of 50}

Name the common factors and the greatest common factor (GCF).

B

18. 6 and 4
19. 8 and 12
20. 21 and 27
21. 16 and 20
22. 5 and 15
23. 9 and 18
24. 20 and 25
25. 5 and 7
26. 2 and 11

Name the GCF.

27. 9 and 12
28. 4 and 10
29. 14 and 18
30. 27 and 45
31. 15 and 16
32. 24 and 30

True or false?

C

33. 1 is a factor of every counting number.
34. Every counting number is a factor of itself.
35. The GCF of two consecutive counting numbers is always 1.
36. The GCF of two odd numbers is always 1.

3-3 *Special Sets of Whole Numbers*

OBJECTIVES

Express an even number in the form $2 \times n$.

Express an odd number in the form $(2 \times n) + 1$.

Identify prime numbers.

Beginning with zero, we count by 2's to name the **even** numbers. Each even number can be expressed in the form $2 \times n$, where n is a whole number.

$2 \times n$
$2 \times 0 = 0$
$2 \times 1 = 2$
$2 \times 2 = 4$
$2 \times 3 = 6$
⋮

→ {the even numbers} = {0, 2, 4, 6, 8, 10, 12, . . .}

A whole number that is not even is an **odd** number. Each odd number can be expressed in the form $(2 \times n) + 1$, where n is a whole number.

$(2 \times n) + 1$
$(2 \times 0) + 1 = 1$
$(2 \times 1) + 1 = 3$
$(2 \times 2) + 1 = 5$
$(2 \times 3) + 1 = 7$
⋮

→ {the odd numbers} = {1, 3, 5, 7, 9, 11, 13, . . .}

A whole number that has exactly two different factors, itself and 1, is a **prime** number.

EXAMPLES

Number	*Set of Factors*	*Prime/Not Prime*
2	{1, 2}	Prime
5	{1, 5}	Prime
1	{1}	Not Prime
15	{1, 3, 5, 15}	Not Prime

Oral EXERCISES

Simplify. Tell whether the result is an odd or an even number.

Sample 1: 2×7 *What you say:* $2 \times 7 = 14$; 14 is an even number.

Sample 2: $(2 \times 4) + 1$ *What you say:* $(2 \times 4) + 1 = 9$; 9 is an odd number.

1. 2×5
2. 2×8
3. $(2 \times 8) + 1$
4. $(2 \times 3) + 1$
5. $(2 \times 25) + 1$
6. 2×25
7. 2×100
8. $(2 \times 100) + 1$
9. $(2 \times 30) + 1$

Written EXERCISES

A

Write in the form $2 \times n$ if possible, where n is a whole number.

Sample 1: 60 *Solution:* $60 = 2 \times 30$

Sample 2: 19 *Solution:* Not possible.

1. 14
2. 20
3. 17
4. 30
5. 7
6. 41
7. 72
8. 0
9. 11

Write in the form $(2 \times n) + 1$ if possible, where n is a whole number.

Sample 1: 15 *Solution:* $15 = 14 + 1 = (2 \times 7) + 1$

10. 9
11. 28
12. 5
13. 23
14. 27
15. 41
16. 50
17. 55
18. 17

Add. Label each number *odd* or *even.*

Sample: $40 + 12$ *Solution:* $40 + 12 = 52$
even + even = even

19. $6 + 8$
20. $12 + 10$
21. $4 + 0$
22. $2 + 16$
23. $7 + 9$
24. $11 + 11$
25. $5 + 1$
26. $3 + 15$
27. $8 + 9$

Complete.

28. The last digit of an even number is 0, 2, _?_, _?_, or _?_.

29. The last digit of an odd number is 1, 3, _?_, _?_, or _?_.

Write the set of factors. Tell which numbers are prime.

Sample: 17: {_?_, _?_} *Solution:* 17: {1, 17}; 17 is prime.

30. 5: {_?_, _?_} **31.** 14: {_?_, _?_, _?_, _?_} **32.** 7: {_?_, _?_}

B **33.** 11 **34.** 2 **35.** 4

36. 23 **37.** 57 **38.** 61

Complete. Use odd or even.

39. even + even = _?_ **40.** odd + odd = _?_

41. odd + even = _?_ **42.** even + even + even = _?_

43. even × 1 = _?_ **44.** even × 3 = _?_

Write each even number as the sum of two prime numbers.

C **45.** 8 **46.** 78 **47.** 50

48. 12 **49.** 100 **50.** 84

SELF-TEST 1

Be sure that you understand these terms.

counting numbers (p. 56) multiple (p. 56)
common multiple (p. 56) least common multiple (p. 56)
factor (p. 59) greatest common factor (p. 59)
even number (p. 62) odd number (p. 62)
prime number (p. 62)

Section 3-1, p. 56 Solve for each variable. Then write the set of multiples.

1. $1 \times 7 = r$
$2 \times 7 = s$
$3 \times 7 = t$

2. $1 \times 3 = d$
$2 \times 3 = e$
$3 \times 3 = f$

3. Name the least common multiple of 7 and 11.

Section 3-2, p. 59 **4.** List the numbers in {the factors of 10}.

5. Name the common factors and the GCF of 6 and 3.

Section 3-3, p. 62 **6.** Write 18 in the form $2 \times n$, where n is a whole number.

7. Write 15 in the form $(2 \times n) + 1$, where n is a whole number.

Check your answers with those printed at the back of the book.

3-4 *Fractions*

OBJECTIVES

Write equivalent forms of a fraction: $\frac{2}{3} = \frac{4}{6} = \frac{6}{9}, \ldots$.

Write a fraction in lowest terms.

Fractions that name the same number are called **equivalent fractions.** To write a fraction in the form of an equivalent fraction, we either multiply or divide both the numerator and the denominator by the same number (except 0).

EXAMPLE 1 $\frac{5}{8} = \frac{5 \times 3}{8 \times 3} = \frac{15}{24}$ ► $\frac{5}{8}$ and $\frac{15}{24}$ are equivalent fractions.

EXAMPLE 2 $\frac{24}{30} = \frac{24 \div 6}{30 \div 6} = \frac{4}{5}$ ► $\frac{24}{30}$ and $\frac{4}{5}$ are equivalent fractions.

A fraction is in **lowest terms** when the greatest common factor (GCF) of the numerator and denominator is 1.

EXAMPLE 3 $\frac{2}{3}, \frac{5}{8}, \frac{3}{4}$, and $\frac{10}{7}$ are fractions in lowest terms.

$\frac{8}{24}, \frac{12}{16}$, and $\frac{20}{15}$ are fractions *not* in lowest terms.

We can divide the numerator and denominator by common factors to write a fraction in lowest terms.

EXAMPLE 4 $\frac{8}{24} = \frac{8 \div 2}{24 \div 2} = \frac{4}{12} = \frac{4 \div 2}{12 \div 2} = \frac{2}{6} = \frac{2 \div 2}{6 \div 2} = \frac{1}{3}$

$\frac{8}{24}$ in lowest terms is $\mathbf{\frac{1}{3}}$.

The quickest way is to divide the numerator and denominator by their GCF.

EXAMPLE 5 $\frac{8}{24} = \frac{8 \div 8}{24 \div 8} = \frac{1}{3}$ ◄ The GCF of 8 and 24 is 8.

Oral EXERCISES

Tell how to complete the pattern of equivalent fractions.

Sample: $\frac{1}{3}, \frac{2}{6}, \frac{3}{9}, \underline{\ ?\ }, \underline{\ ?\ }, \underline{\ ?\ }$ *What you say:* $\frac{4}{12}, \frac{5}{15}, \frac{6}{18}$

1. $\frac{1}{5}, \frac{2}{10}, \frac{3}{15}, \underline{\ ?\ }, \underline{\ ?\ }, \underline{\ ?\ }$
2. $\frac{2}{3}, \frac{4}{6}, \frac{6}{9}, \underline{\ ?\ }, \underline{\ ?\ }, \underline{\ ?\ }$
3. $\frac{3}{2}, \frac{6}{4}, \frac{9}{6}, \underline{\ ?\ }, \underline{\ ?\ }, \underline{\ ?\ }$
4. $\frac{6}{12}, \frac{7}{14}, \frac{8}{16}, \underline{\ ?\ }, \underline{\ ?\ }, \underline{\ ?\ }$
5. $\frac{7}{8}, \frac{14}{16}, \frac{21}{24}, \underline{\ ?\ }, \underline{\ ?\ }, \underline{\ ?\ }$
6. $\frac{2}{5}, \underline{\ ?\ }, \underline{\ ?\ }, \underline{\ ?\ }, \frac{10}{25}, \frac{12}{30}$

Tell whether or not the fraction is in lowest terms. Explain.

Sample 1: $\frac{7}{8}$ *What you say:* $\frac{7}{8}$ is in lowest terms because the GCF of 7 and 8 is 1.

Sample 2: $\frac{9}{12}$ *What you say:* $\frac{9}{12}$ is not in lowest terms because the GCF of 9 and 12 is 3.

7. $\frac{3}{4}$
8. $\frac{2}{10}$
9. $\frac{14}{15}$
10. $\frac{6}{8}$
11. $\frac{10}{16}$
12. $\frac{15}{36}$
13. $\frac{7}{8}$
14. $\frac{5}{4}$

Written EXERCISES

Solve.

Sample 1: $\frac{3 \times 2}{10 \times 2} = t$ *Solution:* $t = \frac{6}{20}$

Sample 2: $\frac{15 \div 5}{20 \div 5} = y$ *Solution:* $y = \frac{3}{4}$

A

1. $\frac{1 \times 5}{2 \times 5} = s$
2. $\frac{1 \times 3}{4 \times 3} = b$
3. $\frac{4 \times 2}{5 \times 2} = k$
4. $\frac{2 \times 5}{3 \times 5} = y$
5. $\frac{2 \div 2}{16 \div 2} = t$
6. $\frac{7 \div 7}{7 \div 7} = n$
7. $\frac{9 \div 3}{24 \div 3} = m$
8. $\frac{10 \div 10}{20 \div 10} = r$
9. $\frac{5 \div 5}{5 \div 5} = a$
10. $\frac{8 \div 8}{8 \div 8} = f$
11. $\frac{3 \times 1}{4 \times 1} = h$
12. $\frac{2 \times 1}{7 \times 1} = d$

Write in lowest terms.

13. $\frac{14}{20}$ 14. $\frac{33}{66}$ 15. $\frac{50}{100}$ 16. $\frac{20}{100}$

17. $\frac{6}{10}$ 18. $\frac{18}{16}$ 19. $\frac{75}{100}$ 20. $\frac{100}{1000}$

21. $\frac{4 + 10}{20}$ 22. $\frac{5 + 5}{4}$ 23. $\frac{4 \times 5}{100}$ 24. $\frac{10 \times 9}{100}$

Replace the variable to name the equivalent fraction.

Sample: $\frac{4}{5} = \frac{n}{20}$ *Solution:* $\frac{4}{5} = \frac{16}{20}$

25. $\frac{3}{10} = \frac{x}{70}$ 26. $\frac{2}{9} = \frac{s}{45}$ 27. $\frac{9}{10} = \frac{a}{100}$

28. $\frac{72}{48} = \frac{y}{2}$ 29. $\frac{25}{100} = \frac{m}{20}$ 30. $\frac{5}{9} = \frac{w}{63}$

31. $\frac{5}{12} = \frac{r}{48} = \frac{t}{36}$ 32. $\frac{10}{15} = \frac{m}{30} = \frac{n}{3}$ 33. $\frac{20}{32} = \frac{h}{8} = \frac{a}{80}$ B

34. $\frac{s}{5} = \frac{40}{100} = \frac{c}{35}$ 35. $\frac{x}{10} = \frac{5}{2} = \frac{y}{16}$ 36. $\frac{m}{21} = \frac{z}{35} = \frac{4}{7}$

Time out

You can use lined 6 × 9 cards to make a "Multiple Sorter." Beginning at the left-hand edge of the long side of each card, mark 22 one–cm intervals. Using a hole puncher, punch holes which are just about centered in each interval. The bottom edge of the hole should just touch the top line on the card.

Now number the cards from 1 through 22. On the first card, number the holes from 1 to 22. On each card cut out the top part of each hole whose number corresponds to a factor of the number named on the card. For example, on the card labeled 16, cut out the tops of the first, second, fourth, eighth, and sixteenth holes.

To find the multiples of 3 which are less than 22, straighten out a paper clip and insert it in the third hole, all the way through the stack. Lift. The cards naming the multiples of 3 will drop off. To find the common multiples of 2 and 3 which are less than 22, insert paper clips in both holes and lift.

3-5 *Ratios*

OBJECTIVE
Use a fraction to express the ratio of two quantities.

Two quantities can be compared by stating the ratio of one to the other.

EXAMPLE 1 □△△△△□ / □ □ □ □ 4 out of 10 of the shapes are triangles.

Ratio of triangles to all the shapes ► 4 to 10, or 4 : 10

Fraction form: $\frac{4}{10}$ or, in lowest terms, $\frac{2}{5}$

Ratio of triangles to squares ► 4 to 6, or 4 : 6

Fraction form: $\frac{4}{6}$ or $\frac{2}{3}$

EXAMPLE 2 There are 15 boys and 12 girls in an algebra class.
Ratio of boys to girls ► 15 to 12, or 15 : 12

Fraction form: $\frac{15}{12} = \frac{5}{4}$

Ratio of girls to boys ► 12 to 15, or 12 : 15

Fraction form: $\frac{12}{15} = \frac{4}{5}$

Oral EXERCISES

Express each ratio as a fraction.

Sample: 8 out of 10 *What you say:* $\frac{8}{10}$

1. 13 out of 40	**2.** 20 out of 50	**3.** 95 out of 100
4. 9 out of 12	**5.** 36 out of 72	**6.** 5 out of 9
7. 15 out of 60	**8.** 17 out of 20	**9.** 10 out of 15
10. 65 out of 80	**11.** 13 out of 30	**12.** 17 out of 20

Write each ratio as a fraction in lowest terms.

Sample: 8 out of 12 *Solution:* $\frac{8}{12} = \frac{2}{3}$

A

1. 10 out of 15	**2.** 28 out of 100	**3.** 19 out of 100
4. 20 out of 40	**5.** 10 out of 12	**6.** 15 out of 25
7. 9 out of 5	**8.** 6 out of 20	**9.** 25 out of 100
10. 10 out of 16	**11.** 8 out of 40	**12.** 7 out of 9

Complete.

Sample: □ □△□ _?_ out of _?_ shapes are squares.

Solution: 3 out of 4 shapes are squares.

B

13. ◆ ◆ ◇ ◇ ◇ _?_ out of _?_ shapes are shaded.

14. ○ ○ ▲ ○ _?_ out of _?_ shapes are triangles.

15. ■△△△■ _?_ out of _?_ of the shapes are triangles.

16. ⬢ ⬡ ⬢ ⬡ _?_ out of _?_ of the shapes are shaded.

17. A, B, C, d, e, f, g _?_ out of _?_ letters are capitals.

Solve. Write all ratios as fractions in lowest terms.

1. A pitcher of lemonade is made from lemon concentrate and water. The ratio of concentrate to water is 1 to 4. What fraction of the pitcher of lemonade is concentrate? What fraction is water?
2. If the vote on an issue is 3725 for and 1250 against, what is the ratio of votes "for" to the total vote cast?
3. For the rectangle shown here, what is the ratio of the length to the width? of the sum of the length and width to the length?

14 cm
6 cm

4. The monthly income of the Jones family is \$650. If they pay \$130 a month for rent, what is the ratio of their rent to their total income?

5. The pitch or slope of a drain pipe is shown in the picture. State the ratio $\frac{\text{rise}}{\text{run}}$ that describes the pitch of the drain pipe.

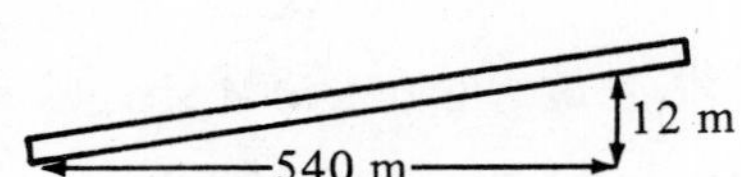

Hint: $\frac{\text{rise}}{\text{run}} = \frac{4}{300} = \underline{\ ?\ }$

6. A construction company is building a new highway. The road bed is to have a 2 meter rise for every 90 meters of run. The picture shows that the road bed rises 12 meters over a distance of 540 meters. Tell whether or not the grading has been done correctly for this part of the road bed.

(*Hint:* are the fractions $\frac{2}{90}$ and $\frac{12}{540}$ equivalent fractions?)

12 m
540 m

7. The front sprocket of a bicycle has 42 teeth and the rear sprocket has 14 teeth. Use $\frac{\text{teeth in front sprocket}}{\text{teeth in rear sprocket}}$ to find the ratio of the sprockets.

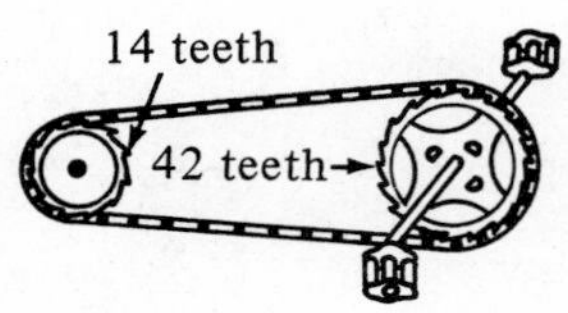

8. A stretch of railroad track going up-grade through the mountains rises 80 meters over a distance of 3200 meters. Over another stretch 10,000 meters in length the rise is 250 meters. How do the grades of these two stretches of track compare?

3-6 *Fractions and Decimals*

OBJECTIVES

Name the decimal equivalent of a fraction.

Read decimal numerals.

Name the fraction equivalent of a decimal.

Recall that a fraction indicates division.

EXAMPLE 1 $\frac{3}{4}$ means $4\overline{)3.00}$ with quotient 0.75, so $\frac{3}{4} = 0.75$.

EXAMPLE 2 $\frac{9}{10}$ means $10\overline{)9.0}$ with quotient 0.9, so $\frac{9}{10} = 0.9$.

EXAMPLE 3 $\frac{3}{2}$ means $2\overline{)3.0}$ with quotient 1.5, so $\frac{3}{2} = 1\frac{1}{2} = 1.5$.

In Examples 1–3, we have found the decimal equivalent of each fraction.

EXAMPLE 4 The decimal equivalent of $\frac{8}{10}$ is 0.8. ◄ Read "eight tenths."

EXAMPLE 5 $4\frac{3}{10} = 4.3$

four and three tenths

Compare these fractions and decimals.

$$\frac{3}{100} = \frac{30}{1000} = \frac{300}{10{,}000} = \dots \quad ► \quad 0.03 = 0.030 = 0.0300 = \dots$$

Once the decimal point is placed in a numeral, extra zeros do not change the value.

EXAMPLE 6 $53 = 53.0 = 53.00 = 53.000 = \dots$

The decimal point is understood to be to the right of the ones' place.

Give the division meaning.

Sample: $\frac{3}{7}$ *What you say:* Three divided by seven.

1. $\frac{9}{10}$ **2.** $\frac{4}{5}$ **3.** $\frac{7}{8}$

4. $\frac{10}{2}$ **5.** $\frac{7}{4}$ **6.** $\frac{9}{1}$

Name the fraction or decimal that is not equivalent to the others.

Sample: 0.60, 0.6, 0.06
What you say: 0.06 is not equivalent to either 0.60 or 0.6.

7. $\frac{3}{10}, \frac{30}{10}, \frac{30}{100}$ **8.** 0.5, 0.05, 0.050

9. 1.5, 0.15, 1.50 **10.** 40.0, 4.000, 4.0

Complete.

11. $0.6 = \frac{?}{10}$ **12.** $0.9 = \frac{?}{10}$ **13.** $0.50 = \frac{?}{100}$

14. $0.38 = \frac{?}{100}$ **15.** $5.7 = 5\frac{7}{?}$ **16.** $0.2 = \frac{2}{?}$

Write the meaning in words.

Sample 1: $\frac{7}{1000}$ *Solution:* seven thousandths

Sample 2: 0.15 *Solution:* fifteen hundredths

A

1. 0.5 **2.** 0.03 **3.** $\frac{23}{100}$ **4.** 6.65

5. 8.40 **6.** $\frac{40}{100}$ **7.** 0.025 **8.** 0.25

9. $\frac{8}{10}$ **10.** 10.8 **11.** 20.00 **12.** $\frac{147}{1000}$

Write as a decimal. Use division.

Sample: $\frac{3}{10}$ *Solution:* $10\overline{)3.0}$ (quotient 0.3); $\frac{3}{10} = 0.3$

13. $\frac{1}{5}$ 14. $\frac{1}{4}$ 15. $\frac{2}{5}$ 16. $\frac{6}{10}$

17. $\frac{4}{5}$ 18. $\frac{3}{4}$ 19. $\frac{7}{10}$ 20. $\frac{5}{5}$

21. $\frac{18}{100}$ 22. $\frac{35}{100}$ 23. $\frac{1}{8}$ 24. $\frac{3}{8}$

Complete.

Sample 1: $\frac{3}{10} = \frac{?}{100} = \frac{?}{1000}$ *Solution:* $\frac{3}{10} = \frac{30}{100} = \frac{300}{1000}$

Sample 2: 0.3 = 0.30 = _?_ = _?_
Solution: 0.3 = 0.30 = 0.300 = 0.3000

25. $\frac{2}{10} = \frac{?}{100} = \frac{?}{1000}$

26. $\frac{?}{10} = \frac{?}{100} = \frac{700}{1000}$

27. $\frac{13}{100} = \frac{?}{1000} = \frac{?}{10{,}000}$

28. $\frac{3}{1} = \frac{?}{10} = \frac{?}{100}$

29. 0.7 = 0.70 = _?_ = _?_
30. 4.3 = 4.30 = _?_ = _?_
31. 0.12 = 0.120 = _?_ = _?_
32. _?_ = _?_ = 2.700 = 2.7000

Write as a fraction in lowest terms.

Sample: 0.6 *Solution:* $0.6 = \frac{6}{10} = \frac{3}{5}$

33. 0.4 34. 0.25 35. 0.75
36. 0.039 37. 0.875 38. 3.5 **B**
39. 0.025 40. 0.625 41. 1.05

Find the decimal equivalent.

Sample: $\frac{1}{3}$ *Solution:* $3\overline{)1.000\ldots}$ = 0.333 . . . $\frac{1}{3} = 0.3333\ldots = 0.\overline{3}$

42. $\frac{2}{6}$ 43. $\frac{1}{6}$ 44. $\frac{2}{3}$ 45. $\frac{5}{9}$ **C**

46. $\frac{5}{11}$ 47. $\frac{5}{6}$ 48. $1\frac{4}{5}$ 49. $2\frac{3}{4}$

3-7 *Fractions, Decimals, and Percents*

OBJECTIVES

Express fractions as percents.

Express decimals as percents.

You are familiar with percent expressions and the percent symbol, %.

50% ► 50 percent   100% ► 100 percent

Percent means *hundredths*. A number given in hundredths can be expressed directly as a percent.

EXAMPLE 1 $\frac{4}{100}$ ► four hundredths ► 4%

0.04 ► four hundredths ► 4%

EXAMPLE 2 $\frac{15}{100} = 15\%$ $0.15 = 15\%$

EXAMPLE 3 $\frac{7}{10} = \frac{70}{100} = 70\%$ $0.7 = 0.70 = 70\%$

A fraction such as $\frac{1}{2}$ or $\frac{17}{25}$ can first be written as hundredths, then as a percent.

EXAMPLE 4 $\frac{1}{2}$ ► $2\overline{)1.00}$ (quotient 0.50) ► $0.50 = 50\%$

EXAMPLE 5 $\frac{17}{25}$ ► $25\overline{)17.00}$ (quotient 0.68) ► $0.68 = 68\%$

Important Pattern ► **To write a decimal as a percent, "move" the decimal point two places to the *right* and add the %. To write a percent as a decimal, "move" the decimal point two places to the *left* and drop the %.**

Decimal ► Percent			Percent ► Decimal		
0.62	=	62%	85.%	=	0.85
0.08	=	8%	250.%	=	2.50

Oral EXERCISES

Express as a percent.

Sample 1: six hundredths *What you say:* 6%

Sample 2: 0.45 *What you say:* 45%

1. eight hundredths **2.** 0.27 **3.** 0.55

4. ninety hundredths **5.** 0.93 **6.** 0.01

7. sixty-one hundredths **8.** 0.04 **9.** $\frac{17}{100}$

Complete.

10. 0.75 = ? % **11.** 0.9 = ? %

12. 1.00 = ? % **13.** 1.85 = ? %

14. 2.00 = ? % **15.** 0.04 = ? %

Written EXERCISES

Write as a decimal and as a percent.

Sample 1: $\frac{24}{100}$ *Solution:* $\frac{24}{100} = 0.24 = 24\%$

Sample 2: $\frac{2}{5}$ *Solution:* $\frac{2}{5} = 0.40 = 40\%$

A

1. $\frac{37}{100}$ **2.** $\frac{49}{100}$ **3.** $\frac{7}{10}$ **4.** $\frac{4}{10}$

5. $\frac{1}{4}$ **6.** $\frac{3}{4}$ **7.** $\frac{5}{8}$ **8.** $\frac{1}{8}$

9. $\frac{4}{4}$ **10.** $\frac{300}{1000}$ **11.** $\frac{450}{1000}$ **12.** $\frac{3}{5}$

Write as a fraction in lowest terms.

Sample: 20% *Solution:* $20\% = \frac{20}{100} = \frac{1}{5}$

13. 15% **14.** 40% **15.** 10%

16. 50% **17.** 25% **18.** 30%

19. 42% **20.** 75% **21.** 100%

Sample: 23.6% *Solution:* $23.6\% = 0.236 = \frac{236}{1000} = \frac{59}{250}$

B

22. 37.5% **23.** 12.5% **24.** 32.4%

25. 87.5% **26.** 2% **27.** 5%

28. 1% **29.** 325% **30.** 140%

Write as a decimal.

Sample: $4\frac{1}{2}\%$ *Solution:* $4\frac{1}{2}\% = 4.5\% = 0.045$

C

31. $3\frac{1}{2}\%$ **32.** $5\frac{1}{4}\%$ **33.** $2\frac{3}{4}\%$

34. $\frac{8}{10}\%$ **35.** $\frac{3}{4}\%$ **36.** $\frac{1}{3}\%$

Problems

Complete. Use the information that is given in the accompanying circle graph. Give fractions in lowest terms.

1. The graph shows that 60% of the students at Lincoln High School are girls and 40% are boys. What fractional part of the student body are the boys? What fractional part of the student body are the girls?

LINCOLN HIGH STUDENT BODY

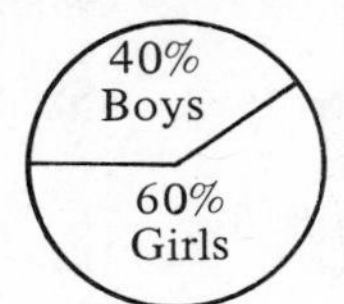

2. This graph shows the percent of students enrolled at each grade level at Harbor High School. What fraction tells what part of Harbor High students are in grade 12?
What fraction tells what part of the students are in grade 9?
What percent tells what part of the students are in grades 9 through 12?

HARBOR HIGH ENROLLMENT

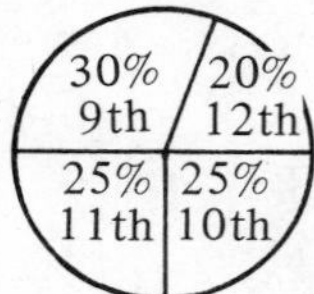

3. What fractional part of the books are non-fiction?
What fractional part of the books are fiction?
What percent of the books are reference?
Which two types of books together make up three-fourths of all the books in the library?

BOOKS IN LIBRARY

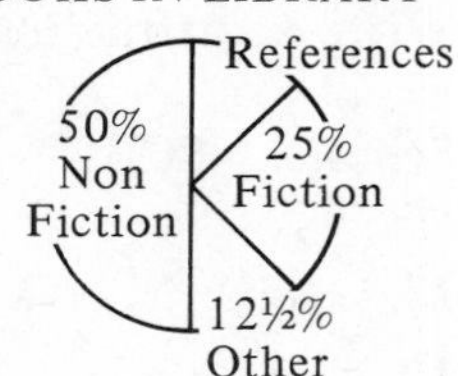

4. Copy and complete the table.

Vehicles	*Decimal*	*Percent*
Vans	0.125	?
Compacts	?	?
Full Size	?	?
Pickups	?	?
TOTALS	1.000	100%

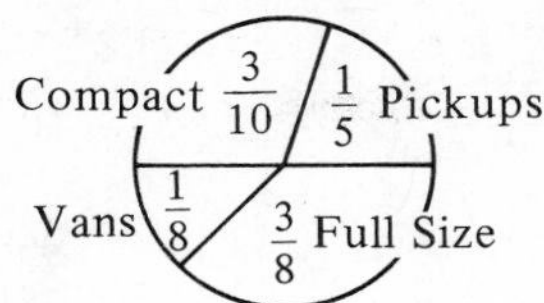

SELF-TEST 2

Be sure that you understand these terms and symbols.

equivalent fractions (p. 65) lowest terms (p. 65)
ratio (p. 68) decimal equivalent (p. 71)
% (p. 74)

1. Replace the variable to name the equivalent fraction: $\frac{5}{7} = \frac{x}{42}$. **Section 3-4, p. 65**

2. Write $\frac{6}{69}$ in lowest terms.

3. Write this ratio as a fraction in lowest terms: 16 out of 28 **Section 3-5, p. 68**

4. Write the meaning of $\frac{7}{8}$ in words. Then write $\frac{7}{8}$ as a decimal. **Section 3-6, p. 71**

5. Write the decimal equivalents of $2\frac{6}{100} = 2\frac{60}{1000} = 2\frac{600}{10,000}$.

Write as a decimal and as a percent. **Section 3-7, p. 74**

6. $\frac{2}{5}$

7. $\frac{4}{20}$

Check your answers with those printed at the back of the book.

3-8 *Metric Measurement*

OBJECTIVES

Express linear measures in meters, centimeters, and millimeters.

Use a metric ruler to draw and to measure line segments.

The meter (m) is the basic unit of length in the metric system. The meter is divided into 100 equal parts called centimeters (cm). The centimeter is divided into 10 equal parts called millimeters (mm).

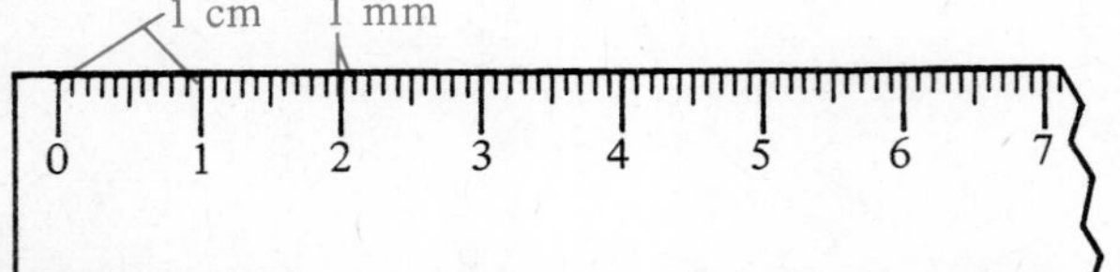

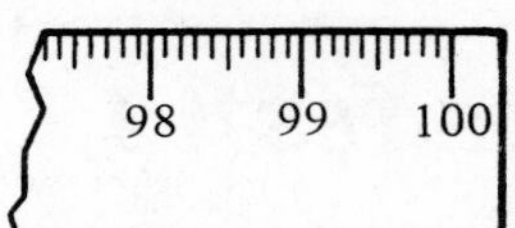

The arrow (↔) means "is the same as."

Equivalent Measures	
1 m ↔ 100 cm ↔ 1,000 mm	1 mm ↔ 0.1 cm ↔ 0.001 m
2 m ↔ 200 cm ↔ 2,000 mm	10 mm ↔ 1 cm ↔ 0.01 m
2.5 m ↔ 250 cm ↔ 2,500 mm	25 mm ↔ 2.5 cm ↔ 0.025 m

Study these examples.

EXAMPLE 1 256 cm ↔ 200 cm and 56 cm ↔ 2 m 56 cm

EXAMPLE 2 3.85 m ↔ 3 m and 0.85 m ↔ 3 m 85 cm

EXAMPLE 3 150 cm ↔ 1 m 50 cm ↔ 1.50 m

EXAMPLE 4 65 mm ↔ 60 mm and 5 mm ↔ 6 cm 5 mm

EXAMPLE 5 278 mm ↔ 270 mm and 8 mm ↔ 27 cm 8 mm
↔ 27.8 cm

Tell how to complete each statement.

1. 3 m ↔ ___?___ cm
2. 1.5 m ↔ ___?___ cm
3. 2.2 m ↔ ___?___ cm
4. 10 cm ↔ ___?___ m
5. 25 cm ↔ ___?___ m
6. 200 cm ↔ ___?___ m
7. 15 cm ↔ ___?___ mm
8. 10 cm ↔ ___?___ mm
9. 100 cm ↔ ___?___ mm
10. 60 mm ↔ ___?___ cm
11. 10 m ↔ ___?___ cm
12. 140 mm ↔ ___?___ cm

Written EXERCISES

Find the length. Use a metric ruler.

Sample:

Solution: 3.5 cm

A

1.
2.
3.
4.
5.
6.
7.
8.

Draw line segments. Use a metric ruler.

9. 10 cm
10. 12 cm
11. 1 cm
12. 4.5 cm
13. 100 mm
14. 75 mm
15. 8 cm 3 mm
16. 5 cm
17. 6.5 cm

Complete.

Sample 1: 145 cm ↔ ___?___ m ___?___ cm

Solution: 145 cm ↔ 1 m 45 cm

Sample 2: 64 mm ↔ ___?___ cm ___?___ mm

Solution: 64 mm ↔ 6 cm 4 mm

Complete.

B

18. 134 cm ↔ __?__ m __?__ cm

19. 95 cm ↔ __?__ m

20. 240 cm ↔ __?__ m __?__ cm

21. 60 cm ↔ __?__ m

22. 395 cm ↔ __?__ m __?__ cm

23. 409 cm ↔ __?__ m __?__ cm

24. 27 mm ↔ __?__ cm __?__ mm

25. 50 mm ↔ __?__ cm

26. 86 mm ↔ __?__ cm __?__ mm

27. 100 mm ↔ __?__ cm

28. 31 mm ↔ __?__ cm __?__ mm

29. 125 mm ↔ __?__ cm __?__ mm

C

Complete.

30. 59 mm ↔ __?__ cm

31. 26 mm ↔ __?__ cm

32. 152 mm ↔ __?__ cm

33. 9.4 cm ↔ __?__ mm

34. 21.8 cm ↔ __?__ mm

35. 0.6 cm ↔ __?__ mm

36. 75 cm ↔ __?__ m

37. 15 cm ↔ __?__ m

38. 8 cm ↔ __?__ m

39. 0.75 m ↔ __?__ cm

40. 0.52 m ↔ __?__ cm

41. 0.6 m ↔ __?__ cm

SELF-TEST 3

Be sure that you understand these terms.

meter (p. 78) centimeter (p. 78) millimeter (p. 78)

Complete.

1. 590 cm ↔ __?__ m __?__ cm

2. 87 cm ↔ __?__ m

Complete.

3. 39 mm ↔ __?__ cm

4. 720 mm ↔ __?__ cm __?__ mm

5. Draw a line segment 7 cm 3 mm long. Use a metric ruler.

Check your answers with those printed at the back of the book.

---

chapter summary

1. The product of a number and any counting number is a **multiple** of the first number.
2. The least number that is a multiple of two given numbers is called their **least common multiple** (LCM).
3. The **divisors** of a number are the factors of that number.
4. The greatest divisor of two numbers is called their **greatest common factor** (GCF).
5. A number that can be expressed in the form $2 \times n$, where n is a whole number, is an **even number.**
6. A number that can be expressed in the form $(2 \times n) + 1$, where n is a whole number, is an **odd number.**
7. A whole number that has exactly two factors, itself and 1, is a **prime** number.
8. Fractions that name the same number are called **equivalent fractions.**
9. When the GCF of the numerator and the denominator of a fraction is 1, the fraction is in lowest terms.
10. A ratio may be expressed as a fraction.
11. The **decimal equivalent** of a fraction can be found by dividing the numerator by the denominator.

calculator corner

You can use your calculator to divide, even if the result is a quotient with remainder. (This will show up as a decimal.) For example, divide 416 by 59. Think of the steps you would use to figure out the division problem without a calculator. Now divide 416 by 59. Multiply the whole number in the quotient by 59. Subtract this new result from 416. The number which is displayed is the remainder. 416 divided by 59 is 7 with a remainder of 3. You can use this method to solve other division problems. Try $728 \div 15$ or $963 \div 38$.

chapter test

Name the sets of multiples and the LCM.

1. 3 and 4

2. 2 and 8

3. 6 and 8

4. 3 and 5

Name the sets of factors and the GCF.

5. 30 and 24

6. 12 and 15

7. 4 and 9

8. 5 and 10

Write in the form $2 \times n$ or $(2 \times n) + 1$.

9. 15 **10.** 12 **11.** 34 **12.** 51

Complete.

13. $\frac{1}{2} = \frac{?}{10}$

14. $\frac{12}{15} = \frac{?}{5}$

15. $\frac{7}{8} = \frac{?}{16}$

16. $\frac{8}{12} = \frac{4}{?}$

Write as a fraction in lowest terms.

17. 9 out of 12

18. 6 out of 30

19. 3 out of 5

20. 10 out of 100

Write the decimal equivalent.

21. $\frac{3}{4}$ **22.** $1\frac{1}{2}$ **23.** $\frac{9}{10}$ **24.** $\frac{25}{100}$

Write as a percent.

25. $\frac{15}{100}$ **26.** $\frac{95}{100}$ **27.** 0.04 **28.** 0.34

Complete.

29. 1 m ↔ __?__ cm

30. 50 cm ↔ __?__ m

31. 1 cm ↔ __?__ mm

32. 10 cm ↔ __?__ mm

33. 1 m ↔ __?__ mm

34. 450 mm ↔ __?__ m

challenge topics *Symmetry*

Study the figure of a moth shown below. Do you agree that the broken line is a **line of symmetry?** That is, if we fold the shape along this line, the two parts will fit over each other exactly. We can test this conclusion by folding the figure along this line to see if the parts fit over each other exactly. Another way to test for a line of symmetry is to place a mirror along the broken line, as shown. If the

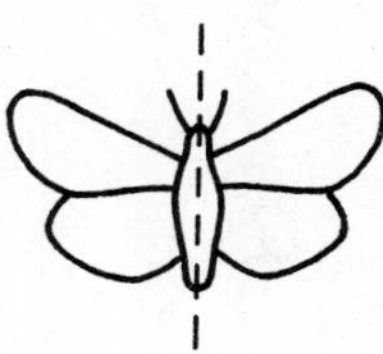

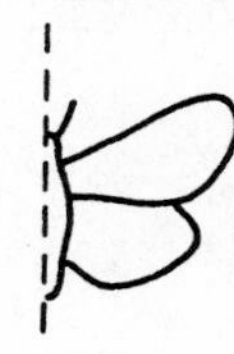

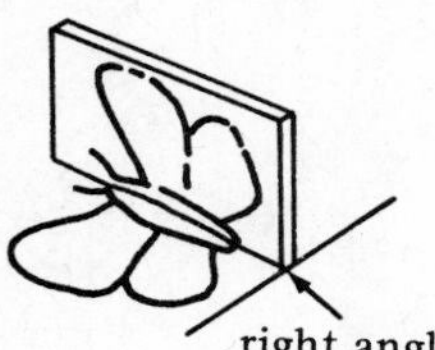

mirror image, the part of the moth that you see in the mirror, is exactly like the part that is hidden behind the mirror, the figure is symmetric about the line determined by the edge of the mirror.

Which of the following figures have at least one line of symmetry?

1. 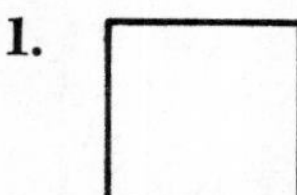

2. 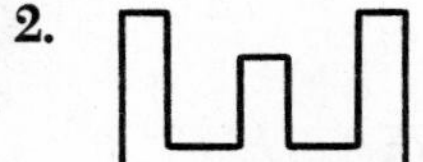

3. 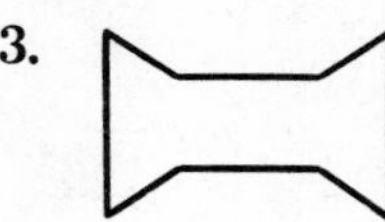

How many lines of symmetry can you find in each figure? Make a copy of each to illustrate your answer.

4. 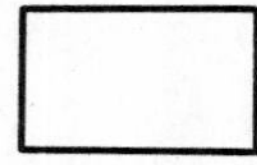

5. 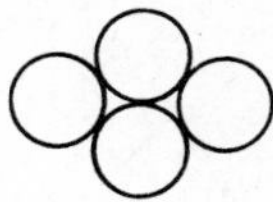

6. TOOT

7. NOON

8. 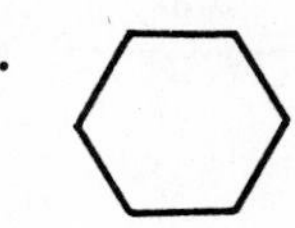

9.

Copy each figure and sketch its mirror image, using the broken line as a line of symmetry for the completed figure.

10. 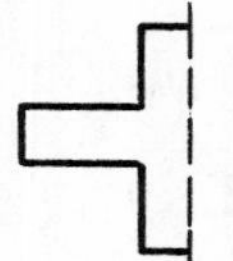

11. 

12. 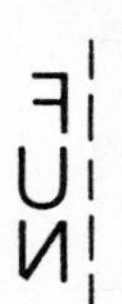

13. 

Review of Skills

Write as a mixed numeral or whole number.

1. $\frac{7}{2}$ **2.** $\frac{15}{6}$ **3.** $\frac{21}{5}$ **4.** $\frac{8}{2}$

Write as a fraction.

5. $2\frac{1}{3}$ **6.** $1\frac{1}{8}$ **7.** $1\frac{1}{7}$ **8.** $2\frac{3}{5}$

Add or subtract.

9. $\begin{array}{r} 5.067 \\ +1.300 \\ \hline \end{array}$ **10.** $\begin{array}{r} 8.46 \\ -2.7 \\ \hline \end{array}$ **11.** $\begin{array}{r} 46.3 \\ -11.8 \\ \hline \end{array}$ **12.** $\begin{array}{r} 3.05 \\ +0.7 \\ \hline \end{array}$

Multiply or divide.

13. $\frac{2}{3} \times \frac{3}{2}$ **14.** $10 \times \frac{1}{10}$ **15.** $\frac{1}{8} \times \frac{8}{7}$

16. $\begin{array}{r} 4.3 \\ \times 6.8 \\ \hline \end{array}$ **17.** $\begin{array}{r} 16.4 \\ \times 3.2 \\ \hline \end{array}$ **18.** $\begin{array}{r} 1.25 \\ \times 64 \\ \hline \end{array}$

19. $5\overline{)86.15}$ **20.** $5\overline{)8.615}$ **21.** $34\overline{)57.8}$

22. $34\overline{)578}$ **23.** $0.8\overline{)184}$ **24.** $8\overline{)1840}$

Find the area. Use the given formula.

25.

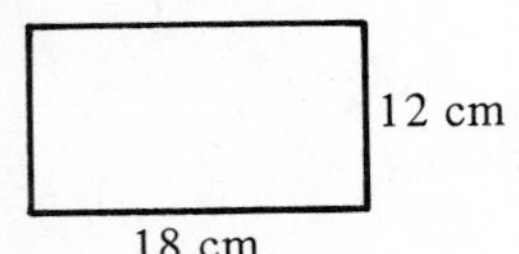

$A = l \times w$ Area: ? cm^2

26.

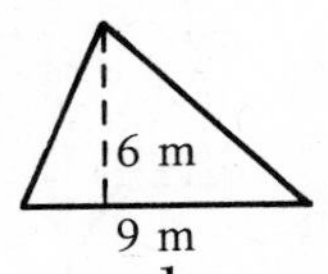

$A = \frac{1}{2} \times b \times h$ Area: ? m^2

Name the number pair graphed by the point.

27. A

28. *B*

29. *C*

30. *D*

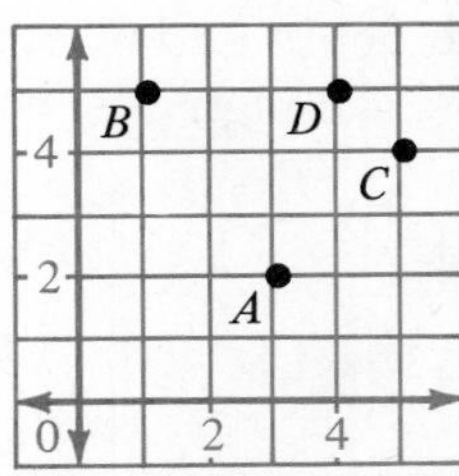

Left: General store, early 1900's.

Right: Clerk using optical scanner. It scans a printed code on the package and records the price automatically.

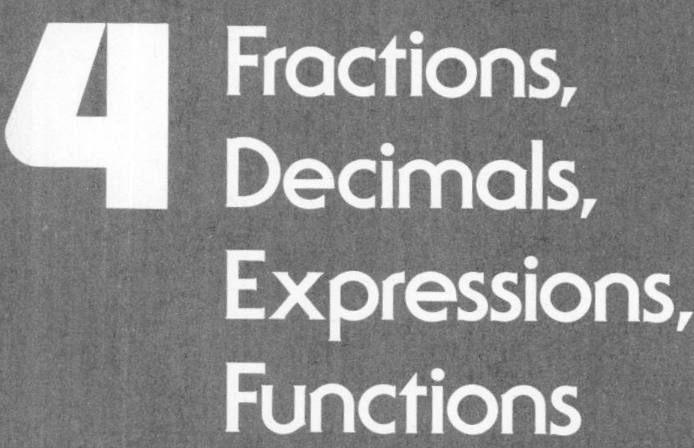

4 Fractions, Decimals, Expressions, Functions

Working with Fractions and Decimals

4-1 *Fractions: Addition and Subtraction*

OBJECTIVE
Add and subtract with fractions.

Adding or subtracting with like fractions is easy. Like fractions have a common denominator.

EXAMPLE 1 $\frac{1}{10} + \frac{8}{10}$ ► Add the numerators. ► Use the common denominator. ► $\frac{1+8}{10} = \frac{9}{10}$

EXAMPLE 2 $\frac{7}{8} - \frac{3}{8}$ ► Subtract the numerators. ► Use the common denominator. ► $\frac{7-3}{8} = \frac{4}{8} = \frac{1}{2}$

Recall that $4\frac{1}{5}$ means $4 + \frac{1}{5}$.

EXAMPLE 3 $4\frac{1}{5} + 2\frac{3}{5} = 4 + 2 + \frac{1}{5} + \frac{3}{5}$ ◄ First add the whole numbers. Then add the fractional numbers.

$= 6 + \frac{4}{5} = 6\frac{4}{5}$

EXAMPLE 4 $5\frac{5}{8} - 4\frac{2}{8} = 5 - 4 + \frac{5}{8} - \frac{2}{8}$ ◄ First subtract the whole numbers. Then subtract the fractional numbers.

$= 1 + \frac{3}{8} = 1\frac{3}{8}$

To add or subtract with unlike fractions, rename the fractions so they have a common denominator.

EXAMPLE 5 $\frac{1}{4} + \frac{1}{6} = \frac{6}{24} + \frac{4}{24} = \frac{6+4}{24} = \frac{10}{24} = \frac{5}{12}$

We can use the LCM of 4 and 6 to rename the fractions. Then our work is simpler.

$$\frac{1}{4} + \frac{1}{6} = \frac{3}{12} + \frac{2}{12} = \frac{3+2}{12} = \frac{5}{12}$$

Name the solution.

Sample: $b = \frac{4+2}{7}$ *What you say:* $b = \frac{6}{7}$

1. $c = \frac{2+1}{8}$

2. $m = \frac{3+6}{9}$

3. $h = \frac{3+4}{10}$

4. $n = \frac{4-3}{5}$

5. $k = \frac{1+1}{3}$

6. $s = \frac{7-6}{2}$

Complete.

Sample: $\frac{1}{2} = \frac{?}{6}$ *What you say:* $\frac{1}{2} = \frac{3}{6}$

7. $\frac{1}{5} = \frac{?}{10}$

8. $\frac{1}{2} = \frac{?}{4}$

9. $\frac{2}{3} = \frac{?}{9}$

10. $\frac{2}{5} = \frac{?}{15}$

11. $\frac{1}{3} = \frac{?}{6}$

12. $\frac{5}{10} = \frac{?}{2}$

Written EXERCISES

A

Add or subtract.

Sample: $\frac{7}{8} - \frac{5}{8}$ *Solution:* $\frac{7-5}{8} = \frac{2}{8} = \frac{1}{4}$

1. $\frac{2}{9} + \frac{5}{9}$

2. $\frac{1}{4} + \frac{2}{4}$

3. $\frac{1}{4} + \frac{1}{4} + \frac{1}{4}$

4. $\frac{3}{5} + \frac{1}{5}$

5. $\frac{9}{10} - \frac{3}{10}$

6. $\frac{3}{5} - \frac{3}{5}$

7. $\frac{5}{12} + \frac{1}{12}$

8. $\frac{3}{4} - \frac{1}{4}$

9. $1\frac{1}{2} - \frac{1}{2}$

Sample: $2\frac{1}{5} + 5\frac{2}{5}$ *Solution:* $2\frac{1}{5} + 5\frac{2}{5} = 2 + 5 + \frac{1}{5} + \frac{2}{5} = 7\frac{3}{5}$

10. $4\frac{1}{3} + 2\frac{1}{3}$

11. $5\frac{1}{2} - 1\frac{1}{2}$

12. $\frac{1}{10} + 2\frac{7}{10}$

13. $6\frac{3}{10} + 1\frac{4}{10}$ 14. $7\frac{1}{3} + 1\frac{2}{3}$ 15. $3\frac{1}{4} - 3$

16. $8\frac{7}{8} - 6\frac{2}{8}$ 17. $4\frac{3}{4} - 3\frac{1}{4}$ 18. $7\frac{2}{5} + 2$

Complete.

Sample: $b = \frac{5}{8} + \frac{1}{4}$

$b = \frac{5}{8} + \frac{?}{8}$

$b = \underline{\ ?\ }$

Solution: $b = \frac{5}{8} + \frac{1}{4}$

$b = \frac{5}{8} + \frac{2}{8}$

$b = \frac{7}{8}$

19. $t = \frac{1}{8} + \frac{1}{2}$

$t = \frac{1}{8} + \frac{?}{8}$

$t = \underline{\ ?\ }$

20. $x = \frac{1}{2} + \frac{1}{3}$

$x = \frac{?}{6} + \frac{?}{6}$

$x = \underline{\ ?\ }$

21. $m = \frac{1}{5} + \frac{3}{10}$

$m = \frac{?}{10} + \frac{3}{10}$

$m = \underline{\ ?\ }$

Solve.

B

22. $s = \frac{3}{4} + \frac{1}{8}$ 23. $\frac{7}{8} - \frac{3}{5} = k$ 24. $h = \frac{1}{2} + \frac{1}{4} + \frac{1}{4}$

25. $n = \frac{3}{4} - \frac{1}{2}$ 26. $5\frac{3}{4} - 2\frac{1}{2} = t$ 27. $q = 4\frac{1}{2} - 2\frac{1}{3}$

28. $z = \frac{4}{5} - \frac{1}{3}$ 29. $6\frac{1}{8} + 5\frac{1}{4} = c$ 30. $r = 5\frac{3}{10} - 2\frac{6}{10}$

Find the value when $x = 2$, $y = 3$, and $z = 5$.

Sample: $\frac{2}{y} + \frac{1}{z}$

Solution: $\frac{2}{y} + \frac{1}{z} = \frac{2}{3} + \frac{1}{5}$

$= \frac{10}{15} + \frac{3}{15} = \frac{13}{15}$

31. $\frac{1}{y} + \frac{2}{y}$ 32. $\frac{1}{x} - \frac{1}{z}$ 33. $\frac{x}{y} + \frac{z}{y}$

34. $\frac{1}{x} + \frac{3}{z}$ 35. $\frac{x}{10} + \frac{y}{10}$ 36. $\frac{x + z}{y}$

37. $\frac{1}{y} + \frac{1}{y} + \frac{1}{y}$ 38. $\frac{y}{2} + \frac{y}{4}$ 39. $\frac{y - x}{z}$

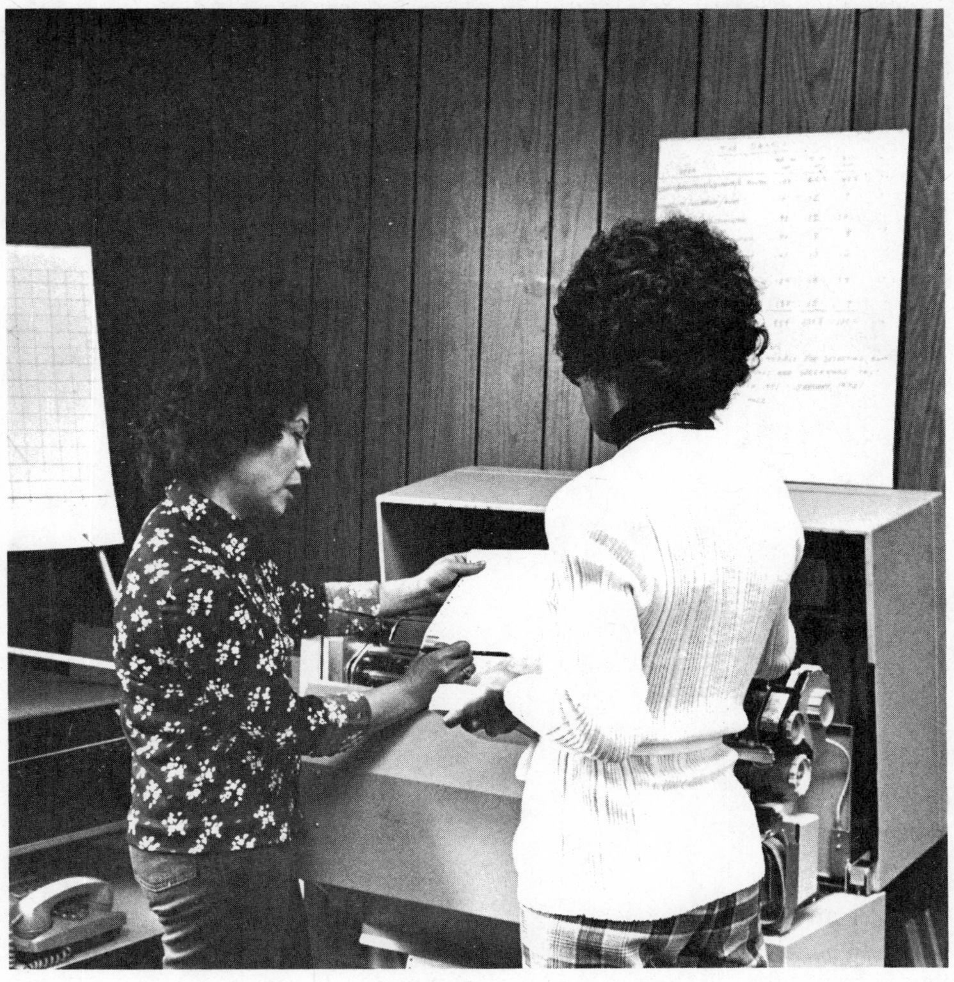

career capsule *Market Researcher*

Market researchers collect, study, and relate facts about company products and services, advertising, sales policies, and consumer opinions. They collect information from company records, personal opinion surveys, and statistics on changes in population.

A market researcher must have an ability to work with figures and an interest and flair for research. A college degree in economics or business administration is generally required. Courses in mathematics and social studies are useful.

4-2 *Fractions: Multiplication and Division*

OBJECTIVES

Multiply numbers in fraction form.

Divide numbers in fraction form.

EXAMPLE 1 $\frac{3}{8} \times \frac{1}{2}$ ► Multiply the numerators. ► Multiply the denominators. $\frac{3 \times 1}{8 \times 2} = \frac{3}{16}$

EXAMPLE 2 $2\frac{1}{2} \times 2\frac{1}{4} = \frac{5}{2} \times \frac{9}{4} = \frac{5 \times 9}{2 \times 4} = \frac{45}{8} = 5\frac{5}{8}$

To divide with fractions, we use reciprocals. Two numbers are **reciprocals** of each other if their product is 1.

EXAMPLE 3 $\frac{2}{3}$ and $\frac{3}{2}$ $\qquad \frac{2}{3} \times \frac{3}{2} = \frac{6}{6} = 1$

reciprocals — The product is 1.

EXAMPLE 4 5 and $\frac{1}{5}$ $\qquad \frac{5}{1} \times \frac{1}{5} = \frac{5}{5} = 1$

reciprocals — The product is 1.

EXAMPLE 5 $1\frac{1}{4}$ and $\frac{4}{5}$ $\qquad 1\frac{1}{4} \times \frac{4}{5} = \frac{5}{4} \times \frac{4}{5} = 1$

Dividing by a number is the same as multiplying by its reciprocal.

EXAMPLE 6 $\frac{1}{2} \div \frac{3}{4} = \frac{1}{2} \times \frac{4}{3}$ ◄ $\frac{4}{3}$ is the reciprocal of $\frac{3}{4}$.

$$= \frac{1 \times 4}{2 \times 3} = \frac{4}{6} = \frac{2}{3}$$

EXAMPLE 7 $\frac{2}{3} \div 1\frac{3}{4} = \frac{2}{3} \div \frac{7}{4} = \frac{2}{3} \times \frac{4}{7}$ ◄ $\frac{4}{7}$ is the reciprocal of $1\frac{3}{4}$.

$$= \frac{2 \times 4}{3 \times 7} = \frac{8}{21}$$

Oral EXERCISES

Name the reciprocal.

Sample: $\frac{4}{3}$ *What you say:* $\frac{3}{4}$

1. $\frac{3}{2}$
2. $\frac{1}{3}$
3. $\frac{7}{10}$
4. $\frac{4}{5}$
5. $\frac{5}{3}$
6. $\frac{6}{1}$

Express as a fraction. Then name the reciprocal.

7. $1\frac{1}{2}$
8. $4\frac{1}{8}$
9. $2\frac{1}{2}$
10. $1\frac{2}{3}$
11. $2\frac{1}{3}$
12. $1\frac{1}{8}$

Written EXERCISES

A

Multiply.

Sample: $\frac{2}{5} \times \frac{1}{3}$ *Solution:* $\frac{2}{5} \times \frac{1}{3} = \frac{2 \times 1}{5 \times 3} = \frac{2}{15}$

1. $\frac{1}{9} \times \frac{2}{3}$
2. $\frac{5}{2} \times \frac{1}{4} \times \frac{1}{4}$
3. $2\frac{1}{5} \times 1\frac{1}{2}$
4. $\frac{3}{5} \times \frac{1}{2}$
5. $\frac{2}{1} \times \frac{1}{2} \times \frac{1}{2}$
6. $1\frac{1}{3} \times 3$
7. $\frac{1}{2} \times \frac{3}{2} \times \frac{1}{5}$
8. $\frac{1}{9} \times \frac{1}{9}$
9. $\frac{2}{3} \times 1\frac{1}{4}$

Copy and complete.

10. $\frac{3}{10} \div \frac{2}{3}$
    $\frac{3}{10} \times \frac{3}{2}$
    $\underline{\ ?\ }$
11. $\frac{1}{4} \div \frac{2}{3}$
    $\frac{1}{4} \times \frac{3}{2}$
    $\underline{\ ?\ }$
12. $\frac{4}{5} \div \frac{3}{1}$
    $\frac{4}{5} \times \underline{\ ?\ }$
    $\underline{\ ?\ }$
13. $\frac{1}{2} \div \frac{3}{5}$
    $\frac{1}{2} \times \frac{5}{3}$
    $\underline{\ ?\ }$
14. $\frac{7}{8} \div \frac{2}{1}$
    $\frac{7}{8} \times \underline{\ ?\ }$
    $\underline{\ ?\ }$
15. $\frac{6}{1} \div \frac{2}{1}$
    $\frac{6}{1} \times \underline{\ ?\ }$
    $\underline{\ ?\ }$

Name the reciprocal.

Sample: $\frac{1}{5}$: ___?___ *Solution:* $\frac{1}{5} : \frac{5}{1}$ or 5

B

16. $\frac{1}{4}$: ___?___
17. $\frac{8}{1}$: ___?___
18. 6 : ___?___
19. $\frac{5}{2}$: ___?___
20. 3 : ___?___
21. $\frac{1}{9}$: ___?___
22. $\frac{10}{1}$: ___?___
23. 7 : ___?___
24. 15 : ___?___
25. 1
26. $\frac{x}{3}$ (x is not zero)
27. $\frac{m}{n}$ (m and n not 0)
28. $\frac{5}{5}$
29. $\frac{a}{5}$ (a is not 0)
30. $\frac{r}{s}$ (r and s not 0)

Solve.

Sample 1: $x = \frac{3}{4} \div \frac{1}{2}$ *Solution:* $x = \frac{3}{4} \div \frac{1}{2} = \frac{3}{4} \times \frac{2}{1}$

$x = \frac{3}{2}$ (or $1\frac{1}{2}$)

31. $k = \frac{4}{5} \div \frac{2}{3}$
32. $t = 2 \div 1\frac{1}{2}$
33. $y = 1\frac{1}{2} \times 1\frac{1}{2}$
34. $b = \frac{2}{3} \div \frac{1}{2}$
35. $r = \frac{1}{2} \times 2$
36. $z = 7 \div 2\frac{1}{3}$
37. $w = \frac{3}{4} \div \frac{7}{8}$
38. $x = \frac{3}{4} \times 1\frac{1}{2}$
39. $c = 6 \div \frac{3}{1}$
40. $\frac{1}{2} \div \frac{7}{9} = n$
41. $2\frac{1}{8} \times \frac{8}{10} = a$
42. $10 \times \frac{1}{10} = m$

Find the value when $a = 1$, $b = 2$, $c = 3$, and $d = 4$.

Sample: $\frac{a}{c} \times \frac{b}{c}$ *Solution:* $\frac{1}{3} \times \frac{2}{3} = \frac{2}{9}$

43. $\frac{a}{b} \times \frac{a}{b}$
44. $\frac{c}{d} \div \frac{c}{d}$
45. $\frac{a}{b} \times \frac{a}{c} \times \frac{a}{d}$
46. $\frac{b}{c} \times \frac{c}{b}$
47. $\frac{d}{a} \div a$
48. $\frac{b}{c} \times \frac{c}{d} \times b$

4-3 *Decimals: Addition and Subtraction*

OBJECTIVES

Add and subtract numbers expressed as decimals, including money.

Estimate sums and differences of numbers expressed as decimals by rounding.

When you work with decimals, it is very important to have decimal points positioned correctly.

EXAMPLE 1 2.075 + 3.4 = ?

$$\begin{array}{r} 2.075 \\ +3.400 \\ \hline 5.475 \end{array}$$

Include extra zeros. Be sure the decimal points are in line.

2.075 + 3.4 = **5.475**

EXAMPLE 2 9.67 − 1.5 = ?

$$\begin{array}{r} 9.67 \\ -1.50 \\ \hline 8.17 \end{array}$$

Include extra zeros. Be sure the decimal points are in line.

9.67 − 1.5 = **8.17**

It's a good idea to check an operation with decimals by rounding to whole numbers and estimating the answer. The exact answer and the estimate should be about the same.

EXAMPLE 3 24.2 − 5.73 = ?

	24.20	rounds to	24
	− 5.73	rounds to	− 6
exact answer ►	18.47	estimate ►	18

EXAMPLE 4 14.79 + 8.26 = ?

	14.79	rounds to	15
	+ 8.26	rounds to	+ 8
exact answer ►	23.05	estimate ►	23

EXAMPLE 5 30.40 − 26.19 = ?

	30.40	rounds to	30
	− 26.19	rounds to	− 26
exact answer ►	4.21	estimate ►	4

EXERCISES

Round to the nearest whole number.

Sample 1: 68.35 *What you say:* 68

Sample 2: 1.821 *What you say:* 2

1. 9.3 **2.** 7.99 **3.** 0.2

4. 10.7 **5.** 3.09 **6.** 0.539

7. 8.5 **8.** 0.8 **9.** 127.099

Round to the nearest dollar.

Sample: $6.89 *What you say:* $7.00

10. $ 5.17 **11.** $7.50 **12.** $10.09

13. $49.95 **14.** $ .89 **15.** $19.89

Written EXERCISES

A

Add or subtract.

Sample: $6.72 + 5.09 = ?$ *Solution:* $6.72 + 5.09 = 11.81$

1. $12.38 + 6.8 =$ ___?___ **2.** $10.75 - 3.44 =$ ___?___

3. $100 - 42.3 =$ ___?___ **4.** $1.84 + 0.95 =$ ___?___

5. $0.008 - 0.003 =$ ___?___ **6.** $4.06 - 0.03 =$ ___?___

7. $6.5 + 2.1 + 3.007 =$ ___?___ **8.** $9.07 - 2.005 =$ ___?___

9. $6.703 - 2.5 =$ ___?___ **10.** $7.0 + 0.3 + 0.024 =$ ___?___

11. $9 + 34 + 5.6 =$ ___?___ **12.** $0.5 + 0.5 =$ ___?___

Add or subtract. Estimate to check your work.

Sample: $94.27 - 13.88 =$ ___?___ *Solution:* $94.27 - 13.88 = 80.39$
Check: $94 - 14 = 80$

13. $2.04 + 8.93 =$ ___?___ **14.** $3.25 + 6.9 =$ ___?___

15. $10.00 - 3.75 =$ ___?___ **16.** $38.1 + 1.5 =$ ___?___

17. $1.007 + 5.901 =$ ___?___ **18.** $8.0039 + 7.001 =$ ___?___

Solve.

Sample: $n = 4.07 + 3.5 + 0.007$

Solution: $n = 4.07 + 3.5 + 0.007 = 7.577$

B

19. $t = 0.08 + 436.2$ **20.** $60.9 - 18 = K$

21. $m = 7.1 + 0.004 + 0.3$ **22.** $0.3 + 0.3 + 0.3 = n$

23. $y = 17.4 - 6.004$

24. $8.204 - 3.204 = a$

25. $149.75 + 99.02 = b$

26. $s = 1.0 + 1.11 + 0.010$

27. $4.8 = x + 2.3$

28. $4.25 + 1.07 + r = 8.5$

29. $9.04 - w = 6.5$

30. $y - 3.01 = 6.275$

31. $38.004 + h = 50$

32. $c + 246.30 = 422.09$

C

Problems

Estimate the answer by rounding each amount to the nearest dollar. Then find the exact answer.

1. A carpenter bought these tools. How much did they cost altogether?

hammer:	$3.19	screw driver:	$.87
saw:	$6.95	wrench:	$2.15

2. Walter's car expenses last week were as follows: gasoline, $19.70; oil, $1.19; new tire, $24.30. What were his total expenses?
3. Arlene took some friends to lunch. The total bill was $13.86. She paid the waiter with a $20 bill. How much change did she receive?

Estimate the answer by rounding each amount to the nearest ten dollars. Then find the exact answer.

4. Harmon bought a new suit for $129.95, a pair of shoes for $32, and a raincoat for $37.50. What was the total cost?
5. Jade bought four new tires for her car. If they cost $39.95 each, how much did she pay for all four tires?

Time out

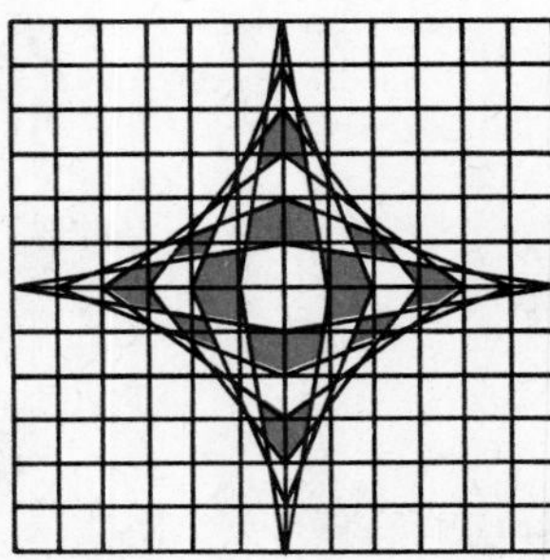

You can make curved designs using straight lines. Take a piece of graph paper. Label a horizontal line from 0 to 6. Starting at 0 label the vertical line through 0 from 1 to 6. With straight lines, connect 1 on the horizontal with 6 on the vertical, 2 on the horizontal with 5 on the vertical, etc. Color in your design. Experiment by combining designs and changing numbers.

4-4 *Decimals: Multiplication and Division*

OBJECTIVES

Multiply and divide numbers expressed as decimals.

Find a percent of a number.

When you multiply or divide with decimals, estimating the answer will help you locate the decimal point.

EXAMPLE 1 $3.2 \times 4.9 = \underline{?}$ ► Estimate: $3 \times 5 = 15$
Exact answer: $3.2 \times 4.9 = 15.68$

EXAMPLE 2 $16.96 \div 5.3 = \underline{?}$ ► Estimate: $17 \div 5$ is about 3.

Exact answer: 16.96 (product) ÷ 5.3 (factor) = **3.2** (factor)

Important Pattern ► **The number of digits after the decimal point in the product is the sum of the numbers of digits after the decimal points in the factors.**

$1.6 \times 3.4 = 5.44$ → $1 + 1 = 2$

$5.46 \div 0.3 = 18.2$ → $2 = 1 + 1$

To find a percent of a number, first write the percent as a decimal. Then multiply.

EXAMPLE 3 15% of 80 is $\underline{?}$ ► $0.15 \times 80 = 12.00 = 12$
15% of 80 is **12.**

EXAMPLE 4 125% of 3.6 is $\underline{?}$ ► $1.25 \times 3.6 = 4.500 = 4.5$
125% of 3.6 is **4.5.**

EXERCISES

Match. Use estimates.

1.	4.8×31	**A.**	0.1488
2.	4.8×3.1	**B.**	148.8
3.	48×31	**C.**	1488
4.	0.48×0.31	**D.**	14.88

Tell where the decimal point should be placed in the answer.

Sample 1: $42.9 \div 3 = 143$ *What you say:* $43 \div 3$ is about 14, so $42.9 \div 3 = \mathbf{14.3}$

Sample 2: $9.0 \div 3.6 = 250$ *What you say:* $9 \div 4$ is about 2, so $9.0 \div 3.6 = \mathbf{2.50}$

5. $11.0 \div 8.8 = 125$

6. $25.96 \div 5.5 = 472$

7. $118.75 \div 0.95 = 125$

8. $81.6508 \div 3.08 = 2651$

9. $3847.2 \div 1.2 = 32060$

10. $46.452 \div 9.8 = 474$

Written EXERCISES

A

Solve. Check by estimating the solution.

Sample: $t = 9.75 \times 6.3$ *Solution:* $t = 9.75 \times 6.3 = 61.425$
Estimate: $10 \times 6 = 60$

1. $n = 4.87 \times 0.95$

2. $40.1 \times 6.85 = y$

3. $b = 24.68 \times 2.35$

4. $8.001 \times 10.1 = w$

5. $m = 1.04 \times 0.008$

6. $1.8 \times 1.8 = s$

7. $x = 3.75 \times 3.0$

8. $8.0 \times 0.8 = t$

Solve. Use an estimate to check your work.

Sample: $19.5 \div 5 = r$ *Solution:* $r = 19.5 \div 5 = 3.9$
Estimate: $20 \div 5 = 4$

9. $87.64 \div 2 = y$

10. $42.03 \div 9 = b$

11. $37.2 \div 12 = n$

12. $46.05 \div 15 = z$

13. $101.01 \div 3 = t$

14. $43.01 \div 5 = s$

15. $\frac{5.73}{3} = a$

16. $22.12 \div 7 = w$

Complete.

Sample: $15\% \times 54 = t$ *Solution:*
$15\% \times 54 = t$
$0.15 \times 54 = t$
$8.1 = t$

17. $24\% \times 75 = m$
$0.24 \times 75 = m$
$\underline{\ ?\ } = m$

18. $12.5\% \times 104 = a$
$0.125 \times 104 = a$
$\underline{\ ?\ } = a$

19. $200\% \times 56 = s$
$2.00 \times 56 = s$
$\underline{\ ?\ } = s$

20. $4\% \times 32 = n$
$0.04 \times 32 = n$
$\underline{\ ?\ } = n$

Solve

B

21. $12.2 \times 0.95 = s$

22. $a = 9.24 \div 0.3$

23. $0.75 \times 3.4 = n$

24. $k = 16.02 \div 0.09$

25. $16 \times \$19.50 = y$

26. $w = \dfrac{41.04}{0.8}$

27. $24 \times \$40.35 = x$

28. $t = \dfrac{\$64.92}{12}$

29. $16\% \times 85 = r$

30. $w = 0.4 \times 0.4 \times 0.4$

31. $75\% \times 1024 = b$

32. $z = 1.0 \times 0.1 \times 0.01$

Complete.

33. $5.0275 \times 1 = \underline{\ ?\ }$
$5.0275 \times 10 = \underline{\ ?\ }$
$5.0275 \times 100 = \underline{\ ?\ }$
$5.0275 \times 1000 = \underline{\ ?\ }$

34. $1674.2 \times 1 = \underline{\ ?\ }$
$1674.2 \times 0.1 = \underline{\ ?\ }$
$1674.2 \times 0.01 = \underline{\ ?\ }$
$1674.2 \times 0.001 = \underline{\ ?\ }$

35. $34.28 \times 1 = \underline{\ ?\ }$
$34.28 \times 10 = \underline{\ ?\ }$
$34.28 \times 100 = \underline{\ ?\ }$
$34.28 \times 1000 = \underline{\ ?\ }$

36. $43.79 \times 1 = \underline{\ ?\ }$
$43.79 \times 0.1 = \underline{\ ?\ }$
$43.79 \times 0.01 = \underline{\ ?\ }$
$43.79 \times 0.001 = \underline{\ ?\ }$

Problems

1. Sarah earns $15,000 each year. She pays 18% of her earnings in income taxes. How much income tax does she pay in a year?
2. An industrial storage bin holds 5000 kilograms of salt. Salt is about 40% sodium. How many kilograms of sodium are in the bin?
3. The total surface area of a cube is 4302.06 square centimeters. What is the area of each of the six faces?
4. Tom works part time. He earns $2.87 per hour. Last week he worked 25 hours. How much did he earn?
5. A three-kilogram roast cost $14.19. What was the cost per kilogram?

SELF-TEST 1

Be sure that you understand these terms.

like fractions (p. 86) unlike fractions (p. 86)
reciprocal (p. 90)

Add or subtract. **Section 4-1, p. 86**

1. $\frac{5}{6} - \frac{2}{6}$ **2.** $\frac{1}{2} + \frac{2}{5}$

Multiply or divide. **Section 4-2, p. 90**

3. $\frac{2}{11} \times \frac{3}{5}$ **4.** $\frac{3}{7} \div \frac{1}{4}$

Add or subtract. Estimate to check your work. **Section 4-3, p. 93**

5. $11.072 - 0.23 = \underline{\ ?\ }$ **6.** $\$5.24 + \$2.57 = \underline{\ ?\ }$

Solve. **Section 4-4, p. 96**

7. $2.03 \times 4.7 = x$ **8.** $69.04 \div 2 = y$

9. $10\% \times 60 = z$

Check your answers with those printed at the back of the book.

consumer notes

Discount and Sales Tax

Maria and Phil went shopping at a discount record shop. They each bought an album which was marked down 25 percent of the original list price of $6.00. Phil went to a cashier who charged a sales tax of 3 percent on the discount price. Maria went to another cashier, who charged a sales tax of 3 percent on the list price and then deducted 25 percent. Maria argued that she was charged sales tax on money that she didn't spend. Phil and Maria then compared costs. How much did Phil spend? How much did Maria spend? What happened?

4-5 *Order of Operations*

OBJECTIVES

Simplify expressions that contain parentheses, brackets, and fraction bars.

Use grouping symbols in expressions to show the order of operations.

Grouping symbols such as parentheses, brackets, and fraction bars are used to show the order in which operations are to be done.

EXAMPLE 1 $4 \times (5 + 7)$ ► First add 5 and 7. ► $4 \times (5 + 7) = 4 \times 12$
Then multiply 4×12. ► $= 48$

EXAMPLE 2 $\frac{10 + 8}{3}$ ► First add 10 and 8. ► $\frac{10 + 8}{3} = \frac{18}{3}$
Then divide 18 by 3. ► $= 6$

When no operation sign, such as $+$, $-$, $\times$, or $\div$, is used between a numeral and an expression within parentheses, the operation intended is multiplication.

EXAMPLE 3 $7(10 + 3)$ ► First add 10 and 3. ► $7(10 + 3) = 7(13)$
Then multiply 7 and 13. ► $= 91$

EXAMPLE 4 $(12 - 5)8$ ► First subtract 5 from 12. ► $(12 - 5)(8) = (7)8$
Then multiply 7 and 8. ► $= 56$

Sometimes two different grouping symbols are used in one expression. We simplify the innermost expression first. Then we simplify the expression in the outer symbol.

EXAMPLE 5 $5[3 + (12 - 8)]$

First subtract 8 from 12. ► $5[3 + (12 - 8)] = 5[3 + 4]$
Then add 3 and 4. ► $= 5[7]$
Then multiply 5 and 7. ► $= 35$

When no grouping symbols are used, first do all multiplications and divisions in order from left to right. Then do all additions and subtractions in order from left to right.

EXAMPLE 6 $3 \times 4 + 7 \times 5$

First multiply 3×4 and 7×5. ► $3 \times 4 + 7 \times 5 = 12 + 35$
Then add 12 and 35. ► $12 + 35 = 47$

Oral EXERCISES

Tell how to simplify the expression.

Sample: $3 + (10 \times 5)$ *What you say:* Multiply 10 and 5, then add 3. The result is 53.

1. $18 \div (2 \times 3)$
2. $(15 + 8) - 10$
3. $(4 + 7)5$
4. $[3(4)] + 6$
5. $(10 - 2)(3)$
6. $\frac{10 + 14}{3}$

Tell what number is named.

Sample 1: $(10 + 20)3$ *What you say:* $(10 + 20)3 = (30)3 = 90$

Sample 2: $\frac{6 + 3}{18}$ *What you say:* $\frac{6 + 3}{18} = \frac{9}{18} = \frac{1}{2}$

7. $10 - (4 + 2)$
8. $(6 + 4)(3 + 1)$
9. $3(5 + 6)$
10. $(2 \times 3 \times 5) + 9$
11. $(2 + 7)5$
12. $6 + [3 + (5 + 2)]$
13. $7(10)$
14. $15 - [2(4 + 1)]$

Written EXERCISES

A

Simplify.

1. $(4 + 5)(2 + 6)$
2. $(2 \times 5 \times 4) + 9$
3. $(1 \times 2 \times 3) + 25$
4. $(17 + 8)6$
5. $4(5 + 3)$
6. $(24 - 6)4$
7. $18 + (34 - 6)$
8. $(9)(4 + 8)$
9. $6\left(\frac{1}{2} + \frac{1}{4}\right)$
10. $(6 + 7)(10 - 3)$

11. $\frac{4 + 9}{3}$

12. $\frac{2 + 6}{(3)(3)}$

13. $\frac{5 + 7 + 8}{4}$

14. $40 \div (6 + 4)$

15. $(6 + 71) - 10$

16. $[(5)(9)] \div 3$

Solve.

Sample: $(18 - 2) - 6 = n$

Solution: $(18 - 2) - 6 = n$
$16 - 6 = n$
$10 = n$

B

17. $(6 + 8)15 = w$

18. $h = (8 + 6)(5 - 1)$

19. $8 + (9 \times 7) = m$

20. $k = 37 - \frac{8 + 4}{9 + 6}$

21. $(5)(7)(4 + 1) = t$

22. $\frac{(45 \div 9) + 3}{6} = b$

23. $5 + \frac{3(8 - 7)}{4} = y$

24. $(15)\left(\frac{6}{2}\right)\left(\frac{3}{3}\right) = s$

25. $z = \frac{6 + 4}{5} + \frac{10 + 4}{10 + 6}$

26. $3^2 + (36 \div 9) = r$

27. $a = \frac{10(3 + 4 + 2)}{9}$

28. $(10^2 + 8^2) - 14 = n$

29. $4[2 + (8 - 1)] = x$

30. $(51 - 27) \div [2(9 + 3)] = b$

31. $5^2 + [(3 + 6) - 4] = m$

32. $\frac{[(25 \times 4) + (15 \div 5)]}{3} = t$

C

33. $4\left[\frac{72 - 24}{6^2}\right] = k$

34. $\left[\frac{9 \times 6}{(3)(3)(2)}\right]5 = a$

Use grouping symbols to show the correct order of operations.

Sample 1: $5 \times 3 + 4 = 19$ *Solution:* $(5 \times 3) + 4 = 19$

Sample 2: $3 + 12 \div 2 = 9$ *Solution:* $3 + (12 \div 2) = 9$

35. $6 \times 4 - 4 = 20$

36. $4 \times \frac{1}{2} \div \frac{1}{2} - 1 = 3$

37. $17 = 3 \times 5 + 2$

38. $32 \div 8 + 2 = 6$

39. $4 + 2 \times 3 \times 1 = 10$

40. $2 \times 3 + 4 \times 1 = 10$

41. $12 \div 4 - 3 = 0$

42. $12 - 2 \times 6 = 0$

43. $8 - 2 \times 3 = 2$

44. $8 \div 2 - 3 = 1$

calculator corner

You can use a calculator and your knowledge of algebra to "guess" a friend's birthday. Give your friend the calculator with instructions to hold it so that you can't see the display. Then have him or her do the following:

1. Punch in the number of the month of his or her birth.
2. Multiply by 5.
3. Add 6.
4. Multiply by 4.
5. Add 9.
6. Multiply by 5.
7. Add the day of birth.
8. Subtract 165.

The display will show your friend's birthday. 1201, for example, means December 1; 207 means February 7.

Maggie Lena Walker 1867–1934

Maggie Lena Walker first entered her career as an insurance and banking executive as an agent for the Woman's Union, an insurance company in Richmond, Virginia. After taking business courses in accounting and sales, she became the executive secretary-treasurer of the Independent Order of St. Luke, a Black fraternal society and cooperative insurance venture. Under her leadership the organization grew in 25 years from 3,400 to 50,000 members. In 1902, Walker began publishing the *St. Luke Herald* which reported the order's affairs. In 1903 the St. Luke Penny Savings Bank was established at her initiative. It grew to become the Consolidated Bank and Trust Company in 1929–1930, with Maggie Lena Walker as president.

4-6 *Evaluating Expressions*

OBJECTIVE

Evaluate an expression by replacing each of the variables by the members of a replacement set.

The **replacement set** for a variable in an expression is the set of numbers that the variable may represent. We **find the value** of an expression by substituting members of the replacement set for each variable.

EXAMPLE 1 Find the value of $2m + 1$. The replacement set for m is $\{0, 2, 4\}$.

If $m = 0$ ► $2(0) + 1 = 0 + 1 = \mathbf{1}$
If $m = 2$ ► $2(2) + 1 = 4 + 1 = \mathbf{5}$
If $m = 4$ ► $2(4) + 1 = 8 + 1 = \mathbf{9}$

EXAMPLE 2 Find the value of $2t + y$. Let $t = 3$ and $y = 7$. (We *could* say "The replacement set for t is $\{3\}$ and for y is $\{7\}$.")

$$2t + y = 2(3) + 7 = 6 + 7 = \mathbf{13}$$

It's important to remember that you must give a variable the same value each time it appears in the expression.

EXAMPLE 3 Find the value of $\frac{2x + 2}{x}$. The replacement set for x is $\{1, 2\}$.

If $x = 1$ ► $\frac{2x + 2}{x} = \frac{2(1) + 2}{1} = \frac{2 + 2}{1} = \mathbf{4}$

If $x = 2$ ► $\frac{2x + 2}{x} = \frac{2(2) + 2}{2} = \frac{4 + 2}{2} = \mathbf{3}$

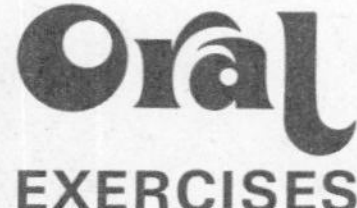

EXERCISES

Name the value of the expression. Let $a = 3$ and $b = 9$.

1. $10a$ **2.** $\frac{a}{b}$ **3.** $4(b)$

4. $2b$ **5.** $\frac{b}{a}$ **6.** $\frac{1}{3}b$

7. $3a$ **8.** $2(a)(b)$ **9.** a^2

Written EXERCISES

Find all values of the expression. The replacement set for m is $\{1, 3, 5, 7\}$.

Sample: $4 + m$ *Solution:* $4 + 1 = 5$
$4 + 3 = 7$
$4 + 5 = 9$
$4 + 7 = 11$

A

1. $m + 10$
2. $5m + 0$
3. $(m + 10) - 8$
4. $16 + m$
5. $\frac{m}{2}$
6. $m(m + 3)$
7. $3m$
8. $\frac{m}{5}$
9. m^2
10. $8m$
11. $2(m + 4)$
12. m^3

Find the value of the expression. Let $r = 2$, $s = 3$, and $t = 5$.

Sample: $rs + t$ *Solution:* $(2)(3) + 5 = 6 + 5 = 11$

13. $rs + rt$
14. $(r \times s) + t^2$
15. rst
16. $s^2 + rt$
17. $\frac{1}{2}rt$
18. $(r + s) - t$

B

19. $r^2 + s^2 + t^2$
20. $t^2 + \frac{r^2}{s^2}$
21. $2r\left(s + \frac{t}{4}\right)$
22. $(6 + r)(t)(s)$
23. $(s - r)(s + r)$
24. $\frac{s + s + s}{(rs)(rs)}$
25. $rs + \frac{t + s}{r}$
26. $\frac{3rt}{5rs} + \left(\frac{s}{t}\right)\left(\frac{r}{t}\right)$

Find the value of the expression. Let $x = 2$ and $y = 7$.

C

27. $x + [y(3 + x)]$
28. $\left[\left(\frac{y}{x}\right) + xy\right] - 12$
29. $y + [2x + (y - x)] + x$
30. $\left[\frac{xy}{x^2} + y\right] - \frac{5}{x}$
31. $y - \left[2\left(\frac{x + y}{3}\right)\right] + 4$
32. $[(x^2 + y^2)(xy)] \div 10$

4-7 *Factors, Coefficients, and Terms*

OBJECTIVES

Factor expressions like $\frac{3n}{2}$.

Name the terms of an expression.

Simplify expressions involving indicated products, such as $(3)(4)(t) = 12t$.

There are many ways to indicate multiplication. In each case, the numbers to be multiplied are called **factors**. The result is called the **product**.

$4 \times 7 = 28$ (4 and 7: factors; 28: product) $\quad 4 \cdot 7 = 28$ (4 and 7: factors; 28: product) $\quad (4)(7) = 28$ (4 and 7: factors; 28: product)

We **factor** a number or an expression by writing it as an indicated multiplication, called a **factorization**. A number or expression may have many factorizations.

EXAMPLE 1 Some factorizations of 10 ► $1 \cdot 10 \quad 2 \cdot 5 \quad \frac{1}{2} \cdot 20$

Any factor of an expression can be called the **coefficient** of the remaining factors. Often the numerical part of a multiplication expression containing variables is called *the* coefficient.

EXAMPLE 2 $6ab$ ► $6a(b)$ ► $6a$ is the coefficient of b.
$3(2ab)$ ► 3 is the coefficient of $2ab$.
$6(ab)$ ► 6 is the coefficient of ab.

EXAMPLE 3 $5x$ ► 5 is the coefficient of x.

EXAMPLE 4 m ► 1 is understood to be the coefficient of m.

The parts of an expression like $3m + 2t$ that are separated by a plus or minus sign are called **terms**.

EXAMPLE 5 $3m + 2t$ (two terms) $\quad 4a + \frac{b}{2} - c$ (three terms) $\quad 3ab$ (one term)

Name the coefficient of the variables.

Sample: $\frac{1}{5}y$ *What you say:* $\frac{1}{5}$ is the coefficient of y.

1. $5m$ **2.** $2.6n$ **3.** $\frac{z}{2}$

4. $7t$ **5.** $3ab$ **6.** $0.75r$

7. $\frac{1}{3}b$ **8.** $10mn$ **9.** $6w^2$

Name the terms.

Sample: $2x + 5$ *What you say:* $2x$ is a term and 5 is a term.

10. $b + c$ **11.** $\frac{a}{b} + \frac{1}{2}$

12. $2t + n$ **13.** $\frac{ab}{c}$

14. $7k - 5$ **15.** $w \div y$

A

Complete each factorization for the given product.

Sample: Product: $8ab$; $8(\underline{\ ?\ })$, $4(\underline{\ ?\ })$, $(\underline{\ ?\ })4a$
Solution: $8(ab)$, $4(2ab)$, $(2b)4a$

1. Product: $10s$; $10(\underline{\ ?\ })$, $5(\underline{\ ?\ })$, $2(\underline{\ ?\ })$
2. Product: $9b$; $3(\underline{\ ?\ })$, $9(\underline{\ ?\ })$, $1(\underline{\ ?\ })$
3. Product: $\frac{1}{8}t$; $(\underline{\ ?\ })t$, $\frac{1}{2}(\underline{\ ?\ })$, $\frac{1}{4}(\underline{\ ?\ })$
4. Product: $5ab$; $\underline{\ ?\ }(ab)$, $5a(\underline{\ ?\ })$, $(\underline{\ ?\ })a$
5. Product: xyz; $x(\underline{\ ?\ })$, $y(\underline{\ ?\ })$, $(\underline{\ ?\ })z$
6. Product: $\frac{rs}{2}$; $\frac{1}{2}(\underline{\ ?\ })$, $\frac{r}{2}(\underline{\ ?\ })$, $\frac{s}{2}(\underline{\ ?\ })$
7. Product: $\frac{2m}{3}$; $\frac{1}{3}(\underline{\ ?\ })$, $\frac{2}{3}(\underline{\ ?\ })$, $(\underline{\ ?\ })\frac{m}{3}$
8. Product: $2abc$; $2a(\underline{\ ?\ })$, $(\underline{\ ?\ })c$, $(\underline{\ ?\ })b$

Show that each factorization has the same value as the given product. Use $k = 4$ and $t = 6$.

Sample: Product: $\frac{3}{4}t$ Factorizations: $\frac{1}{4}(3t)$; $3\left(\frac{t}{4}\right)$

Solution: $\frac{3}{4}t = \frac{3}{4} \cdot 6 = 4\frac{1}{2}$

$\frac{1}{4}(3t) = \frac{1}{4} \cdot 18 = 4\frac{1}{2}$

$3\left(\frac{t}{4}\right) = 3 \cdot \frac{6}{4} = 4\frac{1}{2}$

9. Product: $8k$ Factorizations: $4(2k)$; $2(4k)$
10. Product: $3tk$ Factorizations: $3t(k)$; $3k(t)$
11. Product: $\frac{kt}{3}$ Factorizations: $\frac{1}{3}(kt)$; $\frac{t}{3}(k)$
12. Product: $\frac{9k}{t}$ Factorizations: $9 \cdot \frac{k}{t}$; $\frac{1}{t} \cdot 9k$
13. Product: $\frac{1}{2}kt$ Factorizations: $\frac{k}{2} \cdot t$; $k \cdot \frac{t}{2}$
14. Product: $\frac{4k}{5t}$ Factorizations: $\frac{4}{5} \cdot \frac{k}{t}$; $4k \cdot \frac{1}{5t}$

Name the product.

Sample 1: $(7)(5)(m)$ *Solution:* $35m$

Sample 2: $c = 2 \times \pi \times r$ *Solution:* $2\pi r$

15. $(3)(2)(x)$
16. $3(t)(n)$
17. $(9)(a)(b)$
18. $(0.5)(5.0)(c)(d)$

B

19. $p = l + l + w + w$
20. $A = \pi \times r \times r$
21. $A = \frac{1}{2} \times b \times h$
22. $v = \frac{4}{3} \times \pi \times r \times r \times r$
23. $(6)(m)(m)(9)$
24. $5(t)(r)\left(\frac{s}{9}\right)$
25. $(3)(b)\left(\frac{c}{5}\right)$
26. $\left(\frac{a}{2}\right)\left(\frac{b}{4}\right)\left(\frac{3}{c}\right)$
27. $\left(\frac{1}{2}\right)(p)(5q)$
28. $a\left(\frac{a}{2}\right)\left(\frac{a}{3}\right)$

Write three different factorizations.

Sample: $12pq$ *Solution:* $12p(q)$; $(3p)(4q)$; $(6q)(2p)$ (Other answers are possible.)

C

29. $8rs$ **30.** $2ab$ **31.** $\frac{3rs}{t}$

32. abc **33.** $2d$ **34.** $\frac{ab}{cd}$

35. $\frac{3t}{10}$ **36.** r^2 **37.** $\frac{a}{cd}$

38. $\frac{xy}{3}$ **39.** $\frac{4cd}{5}$ **40.** $\frac{1}{rst}$

Problems

Solve.

Sample: The area of a rectangle is $5ab$. If the length is $5a$, what is the width?

Solution Use $A = lw$, where $A = 5ab$ and $l = 5a$.
$5ab = (5a)(b)$, so the width is b.

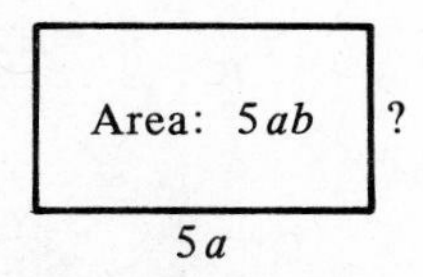

1. The area of a rectangle is $18cd$. If the length is $9c$, what is the width? Use $A = lw$.

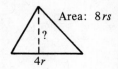

2. The area of a triangle is $8rs$. If the length of the base is $4r$, what is the height? Use $A = \frac{1}{2}bh$.

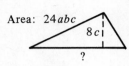

3. The area of a triangle is $24abc$. If the height is $8c$, what is the base? Use $A = \frac{1}{2}bh$.

4. The dimensions of two rectangles are shown. Compare their areas. Use $A = lw$.

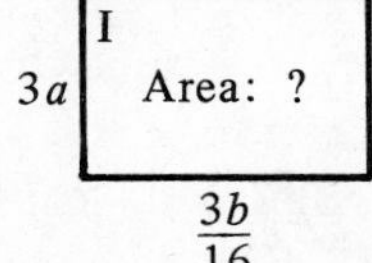

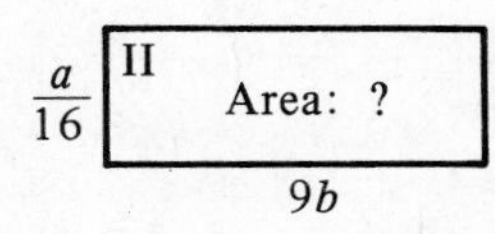

4-8 *Functions*

OBJECTIVES

Use an algebraic expression as a rule for finding a set of ordered pairs that is a function.

Graph a function.

In Chapter 2 you learned about ordered pairs of numbers and their graphs. Now we use those ideas in working with mathematical functions.

Suppose you have a "function machine." When a card bearing a number is fed in, the machine names another number according to a stated rule. Let's call the number on the card an **input** number and the machine's response an **output** number. We can write a set of ordered pairs of the form (**input, output**).

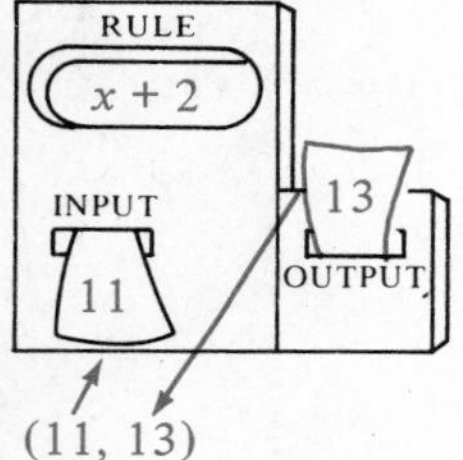

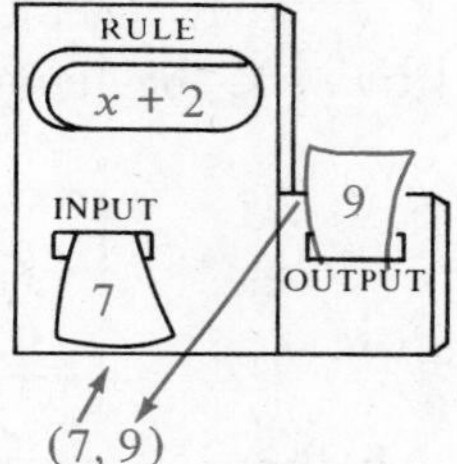

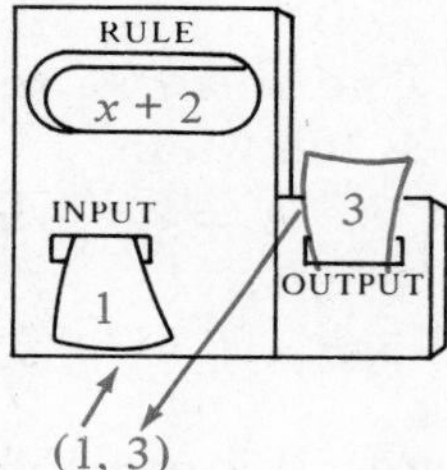

EXAMPLE 1 Let's use a function machine with the rule $x + 2$. The table shows the ordered pairs that result when the counting numbers are fed in.

Input Number: x	*Output Number:* $x + 2$	*Ordered Pair:* $(x, x + 2)$
1	3	(1, 3)
2	4	(2, 4)
3	5	(3, 5)
4	6	(4, 6)
.	.	.
.	.	.
.	.	.

Notice the three dots. They show that the set continues on indefinitely.

We get the set of ordered pairs $\{(1, 3), (2, 4), (3, 5), (4, 6), \ldots\}$. This set is called a **function.**

EXAMPLE 2 Let us use the "function machine" with the rule $\frac{n}{3}$ to generate a different set of ordered pairs.

Input Number: n	*Output Number:* $\frac{n}{3}$	*Ordered Pair:* $\left(n, \frac{n}{3}\right)$
1	$\frac{1}{3}$	$\left(1, \frac{1}{3}\right)$
2	$\frac{2}{3}$	$\left(2, \frac{2}{3}\right)$
3	1	(3, 1)
4	$1\frac{1}{3}$	$(4, 1\frac{1}{3})$
5	$1\frac{2}{3}$	$(5, 1\frac{2}{3})$

The function that results is $\left\{\left(1, \frac{1}{3}\right), \left(2, \frac{2}{3}\right), (3, 1), (4, 1\frac{1}{3}), (5, 1\frac{2}{3})\right\}$.

Many rules can be used to form sets of ordered pairs that are functions. Notice that for a set of ordered pairs to be a function, no two different pairs can have the same first number.

Functions	*Not Functions*
{(0, 7), (1, 8), (2, 9), (3, 10)}	{(2, 0), (2, 5), (3, 6), (4, 9)} same first member
{(1, 2), (2, 3), (3, 5), (5, 7), . . .}	{(2, 2), (4, 4), (2, 6), (4, 6), . . .}

We can graph a function by locating on a set of axes the points that represent the ordered pairs in the set.

EXAMPLE 3

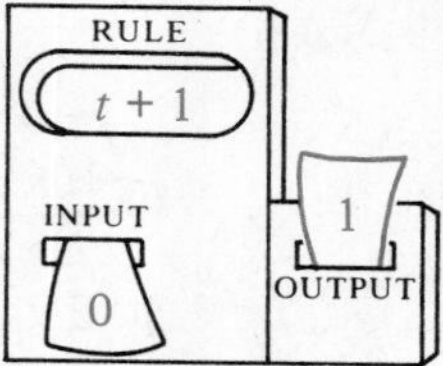

Input Number *t*	*Output Number* *t + 1*	*Ordered Pair* *(t, t + 1)*
0	1	(0, 1)
1	2	(1, 2)
2	3	(2, 3)
3	4	(3, 4)

Graph:

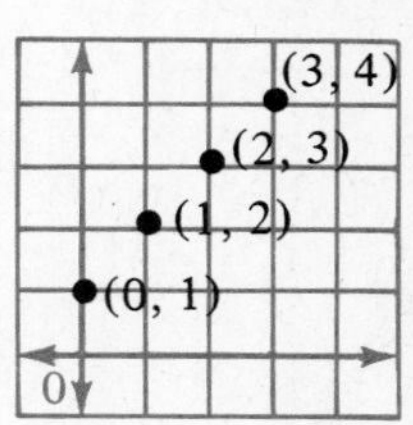

Function: {(0, 1), (1, 2), (2, 3), (3, 4)}

Tell how to complete the table.

1. Rule: $s - 3$

Input Number	*Output Number*	*Number Pair*
3	0	(3, 0)
5	2	(?, ?)
7	4	(?, ?)
9	?	(9, 6)
11	?	(11, 8)

2. Rule: $\frac{w}{2}$

Input Number	*Output Number*	*Number Pair*
2	1	(2, 1)
3	$1\frac{1}{2}$	(?, ?)
5	?	$(5, 2\frac{1}{2})$
7	?	$(7, 3\frac{1}{2})$
9	?	(?, ?)

Tell whether or not the set of ordered pairs is a function.

3. $\{(0, 4), (1, 8), (2, 16), (3, 32)\}$
4. $\{(1, 2), (1, 3), (1, 4), (2, 6), (2, 8), (2, 10)\}$
5. $\{(1, 5), (2, 5), (3, 5), (4, 6), (5, 6), (6, 6), \ldots\}$
6. $\left\{\left(\frac{1}{2}, \frac{1}{3}\right), \left(\frac{1}{3}, \frac{1}{4}\right), \left(\frac{1}{4}, \frac{1}{5}\right), \left(\frac{1}{5}, \frac{1}{6}\right)\right\}$

Written EXERCISES

Complete the set of ordered pairs by using the given rule.

Sample: $r + 3$: {(5, 8), (7, 10), (9, _?_), (11, _?_), (13, _?_)}
Solution: {(5, 8), (7, 10), (9, 12), (11, 14), (13, 16)}

A

1. $b - 5$: {(5, 0), (6, 1), (7, _?_), (8, _?_), (9, _?_), (10, 5)}
2. $4 + s$: {(1, 5), (2, 6), (3, _?_), (4, _?_), (5, _?_), (6, _?_), (7, _?_)}
3. $\frac{t}{5}$: $\left\{(0, 0), \left(4, \frac{4}{5}\right)\right.$, (8, _?_), (12, _?_), (16, _?_), (20, _?_), (24, _?_)}
4. $k + 0$: {(0, 0), (1, 1), (2, 2), (3, _?_), (4, _?_), (5, _?_), (6, _?_)}
5. w^2: {(1, 1), (2, _?_), (3, _?_), (4, 16), (5, 25), (6, _?_), (7, _?_)}
6. $2(x + 1)$: {(10, 22), (20, 42), (30, 62), (40, _?_), (50, _?_), (60, _?_)}

Graph the function.

Sample: {(0, 4), (1, 3), (2, 2), (3, 1)} *Solution:*

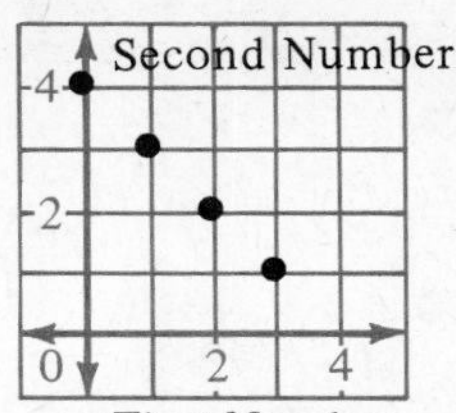

7. {(0, 0), (1, 1), (2, 2), (3, 3), (4, 4), (5, 5)}
8. {(1, 0), (2, 1), (3, 2), (4, 3), (5, 4), (6, 5)}
9. $\left\{\left(0, \frac{1}{2}\right), (1, 1\tfrac{1}{2}), (1\tfrac{1}{2}, 2), (2, 2\tfrac{1}{2}), (2\tfrac{1}{2}, 3), (3, 3\tfrac{1}{2}), (3\tfrac{1}{2}, 4)\right\}$

Match each set of ordered pairs with the correct rule.

10. {(0, 2), (1, 4), (2, 6), (3, 8), (4, 10)} **A.** $n + 0.3$
11. $\left\{\left(\frac{1}{7}, 1\right), \left(\frac{2}{7}, 2\right), \left(\frac{3}{7}, 3\right), \left(\frac{4}{7}, 4\right), \left(\frac{5}{7}, 5\right)\right\}$ **B.** $2(x + 1)$
12. {(1, 1.3), (2, 2.3), (3, 3.3), (4, 4.3)} **C.** $7w$
13. {(0, 0), (2, 1), (4, 2), (6, 3), (8, 4)} **D.** $\frac{s}{3}$
14. $\{(6, 2), (7\tfrac{1}{2}, 2\tfrac{1}{2}), (9, 3), (10\tfrac{1}{2}, 3\tfrac{1}{2})\}$ **E.** $y \div 2$

Complete.

	Input Number m	*Output Number* $0.5 + m$	*Ordered Pair* $(m, 0.5 + m)$
15.	0	0.5	?
16.	1.0	1.5	?
17.	1.5	?	?
18.	2.0	?	?
19.	2.5	?	?

RULE
0.5 + *m*
INPUT
0
0.5
OUTPUT

B

	n	$\frac{n + 2}{3}$	$\left(n, \frac{n + 2}{3}\right)$
20.	2	$1\frac{1}{3}$	?
21.	4	?	?
22.	6	?	?
23.	8	?	?
24.	10	?	?
25.	12	?	?

Write an expression that is a function rule for the set of ordered pairs.

Sample: $\{(2, 4\frac{1}{2}), (3, 5\frac{1}{2}), (4, 6\frac{1}{2}), (6, 8\frac{1}{2})\}$ *Solution:* $x + 2\frac{1}{2}$

C **26.** $\{(2, 10), (3, 15), (4, 20), (5, 25), (6, 30)\}$

27. $\left\{(0, 0), \left(1, \frac{1}{2}\right), (2, 1), (3, 1\frac{1}{2}), (4, 2), (5, 2\frac{1}{2})\right\}$

28. $\{(0, 0), (1, 1), (2, 2), (3, 3), (8, 8), (9, 9), (10, 10)\}$

29. $\{(1, 1), (2, 4), (3, 9), (4, 16), (5, 25), (6, 36)\}$

30. $\{(1, 0.75), (2, 1.5), (3, 2.25), (4, 3), (5, 3.75)\}$

31. $\left\{\left(1, \frac{1}{10}\right), \left(2, \frac{1}{5}\right), \left(3, \frac{3}{10}\right), \left(4, \frac{2}{5}\right), \left(5, \frac{1}{2}\right), \left(6, \frac{3}{5}\right)\right\}$

SELF-TEST 2

Be sure that you understand these terms.

replacement set (p. 104)	coefficient (p. 106)
terms (p. 106)	function (p. 110)

Section 4-5, p. 100 **1.** Simplify $15 \div (3 - 2)$.

Section 4-6, p. 104 **2.** Show that both expressions have the same value when $x = 2$ and $y = 7$: $3(xy) = 3x(y)$

3. Find the value of $(r + s^2)t$ if $r = 5$, $s = 3$, and $t = 2$.

Section 4-7, p. 106 **4.** Complete the following factorizations of $\frac{2s}{7}$:

$\frac{1}{7}(\underline{\ ?\ })$, $\frac{2}{7}(\underline{\ ?\ })$, $(\underline{\ ?\ })\frac{s}{7}$

5. Simplify $(3)(x)(y)(2)$.

Section 4-8, p. 110 **6.** Complete the set of number pairs by using the rule $t + 7$: $\{(0, 7), (1, \underline{\ ?\ }), (2, \underline{\ ?\ }), (3, \underline{\ ?\ }), (4, \underline{\ ?\ }), (5, \underline{\ ?\ }), (6, \underline{\ ?\ })\}$.

7. Graph $\{(0, 0), (1, 1), (2, 4), (3, 9), (4, 16)\}$.

Check your answers with those printed at the back of the book.

---

chapter summary

1. To add (or subtract) with fractions that have a common denominator, add (or subtract) the numerators and use the common denominator.
2. To add (or subtract) with fractions that do not have a common denominator, first rename one or both fractions so they have a common denominator. Then add or subtract.
3. To multiply with fractions, multiply the numerators and the denominators.
4. Two numbers are **reciprocals** of each other if their product is 1.
5. Dividing by a number is the same as multiplying by its reciprocal.
6. When we multiply or divide with decimals, the number of digits after the decimal point in the product is the sum of the numbers of digits after the decimal points in the factors.
7. To find a percent of a number, multiply the number by the percent written in decimal form.
8. Values of an expression containing a variable are found when the variable is replaced with the members of the specified replacement set.
9. Any factor of an expression can be called the **coefficient** of the remaining factors.

chapter test

Add or subtract.

1. $\frac{5}{8} + \frac{1}{8}$
2. $\frac{9}{10} - \frac{8}{10}$
3. $\frac{1}{2} + \frac{3}{8}$
4. $2\frac{2}{5} + 4\frac{1}{5}$
5. $7\frac{3}{4} - 4\frac{1}{4}$
6. $\frac{4}{5} - \frac{2}{3}$

Multiply or divide.

7. $\frac{5}{8} \times \frac{1}{3}$
8. $1\frac{1}{2} \div \frac{1}{4}$
9. $2\frac{1}{3} \div 4$

10. $\frac{2}{3} \div \frac{3}{5}$

11. $\frac{1}{2} \times 4\frac{1}{3}$

12. $6 \times 1\frac{1}{8}$

Find the value when $a = 1$, $b = 2$, and $c = 3$.

13. $\frac{a}{6} + \frac{a}{c}$

14. $\frac{c}{b} \times \frac{a}{b}$

15. $\frac{a}{b} \times \frac{a}{c} \times \frac{b}{c}$

Solve.

16. $t = 27.1 + 3.8$

17. $x = 58.09 - 12.25$

18. $s = 13.04 \times 5.7$

19. $t = 119.7 \div 0.95$

Find the percent.

20. $32\% \times 65$

21. $8\% \times \$125$

Simplify.

22. $(10 - 6)(3 + 7)$

23. $[(3)(4)]$

24. $\frac{8 + 7}{3}$

25. $5a(b)(c)$

Find the values of the expression. The replacement set for t is $\{2, 4, 6\}$.

26. $3t + 15$

27. $5(t + 3)$

Complete each factorization of the given product.

28. Product: $6bc$; $6(\underline{\ ?\ })$, $3(\underline{\ ?\ })$, $2b(\underline{\ ?\ })$

29. Product: $\frac{3t}{5}$; $\frac{3}{5}(\underline{\ ?\ })$, $3(\underline{\ ?\ })$, $\frac{1}{5}(\underline{\ ?\ })$

Complete the table and graph the function.

30.

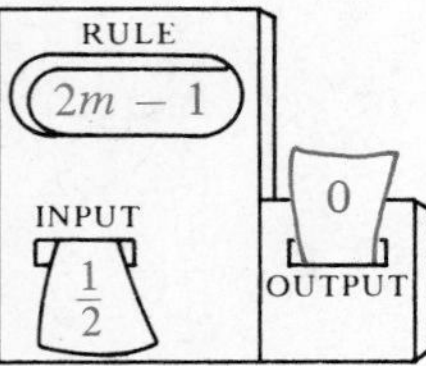

Input Number	*Output Number*	*Ordered Pair*
$\frac{1}{2}$	0	$\left(\frac{1}{2}, 0\right)$
1	1	?
$1\frac{1}{2}$	2	?
2	?	?
$2\frac{1}{2}$	?	?

challenge topics

Decimal Slide Ruler

Make a pair of scales from heavy paper, as shown below. Each scale is marked off in centimeters and millimeters which will be used to add and subtract with decimals.

These scales are arranged to show that 3.5 + 4.3 = 7.8

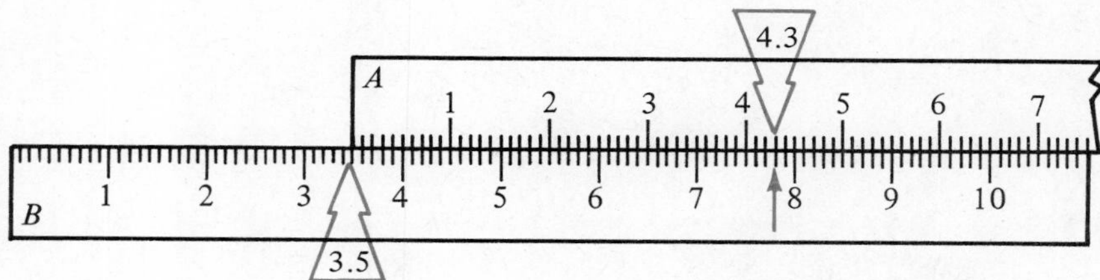

Read the answer 7.8 from the *B* scale.

To complete the subtraction 8.9 − 2.4 = __?__ the scales are arranged like this:

Read the answer 6.5 from the *A* scale.

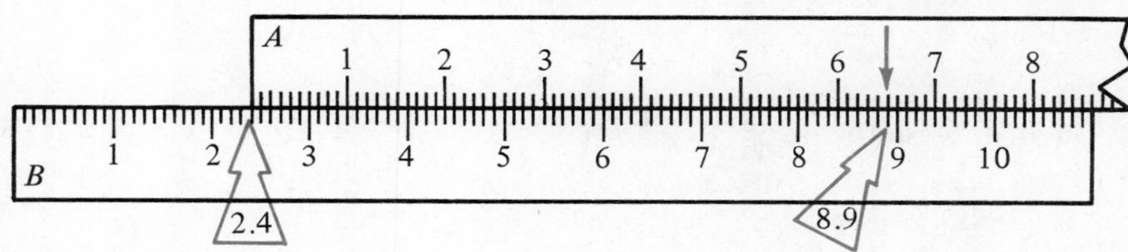

Add or subtract. Use the decimal slide ruler.

1. 2.8 + 6.9 **2.** 4.0 + 5.5 **3.** 0.6 + 3.7

4. 6.2 − 3.1 **5.** 10.0 − 4.7 **6.** 7.3 − 2.4

Review of Skills

Write using exponents.

Sample: $8 \cdot 8 \cdot 8$ *Solution:* $8 \cdot 8 \cdot 8 = 8^3$

1. $10 \cdot 10$
2. $2 \cdot 2 \cdot 2 \cdot 2 \cdot 2 \cdot 2$
3. $5 \cdot 5 \cdot 5 \cdot 5 \cdot 5$
4. $3 \cdot 3 \cdot 3 \cdot 3$
5. $n \cdot n \cdot n$
6. $7 \cdot 7 \cdot 7$

Multiply.

7. $9 \cdot 5$
8. $9 \cdot 9$
9. $7 \cdot 5 \cdot 14$
10. $6 \cdot 7$
11. $7 \cdot 8 \cdot 2 \cdot 0$
12. $5 \cdot 12 \cdot 9$
13. $4 \cdot 4 \cdot 4$
14. $10 \cdot 10 \cdot 15$
15. $7 \cdot 8 \cdot 18$

Tell whether the statement is true or false.

16. $8 + 3 < 11$
17. $(2 \cdot 5) + 1 > 10$
18. $3 \times 5 < 10$
19. $\frac{7}{3} + 2 > 3$

Divide.

20. $36 \div 9$
21. $56 \div 8$
22. $64 \div 8$
23. $63 \div 7$
24. $72 \div 9$
25. $40 \div 5$

Add.

26.
```
 477
 209
  83
----
```

27.
```
$  47.10
   65.28
  300.00
--------
```

28. $9.24 + $18.37 + $15.80

Write the fraction in lowest terms.

29. $\frac{15}{20}$
30. $\frac{3}{9}$
31. $\frac{12}{48}$
32. $\frac{50}{100}$
33. $\frac{18}{30}$
34. $\frac{19}{57}$
35. $\frac{36}{48}$
36. $\frac{75}{100}$

Left: Telephone switchboard, 1908.

Right: Modern electronic switching system.

5 Equations and Inequalities

Solution Sets and Strategies

5-1 *Equations and Inequalities*

OBJECTIVES

Classify number sentences as equations or inequalities.

Use the symbols $=$, $\neq$, $<$, and $>$ to write number sentences.

You recall that a number sentence which contains the symbol $=$ is called an **equation.** A number sentence which contains one of the symbols $<$, $>$, or $\neq$ is called an **inequality.**

EXAMPLE 1 The sum of 10 and 9 is not equal to 20.

$$10 + 9 \neq 20$$

This statement is **true.**

EXAMPLE 2 The product of 5 and 9 is less than 40.

$$5 \cdot 9 < 40$$

This statement is **false.**

An equation or inequality that contains a variable is neither true nor false until the variable is replaced by a member of a specified replacement set.

EXAMPLE 3 The sum of 6 and some number is less than 15.

$$6 + n < 15$$

This sentence is **neither** true nor false.

EXAMPLE 4 The quotient of 20 and 5 is greater than some number.

$$20 \div 5 > x$$

This sentence is neither true nor false.

EXAMPLE 5 The product of 2 and some number is less than 2.

$$2m < 2$$

This sentence is neither true nor false.

Tell whether the sentence is an equation or an inequality.

1. $\frac{5}{t} + 3 = 8$
2. $2w + 3 = 20$
3. $7 + 4 < 18$
4. $7 + 4x \neq 15$
5. $9 \neq 3 \cdot 3 \cdot 3$
6. $4 + 0 > 4 \cdot 0$

Tell whether the sentence is *true, false,* or *neither.*

Sample 1: $9 - 2 > 4$ *What you say:* True

Sample 2: $2 \cdot k = 14$ *What you say:* Neither

7. $4 \cdot 7 > 7 \cdot 4$
8. $x - 1 = 6$
9. $3 + 2 < 8$
10. $2(1 + 5) = 12$
11. $16 \div 4 \neq 4$
12. $1.01 < 1.001$

Written EXERCISES

A

Match each number sentence in Column 1 with the correct item in Column 2.

COLUMN 1	COLUMN 2
1. $x^2 + 2 = 3$	A. 10 is less than 5 times x^3.
2. $14 > 2x$	B. 4 times x is not the same as 6^2.
3. $26 + x < 4x$	C. 2 plus the square of some number is three.
4. $10 < 5 \cdot x^3$	D. 5 is x less than the square of 15.
5. $6 + x^2 < 20$	E. 16.2 is x less than 2.1.
6. $15^2 - x = 5$	F. x added to 26 is less than 4 times x.
7. $4x \neq 6^2$	G. 2 times x is less than 14.
8. $2.1 - x = 16.2$	H. 6 plus the square of x is less than 20.

Write a number sentence.

Sample: Some number is greater than the product of 6 and 7.
Solution: $k > 6 \cdot 7$.

9. 8 more than some number is 23.
10. 8 less than some number is 23.

11. 3 times the cube of some number is greater than 7.
12. Some number times 9 is not equal to 13.
13. The product of 3.4 and some number is greater than 100.
14. Three-fourths of some number is not equal to 3.

B

15. Twice the square of some number is greater than 5.
16. The sum of 8 and 7 is greater than the product of some number and 3.
17. One more than four times some number is less than 20.
18. Four less than the cube of some number is not equal to 62.

Write a word statement.

Sample: $m - 5 > 7$ *Solution:* m minus 5 is greater than 7. (Other answers are possible.)

19. $7 < t - 2$
20. $16 \neq 1.8b + 1$
21. $5^2 + s \neq 8$
22. $22 < m - 6 \cdot 7$
23. $3 + 2r < 11$
24. $r^2 - 1 \neq 0$
25. $a^2 - 3 > 10$
26. $5 + c^2 < 24$

consumer notes *Packaging*

Packages are designed to attract consumers visually. Many times bigger looking packages or bottles do not contain larger amounts of items.

Go into a food store and compare soft drink bottles. Often two bottles *appear* to be the same size. Choose two brands. Which bottle seems to contain more? Read the labels and compare the volumes of the bottles. Which bottle actually contains more beverage? You can compare potato chips in the same way. Choose a bag of potato chips which contains two or more separate parts. Choose a single bag of chips of the same size. Read both labels. Which bag contains more? Which has the lower unit price? Think of other items you can compare. A wise consumer reads labels, rather than trusts appearances.

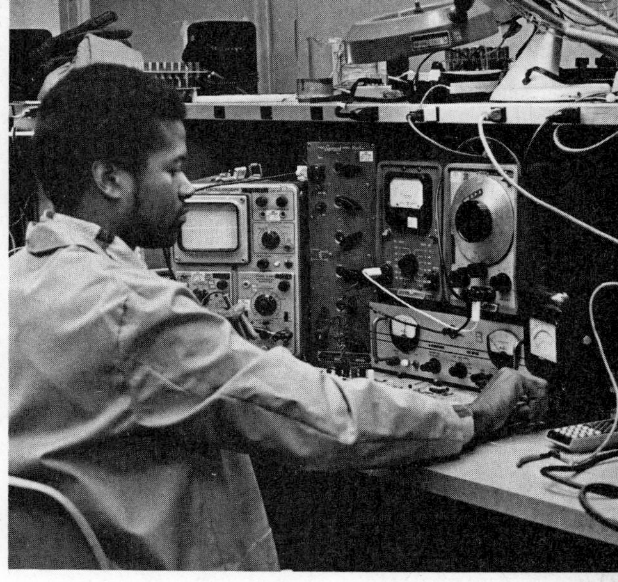

career capsule

Instrument Maker

Instrument makers redesign or build mechanical or electronic instruments. Often they work in cooperation with engineers and scientists in developing laboratory equipment and experimental models. They work from blueprints, rough sketches, or verbal instructions. Instrument makers must have an interest in mechanics and the ability to work with their hands. They must study each individual part and understand its relationship to the whole machine.

A four or five year apprenticeship is usually required. High school courses in algebra, geometry, trigonometry, science and machine shop are very useful.

5-2 *Equations and Solution Sets*

OBJECTIVES

Use tables to find solutions of equations.

Write and graph solution sets of equations.

We have seen that an equation such as $4 + t = 19$ is neither true nor false until a value is given to t. If a replacement set for t is specified, we can substitute members to see which, if any, make the equation true. Sometimes a table is helpful.

EXAMPLE 1 $4 + t = 19$; replacement set: $\{5, 10, 15, 20\}$

Replacement	$4 + t = 19$	*True/False*
5	$4 + 5 = 19$	False
10	$4 + 10 = 19$	False
15	$\mathbf{4 + 15 = 19}$	**True**
20	$4 + 20 = 19$	False

15 is a **solution.** It is the only replacement that makes the equation true. The **solution set** is $\{15\}$.

EXAMPLE 2 $2m = 7 + 1$; replacement set: $\{0, 2, 5\}$

Replacement	$2m = 7 + 1$	*True/False*	*Solution?*
0	$0 = 7 + 1$	False	No
2	$4 = 7 + 1$	False	No
5	$10 = 7 + 1$	False	No

There are no solutions. Solution set: $\emptyset$ ◄ the empty set

Once an equation is solved, we can graph its solution set.

EXAMPLE 3 $x \cdot 0 = 0$; replacement set: $\{1, 1\frac{1}{2}, 2, 3\}$

Replacement	$x \cdot 0 = 0$	*True/False*	*Solution?*
1	$1 \cdot 0 = 0$	True	YES
$1\frac{1}{2}$	$1\frac{1}{2} \cdot 0 = 0$	True	YES
2	$2 \cdot 0 = 0$	True	YES
3	$3 \cdot 0 = 0$	True	YES

All the replacements are solutions. Solution set: $\{1, 1\frac{1}{2}, 2, 3\}$

Graph: 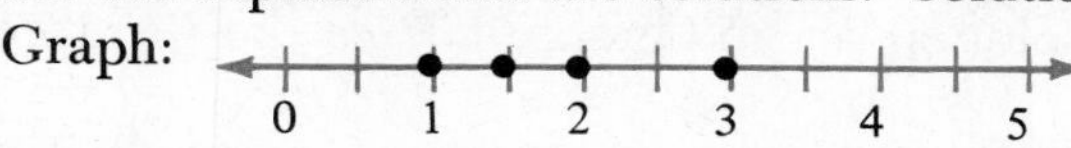

Name the solution set for each equation. The replacement set for each variable is $\{1, 3, 5\}$.

Sample 1: $t - 1 = 2$ *What you say:* $\{3\}$

Sample 2: $6 + k = 4$ *What you say:* $\emptyset$

1. $4 + n = 9$
2. $2t = 2$
3. $m - 5 = 2$
4. $s \div 3 = 1$
5. $5 + 4 = 3r$
6. $10 \div b = 2$
7. $16 + d = 0$
8. $n^2 \cdot 0 = 0$

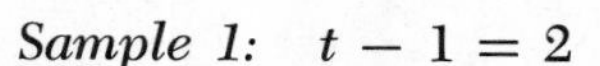

Make a table to find the solution set. Use the given replacement set.

Sample: $m^2 - 1 = 8$; $\{3, 4, 5\}$

Solution:

Replacement	$m^2 - 1 = 8$	*True/False*
3	$3^2 - 1 = 8$	True
4	$4^2 - 1 = 8$	False
5	$5^2 - 1 = 8$	False

The solution set is $\{3\}$.

A

1. $m - 4 = 6 + 2$; $\{10, 12, 14\}$
2. $n^2 + 1 = 26$; $\{3, 4, 5\}$
3. $2m + 5 = 17$; $\{6, 7, 8\}$

4. $10 - b = 2$; $\{6, 8, 10\}$
5. $4 - 2b = 0$; $\{0, 2, 4\}$
6. $7.2 + m = 10.2$; $\{1, 3, 5, 7\}$
7. $3(1 + s) = 12$; $\{0, 1, 2, 3\}$
8. $t \cdot 0 + 1 = t$; $\{0, 1, 2, 3\}$
9. $d + 3d = 8$; $\{0, 1, 2, 3\}$
10. $2t + 4 = 2(t + 2)$; $\{2, 4, 6, 8\}$

Find the solution set and graph it. Use the specified replacement set.

Sample: $7k - 14 = 7(k - 2)$; $\{3, 4\}$

Solution:

Replacement	$7k - 14 = 7(k - 2)$	*True/False*
3	$21 - 14 = 7(1)$	True
4	$28 - 14 = 7(2)$	True

Solution set: $\{3, 4\}$

Graph: 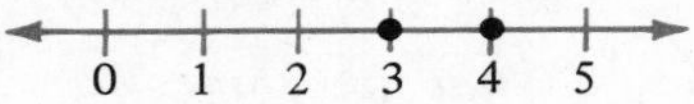

B

11. $10 - a = 20 - 3a$; $\{0, 5, 10\}$
12. $2m + 5 = 6$; $\{1, 2, 3\}$
13. $2s = 3s - 7$; $\{3, 5, 7\}$
14. $m(3 + 5) = 7m + m$; $\{0, 1, 2\}$
15. $5k + 2 = k + 10$; $\{0, 2, 4, 6\}$
16. $b + b + 2b = 4b$; $\{1, 2, 3\}$
17. $n(n - 1) = 6$; $\{0, 1, 2\}$
18. $2t + 0 \cdot t = t + t$; $\{0, 1, 2, 3\}$
19. $r + r = r^2$; $\{0, 1, 2\}$
20. $t + t = t^2$; $\{0, 3, 5\}$
21. $4n - 5 = 3$; $\{2, 3, 4, 5\}$
22. $2m - 1 = 5$; $\{1, 2, 3, 4\}$
23. $b + 2b = 4b$; $\{0, 2, 4\}$
24. $4x - 2 = 0$; $\left\{0, \frac{1}{2}, 1, 1\frac{1}{2}\right\}$
25. $\frac{2}{3}t + 4 = 6$; $\{2, 4, 6, 8\}$
26. $m^2 - 1 = 0$; $\{0, 1, 2, 3\}$

5-3 *Equation Solving Strategies*

OBJECTIVES

Solve an equation by adding the same number to both members.

Solve an equation by subtracting the same number from both members.

The fact that an equation is like a balanced scale can be used in solving equations.

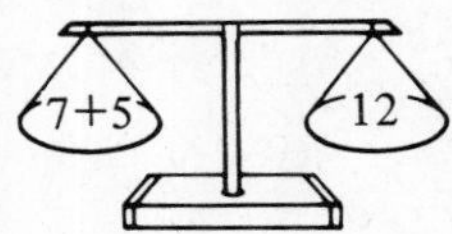

Add 3 to both sides.
The scale is still balanced.

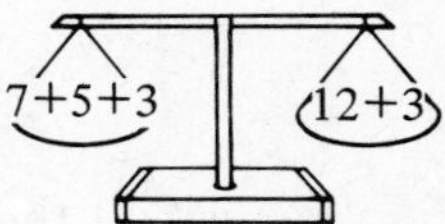

You will agree that $7 + 5 = 12$ is a true statement. Note that when the same number is added to both members of the equation, another true statement results. A true statement also results if we subtract the same number from both members.

$7 + 5 = 12$ ◀ True
$7 + 5 + 3 = 12 + 3$ ◀ Also true
$15 = 15$

$7 + 5 = 12$ ◀ True
$7 + 5 - 2 = 12 - 2$ ◀ Also true
$10 = 10$

These ideas can help us solve an equation that contains a variable. The basic strategy is to get the variable to stand alone as one member of the equation. In working with the following equations, let us agree to use as the replacement set {0 and all numbers to the right of zero on the number line}. We shall call this set {the numbers of arithmetic}.

EXAMPLE 1

$x + 9 = 14$
$x + 9 - 9 = 14 - 9$ ◀ Subtract 9 from both members.
$x = 5$

Solution: 5

EXAMPLE 2

$8 = m - 1$
$8 + 1 = m - 1 + 1$ ◀ Add 1 to both members.
$9 = m$

Solution: 9

Oral EXERCISES

True or false?

1. $5 - 5 = 0$
2. $3\frac{1}{2} - 3\frac{1}{2} = 0$
3. $9 + 3 - 3 = 3$
4. $10 + 5 - 5 = 10$
5. $2m - m = m$
6. $4.7 + 2 - 2 = 4.7$

Simplify.

Sample: $23 + 2 - 2$ *What you say:* 23

7. $15 + 7 - 7$
8. $17 - 1 + 1$
9. $15 - c + c$
10. $32 + 2 - 2$
11. $10 + b - b$
12. $m + 3 - 3$

Written EXERCISES

Add the given number to both members. Simplify the result.

Sample: $11 + 5 = 16$; add 3 *Solution:* $11 + 5 + 3 = 16 + 3$
$19 = 19$

A

1. $2 + 8 = 10$; add 3
2. $4 = 1 + 3$; add 10
3. $15 = 6 + 9$; add 1
4. $4 + 1 = 5$; add $\frac{1}{2}$
5. $4.5 = 1 + 3.5$; add 1.5
6. $6 - 2 = 3 + 1$; add 0

Subtract the given number from both members. Simplify the result.

7. $4 + 8 = 12$; subtract 5
8. $3 + 5 = 8$; subtract 2
9. $35 = 10 + 25$; subtract 4
10. $5.0 + 2.5 = 7.5$; subtract 2.5
11. $3 + 9 = 3 + 4 + 5$; subtract 0
12. $18 - 1 = 10 + 7$; subtract 7

Add or subtract. Simplify the result.

Sample: $m + 2$; subtract 2 *Solution:* $m + 2 - 2 = m$

13. $x + 10$; subtract 10
14. $w + 9$; subtract 9
15. $n - 17$; add 17
16. $y - \frac{1}{2}$; add $\frac{1}{2}$
17. $10 + z$; subtract 10
18. $s - 2.7$; add 2.7
19. $3.9 + m$; subtract 3.9
20. $a - b$; add b

Complete the solution. The replacement set is {the numbers of arithmetic}.

21. $w + 1 = 8$
$w + 1 - 1 = 8 - 1$
$w = \underline{\ ?\ }$

22. $k + 10 = 40$
$k + 10 - 10 = 40 - 10$
$k = \underline{\ ?\ }$

23. $a - 5 = 25$
$a - 5 + 5 = 25 + 5$
$a = \underline{\ ?\ }$

24. $t - 6 = 18$
$t - 6 + 6 = 18 + 6$
$t = \underline{\ ?\ }$

B

25. $14 = n + 6\frac{1}{2}$
$14 - 6\frac{1}{2} = n + 6\frac{1}{2} - 6\frac{1}{2}$
$\underline{\ ?\ } = n$

26. $18.7 = y - 4.1$
$18.7 + 4.1 = y - 4.1 + 4.1$
$\underline{\ ?\ } = y$

27. $2x = 5 + x$
$2x - x = 5 + x - x$
$x = \underline{\ ?\ }$

28. $s + 2 = 2$
$s + 2 - 2 = 2 - 2$
$s = \underline{\ ?\ }$

29. $r + \frac{2}{3} = 4$
$r + \frac{2}{3} - \frac{2}{3} = 4 - \frac{2}{3}$
$r = \underline{\ ?\ }$

30. $7 + m = 2m$
$7 + m - m = 2m - m$
$\underline{\ ?\ } = m$

C

31. $21 = m^2 - 4$
$21 + 4 = m^2 - 4 + 4$
$\underline{\ ?\ } = m^2$
$\underline{\ ?\ } = m$

32. $x^2 + 3 = 19$
$x^2 + 3 - 3 = 19 - 3$
$x^2 = \underline{\ ?\ }$
$x = \underline{\ ?\ }$

33. $t^2 - 7 = 29$
$t^2 - 7 + 7 = 29 + 7$
$t^2 = \underline{\ ?\ }$
$t = \underline{\ ?\ }$

34. $2n^2 = n^2 + 100$
$2n^2 - n^2 = n^2 - n^2 + 100$
$n^2 = \underline{\ ?\ }$
$n = \underline{\ ?\ }$

Solve. Add or subtract as indicated.

35. $a + 12 = 33$; subtract 12 from both members

36. $27 = y + 14$; subtract 14 from both members

37. $b - 29 = 50$; add 29 to both members

38. $m - 8 = 19 + 10$; add 8 to both members

39. $r - \frac{1}{2} = 6$; add $\frac{1}{2}$ to both members

40. $8 = t + \frac{5}{8}$; subtract $\frac{5}{8}$ from both members

5-4 *More Equation Solving Strategies*

OBJECTIVES

Solve an equation by multiplying both members by the same number.

Solve an equation by dividing both members by the same number.

Let's use the true statement $2 + 6 = 8$ to see what happens when both members are multiplied by the same number or divided by the same number.

Multiply both members by 3:		Divide both members by 4:
$2 + 6 = 8$	◄ True ►	$2 + 6 = 8$
$3(2 + 6) = 3 \times 8$	◄ Also true ►	$\frac{2 + 6}{4} = \frac{8}{4}$
$24 = 24$		$2 = 2$

When both members of a true equation are multiplied or divided by the same number, the result is another true equation. We can use this idea to solve equations. Again our strategy is based on getting the variable to stand alone as one member.

EXAMPLE 1

$$\frac{1}{3} \cdot x = 4$$

$$3 \cdot \frac{1}{3} \cdot x = 3 \cdot 4$$ ◄ Multiply both members by 3.

$$x = 12$$

EXAMPLE 2

$$\frac{m}{2} = 8$$ ◄ Recall that $\frac{m}{2}$ means $\frac{1}{2} \cdot m$.

$$2 \cdot \frac{m}{2} = 2 \cdot 8$$ ◄ Multiply both members by 2.

$$m = 16$$

EXAMPLE 3

$$5t = 35$$

$$\frac{5t}{5} = \frac{35}{5}$$ ◄ Divide both members by 5.

$$t = 7$$

True or false?

1. $3 \cdot \frac{1}{3} = 1$
2. $\frac{4}{4} = 0$
3. $2 \cdot \frac{1}{2} = 1$
4. $\frac{3n}{3} = n$
5. $\frac{x}{10} = 10x$
6. $3m = m \cdot 3$
7. $\frac{1}{2} \cdot k = \frac{k}{2}$
8. $\frac{2t}{2} = 1$
9. $5 \cdot \frac{s}{5} = 5s$

Written EXERCISES

Multiply or divide both members. Simplify the result.

Sample: $3 + 12 = 15$; divide by 3 *Solution:*

$$3 + 12 = 15$$
$$\frac{3 + 12}{3} = \frac{15}{3}$$
$$5 = 5$$

A

1. $10 + 8 = 18$; divide by 9
2. $15 = 9 + 6$; multiply by 3
3. $6 = 2 \cdot 3$; multiply by 5
4. $\frac{9}{2} = 4.5$; multiply by 2
5. $24 = 3 \cdot 8$; divide by 6
6. $3 + 9 = 6 + 6$; divide by 4
7. $\frac{16}{2} = \frac{24}{3}$; multiply by 3
8. $6 \cdot 5 = 3 \cdot 10$; divide by 5
9. $6^2 = 36$; divide by 6
10. $1 = \frac{7}{7}$; multiply by 0
11. $2 \cdot 8 = 4 \cdot 4$; multiply by $\frac{1}{2}$
12. $21 = 14 + 7$; multiply by $\frac{1}{3}$

Complete.

Sample: $\frac{3y}{3} = \underline{\ ?\ }$ *Solution:* $\frac{3y}{3} = y$

13. $\frac{8n}{8} = \underline{\ ?\ }$
14. $\frac{5m}{5} = \underline{\ ?\ }$

15. $\frac{4x}{4} = \underline{\ ?\ }$

16. $3 \cdot \frac{d}{3} = \underline{\ ?\ }$

17. $7 \cdot \frac{h}{7} = \underline{\ ?\ }$

18. $\frac{6s}{?} = s$

Copy and complete.

Sample:

$$\frac{w}{7} = 1 + 5$$
$$7 \cdot \frac{w}{7} = 7(1 + 5)$$
$$w = \underline{\ ?\ }$$

Solution:

$$\frac{w}{7} = 1 + 5$$
$$7 \cdot \frac{w}{7} = 7(1 + 5)$$
$$w = 42$$

19.
$$\frac{t}{3} = 7$$
$$3 \cdot \frac{t}{3} = 3 \cdot 7$$
$$t = \underline{\ ?\ }$$

20.
$$\frac{b}{10} = 8$$
$$10 \cdot \frac{b}{10} = 10 \cdot 8$$
$$b = \underline{\ ?\ }$$

21.
$$4m = 72$$
$$\frac{4m}{4} = \frac{72}{4}$$
$$m = \underline{\ ?\ }$$

22.
$$45 = 9k$$
$$\frac{45}{9} = \frac{9k}{9}$$
$$\underline{\ ?\ } = k$$

23.
$$\frac{n}{7} = 40 + 2$$
$$7 \cdot \frac{n}{7} = 7(40 + 2)$$
$$n = \underline{\ ?\ }$$

24.
$$15 = \frac{x}{3}$$
$$3 \cdot 15 = 3 \cdot \frac{x}{3}$$
$$\underline{\ ?\ } = x$$

To solve, multiply or divide as indicated.

Sample: $10t = 65$; divide by 10

Solution:

$$10t = 65$$
$$\frac{10t}{10} = \frac{65}{10}$$
$$t = 6.5$$

B

25. $8w = 104$; divide by 8

26. $1.5t = 7.5$; divide by 1.5

27. $80 = \frac{y}{5}$; multiply by 5

28. $17 = \frac{a}{3}$; multiply by 3

29. $\frac{1}{5} \cdot x = 6.5$; multiply by 5

30. $n \cdot 4 = 280$; divide by 4

31. $3.2z = 16$; divide by 3.2

32. $0.5w = 9$; divide by 0.5

33. $\frac{2m}{3} = 15$; multiply by 3, then divide by 2

C

34. $\frac{4t}{5} = 20$; multiply by 5, then divide by 4

35. $\frac{9r}{2} = 27$; multiply by 2, then divide by 9

SELF-TEST 1

Be sure that you understand these terms and symbols.

equation (p. 120) inequality (p. 120)
solution (p. 124) solution set (p. 124)
Ø (p. 124)

Write an open sentence for each of the following. Section 5-1, p. 120

1. k increased by 2 is less than 14.
2. The product of r and 7 is greater than 5.

Write a word statement for each of the following.

3. $3m > 1$

4. $4(n - 3) < 10$

Make a table to find the solution set for the given replacement set. Section 5-2, p. 124

5. $a + 1 = 9$; {6, 7, 8}

6. $b^2 - 1 = 24$; {4, 5, 6}

Solve. Add or subtract as indicated. Section 5-3, p. 127

7. $x + 6 = 10.5$; subtract 6

8. $y - 4 = 6$; add 4

Solve. Multiply or divide as indicated. Section 5-4, p. 130

9. $\frac{r}{3} = 4$; multiply by 3

10. $7s = 56$; divide by 7

Check your answers with those printed at the back of the book.

Equations and Word Problems

5-5 *Writing Expressions Using Variables*

OBJECTIVE

Write expressions containing variables to represent given information.

The following steps are helpful in preparing to solve an algebraic problem:

1. Read the problem carefully, two or three times if necessary.
2. Identify all the information given.
3. Make a sketch of the problem if you can.
4. Use symbols of algebra to express the given information.

EXAMPLE 1 The large container holds 8 liters of water. Each of the other containers holds t liters of water. How can you express the total amount of water?

Solution: $8 + 2t$

EXAMPLE 2 Two cars are parked bumper to bumper in a parking space 14 meters long. Each car is x meters long. How much of the space is not being used?

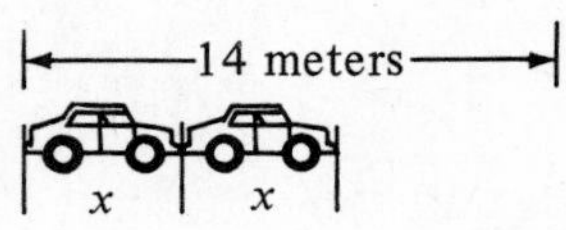

Solution: $14 - 2x$

EXERCISES

State an algebraic expression.

1. Preston has one bank for saving nickels and one for saving dimes. He has n nickels and d dimes.
   a. What is the value in cents of the coins in the nickel bank?
   b. What is the value in cents of the coins in the dime bank?

2. Maria had k hockey pucks and lost 2 pucks. How many pucks were left?

3. Frank could jump b centimeters last year. This year he can jump one centimeter less than twice as far as last year. How far can he jump this year?
4. The Stevenson High baseball team spends d hours each week at practice. Batting practice takes up one-half that time. How much time is left for other activities?
5. Larry has d dimes and Karen has n nickels. How much money do they have altogether?
6. The width of a playing field is y meters. The length is 80 meters. What is the area?

Written EXERCISES

Write an algebraic expression to answer the question.

Sample: Given the number z, what is 1 less than half that number?

Solution: $\frac{1}{2}z - 1$ or $\frac{z}{2} - 1$

A

1. Given the number a, what is two-thirds that number?
2. Given the number b, what is 7 more than that number?
3. Given the number c, what is one less than the square of that number?
4. Given the number d, what is one more than five times that number?
5. Given the number m, what is two more than three-fourths that number?
6. Given the number $9n$, what is one less than half that number?

Write an algebraic expression.

7. 2 less than x
8. z less than t
9. 5 more than y
10. $5k$ more than $4j$
11. 1 less than one-third z
12. 2 less than 4 times f
13. 5 more than $10a$
14. three-fourths the product of 3 and r

15. b more than t
16. one-half the sum of x and y
17. $5r$ less than 100
18. $2m$ more than j
19. $2k$ less than 5 times n
20. one-third the sum of $2m$ and n

Write the algebraic expression indicated. Use a variable to stand for any missing values.

B 21. The area of the smaller rectangle pictured is one-fourth the area of the other rectangle. Name the area of the smaller rectangle.

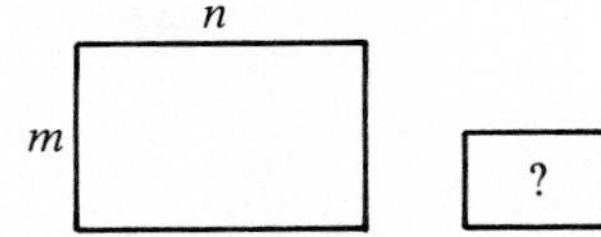

22. If the width of each volume of an encyclopedia is k centimeters, how much shelf space is needed for all 24 volumes?
23. Let n represent an odd number. Name the odd number which precedes n.
24. Let m represent an even number. Name the next two even numbers greater than m.
25. The members of the swimming team scored a, b, and c points. What was the team average?

C 26. A table cloth x centimeters long and w centimeters wide is hemmed on all four sides. How long is the hem?
27. What is the total value of d dimes, n nickels, and p pennies?

Evariste Galois 1811–1832

Evariste Galois began his short mathematical career at an early age. When he was 16 he began to develop theories about solving algebraic equations. Galois met with many misfortunes during his lifetime. He failed his school entrance examinations twice. He wrote two papers involving significant mathematical discoveries which were lost before being read. He died at the age of 21 in a duel. At the time of his death he had begun work on a theory of functions which was completed years later by another famous mathematician, Bernhard Riemann.

5-6 *Using Formulas to Solve Problems*

OBJECTIVE
Use perimeter and area formulas to solve problems.

Formulas, which are special kinds of equations, can often be used in solving problems.

EXAMPLE The mainsail on a boat has the shape of a triangle, with a base 6 meters in length. The height of the sail is 8.5 meters. What is the area of the sail in square meters (m^2)?

The area formula for triangles is $A = \frac{bh}{2}$.

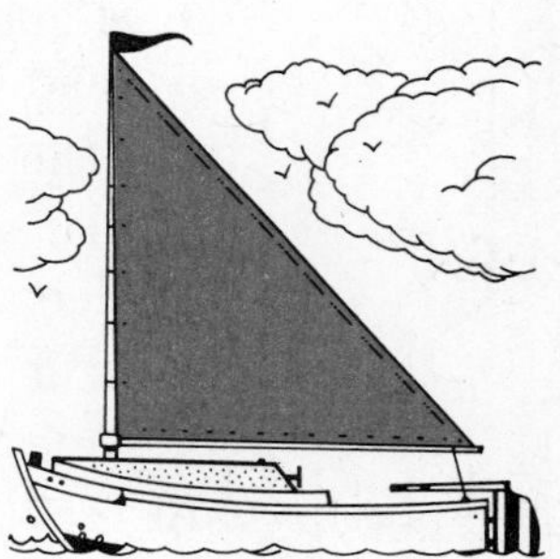

Replacements for variables ► A is unknown.
$b = 6$
$h = 8.5$

Equation ► $A = \frac{bh}{2} = \frac{6(8.5)}{2}$

$= \frac{51}{2} = 25.5$

The area of the sail is $25.5\ m^2$.

Oral EXERCISES

Match each description in Column 1 with the correct formula in Column 2.

COLUMN 1	COLUMN 2
1. Perimeter of a square	**A.** $A = lw$
2. Area of a square	**B.** $P = a + b + c$
3. Perimeter of a rectangle	**C.** $P = 4s$
4. Area of a rectangle	**D.** $A = \frac{1}{2}bh$
5. Perimeter of a triangle	**E.** $C = \pi d$
6. Area of a triangle	**F.** $A = s^2$
7. Circumference of a circle	**G.** $A = \pi r^2$
8. Area of a circle	**H.** $P = 2l + 2w$

Written EXERCISES

Tell which formula is required. Then complete the solution. Where π is used, let $\pi = \frac{22}{7}$.

Sample: Find the perimeter of a triangle with sides of length 6 centimeters, 8 centimeters, and 12 centimeters.

Solution: $P = a + b + c$
$P = 6 + 8 + 12$
$P = 26$ centimeters

A

1. Find the area of a rectangle with width 10 centimeters and length 11.5 centimeters.
2. Find the perimeter of a square if the length of a side is 22 millimeters.
3. Find the area of a triangle with base of length 13 centimeters and height 10 centimeters.
4. The radius of a circle is 49 millimeters. Find the area.
5. The lengths of the sides of a triangle are 1.5 meters, 0.9 meters and 2 meters. Find the perimeter.
6. The length of the side of a square is 15 meters. Find the area.
7. The perimeter of a square is 144 centimeters. Find the length of each side.
8. A circle has radius 35 centimeters. Find the circumference.
9. The width of a rectangle is 8.2 centimeters and the length is 41 centimeters. Find the area.

B

10. Find the perimeter of a square if the area is 64 square centimeters.
11. The circumference of a circle is 132 centimeters. Find the radius.

C

12. The circumference of a circle is 88 centimeters. Find the area.
13. Find the distance around the figure.

a.

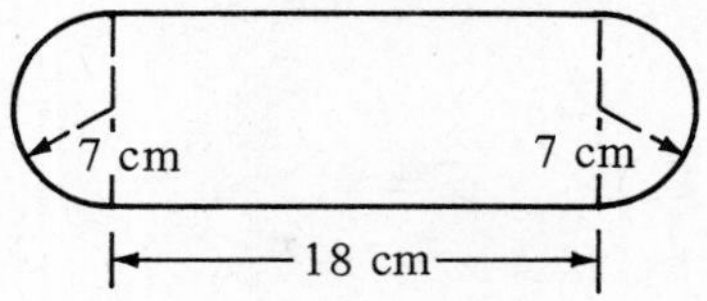

7 cm
7 cm
18 cm

b.

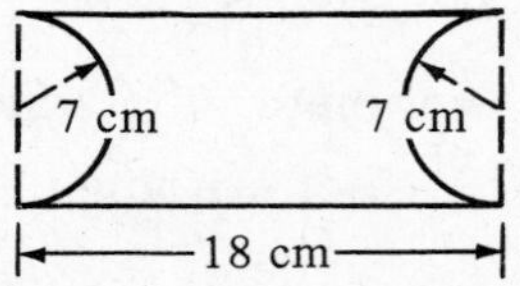

7 cm
7 cm
18 cm

14. Find the area of the shaded part of the figure.

a. 10 cm; 20 cm

b. 14 cm; 30 cm

c. 28 cm

d.

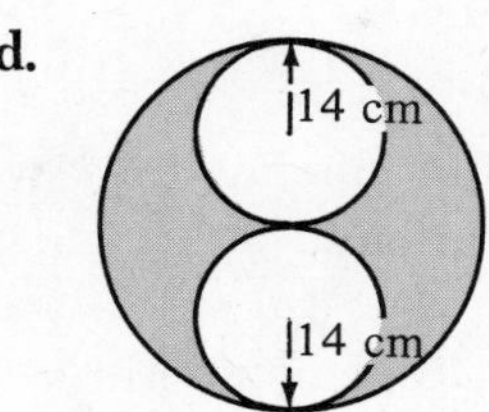

SELF-TEST 2

Write an algebraic expression.

1. 1.3 less than 4 times k — **Section 5-5, p. 134**

2. Let m represent a multiple of 7. What are the multiples of 7 which precede and follow m?

Tell what formula is needed to solve the problem. Then complete the solution. — **Section 5-6, p. 137**

3. The width of a rectangle is 10 centimeters and the length is 13 centimeters. What is the perimeter?
4. The length of the side of a square is 7.5 meters. What is the area?

Check your answers with those printed at the back of the book.

5-7 *Solving Inequalities: The < and > Relationships*

OBJECTIVES

Solve inequalities that involve the < and the > relationships.

Write and graph the solution set of an inequality.

For solving and graphing inequalities, we can use tables and the number line as we did with equations.

EXAMPLE 1 $n + 3 < 8$; replacement set: {1, 3, 5, 7}

Replacement	$n + 3 < 8$	*True/False*	*Solution?*
1	$1 + 3 < 8$	True	YES
3	$3 + 3 < 8$	True	YES
5	$5 + 3 < 8$	False	No
7	$7 + 3 < 8$	False	No

The solutions are 1 and 3. Solution set: {1, 3}

EXAMPLE 2 $3x + 1 > 7$; replacement set: {the counting numbers}

Replacement	$3x + 1 > 7$	*True/False*	*Solution?*
1	$3(1) + 1 > 7$	False	No
2	$3(2) + 1 > 7$	False	No
3	$3(3) + 1 > 7$	True	YES
4	$3(4) + 1 > 7$	True	YES
5	$3(5) + 1 > 7$	True	YES
.	.	.	.
.	.	.	.
.	.	.	.

3, 4, and 5 are solutions. You can see that, in fact, any counting number greater than 3 is a solution. The solution set is {3, 4, 5, . . .}.

It is often easiest to show the solution set of an inequality with a number line graph.

Recall that this set includes 0 and all the numbers to the right of 0 on the number line.

EXAMPLE 3 $3y > 9$; replacement set: {the numbers of arithmetic}
$3y > 9$ is a true statement when y is replaced by any number greater than 3.
Solution set: {the numbers of arithmetic greater than 3}
Graph:

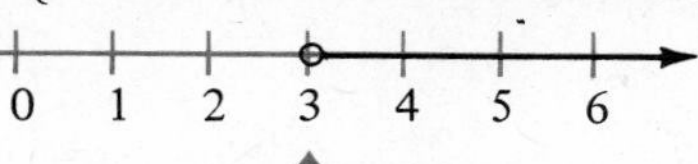

The hollow dot shows that 3 is *not* included.

Oral EXERCISES

State the question that is suggested by the inequality. The replacement set is {the numbers of arithmetic}.

Sample 1: $m > 10$ *What you say:* Which numbers of arithmetic are greater than 10?

Sample 2: $\frac{k}{2} < 8$ *What you say:* Which numbers of arithmetic, when divided by 2, are less than 8?

1. $r < 9$
2. $\frac{1}{2}a > 10$
3. $5s < 10$
4. $b - 5 < 2$
5. $t + 1 > 14$
6. $c + 1 > 5$

Written EXERCISES

Tell whether the resulting statement is true or false when these replacements are used for the variables: $a = 1$, $b = 3$, $c = 5$.

Sample: $2a - 1 < 10$ *What you say:* $2 - 1 < 10$
$1 < 10$; True

A

1. $5a < 9$
2. $a + b < 10$
3. $2b > 6$
4. $6a + 1 > 2$
5. $4c < 16$
6. $7b - 8 > 15$
7. $2a > 4$
8. $b + b > b^2$

For each member of the replacement set, show whether a true or a false statement results when the variable in the sentence is replaced by the number.

Sample: $k - 7 < 10$; {16, 16.5, 17}

Solution:
$16 - 7 < 10 \blacktriangleright 9 < 10$ True
$16.5 - 7 < 10 \blacktriangleright 9.5 < 10$ True
$17 - 7 < 10 \blacktriangleright 10 < 10$ False

9. $5 < a + 1$; {0, 5, 10}
10. $10 > b - 8$; {10, 15, 20}
11. $3c + 5 < 14$; {0, 1, 2, 3}
12. $21 > m \cdot m$; {3, 4, 5, 6}
13. $5n < 14$; {0, 1, 2, 3}
14. $3p > 10$; {1, 3, 5, 7}

B

15. $m^2 > m + m$; {0, 1, 2, 3}
16. $k \div 3 < 7$; {0, 5, 10, 15}
17. $4.2 + h > 4$; {0, 1, 2}
18. $4.2 - h < 4$; {0, 1, 2, 3}
19. $6k < 2$; $\left\{0, \frac{1}{2}, \frac{1}{3}, \frac{1}{4}\right\}$
20. $m^3 < 10$; {0, 1, 2}

Find the solution set if the replacement set is {the numbers of arithmetic}. Graph the solution set on the number line.

Sample 1: $2a > 8$

Solution: {the numbers of arithmetic greater than 4}

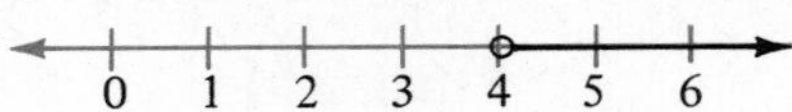

Sample 2: $16 + b < 20$

Solution: {the numbers of arithmetic less than 4}

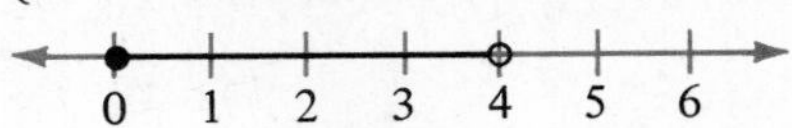

21. $m < 7$
22. $2n < 12$
23. $r > 4$
24. $3s > 15$
25. $t > 2.5$
26. $6 > 2a$
27. $k - 5 > 6$
28. $m - 1 < 3$
29. $n + 7 > 5.2$

C

30. $p - 4 < 6.8$
31. $\frac{r}{3} > 7$
32. $\frac{s}{4} < 10.1$
33. $\frac{t}{3} > 0$
34. $\frac{z}{5} < 1$
35. $x^2 + 3 > 50$
36. $2x - 1 < 7$
37. $\frac{y}{5} > 2$
38. $x^2 > 1$
39. $\frac{2n}{3} > 1$
40. $\frac{x - 1}{2} < 1$
41. $m^2 > 4$

5-8 *Solving Inequalities: The ≤ and ≥ Relationships*

OBJECTIVES

Solve inequalities that involve the ≤ and ≥ relationships.

Write and graph the solution set of an inequality.

When the symbols ≤ and ≥ are used in sentences

≤ means is less than or equal to
≥ means is greater than or equal to.

EXAMPLE 1 $m + 3 \geq 7$; replacement set: {the numbers of arithmetic}

This statement is true when m is replaced by 4 or any number greater than 4.

Solution set: {the numbers of arithmetic greater than or equal to 4} Graph:

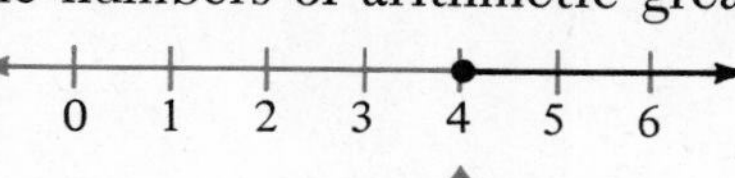

The solid dot shows that 4 is included.

EXAMPLE 2 $t + 1\frac{1}{2} \leq 4$; replacement set: {the numbers of arithmetic}

This statement is true when t is replaced by $2\frac{1}{2}$ or any number less than $2\frac{1}{2}$.

Solution set: {the numbers of arithmetic less than or equal to $2\frac{1}{2}$}
Graph:

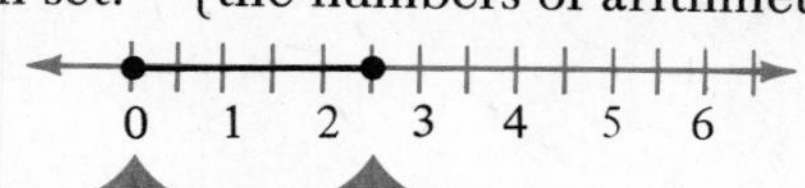

Solid dots at 0 and $2\frac{1}{2}$.

EXAMPLE 3 $h \leq \frac{1}{2}$; replacement set: {all the numbers on the number line}

This statement is true when n is replaced by $\frac{1}{2}$ or any number less than $\frac{1}{2}$.

Solution set: {all the numbers on the number line less than or equal to $\frac{1}{2}$} Graph:

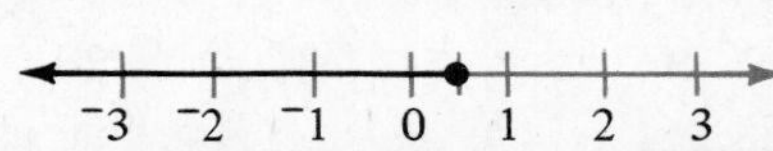

EXERCISES

State the question that is suggested by the inequality. The replacement set is {the numbers of arithmetic}.

Sample: $\frac{1}{3}k \le 6$ *What you say:* Which numbers of arithmetic, when divided by 3, are less than or equal to 6?

1. $a \le 5$
2. $b \ge 10$
3. $c \le 1.1$
4. $3k \le 20$
5. $4m \ge 18$
6. $n + 1 \ge 9$

Tell whether the resulting statement is true or false when these replacements are used for the variables: $r = 2$, $s = 3$, $t = 6$.

7. $r \le 10$
8. $s \ge 5$
9. $t \le 6$
10. $s + 1 \ge 3$
11. $t - 1 \ge 6$
12. $2r + 1 \le 5$

Written

EXERCISES

For each member of the replacement set, show whether a true or a false statement results when the variable is replaced by the number.

Sample: $m + 4 \ge 10$; $\{4, 6, 8\}$

$4 + 4 \ge 10$ ► $8 \ge 10$ False
$6 + 4 \ge 10$ ► $10 \ge 10$ True
$8 + 4 \ge 10$ ► $12 \ge 10$ True

A

1. $p \le 4$; $\{2, 4, 6\}$
2. $q \ge 5$; $\{3, 5, 7\}$
3. $r \ge 1.5$; $\{0, 1, 2\}$
4. $s \le 7.8$; $\{7, 8, 9\}$
5. $x + 1 \le 8$; $\{5, 6, 7\}$
6. $y + 7 \ge 10$; $\{1, 2, 3\}$
7. $z - 10 \le 6$; $\{16, 17, 18\}$
8. $2a \le 11$; $\{2, 4, 6\}$
9. $3b \ge 14$; $\{3, 5, 7\}$
10. $c + 6 \ne 8$; $\{1, 2, 3\}$
11. $2d + 1 \le 13$; $\{6, 7, 8\}$
12. $5n + 6 \ne 18$; $\{2, 3, 4\}$

B

13. $3b + 6 \le 80$; $\{10, 20, 30\}$
14. $4j - 9 \ge 37$; $\{10, 20, 30\}$
15. $t \le {}^-1$; $\{2, 3, {}^-2, {}^-3\}$
16. ${}^-2 \ge x$; $\{{}^-3, {}^-2, {}^-1, 0\}$

Match each inequality in Column 1 with the graph of its solution in Column 2. The replacement set is {the numbers of arithmetic}.

17. $3a \leq 4$ A.

18. $\frac{1}{2}b \geq 1$ B.

19. $3c \leq 6$ C.

20. $4d \neq 8$ D.

21. $k \leq 1$ E.

Describe the set of numbers represented by the number line graph.

Sample:

Solution: {the numbers of arithmetic less than or equal to $3\frac{1}{2}$}

22. 23.

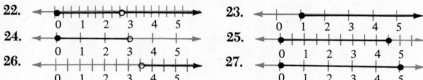

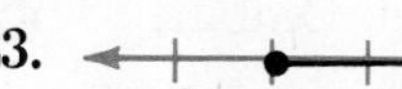

24. 25.

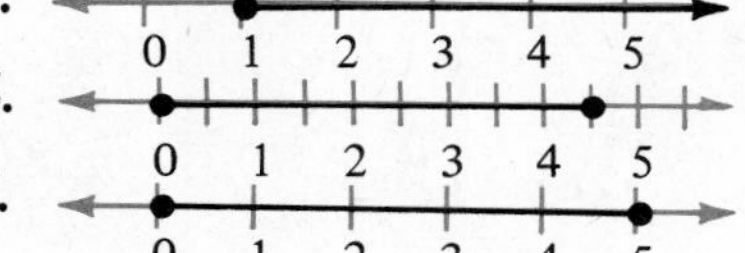

26. 27.

Describe the solution set. The replacement set is {all the numbers on the number line}.

Sample: $k \div 3 \leq 10$
Solution: {the numbers on the number line less than or equal to 30}

28. $g \geq 2\frac{1}{2}$ 29. $h \leq 0$

30. $k \geq {}^{-}1$ 31. $m \leq {}^{-}3$

32. $3s - 4 \geq 10.1$ 33. $9x + 1 \neq 28$

C

Graph the solution on the number line. The replacement set is {all the numbers on the number line}.

Sample: $r \leq 1$
Solution:

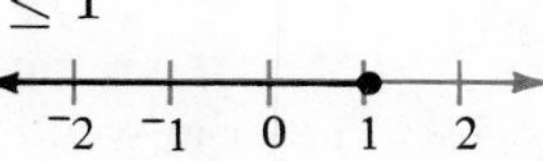

34. $s \leq 2\frac{1}{2}$ 35. $t \geq 0$

36. $x \geq {}^{-}2$ 37. $y \neq {}^{-}1$

38. $4z \leq 6$ 39. $3a \geq 2$

5-9 *Using Inequalities to Solve Problems*

OBJECTIVE

Solve problems by writing inequalities and finding their solution sets.

When a problem involves the idea of *less than* or *greater than,* an inequality can be used to solve it.

EXAMPLE Ted has two pieces of string. Their combined length is less than 25 centimeters. The longer piece is 16 centimeters long. What can we say about the length of the shorter piece?

Let s = the length of the shorter piece.
16 = the length of the longer piece.

Then $s + 16$ = the combined length.

Equation: $\underbrace{\text{The combined length}}_{s + 16}$ $\underbrace{\text{is less than}}_{<}$ $\underbrace{\text{25 centimeters.}}_{25}$

$$s < 9$$

This statement is true when s is replaced by any number of arithmetic less than 9.

Solution set: {the numbers of arithmetic < 9}
The length of the shorter piece is less than 9 cm.

EXERCISES

Name the solution set for the open sentence suggested. The replacement set is {the numbers of arithmetic}.

Sample: If a number is added to 6, the sum is greater than or equal to 13. What numbers meet this condition? (*Hint:* $6 + m \geq 13$)

Solution: Since $6 + 7 = 13$, we see that if m is any number greater than 7, $6 + m > 13$. Thus the solution set is

{the numbers of arithmetic ≥ 7}.

1. The difference between 9 and a number is at least 6. What numbers can meet this condition? (*Hint:* $k - 9 \geq 6$)

2. The sum of the ages of a brother and sister is no more than 21 years. If one is 16, what can we say about the age of the other? (*Hint:* $m + 16 \leq 21$)
3. An auditorium has a capacity of 600 people. If 289 people have been seated, at most how many more may be seated? (*Hint:* $289 + n \leq 600$)
4. The perimeter of a square must be less than 44 meters. What is the range of values for the length of one side? (*Hint:* $4s < 44$)
5. The perimeter of a given rectangle cannot exceed 240 meters. If the width is 20 meters, what is the range of values for the length? (*Hint:* $(2 \cdot 20) + (2 \cdot l) \leq 240$)
6. A carrying case for records is designed to hold 48 records. If 29 records are in the case, what is the possible number of records which can be added? (*Hint:* $29 + z \leq 48$)
7. The perimeter of a square table must be at least 320 centimeters but it cannot exceed 400 centimeters. What are the possible lengths of one side? (*Hint:* $4s \geq 320$ and $4s \leq 400$)

Problems

Write an inequality. Then write the solution set if the replacement set is {the numbers of arithmetic}.

Sample: A square has an area which is at most 100 square meters. What numbers might describe the length of one side?

Solution: Let s stand for the length of one side in meters. Then

$$s \cdot s \leq 100$$
$$s \leq 10$$

The solution set is {the numbers of arithmetic ≤ 10}.

A

1. The perimeter of a square is less than 50 meters. What numbers might describe the length of one side?
2. 41 minus some number is less than 13. What are the possible values of the other number?
3. Aurelia lost her wallet. She knew that she had no more than $18. She also remembered that she had a $10 bill. What numbers represent the amount which may have been lost?
4. The sum of 12 and some number is greater than 40. What are the possible values of the other number?

5. When $2\frac{1}{3}$ is increased by some number, the resulting number is less than 14. What numbers meet these conditions?

6. Joe is having a party. There will be 15 people there. He plans on each person eating at most three pieces of pizza. What numbers represent the number of pieces of pizza Joe may buy?

B

7. The perimeter of a rectangle is at most 100 centimeters. If the width is 10 centimeters, what numbers represent the possible values of the length?

8. If the area of a rectangle is less than 100 square centimeters and the length is 15 centimeters, what numbers may represent the width in centimeters?

9. The circumference of a circle is at least 44 centimeters. What are the possible values of the diameter? Radius?

10. A rectangle has a perimeter which is at least 120 centimeters. If the length is 40 centimeters, what are the possible values of the width?

SELF-TEST 3

Be sure that you understand these symbols.

A hollow dot on a number line graph (p. 141)
A solid dot on a number line graph (p. 143)
$\leq$ (p. 143) $\geq$ (p. 143)

Section 5-7, p. 140

1. Indicate whether each replacement makes the statement true or false: $3k - 1 < 14$; $\{1, 3, 5\}$

2. Solve $3r > 12$ and graph the solution set. The replacement set is {the numbers of arithmetic}.

Section 5-8, p. 143

3. Indicate whether each replacement makes the statement true or false: $\frac{1}{2}t + 1 \geq 10$; $\{0, 9, 18\}$

4. Graph the solution set of this inequality: $2s - 1 \leq 7$.

Write an inequality for each problem. Then write the solution set if the replacement set is {the numbers of arithmetic}. Section 5-9, p. 146

5. The area of a rectangle with width 8 meters is at most 120 square meters. What are the possible values of the length?
6. When 7 is increased by 2 times a number, the total is less than 19. What are the possible values of the number?

Check your answers with those printed at the back of the book.

---

chapter summary

1. Number sentences that contain the symbol $=$ are called **equations.** Those that contain the symbols $\neq$, $<$, $>$, $\leq$, or $\geq$ are called **inequalities.**
2. A number sentence that contains a variable is neither true nor false until the variable is replaced by a member of a specified **replacement set.**
3. To solve an equation or inequality the variable in the equation or inequality is replaced by members of the replacement set. The result is either a true statement or a false statement. Each replacement that results in a true statement is a **solution** and all such replacements make up the **solution set.**
4. A solution set that contains no members is called the **empty set** and is indicated by the symbol $\emptyset$.
5. When the same number is added to both members of an equation, or subtracted from both members of an equation, the meaning of the equation remains unchanged.
6. When both members of an equation are multiplied by the same number, or both members are divided by the same number, the meaning of the equation remains unchanged.
7. **Variables** are used to represent missing values in equations.
8. Equations used to solve problems that occur frequently, are called **formulas.**

chapter test

Write a number sentence. Do not determine the solution set.

1. If some number is increased by 10, the result is 13.
2. If 18 is decreased by some number, the difference is 13.
3. If some number is multiplied by 4, the product is less than 15.

Find the solution set. The replacement set is given.

4. $m + 8 = 2m + 4$; $\{0, 2, 4, 6\}$
5. $n^2 = 2n$; $\{0, 1, 2, 3\}$
6. $2k < 10$; $\{1, 3, 5, 7\}$
7. $2h + 4 \geq 12$; $\{2, 4, 6, 8\}$

To solve, perform the operation as indicated.

8. $3k = 12$; divide by 3
9. $m + 4 = 8$; subtract 4
10. $n - 8 = 1$; add 8
11. $\frac{r}{3} = 7$; multiply by 3
12. $s + 7 = 11$; subtract 7
13. $t - \frac{1}{3} = 4$; add $\frac{1}{3}$

Graph the solution set on the number line. The replacement is {the numbers of arithmetic}.

14. $2a > 6$
15. $b - 4 < 10$

Write an algebraic expression.

16. The sum of a number and 2, multiplied by 3
17. 4 times a given number, increased by 3
18. The perimeter of a rectangle with width n centimeters and length 12 centimeters

Write a number sentence. Then solve it to answer the question.

19. If the length of a rectangle is 10 meters and the width is 8 meters, what is the perimeter?
20. Teresa's mother is more than twice as old as she. If Teresa is 17, what numbers represent how old her mother might be?

challenge topics

Triangular Numbers

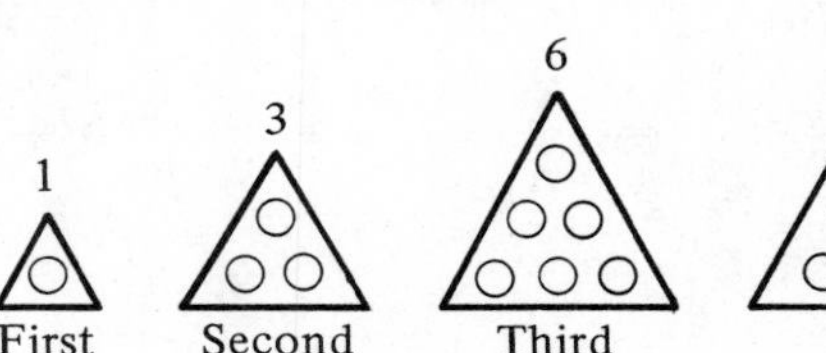

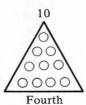

Study the triangular arrays of dots shown above. The number of dots in each array is called a **triangular** number. Can you find a pattern that will help you predict the next triangular number?

1. What are the first fifteen numbers in the set of triangular numbers? Use this pattern:

1st	2nd	3rd	4th	. . .	15th
1	3	6	10	. . .	?
1	(1 + 2)	(3 + 3)	(6 + 4)		

2. The set of counting numbers is $\{1, 2, 3, 4, 5, \ldots\}$.
From your completed pattern in Question 1, notice that:
The **second** triangular number is the sum of the first **two** counting numbers.
The **third** triangular number is the sum of the first __?__ counting numbers.
The **fourth** triangular number is the sum of the first __?__ counting numbers.
The **fifth** triangular number is the sum of the first __?__ counting numbers.

3. In general, to find the nth triangular number, you find the sum of the first __?__ counting numbers.
A short cut for finding this sum is to find the value of
$\frac{n \cdot (n+1)}{2}$, where n stands for the number of counting numbers. Thus the sum of the first 5 counting numbers is
$\frac{5 \cdot (5+1)}{2} = \frac{5 \cdot 6}{2} = 15$. Then the **fifth** triangular number is **15.**

What is the fifteenth triangular number?
What is the twentieth triangular number?
What is the fifty-first triangular number?

REVIEW OF SKILLS

Simplify.

1. $6 \cdot (10 + 2)$ **2.** $8 \cdot (9 - 2)$ **3.** $6(7 \cdot 5)$

4. $2\frac{1}{2} + 3\frac{1}{4}$ **5.** $\frac{2}{5} + \left(\frac{1}{4} + \frac{1}{2}\right)$ **6.** $8.6 + 9.3$

7. $\frac{30 - 18}{2}$ **8.** $\frac{1.8}{6} + 4.2$ **9.** $\frac{1}{2}(15 + 7)$

10. $2 \cdot 5\frac{3}{8} \cdot 1$ **11.** $25 + \frac{300}{3}$ **12.** $0 + \frac{5}{8}$

Name the value of the expression. Let $m = 3$ and $n = 4$.

13. $4 + 7m$ **14.** $m^2 + 4$ **15.** $3n - 4m$

16. $n(6 + 2)$ **17.** $(m + 8)m$ **18.** $n^2 \cdot n$

True or false?

19. $4 + 6 = 10$, so $6 + 4 = 10$

20. $5.7 + 2.1 = 7.8$, so $2.1 + 5.7 = 7.8$

21. $\frac{18}{6} = 3$, so $\frac{6}{18} = 3$ **22.** $\frac{42}{6} = \frac{12}{6} + \frac{30}{6}$

23. $647 = 600 + 40 + 7$ **24.** $10 - 3 = 7$, so $3 - 10 = 7$

25. $4 \cdot (5 \cdot 1) = (4 \cdot 5) \cdot 1$ **26.** $18 - (6 - 2) = (18 - 6) - 2$

27. $20 + (8 - 3) = (20 + 8) - 3$ **28.** $8^2 \cdot 1 = 1 \cdot 8^2$

Complete.

29. $8 + 0 =$ _?_ **30.** $0 + 15 =$ _?_ **31.** $0 \cdot 43 =$ _?_

32. $1 \cdot 19 =$ _?_ **33.** $0 + 2.5 =$ _?_ **34.** $0 \cdot 6.7 =$ _?_

35. $\frac{0}{8} =$ _?_ **36.** $1 \cdot 4\frac{7}{8} =$ _?_ **37.** $\frac{12}{1} =$ _?_

Name the solution set. Use the given replacement set.

38. $m \cdot 0 = 0$; $\{1, 2, 3, 4\}$ **39.** $0 \cdot 8 = t$; $\{0, 2, 4, 6, 8\}$

40. $x = \frac{15}{3}$; $\{1, 3, 5, 7\}$ **41.** $\frac{s}{4} = 1$; $\{2, 4, 6, 8\}$

Left: Farmer with tractor, early 1900's.

Right: Farmer using modern combine to harvest wheat.

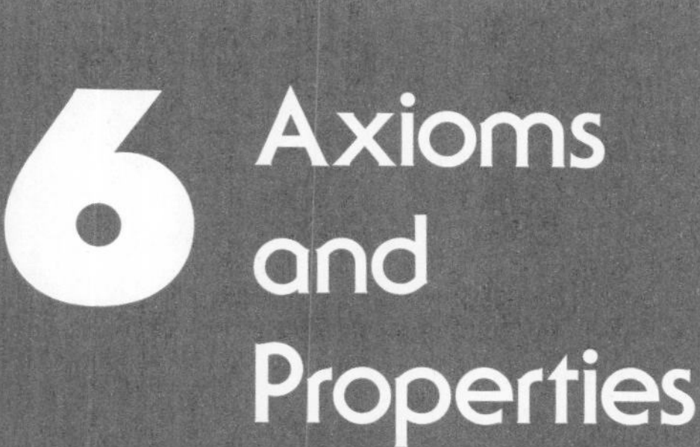

6 Axioms and Properties

Some Basic Properties

6-1 *Basic Axioms of Equality*

OBJECTIVES
Identify and apply these properties of equality:

1. **The reflexive property**
2. **The symmetric property**
3. **The transitive property**

In mathematics there are certain ideas that we must assume to be true. They provide the basis for rules which we develop about numbers and operations with numbers. For example, any number is equal to itself. This property can be stated in terms of a variable.

The Reflexive Property of Equality ► **For any number r, $r = r$.**

EXAMPLES $15 = 15$
$42 + 3 = 42 + 3$
$a + 7 = a + 7$ for every number a.

The left and right members of any equation may be interchanged.

The Symmetric Property of Equality ► **For any numbers r and s, if $r = s$, then $s = r$.**

EXAMPLES $5 + 7 = 12$, so $12 = 5 + 7$.
If $m + 2 = 8$, then $8 = m + 2$.
If $t^2 - 6 = m + 7$, then $m + 7 = t^2 - 6$.

If one number is equal to a second number, and the second number is equal to a third, the first and third numbers are equal.

The Transitive Property of Equality ► **For any numbers r, s, and t, if $r = s$ and $s = t$, then $r = t$.**

EXAMPLES $4 + 5 = 3 + 6$ and $3 + 6 = 7 + 2$, so $4 + 5 = 7 + 2$.
If $a - 3 = b + 1$ and $b + 1 = c$, then $a - 3 = c$.

Tell which property of equality is illustrated.

Sample 1: $12 \div 4 = 3$, so $3 = 12 \div 4$.
What you say: The symmetric property of equality

Sample 2: $3 + 8 = 3 + 8$
What you say: The reflexive property of equality

1. $3 + 4 = 3 + 4$

2. $6 + 2 = 8$ and $8 = 4 + 4$, so $6 + 2 = 4 + 4$.

3. $3 + 3 + 3 = 9$, so $9 = 3 + 3 + 3$.

4. $4 \cdot 4 \cdot 4 = 64$, so $64 = 4 \cdot 4 \cdot 4$.

5. If $a = 9$, then $9 = a$.

6. If $a + 2 = b$ and $b = 7$, then $a + 2 = 7$.

7. $a \div k = a \div k$

8. If $2 + a = b$, then $b = 2 + a$.

9. If $14m = 10n$, then $10n = 14m$.

10. $r + 7 = r + 7$

Written EXERCISES

A

Use the expression to illustrate the reflexive property of equality.

Sample: $4 + k$ *Solution:* $4 + k = 4 + k$

1. m **2.** $9 + n$

3. $a + b^3$ **4.** $x^2 + 5x + 8$

Assume the equation is true. Use the symmetric property of equality to write another equation.

Sample: $b + 2 = 11$ *Solution:* $11 = b + 2$

5. $m + 4 = 10$ **6.** $a + k = 15$

7. $b + 2c = p$ **8.** $4(q - 8) = 4q - 32$

9. $k^3 + k^2 + k = k(k^2 + k + 1)$ **10.** $12 - m + n = b + c$

Use the transitive property of equality to complete the statement.

Sample: $3 = 2 + 1$ and $2 + 1 = 3 + 0$, so __?__.
Solution: $3 = 2 + 1$ and $2 + 1 = 3 + 0$, so $3 = 3 + 0$.

11. $7 = 6 + 1$ and $6 + 1 = 5 + 2$, so __?__.

12. $13 + 4 = 17$ and $17 = 10 + 7$, so __?__.

13. $48 \div 12 = 4$ and $4 = 2^2$, so _?_.

B

14. $3 + 4 = 7$ and _?_, so $3 + 4 = 6 + 1$.
15. If $k - 8 = q$ and _?_, then $k - 8 = 13$.
16. If _?_ and $r = s - 1$, then $10 = s - 1$.
17. If $x^2 + 1 = 10$ and $10 = p^3$, then _?_.
18. If $m + n = 100$ and $100 = rs$, then _?_.
19. If _?_ and $r^2 + t = 8$, then $m = 8$.
20. If $v^2 + w^2 = 1$ and _?_, then $v^2 + w^2 = rst$.

Tell which property of equality is used to reach each conclusion.

C

21. $6 \div 2 = 3$ and $9 \div 3 = 3$, so
    (1) $3 = 9 \div 3$
    (2) and $6 \div 2 = 9 \div 3$.
22. If $rk = 10$ and $m + n = 10$, then
    (1) $10 = m + n$
    (2) and $rk = m + n$
23. $2(6 + 2) = 2(8)$, and $2(8) = 16$, and $16 = 10 + 6$, so
    (1) $2(6 + 2) = 16$
    (2) and $2(6 + 2) = 10 + 6$
24. $12 \times \frac{1}{3} = 12 \div 3$, and $12 \div 3 = 0 + 4$, and $0 + 4 = 2^2$, so
    (1) $12 \div 3 = 2^2$
    (2) and $12 \times \frac{1}{3} = 2^2$
25. If $mn = 4$ and $m + n = 4$, then
    (1) $4 = m + n$
    (2) and $mn = m + n$
26. If $2xy = 21 - x$ and $21 - x = 9$, then
    (1) $2xy = 9$
    (2) and $9 = 2xy$
27. $4(3 + 2) = 4(5)$, and $4(5) = 20$, and $20 = \frac{100}{5}$, so
    (1) $4(3 + 2) = 20$
    (2) and $4(3 + 2) = \frac{100}{5}$
28. If $rs = 100$ and $100 = 2r + 8s$, then
    (1) $rs = 2r + 8s$
    (2) and $2r + 8s = rs$

6-2 *The Closure Property and the Substitution Principle*

OBJECTIVES

Determine whether sets of numbers are closed under specified operations.

Use the substitution principle.

If you add any two whole numbers, the result is always a whole number. We say the set of whole numbers is **closed under addition.** If you multiply any two whole numbers, the product is always a whole number. We say the set of whole numbers is **closed under multiplication.**

The Closure Property ► **A set of numbers is closed under an operation if performing the operation on any two members of the set results in a member of the set.**

EXAMPLE 1 The sum of any two even numbers is an even number. The set of even numbers is closed under addition.

$$2 + 2 = 4 \qquad 220 + 80 = 300$$

EXAMPLE 2 The sum of any two odd numbers is an even number. The set of odd numbers is **not** closed under addition.

$$13 + 9 = 22 \qquad 71 + 23 = 94$$

You know that any given number may have many names. We use this idea to simplify an expression.

$$\underbrace{3 + 6} + 10$$

$$\underbrace{9 + 10}$$ ◄ **Substitute 9 for 3 + 6.**

$$19$$ ◄ **Substitute 19 for 9 + 10.**

The Substitution Principle ► **A numeral may be substituted for any other numeral that names the same number.**

EXAMPLE 3 Simplify $\frac{2}{5} + \frac{1}{5} + 4.$ ► $\underbrace{\frac{2}{5} + \frac{1}{5}} + 4$

$$\underbrace{\frac{3}{5} + 4}$$

$$4\frac{3}{5}$$

Oral EXERCISES

Tell whether or not the specified set of numbers is closed under the indicated operation. If it is *not closed,* give at least one example to support your answer.

Sample {0, 1}; addition
What you say: Not closed; 1 + 1 = 2, and 2 is not a member of {0, 1}.

1. {2, 4, 6, 8, 10, 12}; addition
2. {1, 2, 3, 4, 5, 6, 7, 8}; multiplication
3. {1, 2, 3, 4, . . .}; division
4. {0, 1, 2}; addition
5. {4, 8, 12, 16, . . .}; addition

Describe the substitutions made in simplifying the expression.

Sample: $\underbrace{5+4}+1+2$ | *What you say:*
$\underbrace{9+1}+2$ | 9 is substituted for 5 + 4
$\underbrace{10+2}$ | 10 is substituted for 9 + 1
12 | 12 is substituted for 10 + 2

6. $\underbrace{8+1}+2+5$
   $\underbrace{9+2}+5$
   $\underbrace{11+5}$
   16

7. $\underbrace{2\cdot 3}\cdot 4\cdot 5$
   $\underbrace{6\cdot 4}\cdot 5$
   $\underbrace{24\cdot 5}$
   120

8. $\underbrace{3\cdot 3}\cdot 3\cdot 3$
   $\underbrace{9\cdot 3}\cdot 3$
   $\underbrace{27\cdot 3}$
   81

9. $\underbrace{5+5}+5+5$
   $\underbrace{10+5}+5$
   $\underbrace{15+5}$
   20

Written EXERCISES

Tell whether or not the set is closed under addition, subtraction, multiplication, and division.

1. {2, 4, 6, 8, 10, . . .}
2. {multiples of 3}
3. {1, 2, 3, 4, . . .}
4. {prime numbers}
5. {1, 3, 5, 7, 9, . . .}
6. {multiples of 10}
7. {1}
8. {2, 4, 6, 8}
9. {1, 2}
10. {1, 3, 5}

Simplify. Use the substitution principle as indicated.

Sample: $\underbrace{\frac{1}{2}\cdot\frac{1}{3}}\cdot\frac{1}{4}\cdot\frac{1}{5}$

$\underbrace{\underline{\ ?\ }\cdot\frac{1}{4}}\cdot\frac{1}{5}$

$\underbrace{\underline{\ ?\ }\cdot\frac{1}{5}}$

$\underline{\ ?\ }$

Solution: $\underbrace{\frac{1}{2}\cdot\frac{1}{3}}\cdot\frac{1}{4}\cdot\frac{1}{5}$

$\underbrace{\frac{1}{6}\cdot\frac{1}{4}}\cdot\frac{1}{5}$

$\underbrace{\frac{1}{24}\cdot\frac{1}{5}}$

$\frac{1}{120}$

11. $\underbrace{\frac{1}{5}\cdot 5}\cdot\frac{1}{2}\cdot 2$

$\underbrace{\underline{\ ?\ }\cdot\frac{1}{2}}\cdot 2$

$\underbrace{\underline{\ ?\ }\cdot 2}$

$\underline{\ ?\ }$

12. $\frac{2}{5}+\underbrace{\frac{4}{5}+1}+\frac{4}{5}$

$\frac{2}{5}+\underbrace{\underline{\ ?\ }+\frac{4}{5}}$

$\underbrace{\frac{2}{5}+\underline{\ ?\ }}$

$\underline{\ ?\ }$

13. $\underbrace{(2\cdot 9)}+\underbrace{(2\cdot 7)}$

$\underbrace{\underline{\ ?\ }+\underline{\ ?\ }}$

$\underline{\ ?\ }$

14. $\underbrace{(12-7)}+\underbrace{(12-5)}$

$\underbrace{\underline{\ ?\ }+\underline{\ ?\ }}$

$\underline{\ ?\ }$

15. $\underbrace{\frac{1}{4}+\frac{2}{4}}+\frac{3}{4}+1$

$\underbrace{\underline{\ ?\ }+\frac{3}{4}}+1$

$\underbrace{\underline{\ ?\ }+1}$

$\underline{\ ?\ }$

16. $\underbrace{3\cdot 6}\cdot 10\cdot\frac{1}{2}$

$\underbrace{\underline{\ ?\ }\cdot 10}\cdot\frac{1}{2}$

$\underbrace{\underline{\ ?\ }\cdot\frac{1}{2}}$

$\underline{\ ?\ }$

17. $\underbrace{1.3+4.8}+7.7+5.6$

$\underbrace{\underline{\ ?\ }+7.7}+5.6$

$\underbrace{\underline{\ ?\ }+5.6}$

$\underline{\ ?\ }$

18. $\underbrace{(5\cdot 8)}+\underbrace{(5\cdot 4)}$

$\underbrace{\underline{\ ?\ }+\underline{\ ?\ }}$

$\underline{\ ?\ }$

B

19. $\underbrace{\left(\frac{1}{3}\cdot\frac{2}{3}\right)}+\underbrace{\left(\frac{1}{9}\cdot 4\right)}$

$\underbrace{\underline{\ ?\ }+\underline{\ ?\ }}$

$\underline{\ ?\ }$

20. $\underbrace{(18-2)}+8-10$

$\underbrace{\underline{\ ?\ }+8}-10$

$\underbrace{\underline{\ ?\ }-10}$

$\underline{\ ?\ }$

21. $\underbrace{\frac{1}{4}\cdot 8}+\underbrace{\frac{1}{4}\cdot 2}$
$\underbrace{\underline{\ ?\ } + \underline{\ ?\ }}$
$\underline{\ ?\ }$

22. $\underbrace{\frac{3}{4}\cdot\frac{1}{2}}+\underbrace{\frac{1}{4}\cdot\frac{3}{2}}$
$\underbrace{\underline{\ ?\ } + \underline{\ ?\ }}$
$\underline{\ ?\ }$

SELF-TEST 1

Be sure that you understand these terms.

Reflexive property of equality (p. 154)
Symmetric property of equality (p. 154)
Transitive property of equality (p. 154)
Substitution principle (p. 157)
Closure (p. 157)

Section 6-1, p. 154 Use the property indicated to complete the statement.

Reflexive: **1.** $6 + x = \underline{\ ?\ }$ **2.** $m(n + 3) = \underline{\ ?\ }$

Symmetric: **3.** $4 + a = 9$, so $\underline{\ ?\ }$ **4.** $x^2 \cdot 6 = z$, so $\underline{\ ?\ }$

Transitive: **5.** $3 - k = 1$ and $1 = m \cdot 5$, so $\underline{\ ?\ }$

6. $\underline{\ ?\ }$ and $m = 2n - 1$, so $k + 3 = 2n - 1$.

Section 6-2, p. 157 Tell whether the set is closed under addition, subtraction, multiplication and division.

7. $\{5, 10, 15, \ldots\}$ **8.** $\{1\}$

Simplify these expressions using the substitution principle.

9. $\underbrace{6 + 7} + 8 + 9$
$\underbrace{\underline{\ ?\ } + 8} + 9$
$\underbrace{\underline{\ ?\ } + 9}$
$\underline{\ ?\ }$

10. $\underbrace{\frac{2}{3}\cdot\frac{3}{4}}\cdot\frac{4}{5}\cdot\frac{1}{6}$
$\underbrace{\underline{\ ?\ }\cdot\frac{4}{5}}\cdot\frac{1}{6}$
$\underbrace{\underline{\ ?\ }\cdot\frac{1}{6}}$
$\underline{\ ?\ }$

Check your answers with those printed at the back of the book.

career capsule *Landscape Architect*

Landscape architects work on parks, gardens, housing developments, school campuses, airports, roads, recreational areas and industrial parks, planning the best design for the land and the objects on it. They study the site, map the slope of the land, and determine the existing soil type. Architects also check building codes and develop blueprints of plans and materials to be used. Many landscape architects also supervise construction.

Landscape architects must have mathematical and artistic ability, an interest in art and nature, and a desire to work outdoors. A college degree in landscape architecture or a related field is required.

6-3 *The Commutative and Associative Properties*

OBJECTIVES

Identify and apply the commutative and associative properties of addition.

Identify and apply the commutative and associative properties of multiplication.

The order in which two numbers are added or multiplied does not affect the result. We say that addition and multiplication are commutative operations.

$$12 + 6 = 18 \qquad 9 \times 4 = 36$$
$$6 + 12 = 18 \qquad 4 \times 9 = 36$$

The Commutative Property of Addition ▶ For every number r and every number s, $r + s = s + r$.

The Commutative Property of Multiplication ▶ For every number r and every number s, $r \cdot s = s \cdot r$.

EXAMPLE 1 $n + 4 = 4 + n$ for every number n
$n \cdot 10 = 10 \cdot n$ for every number n

Subtraction and division are *not* commutative operations.

EXAMPLE 2 $15 - 8 \neq 8 - 15$
$12 \div 6 \neq 6 \div 12$

When three or more numbers are added or multiplied, the way in which we group the numbers does not affect the result. We say that addition and multiplication are associative operations.

$2 + 8 + 7$ ▶ $(2 + 8) + 7 = 17$, $2 + (8 + 7) = 17$ $\qquad$ $5 \times 6 \times 2$ ▶ $(5 \times 6) \times 2 = 60$, $5 \times (6 \times 2) = 60$

The Associative Property of Addition ▶ For every number r, every number s, and every number t, $r + (s + t) = (r + s) + t$.

The Associative Property of Multiplication ▶ For every number r, every number s, and every number t, $r(st) = (rs)t$.

EXAMPLE 3 $(3 + b) + 8 = 3 + (b + 8)$ for every number b
$(2b)y = 2(by)$ for all numbers b and y

Subtraction and division are *not* associative.

EXAMPLE 4 $12 - (4 - 2) \neq (12 - 4) - 2$
$24 \div (8 \div 2) \neq (24 \div 8) \div 2$

Tell which property of addition or multiplication is illustrated.

Sample 1: $3 \cdot 9 = 9 \cdot 3$
What you say: Commutative property of multiplication

Sample 2: $2(3 \cdot 9) = (2 \cdot 3)9$
What you say: Associative property of multiplication

1. $\frac{1}{2} + \frac{1}{3} = \frac{1}{3} + \frac{1}{2}$
2. $(2 \cdot 3)4 = 2(3 \cdot 4)$
3. $2 + 7 = 7 + 2$
4. $\frac{1}{2} + \left(\frac{1}{3} + \frac{1}{4}\right) = \left(\frac{1}{2} + \frac{1}{3}\right) + \frac{1}{4}$
5. $\frac{5}{8} + \frac{1}{6} = \frac{1}{6} + \frac{5}{8}$
6. $\frac{1}{3} \cdot \frac{3}{4} = \frac{3}{4} \cdot \frac{1}{3}$
7. $8 \cdot 9 = 9 \cdot 8$
8. $5 + (2 + 3) = (5 + 2) + 3$
9. $8 + (6 + 2) = 8 + (2 + 6)$
10. $9(8 \cdot 4) = 9(4 \cdot 8)$
11. $2 + (3 + 5) = (2 + 3) + 5$
12. $7 \cdot 9 = 9 \cdot 7$
13. $8 + 4 = 4 + 8$

Show that the sentence is true. Name the property illustrated.

Sample: $4(10 \cdot 3) = (4 \cdot 10)3$

Solution: $4(10 \cdot 3) = (4 \cdot 10)3$

$4 \cdot 30$	$40 \cdot 3$
120	120

Associative property of multiplication

A

1. $10 + (8 + 9) = (10 + 8) + 9$
2. $2\frac{1}{2} + 3\frac{1}{8} = 3\frac{1}{8} + 2\frac{1}{2}$
3. $3.6 + (8.2 + 9.4) = 3.6 + (9.4 + 8.2)$
4. $\frac{1}{2}\left(\frac{1}{3} \cdot \frac{1}{4}\right) = \left(\frac{1}{2} \cdot \frac{1}{3}\right)\frac{1}{4}$
5. $6 + \left(\frac{1}{2} \cdot \frac{1}{3}\right) = 6 + \left(\frac{1}{3} \cdot \frac{1}{2}\right)$
6. $0.8(6 + 0.5) = 0.8(0.5 + 6)$
7. $\left(1 + \frac{3}{4}\right) + \frac{2}{4} = 1 + \left(\frac{3}{4} + \frac{2}{4}\right)$
8. $\frac{2}{5} \cdot \frac{5}{2} = \frac{5}{2} \cdot \frac{2}{5}$
9. $(0.03 + 0.58)3 = 3(0.03 + 0.58)$
10. $(1\frac{1}{3} \cdot 2\frac{3}{4})\frac{1}{2} = 1\frac{1}{3}\left(2\frac{3}{4} \cdot \frac{1}{2}\right)$

Let $r = 1.2$, $s = 4$ and $t = 0.03$. Show that the statement is true. Name the property illustrated.

Sample: $(rs)t = r(st)$ *Solution:* $(rs)t = r(st)$

(4.8)(0.03)	(1.2)(0.12)
0.144	0.144

Associative property of multiplication.

B

11. $r + t = t + r$
12. $s \cdot t = t \cdot s$
13. $r + (s + t) = (r + s) + t$
14. $(r + s)t = (s + r)t$
15. $(r + s)t = t(r + s)$
16. $r(s + t) = r(t + s)$
17. $s + (r + t) = (s + r) + t$
18. $s + (r + t) = s + (t + r)$
19. $s(tr) = (tr)s$
20. $t(rs) = (tr)s$

Justify each step.

Sample:

$$\frac{1}{2} + \left(2 + \frac{1}{2}\right) = \left(2 + \frac{1}{2}\right) + \frac{1}{2}$$ Commutative property of addition

$$= 2 + \left(\frac{1}{2} + \frac{1}{2}\right)$$ Associative property of addition

$$= 2 + 1$$ Substitution principle

$$= 3$$ Substitution principle

Solution: (given at right of each step above)

21. $7 + (8 + 3) = 7 + (3 + 8)$
$= (7 + 3) + 8$
$= 10 + 8$
$= 18$

22. $16 + (8 + 4) = 16 + (4 + 8)$
$= (16 + 4) + 8$
$= 20 + 8$
$= 28$

23. $5(17 \cdot 6) = 5(6 \cdot 17)$
$= (5 \cdot 6)17$
$= 30 \cdot 17$
$= 510$

24. $(9 \cdot 5)\frac{2}{3} = (5 \cdot 9)\frac{2}{3}$
$= 5\left(9 \cdot \frac{2}{3}\right)$
$= 5 \cdot 6$
$= 30$

Replace the __?__ with $=$ or $\neq$ to make a true statement. Use {the numbers of arithmetic} as replacement set for the variables.

25. $16 \cdot 17$ __?__ $17 \cdot 16$

26. $4 \div 2$ __?__ $2 \div 4$

27. $a(b \cdot c)$ __?__ $(a \cdot b)c$

28. $6 + \frac{1}{2}$ __?__ $\frac{1}{2} + 6$

29. $3 \cdot 4$ __?__ $4 + 3$

30. $6 - 7$ __?__ $7 - 6$

31. $(3 + 1)4$ __?__ $4(3 + 1)$

32. $6(5 + 8)$ __?__ $6(8 + 5)$

33. $d + (ef)$ __?__ $(ef) + d$

34. $(3 + 1) \div 2$ __?__ $2 \div (3 + 1)$

35. $(4 + 5) \div 3$ __?__ $(5 + 4) \div 3$

36. $1 \div a$ __?__ $a \div 1$

37. $\frac{2 + 1}{3} + 6$ __?__ $6 + \frac{2 + 1}{3}$

6-4 *The Distributive Property*

OBJECTIVE
Identify and apply the distributive property.

Recall that the formula for the perimeter of a rectangle can be written as $P = 2l + 2w$, or as $P = 2(l + w)$. Since 2 is a common factor of the terms of $2l + 2w$, $2(l + w) = 2l + 2w$. We say that multiplication is distributive over addition.

The Distributive Property ► **For every number r, every number s, and every number t, $r(s + t) = rs + rt$.**

EXAMPLE 1 Find P, the perimeter of the rectangle shown.

15 cm
30 cm

$$P = 2l + 2w = 2(30) + 2(15) = 60 + 30 = 90\text{(cm)}$$

$$P = 2(l + w) = 2(30 + 15) = 2(45) = 90\text{(cm)}$$

EXAMPLE 2 $4(62) = 4(60 + 2) = 4(60) + 4(2) = 240 + 8 = 248$

EXAMPLE 3 $5 \cdot 3\frac{1}{8} = 5\left(3 + \frac{1}{8}\right) = 5(3) + 5\left(\frac{1}{8}\right) = 15 + \frac{5}{8} = 15\frac{5}{8}$

From the commutative property, we know that $r(s + t) = (s + t)r$ and $rs + rt = sr + tr$. Then we can also state the distributive property as follows.

The Distributive Property ► **For every number r, every number s, and every number t, $(s + t)r = sr + tr$.**

EXERCISES

Tell how to complete the sentence to illustrate the distributive property.

Sample: $4(7 + 6) = \underline{\ ?\ }$ *What you say:* $4(7 + 6) = 4 \cdot 7 + 4 \cdot 6$

1. $2(3 + 4) = \underline{\ ?\ }$
2. $\underline{\ ?\ } = 2 \cdot 6 + 2 \cdot 8$
3. $\underline{\ ?\ } = 5(6 + 1)$
4. $8(9 + 3) = \underline{\ ?\ }$
5. $2(7 + 7) = \underline{\ ?\ }$
6. $\underline{\ ?\ } = 6(9 + 1)$

7. $\underline{\ ?\ } = 4(5 + 3)$

8. $a(b + 2) = \underline{\ ?\ }$

9. $(k + 3)4 = \underline{\ ?\ }$

10. $5(n + m) = \underline{\ ?\ }$

Written EXERCISES

Show that the statement is true.

Sample 1: $6(9 + 2) = 6(9) + 6(2)$

Solution: $6(9 + 2) = 6(9) + 6(2)$

$6 \cdot 11$	$54 + 12$
66	66

A

1. $3(4 + 5) = 3 \cdot 4 + 3 \cdot 5$
2. $(7 + 3)5 = 7 \cdot 5 + 3 \cdot 5$
3. $8 \cdot 9 + 8 \cdot 4 = 8(9 + 4)$
4. $6 \cdot 7 + 8 \cdot 7 = (6 + 8)7$
5. $10 \cdot 7 + 13 \cdot 7 = (10 + 13)7$
6. $0(5 + 9) = 0 \cdot 5 + 0 \cdot 9$
7. $1(3 + 9) = 1 \cdot 3 + 1 \cdot 9$
8. $\frac{1}{2}(3 + 5) = \frac{1}{2} \cdot 3 + \frac{1}{2} \cdot 5$
9. $0.6(5 + 0.3) = (0.6)5 + (0.6)(0.3)$
10. $8 \cdot \frac{3}{4} + 6 \cdot \frac{3}{4} = (8 + 6)\frac{3}{4}$

Apply the distributive property to complete. Use the substitution principle as shown in the sample.

Sample: $316 \cdot 4$ *Solution:*

$$\begin{aligned} 316 \cdot 4 &= (300 + 10 + 6) \cdot 4 \\ &= 300 \cdot 4 + 10 \cdot 4 + 6 \cdot 4 \\ &= 1200 + 40 + 24 \\ &= 1264 \end{aligned}$$

B

11. $3 \cdot 612$
12. $5 \cdot 115$
13. $2 \cdot 461$
14. $213 \cdot 7$
15. $618 \cdot 6$
16. $139 \cdot 9$
17. $419 \cdot 7$
18. $6 \cdot 792$
19. $2 \cdot 6248$
20. $5 \cdot 6798$
21. $4113 \cdot 9$
22. $9999 \cdot 8$

Justify each step by naming the principle or property used.

23. $16 \cdot 4 = 4 \cdot 16$
$= 4(10 + 6)$
$= 4 \cdot 10 + 4 \cdot 6$
$= 40 + 24$
$= 64$

24. $2(619) = 2(600 + 10 + 9)$
$= 2 \cdot 600 + 2 \cdot 10 + 2 \cdot 9$
$= 1200 + 20 + 18$
$= 1238$

25. $7 \cdot 35 = 7(30 + 5)$
$= 7 \cdot 30 + 7 \cdot 5$
$= 35 + 210$
$= 245$

26. $298 \cdot 6 = (200 + 90 + 8)6$
$= 200 \cdot 6 + 8 \cdot 6 + 90 \cdot 6$
$= 1200 + 48 + 540$
$= 1788$

Tell whether or not the statement is true for all members of {the numbers of arithmetic}.

C

27. $mn + mp = m(n + p)$

28. $ab + ac + ad = a(b + c + d)$

29. $(r + s + t)x = rx + sx + tx$

30. $mn(x + y) = mnx + mny$

calculator corner

There are some multiplication problems which have answers too large for a calculator display. However, you can still use your calculator to solve them if you also use some algebra. To solve 32,051 × 4060 use the distributive property, 32,051 × 4060 = 32,051(4000 + 60) = 32,051(4000) + 32,051(60) = 32,051(4)(1000) + 32,051(60). You can solve 32,051 × 4 with a calculator and multiply by 1000 by adding three zeros. You can solve 32,051(60) with an 8-digit calculator directly or with a 6-digit calculator by solving 32,051(6)(10). Now add both answers to obtain 32,051 × 4060. Make up and solve a multiplication problem too large for your calculator's display.

6-5 *More about the Distributive Property*

OBJECTIVE

Apply the distributive property to subtraction and to division.

We usually think of the distributive property as applying to multiplication and addition. However, multiplication is also **distributive over subtraction.**

$$7(58) = 7(60 - 2) = 7(60) - 7(2)$$
$$= 420 - 14 = 406$$

The Distributive Property ► **For every number r, every number s, and every number t, $r(s - t) = rs - rt$, and $(s - t)r = sr - tr$.**

EXAMPLE 1

$$\frac{1}{3}(17) = \frac{1}{3}(18 - 1)$$
$$= \frac{1}{3}(18) - \frac{1}{3}(1)$$
$$= 6 - \frac{1}{3} = 5\tfrac{2}{3}$$

Dividing by a number is the same as multiplying by the reciprocal of the number. Then we can also apply the distributive property to distributing division over either addition or subtraction.

EXAMPLE 2

$$396 \div 3 = 396 \times \frac{1}{3} = (300 + 90 + 6)\frac{1}{3}$$
$$= 100 + 30 + 2 = 132$$

EXAMPLE 3

$$19\tfrac{1}{2} \div 4 = \left(20 - \frac{1}{2}\right) \div 4 = 20\left(\frac{1}{4}\right) - \left(\frac{1}{2}\right)\left(\frac{1}{4}\right)$$
$$= 5 - \frac{1}{8} = 4\tfrac{7}{8}$$

Oral EXERCISES

Tell how to complete to illustrate the distributive property.

Sample 1: $\frac{600 + 60 + 9}{3} = \underline{\ ?\ }$

What you say: $\frac{600 + 60 + 9}{3} = \frac{600}{3} + \frac{60}{3} + \frac{9}{3}$

Sample 2: $5(70 - 8) = \underline{\ ?\ }$
What you say: $5(70 - 8) = 5 \cdot 70 - 5 \cdot 8$

1. $6(8 - 2) = \underline{\ ?\ }$
2. $\frac{1}{2}\left(9 - \frac{1}{2}\right) = \underline{\ ?\ }$
3. $\left(7 - \frac{2}{3}\right)\frac{3}{4} = \underline{\ ?\ }$
4. $(x - y)4 = \underline{\ ?\ }$
5. $(z - 3)5 = \underline{\ ?\ }$
6. $\frac{800 + 40 + 6}{2} = \underline{\ ?\ }$
7. $\frac{600 + 90 + 3}{3} = \underline{\ ?\ }$
8. $\underline{\ ?\ } = \frac{1000}{5} + \frac{50}{5} + \frac{5}{5}$
9. $\underline{\ ?\ } = 3 \cdot 5 - 3 \cdot 2$
10. $\underline{\ ?\ } = \frac{1}{4} \cdot 7 - \frac{1}{4} \cdot 3$

Written EXERCISES

Show that the statement is true.

Sample: $4(30 - 8) = 4 \cdot 30 - 4 \cdot 8$
Solution: $4(30 - 8) = 4 \cdot 30 - 4 \cdot 8$

$4(30 - 8)$	$4 \cdot 30 - 4 \cdot 8$
$4 \cdot 22$	$120 - 32$
88	88

A

1. $(10 - 3)4 = 10 \cdot 4 - 3 \cdot 4$
2. $\left(8 - \frac{1}{2}\right)\frac{1}{2} = 8 \cdot \frac{1}{2} - \frac{1}{2} \cdot \frac{1}{2}$
3. $\frac{300 + 60 + 9}{3} = \frac{300}{3} + \frac{60}{3} + \frac{9}{3}$
4. $\frac{400 + 40 + 8}{8} = \frac{400}{8} + \frac{40}{8} + \frac{8}{8}$
5. $5(40 - 7) = 5 \cdot 40 - 5 \cdot 7$
6. $\left(9 - \frac{1}{4}\right)\frac{1}{3} = 9 \cdot \frac{1}{3} - \frac{1}{4} \cdot \frac{1}{3}$
7. $(7 - 0.3)5 = 7 \cdot 5 - 0.3 \cdot 5$

8. $\left(\frac{3}{4} - \frac{1}{2}\right)\frac{1}{3} = \frac{3}{4} \cdot \frac{1}{3} - \frac{1}{2} \cdot \frac{1}{3}$

9. $\left(100 - \frac{1}{10}\right)\frac{1}{5} = 100 \cdot \frac{1}{5} - \frac{1}{10} \cdot \frac{1}{5}$

10. $(100 - 0.2)6 = 100 \cdot 6 - 0.2 \cdot 6$

Complete. Use the substitution principle and the distributive property.

Sample 1: $4 \cdot 67$ *Solution:* $4 \cdot 67 = 4(70 - 3)$
$= 4 \cdot 70 - 4 \cdot 3$
$= 280 - 12 = 268$

Sample 2: $844 \div 4$ *Solution:* $844 \div 4 = \frac{800 + 40 + 4}{4}$
$= \frac{800}{4} + \frac{40}{4} + \frac{4}{4}$
$= 200 + 10 + 1 = 211$

B

11. $3 \cdot 39$
12. $\frac{135}{5}$
13. $\frac{448}{8}$
14. $10 \cdot 11.9$
15. $\frac{866}{2}$
16. $99 \cdot 9$
17. $\frac{284}{4}$
18. $5 \cdot 69$
19. $\frac{245}{5}$
20. $119 \cdot 3$
21. $\frac{428}{4}$
22. $7 \cdot 5\frac{6}{7}$
23. $8.9 \cdot 6$
24. $3 \cdot 12\frac{2}{3}$
25. $9 \cdot 8\frac{5}{6}$

Replace the _?_ with $=$ or $\neq$ to make a true statement.

Sample: $(10 \cdot 5) + 6$ _?_ $10 \cdot 5 + 10 \cdot 6$

Solution: $(10 \cdot 5) + 6 \neq 10 \cdot 5 + 10 \cdot 6$

26. $6(30 + 7)$ _?_ $6 \cdot 30 + 6 \cdot 7$

27. $5 \cdot \frac{1}{2} + 6 \cdot \frac{1}{2}$ _?_ $(5 + 6)\frac{1}{2}$

28. $2 \cdot 3 + 2 \cdot 4 + 2 \cdot 5$ _?_ $(3 + 4 + 5)2$

29. $(4 + 5)8$ _?_ $(4 + 8)(5 + 8)$

30. $3 + (4 \cdot 6)$ _?_ $(3 + 4)(3 + 6)$

SELF-TEST 2

Be sure that you understand these terms.

Commutative property (p. 162) Associative property (p. 162)
Distributive property (p. 166)

Show that the statement is true. Name the property illustrated.

Section 6-3, p. 162

1. $3 \cdot 4 = 4 \cdot 3$
2. $2 + (3 + 4) = (3 + 4) + 2$
3. $2\left(4 \cdot \frac{1}{2}\right) = \left(4 \cdot \frac{1}{2}\right)2$
4. $6(10 \cdot 8) = (6 \cdot 10)8$

Section 6-4, p. 166

5. $6(10 + 4) = (6 \cdot 10) + (6 \cdot 4)$
6. $(10 - 5)3 = (10 \cdot 3) - (5 \cdot 3)$

Use the distributive property and the substitution principle to complete.

7. $4 \cdot 316 = (4 \cdot 300) + (4 \cdot 10) + (4 \cdot 6) = \underline{\ ?\ }$

Section 6-5, p. 169

8. $6 \cdot 89 = (6 \cdot 90) - (6 \cdot 1) = \underline{\ ?\ }$

Complete. Use the distributive property.

9. $\frac{488}{2} = \frac{400}{2} + \frac{80}{2} + \frac{8}{2} = \underline{\ ?\ }$

10. $\frac{369}{3} = \underline{\ ?\ }$

Check your answers with those printed at the back of the book.

Time out

Two jet planes, A and B, are flying in the same direction. Plane B is 800 kilometers ahead of plane A.

If plane A flies at a speed of 880 kilometers per hour and plane B flies at 800 kilometers per hour, how long will it take plane A to catch plane B? How far will plane A have flown by the time it catches up with B?

Properties of 0 and 1; Functions

6-6 *The Properties of Zero and One*

OBJECTIVES

Apply the additive property of 0.

Apply the multiplicative properties of 0 and 1.

When you add 0 to any number, the sum is the number that was added to 0. We call 0 the **additive identity element.**

The Additive Property of 0 ► For every number r, $r + 0 = 0 + r = r$.

EXAMPLES $0 + 9 = 9$ $3\frac{1}{2} + 0 = 3\frac{1}{2}$ $2.3 + 0 = 2.3$

When any number is multiplied by 0, the product is 0.

The Multiplicative Property of 0 ► For every number r, $r \cdot 0 = 0 \cdot r = 0$.

EXAMPLES $0 \cdot 17 = 0$ $4 \cdot 3 \cdot 0 = 0$ $0 \cdot 0 = 0$

There is no similar division property of 0. Division by 0 is not possible.

When you multiply any number by 1, the product is the number that was multiplied by 1. We call 1 the **multiplicative identity element.**

The Multiplicative Property of 1 ► For every number r, $r \cdot 1 = 1 \cdot r = r$.

There is no similar division property of 1. Note that $12 \div 1 = 12$ is true, but $1 \div 12 = 12$ is not true.

EXAMPLES $1 \cdot 75 = 75$ $\frac{3}{4} \cdot 1 = \frac{3}{4}$ $m \cdot 1 = m$

EXERCISES

Tell whether the expression names the number 1 or the number 0.

1. $1 \div 1$ **2.** $0 \div 1$ **3.** $1 - 0$

4. $0 - 0$ **5.** $0 + 0$ **6.** $1 + 0$

Solve.

7. $m \div 12 = 1$
8. $6 + r = 6$
9. $\frac{3}{4} \cdot \frac{4}{3} = s$
10. $\frac{1}{2} = t \cdot 1$
11. $k(12 - 1) = 1$
12. $0 + k = 0$

Written EXERCISES

Solve.

A

1. $4 \cdot m = 4$
2. $\frac{6}{6} \cdot r = 7$
3. $2 \cdot 3 + m = 6$
4. $2(5 + m) = 10$
5. $(8 + 4)0 = n$
6. $p\left(\frac{3}{3} + 4\right) = 10$
7. $q\left(\frac{2}{2} + 7\right) = 0$
8. $4\left(\frac{3}{3} + \frac{2}{2}\right) = a$
9. $5\left(\frac{7}{7} + b\right) = 10$
10. $8\left(\frac{3}{3} + c\right) = 8$
11. $(4 \div 4)d = 2$
12. $f + 0.125 = 0.125$
13. $(0 + 1.8)k = 0$
14. $2^2 \cdot m = 4$
15. $n^2 \cdot 10 = 0$
16. $12^2 \cdot 0 = w$

B

17. $b + b + b = 0$
18. $a + a + a = 3$
19. $0 - y = y$
20. $0 + r = r + 0$
21. $t - 0 = t$
22. $m \cdot 1 = m$
23. $n + 0 = n$
24. $(8 + 1) = y(8 + 1)$
25. $r \cdot 0 = 0$
26. $\frac{s}{s} = 1$
27. $m \div m = 1$
28. $k^2 = (0 + 1)^2$

C

29. $\frac{n}{n} \cdot 1 = 3$
30. $m^2 \cdot \frac{6}{6} = 36$
31. $\frac{2}{2}(0 + 2) = v$
32. $\frac{y}{y} + 0 = 1$
33. $5 + z^3 = 6$
34. $3^2 \cdot m^2 = 9$
35. $k \cdot 1 = k + 0$
36. $\frac{x}{x} \cdot 0 = 1$
37. $n^2 \cdot 5^2 = 0$
38. $1 + x^3 = 2$

6-7 *Function Equations*

OBJECTIVE
Use a function equation and replacement set to write and graph number pairs.

Earlier we used a "function machine" and a rule such as $x - 4$ to develop a set of ordered number pairs called a **function.** Number pairs in a function table are in the form (input, output). **Input values** are specified numbers used to replace x in the rule. The resulting values from the rule are the output numbers. We call each **output number** a **value of the function for x,** which we indicate by the symbol $f(x)$.

EXAMPLE 1 $f(x) = x - 4$; replacement set: $\{5, 10, 15, 20\}$

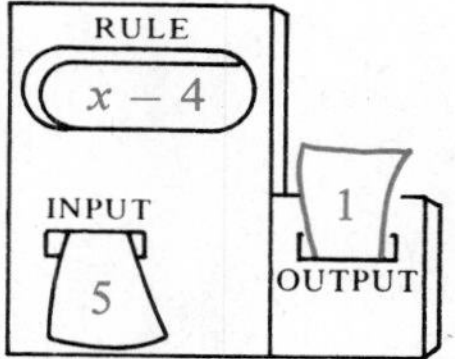

Input → x, **Output** → $f(x)$, **Ordered pair** → $(x, f(x))$

x	$f(x)$	$(x, f(x))$
5	1	(5, 1)
10	6	(10, 6)
15	11	(15, 11)
20	16	(20, 16)

Function: $\{(5, 1), (10, 6), (15, 11), (20, 16)\}$

To graph ordered pairs from a function equation, we label the horizontal axis x and the vertical axis $f(x)$.

EXAMPLE 2 $f(x) = 2x - 1$; replacement set: $\{1, 2, 3\}$

x	$f(x)$	$(x, f(x))$
1	1	(1, 1)
2	3	(2, 3)
3	5	(3, 5)

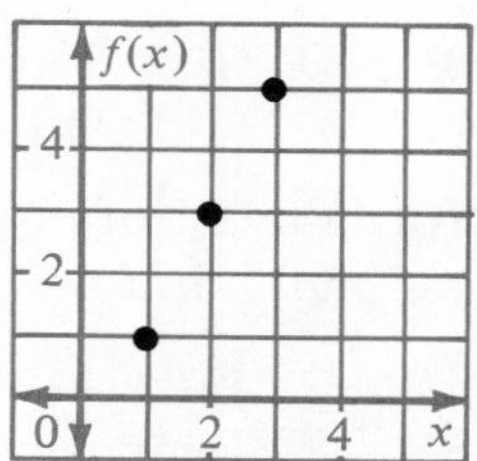

Function: $\{(1, 1), (2, 3), (3, 5)\}$

EXERCISES

Use the function machine and tell how to complete the table.

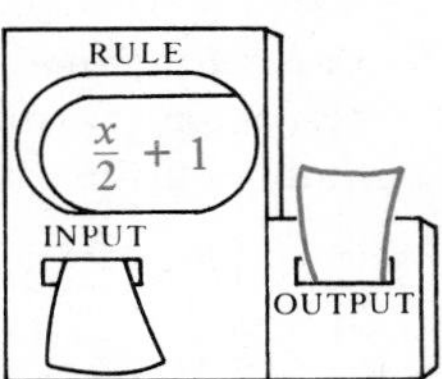

Rule: $\frac{x}{2} + 1$

	x	$f(x)$	$(x, f(x))$
1.	0	?	?
2.	2	?	?
3.	4	?	?
4.	8	?	?
5.	12	?	?
6.	16	?	?

Written EXERCISES

A

Complete the table.

	x	$f(x) = \frac{1}{2}x$	$(x, f(x))$
1.	0	0	?
2.	1	$\frac{1}{2}$	?
3.	2	1	?
4.	3	?	?
5.	4	?	?
6.	5	?	?

	m	$f(m) = m + \frac{1}{2}$	$(m, f(m))$
7.	0	$\frac{1}{2}$	?
8.	3	$3\frac{1}{2}$	?
9.	6	?	?
10.	9	?	?
11.	12	?	?
12.	15	?	?

	n	$f(n) = 3n + 1$	$(n, f(n))$
13.	0	1	?
14.	1	4	?
15.	4	?	?
16.	9	?	?
17.	10	?	?
18.	20	?	?

	s	$f(s) = s^2 - s$	$(s, f(s))$
19.	0	?	?
20.	1	?	?
21.	3	?	?
22.	4	12	?
23.	6	?	?
24.	9	?	?

Write the set of ordered pairs that represents the function. Draw axes and graph the ordered pairs.

Sample: Rule: $3t$
Replacement set:
$\left\{0, \frac{1}{2}, 1\right\}$

Solution:
$\left\{(0, 0), \left(\frac{1}{2}, 1\frac{1}{2}\right), (1, 3)\right\}$

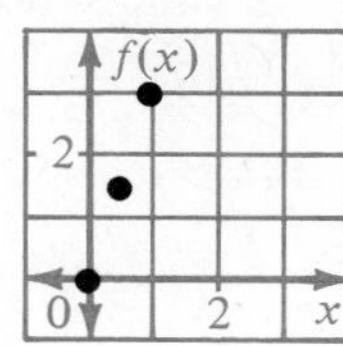

B

25. Rule: $m^2 + 1$
Replacement set:
$\{0, 1, 2\}$

26. Rule: $2n - 1$
Replacement set:
$\{1, 2, 3\}$

27. $\frac{1}{3}s + \frac{1}{2}$
Replacement set:
$\{0, 3, 6\}$

28. Rule: $2a \cdot \frac{1}{a}$
Replacement set:
$\{1, 2, 3, 4\}$

29. $\frac{3}{4} + \frac{b}{4}$
Replacement set:
$\{0, 1, 2, 3\}$

30. $1 + \frac{c}{c}$
Replacement set:
$\{1, 2, 3, 4, 5\}$

31. $p^2 + p$
Replacement set:
$\{0, 1, 2\}$

32. $3r - 3$
Replacement set:
$\{1, 2, 3\}$

Use the given equation and replacement set to make a table of values of the variable, function of the variable, and the resulting number pairs.

Sample: $f(s) = 2s^2 - 1$ $\{1, 3, 5, 7\}$ *Solution:*

s	$f(s) = 2s^2 - 1$	$(s, f(s))$
1	1	(1, 1)
3	17	(3, 17)
5	49	(5, 49)
7	97	(7, 97)

33. $f(a) = 2a + 1$
$\{0, 3, 6, 9\}$

34. $f(b) = (b + 1)^2$
$\{0, 1, 2, 3\}$

35. $f(c) = c^2 - 4$
$\{2, 5, 8, 11\}$

36. $f(d) = \frac{1}{2}(d + 3)$
$\{1, 5, 9, 13\}$

37. $f(g) = 29 - g^3$
$\{0, 1, 2, 3\}$

38. $f(r) = \frac{1}{3}(r^3 + 1)$
$\{0, 2, 3, 5\}$

Use the given equation to complete the set of ordered pairs.

Sample: $f(z) = 6z - 5$; $\{(1, 1), (2, 7), (3, \underline{?}), (4, \underline{?}), (5, \underline{?})\}$
Solution: $\{(1, 1), (2, 7), (3, 13), (4, 19), (5, 25)\}$

C

39. $f(n) = n^2 + n$; $\{(0, 0), (1, 2), (2, \underline{?}), (3, \underline{?}), (4, \underline{?})\}$

40. $f(r) = r^2 + r + 1$;
$\{(0, 1), (1, 3), (2, \underline{?}), (3, \underline{?}), (4, \underline{?}), (5, \underline{?})\}$

41. $f(y) = y^2 - y + 2$;
$\{(0, 2), (1, 2), (2, \underline{?}), (3, \underline{?}), (4, \underline{?}), (5, \underline{?})\}$

42. $f(x) = \frac{1}{2}(x - 2)$; $\{(2, 0), (4, \underline{?}), (6, \underline{?}), (8, \underline{?}), (10, \underline{?})\}$

43. $f(m) = m^2 + \frac{1}{m}$; $\{(1, 2), (2, 4\frac{1}{2}), (3, \underline{?}), (4, \underline{?}), (5, \underline{?})\}$

44. $f(a) = \pi - a$ for $\pi = \frac{22}{7}$;
$\left\{\left(0, \frac{22}{7}\right), \left(\frac{1}{7}, \underline{?}\right), (1, \underline{?}), (2, \underline{?}), (2\frac{3}{7}, \underline{?})\right\}$

SELF-TEST 3

Be sure that you understand these terms.

Additive property of zero (p. 173)
Multiplicative property of zero (p. 173)
Multiplicative property of one (p. 173)
$f(x)$ (p. 175)

Section 6-6, p. 173 Solve.

1. $5 \cdot b = 0$
2. $\left(\frac{7}{7}\right) \cdot r = r$
3. $a \cdot 0 = 1$
4. $t \div t = 1$

Section 6-7, p. 175 Write the set of ordered pairs that represents the function. Draw axes and graph the ordered pairs.

5. $f(x) = x + 3$; replacement set: $\left\{0, \frac{1}{2}, 1, 1\frac{1}{2}\right\}$
6. $f(x) = x - 2$; replacement set: $\{2, 3, 4\}$

Check your answers with those printed at the back of the book.

---

chapter summary

1. The **reflexive property:** $r = r$
The **symmetric property:** If $r = s$, then $s = r$.
The **transitive property:** If $r = s$ and $s = t$, then $r = t$.

2. A set of numbers is **closed** under an operation performed on its members if the operation always gives a result that is a member of that set. This is called the **closure** property.

3. The order in which two numbers are added or multiplied does not affect the result.

   The **commutative property of addition:** $r + s = s + r$
   The **commutative property of multiplication:** $rs = sr$

4. The way in which three or more numbers are grouped for addition or multiplication does not affect the result.

   The **associative property of addition:** $r + (s + t) = (r + s) + t$
   The **associative property of multiplication:** $r \cdot (st) = (rs) \cdot t$

5. Multiplication is distributive over addition.
The **distributive property:** $r(s + t) = rs + rt$.

6. The **additive property of 0:** $r + 0 = 0 + r = r$
The **multiplicative property of 1:** $r \cdot 1 = 1 \cdot r = r$
The **multiplicative property of 0:** $r \cdot 0 = 0 \cdot r = 0$
Division by 0 is not possible.

Time out

Draw a circle with a compass. Mark off the circumference into 16 equal parts. Label the marks clockwise from 1 to 16. With straight lines, connect 1 with 6, 2 with 7, 3 with 8 and so on. Color in your design. Experiment by dividing the circle into a different number of equal parts. What happens if the parts are unequal?

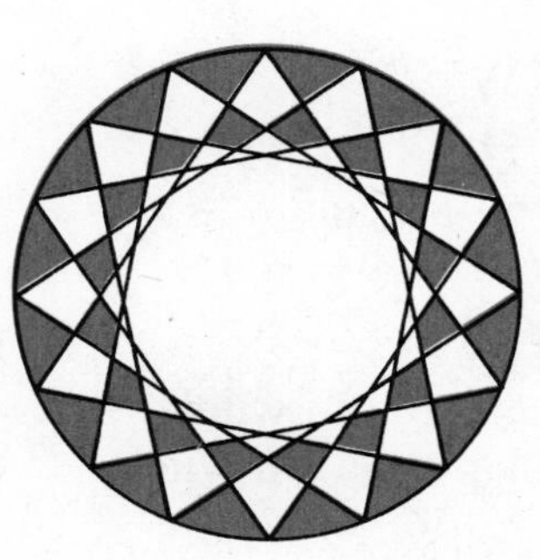

chapter test

Match each statement or equation in Column 1 with the appropriate property in Column 2. You may use a property more than once.

COLUMN 1

1. $1 \cdot 14 = 14$
2. $2(3 + x) = 2 \cdot 3 + 2 \cdot x$
3. $k(j + 4) = k(j + 4)$
4. $7 + x = x + 7$
5. $8 + (2 + 7) = (8 + 2) + 7$
6. $pr^2 + 0 = pr^2$
7. $3 \cdot \frac{2}{2} = 3 \cdot 1$
8. If $2x = 3 + b$, then $3 + b = 2x$.
9. $(x + 1)(x + 2) = (x + 2)(x + 1)$
10. $(7 - 2)6 = 7 \cdot 6 - 2 \cdot 6$
11. Since 3 and 4 are whole numbers, $3 \cdot 4$ is a whole number.
12. $x(yz) = (xy)z$
13. $r(xyz) = (xyz)r$
14. $3 + (a + 4) = (a + 4) + 3$
15. $\frac{1}{2} = \frac{2}{4}$ and $\frac{2}{4} = \frac{3}{6}$, so $\frac{1}{2} = \frac{3}{6}$.
16. $(x^2y^2z^2) \cdot 0 = 0$
17. $6(x + 9) = 6(9 + x)$
18. $3 + 4 = 5 + 2$ and $5 + 2 = 6 + 1$, so $3 + 4 = 6 + 1$.
19. $8 + (2 - 2) = 8 + 0$
20. Since 7 and 10 are whole numbers, $7 + 10$ is a whole number.

COLUMN 2

A. Reflexive property of equality
B. Symmetric property of equality
C. Transitive property of equality
D. Closure under addition
E. Closure under multiplication
F. Substitution principle
G. Commutative property of addition
H. Commutative property of multiplication
I. Associative property of addition
J. Associative property of multiplication
K. Distributive property
L. Additive property of zero
M. Multiplicative property of zero
N. Multiplicative property of one

Complete.

21. $f(p) = p^2 - 4$; replacement set: $\{2, 5, 8, 10\}$

p	$f(p) = p^2 - 4$	$(p, f(p))$
2	?	?
5	?	?
8	?	?
10	?	?

challenge topics

Symmetry in Three Dimensions

A cube-shaped box just fits into a larger packing box. One face has "THIS SIDE UP" written on it. In how many different ways can the smaller box be placed properly inside the larger one?

A child's cube-shaped play block has the letters A, B, C, D, E, F on the faces. The play block just fits into a box. In how many different ways can the block be placed in the box?

In how many ways can each object be placed in the "box" below it?

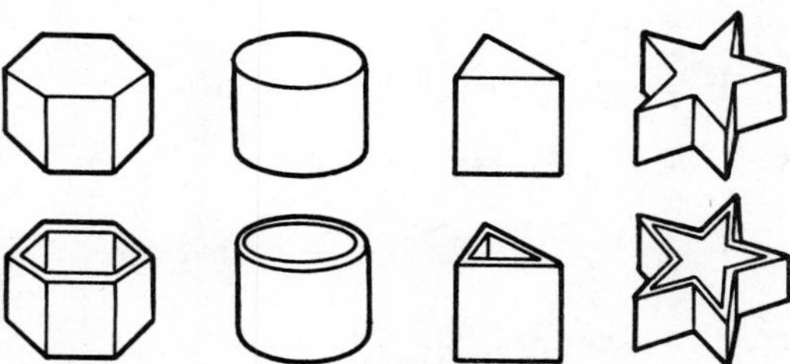

review of skills

Multiply.

1. $10(4)$
2. $(3)(8)$
3. $8(2x + 4)$
4. $3(5 + n)$
5. $(2a + 3)6$
6. $4(4h + 2)$
7. $5(3n + 2)$
8. $(4s + 6)2$
9. $(8 + 2)m$
10. $x(4 + 1)$
11. $y(2 + 3)$
12. $(5 + 6)n$

Simplify.

13. $10 + \frac{5}{8}$
14. $\frac{4}{5} - \frac{2}{5}$
15. $\frac{9}{10} - \frac{3}{10}$
16. $0.77 - 0.34$
17. $1.07 - 0.25$
18. $\frac{3}{4} - \frac{3}{4}$
19. $0.45 - 0.45$
20. $6 + \frac{2}{3}$
21. $\frac{750}{25}$
22. $\frac{120}{15}$
23. $\frac{42}{14}$
24. $8 \div 20$
25. $\frac{1}{2} \cdot 2$
26. $4 \cdot 2\frac{1}{2}$
27. $6 \cdot \frac{1}{3}$
28. $4 \cdot \frac{1}{5}$
29. $\frac{1}{7} \cdot 7$
30. $5 \cdot \frac{1}{5}$

Tell what number makes each statement true.

31. $9 + 3 = 9 + \underline{?}$
32. $16 - \underline{?} = 16 - 10$
33. $8 + 2 = \underline{?} + 2$
34. $\frac{1}{2} \cdot \underline{?} = 1$
35. $\frac{1}{5} \cdot \underline{?} = 1$
36. $7 - 3 = \underline{?} - 3$
37. $(7 + 1) + \underline{?} = (4 + 4) + \underline{?}$
38. $(9 + 2) + \underline{?} = 11 + \underline{?}$
39. $(20 - 6) + \underline{?} = 14 + \underline{?}$
40. $10 + \underline{?} = (12 - 2) + 3$
41. $\frac{6 \cdot 3}{2} = \frac{18}{?}$
42. $\frac{2 \cdot ?}{2} = 8$

Left: Astronomers using telescope.

Right: Astronomer using solar-image display system to analyze space flight data.

7 Equations and Problem Solving

7-1 *Combining Similar Terms*

OBJECTIVE
Simplify expressions by combining similar terms.

We can simplify an expression like $4t + 3t$. We justify the idea that $4t + 3t = 7t$ by using the distributive property: $4t + 3t = (4 + 3)t = 7t$.

Terms such as $4t$ and $3t$ which contain the same variables are called **similar terms** or **like terms.** Terms which contain no variables are also called similar terms.

$5x + 7x$	$8rs + 7 - 1$	$a^2 + 3a - a$
similar terms	similar terms	similar terms

These examples further illustrate how we use the distributive property to combine similar terms.

EXAMPLE 1 $8mn + 6mn = (8 + 6)mn$ ◄ The Distributive Property
$= 14mn$

EXAMPLE 2 $5a - a = 5a - 1a$ ◄ $a = 1 \cdot a$
$= (5 - 1)a$ ◄ The Distributive Property
$= 4a$

EXAMPLE 3 $5t + 9s$ ◄ The terms are unlike. The expression cannot be simplified any further.

EXAMPLE 4 $5x^2 + 4x + 2x = 5x^2 + (4 + 2)x$
$= 5x^2 + 6x$

EXERCISES

Simplify.

Sample: $6m - 2m$ *What you say:* $(6 - 2)m = 4m$

1. $5a + 2a$
2. $3b + 5b$
3. $10k - 4k$
4. $2m + 3m + 4m$
5. $5r + r$
6. $10s + 10s$
7. $k + k$
8. $6xy + 4xy$
9. $6y - y - y$

Written EXERCISES

Combine similar terms to simplify.

Sample 1: $2b + 6b + 4c$

Solution: $8b + 4c$

Sample 2: $2(6 + 5m) - 4m$

Solution: $12 + 10m - 4m = 12 + 6m$

A

1. $5r + 6r$
2. $2t + 7t + 4t$
3. $16s - 9s$
4. $3k + k + 9k$
5. $14 + 3p + 2p$
6. $5ab + ab + 3ab$
7. $cd + 5cd - 2cd$
8. $12rs + rs + rs$
9. $2(2t + 2) + 1$
10. $2(2t + 2) + t$
11. $6k + 4t + 3k + 8t$
12. $5rs + 2b + 3b + 4rs$
13. $2m + 6m - 3m$
14. $3(6 + b) + 4b$
15. $3mn + 2(4 + 2mn)$
16. $8 + 3(2d + 5)$

B

17. $(5k - 2k) + 8k$
18. $(14m - 2m) - m$
19. $6a + 2b + 3b - 2a$
20. $8r + 3r + 5t + 7$
21. $16s + 5 - 9s - 2$
22. $3r + 5t - r + 6r - 4t$
23. $100 - 80 + 16q - 4q - 20$
24. $r + s + s + r + 3$
25. $14ab - 3ab + 14a + ab$
26. $6s + 5t - s - t + 2$

Sample: $4(r + s) + 3(2r + 3s)$

Solution: $4(r + s) + 3(2r + 3s) = 4r + 4s + 6r + 9s$
$= 10r + 13s$

27. $5(a + b) + 6(a + b)$
28. $3(r + 4) + 5(r + 6)$
29. $7(k + m) + 2(k + m)$
30. $2(2k + 4) + 3(3k - 2)$
31. $8(4x + 3) + 7(2x - 3)$
32. $9(2z + 6) + 4(3z - 8)$
33. $8(5f + 4g) + 2(f - 9g)$
34. $(5n + 4)6 + 2(9n - 8)$
35. $2(3x + 2y + 4) + 3(4x + 8)$
36. $7(5a + 5b + 2) + 4(2a - 3b)$

C

37. $4[2(3k + m) + 2k] + 3m$
38. $7s + 5[(6r + 2s)4 + 2r]$
39. $[(3 + 2c + 4d)5 + 2d]3$
40. $4t + 2[3(m + r) + 5m]$
41. $2m[4(m + 3) + 5n] + [2(m + n)4]$
42. $[3(y + x) + 4(y + x)]2x + 2(x^2 + xy)$

7-2 *Addition and Subtraction Properties of Equality*

OBJECTIVES

Use the addition property of equality to solve equations.

Use the subtraction property of equality to solve equations.

Recall that if the same number is added to both members of an equation, the truth of the equation is unchanged.

If $x - 3 = 9$, then $x - 3 + 3 = 9 + 3$, and $x = 12$.

3 is added to both members.

The Addition Property of Equality ► **For every number r, every number s, and every number t, if $r = s$, then $r + t = s + t$.**

EXAMPLE 1 Solve:

$$x - 10 = 8$$
$$x - 10 + 10 = 8 + 10 \quad \text{◄ Add 10 to both members.}$$
$$x = 18 \quad \text{◄ Solution}$$

We check the work by replacing x with 18 in the given equation. ►

$x - 10$	$= 8$
$18 - 10$	8
8	8 ✓

If we subtract the same number from both members of an equation, the truth of the equation is unchanged.

If $m + 7 = 19$, then $m + 7 - 7 = 19 - 7$, and $m = 12$.

7 is subtracted from both members.

The Subtraction Property of Equality ► **For every number r, every number s, and every number t, if $r = s$, then $r - t = s - t$.**

EXAMPLE 2 Solve:

$$a + 3 = 15$$
$$a + 3 - 3 = 15 - 3 \quad \text{◄ Subtract 3 from both members.}$$
$$a = 12 \quad \text{◄ Solution}$$

The addition property and the subtraction property are part of our basic equation solving strategy. We change (or *transform*) the equation so the variable stands alone as one member. The successive changes are called transformations.

Oral EXERCISES

Give the simplest name.

Sample 1: $6 + 4 - 4$ *What you say:* 6

Sample 2: $m - 7 + 7$ *What you say:* m

1. $a - 3 + 3$

2. $b + 8 - 8$

3. $14 + 2 - 2$

4. $k + 9 - 9$

5. $m + \frac{2}{3} - \frac{2}{3}$

6. $r - \frac{1}{2} + \frac{1}{2}$

Tell how to change the expression so the variable will stand alone.

Sample: $r + 4$ *What you say:* Subtract 4.

7. $r + 8$

8. $z - 10$

9. $t - 0.5$

10. $s + 4$

11. $a + \frac{1}{2}$

12. $k + 0.24$

Written EXERCISES

Complete. Then check the solution.

Sample:

$$t + 4 = 11$$
$$t + 4 - 4 = 11 - 4$$
$$t = \underline{\ ?\ }$$

Solution:

$$t + 4 = 11$$
$$t + 4 - 4 = 11 - 4$$
$$t = 7$$

Check: $t + 4 = 11$

$7 + 4$	11
11	11 ✓

A

1.
$$m - 6 = 3$$
$$m - 6 + 6 = 3 + 6$$
$$m = \underline{\ ?\ }$$

2.
$$n - 1 = 24$$
$$n - 1 + 1 = 24 + 1$$
$$n = \underline{\ ?\ }$$

3.
$$p + 7 = 13$$
$$p + 7 - 7 = 13 - 7$$
$$p = \underline{\ ?\ }$$

4.
$$s + 9 = 13$$
$$s + 9 - 9 = 13 - 9$$
$$s = \underline{\ ?\ }$$

5.
$$n + \frac{2}{3} = 6$$
$$n + \frac{2}{3} - \frac{2}{3} = 6 - \frac{2}{3}$$
$$n = \underline{\ ?\ }$$

6.
$$a + 0.1 = 4$$
$$a + 0.1 - 0.1 = 4 - 0.1$$
$$a = \underline{\ ?\ }$$

7.
$$36 = k + 10$$
$$36 - 10 = k + 10 - 10$$
$$\underline{\ ?\ } = k$$

8.
$$0.62 = r + 0.38$$
$$0.62 - 0.38 = r + 0.38 - 0.38$$
$$\underline{\ ?\ } = r$$

Solve. Begin by stating what number should be added to or subtracted from both members.

Sample: $m - 2 = 8$

Solution: Add 2 to both members.

$$m - 2 + 2 = 8 + 2$$
$$m = 10$$

Check: $m - 2 = 8$

$10 - 2$	8
8	8 ✓

9. $r + 3 = 11$

10. $s - 2 = 14$

11. $t + 8 = 13$

12. $p - 4 = 7$

13. $q + \frac{1}{2} = 4$

14. $a + \frac{2}{3} = 1$

15. $b - \frac{1}{5} = \frac{3}{5}$

16. $c - \frac{1}{3} = 4$

17. $100 + r = 167$

18. $r + 0.3 = 6$

B

19. $\frac{5}{6} = a - 1$

20. $\frac{13}{9} = b + \frac{5}{9}$

21. $\frac{5}{4} = r - \frac{1}{4}$

22. $\frac{3}{7} = s - \frac{3}{7}$

23. $\frac{7}{8} = y + \frac{1}{8}$

24. $0.05 = k + 0.01$

Solve and check.

Sample: $x - 7 = 9$

Solution:

$$x - 7 = 9$$
$$x - 7 + 7 = 9 + 7$$
$$x = 16$$

Check: $x - 7 = 9$

$16 - 7$	9
9	9 ✓

25. $a - 2 = 37$

26. $b - 19 = 61$

27. $25 = c - 17$

28. $92 = r - 47$

29. $s + 14 = 88$

30. $t + 19 = 101$

31. $r - 26 = 26$

32. $s - 14 = 0$

33. $k + 2.7 = 3.6$

34. $m - 1.8 = 5.9$

35. $p + 1.08 = 1.09$

36. $q - 1.08 = 0.071$

C

37. $\frac{3}{4} + a = \frac{5}{4}$

38. $\frac{2}{3} + b = 1$

39. $a - \frac{2}{5} = \frac{1}{5}$

40. $k - \frac{7}{8} = \frac{7}{8}$

7-3 *The Division Property of Equality*

OBJECTIVE

Use the division property of equality to solve equations.

If both members of an equation are divided by the same number, the truth of the equation is unchanged.

$$\text{If } 7x = 21, \text{ then } \frac{7x}{7} = \frac{21}{7}, \text{ and } x = 3.$$

Both members are divided by 7.

The Division Property of Equality ► **For every number r, every number s, and every number t except 0, if $r = s$, then $\frac{r}{t} = \frac{s}{t}$.**

EXAMPLE 1 Solve:

$$9n = 12 + 6$$

$$\frac{9n}{9} = \frac{12 + 6}{9} \quad \blacktriangleleft \text{ Divide both members by 9.}$$

$$n = \frac{18}{9} = 2 \quad \blacktriangleleft \text{ Solution}$$

Check: $9n = 12 + 6$

9(2)	12 + 6
18	18 ✓

Sometimes solving an equation requires the use of more than one property of equality.

EXAMPLE 2 Solve:

$$2k - 5 = 19$$

$$2k - 5 + 5 = 19 + 5 \quad \blacktriangleleft \text{ Add 5 to both members.}$$

$$2k = 24$$

$$\frac{2k}{2} = \frac{24}{2} \quad \blacktriangleleft \text{ Divide both members by 2.}$$

$$k = 12 \quad \blacktriangleleft \text{ Solution}$$

Check: $2k - 5 = 19$

2(12) − 5	19
24 − 5	19
19	19 ✓

Oral EXERCISES

Tell how to change the equation so that the variable will stand alone. Do not solve the equation.

Sample: $8k = 40$ *What you say:* Divide both members by 8.

1. $3t = 21$
2. $7r = 49$
3. $36 = 6b$
4. $29m = 290$
5. $5p = 60$
6. $15y = 2$
7. $3r = 1$
8. $0.2t = 1$
9. $24 = 5n$

Written EXERCISES

Solve. Check your answer.

Sample:

$$3s + 2 = 14$$
$$3s + 2 - 2 = 14 - 2$$
$$3s = 12$$
$$\frac{3s}{3} = \frac{12}{3}$$
$$s = 4$$

Check: $3s + 2 = 14$

$3(4) + 2$	14
$12 + 2$	14
14	14 ✓

A

1. $8m = 56$
2. $9n = 72$
3. $13a = 52$
4. $12b = 156$
5. $8r = 92$
6. $35s = 105$
7. $92 = 14t$
8. $16a = 12$
9. $1 = 20b$
10. $36 = 5c$
11. $\frac{1}{2} = 4x$
12. $6m = 6.66$
13. $5n = 0$
14. $3a + 1 = 10$
15. $5b - 1 = 29$
16. $2x + 7 = 31$
17. $7c - 4 = 52$
18. $4c + 5c = 81$

B

19. $18 = 4a + 2$
20. $6b - 6 = 0$
21. $5 + 3x = 38$
22. $7z + 8 = 64$
23. $14 + 18k = 14$
24. $9m - 1 = 14 + 12$
25. $0.06p - 0.2 = 1$
26. $21 + 3q = 30$
27. $0 = 4t - 22$
28. $13 = 9d + 13$

C

29. $\frac{1}{2} + 4n = 6\frac{1}{2}$
30. $0.7 + 2r = 1.8$
31. $5s - 0.01 = 1.44$
32. $0.2t - 6.21 = 18.95$
33. $6.1285 = 2m + 0.0085$
34. $0.12 + 7k = 1.07 + 0.03$

7-4 *The Multiplication Property of Equality*

OBJECTIVE

Use the multiplication property of equality to solve equations.

An equation like $\frac{t}{5} = 3$ can be solved by multiplying both members by the same number.

$$\text{If } \frac{t}{5} = 3, \text{ then } 5 \cdot \frac{t}{5} = 5 \cdot 3, \text{ and } t = 15.$$

The Multiplication Property of Equality ► **For every number r, every number s, and every number t, if $r = s$, then $rt = st$.**

EXAMPLE 1 Solve:

$$\frac{w}{7} = 2$$

$$7 \cdot \frac{w}{7} = 7 \cdot 2 \quad \blacktriangleleft \text{ Multiply both members by 7.}$$

$$w = 14 \quad \blacktriangleleft \text{ Solution}$$

Check:

$$\frac{w}{7} = 2$$

$\frac{14}{7}$	2
2	2 ✓

EXAMPLE 2 Solve:

$$\frac{2y}{3} = 6$$

$$3\left(\frac{2y}{3}\right) = 3(6) \quad \blacktriangleleft \text{ Multiply both members by 3.}$$

$$2y = 18$$

$$\frac{2y}{2} = \frac{18}{2} \quad \blacktriangleleft \text{ Divide both members by 2.}$$

$$y = 9 \quad \blacktriangleleft \text{ Solution}$$

The transformations in Example 2 could have been done in the opposite order. We could have divided by 2 first, and then multiplied by 3. The final result would have been the same: $y = 9$.

EXERCISES

Tell how to change the equation so that the variable will stand alone. Do not solve the equation.

Sample: $\frac{k}{4} = 5$ *What you say:* Multiply both members by 4.

1. $\frac{c}{5} = 2$
2. $\frac{d}{4} = 1$
3. $\frac{m}{2} = 0.5$
4. $\frac{n}{19} = 1$
5. $\frac{a}{6} = 0.214$
6. $\frac{b}{41} = 1$

Solve. Begin by telling the number by which both members are to be multiplied.

Sample: $\frac{f}{6} = 7$ *What you say:* Multiply both members by 6.

$f = 42$

7. $\frac{a}{2} = 10$
8. $\frac{b}{3} = 6$
9. $\frac{m}{2} = 26$
10. $6 = \frac{n}{10}$
11. $\frac{1}{3}y = 4$
12. $\frac{1}{5}z = \frac{1}{2}$

Written

EXERCISES

Solve. Check your answer.

1. $\frac{m}{2} = 8$
2. $\frac{n}{6} = 1.2$
3. $\frac{a}{5} = 0.5$

A

4. $\frac{b}{2} = 1.04$
5. $\frac{m}{10} = 0.018$
6. $\frac{3}{4}q = 4$
7. $\frac{3}{4}k = 3$
8. $\frac{5}{8}x = 0$
9. $\frac{5}{8}y = 1$
10. $\frac{z}{2} = \frac{1}{2}$
11. $\frac{t}{3} = 8 + 9$
12. $\frac{2x}{3} = 6$
13. $\frac{4x}{3} = 6$
14. $\frac{2}{1}m = 9$
15. $\frac{7a}{3} = 14$

B

16. $\frac{7}{9}a = 7$
17. $0.2 = \frac{8}{7}b$
18. $0 = \frac{3}{2}c$
19. $\frac{13m}{4} = 0.26$
20. $\frac{4}{3}d = 1$
21. $3 = \frac{1}{3}w$

22. $\frac{2}{3} = \frac{3}{4}x$

23. $\frac{1}{7}x = \frac{2}{3}$

24. $\frac{7}{8}y = \frac{7}{9}$

25. $5m \div 2 = 1.5$

26. $\frac{n}{0.7} = 6.3$

27. $\frac{3z}{2} = 2\frac{1}{2}$

C

28. $\frac{1}{5}n = 1.21$

29. $\frac{5}{4}k = 0.4$

30. $\frac{x+3}{5} = 4$

31. $\frac{y-2}{4} = 1$

32. $\frac{2y}{5} = 3.4$

33. $\frac{7y}{5} = 0.14$

34. $\frac{2n+1}{3} = 7$

35. $\frac{3y-2}{4} = 1$

36. $30 = 2w \div 7$

37. $v \div 1\frac{1}{3} = 33$

38. $\frac{2n}{3} + 1 = 7$

39. $\frac{3y}{4} - 2 = 1$

SELF-TEST 1

Be sure that you understand these terms.

similar terms (p. 184)
like terms (p. 184)
unlike terms (p. 184)
addition property of equality (p. 186)
subtraction property of equality (p. 186)
division property of equality (p. 189)
multiplication property of equality (p. 191)

Combine similar terms to simplify. **Section 7-1, p. 184**

1. $3a + 4a$
2. $2r + 2s - r$
3. $5(t + 1) - t$
4. $3mn + 4m + mn$

Solve.

5. $t - 7 = 18$
6. $1.7 + s = 10$ **Section 7-2, p. 186**
7. $6x = 48$
8. $0.4z = 0.36$ **Section 7-3, p. 189**
9. $\frac{1}{3}a = 5$
10. $\frac{b}{2} = 0.8$ **Section 7-4, p. 191**

Check your answers with those printed at the back of the book.

7-5 *More about Equation Solving Strategy*

OBJECTIVE
Solve equations by combining terms and making transformations.

We are now ready to solve more complicated equations, such as $4x + 2x - 3 = 10 + 5$. We need to use a combination of transformations, but it's easy if we proceed logically, step by step.

Step 1 Where possible, combine like terms.
Step 2 Transform the equation so that the term that contains the variable stands alone as one member.
Step 3 Transform the equation so that the coefficient of the variable is 1.

EXAMPLE 1 Solve:

$$4x + 2x - 3 = 10 + 5$$
$$6x - 3 = 15 \quad \blacktriangleleft \text{ Combine terms.}$$
$$6x - 3 + 3 = 15 + 3 \quad \blacktriangleleft \text{ Add 3 to both members.}$$
$$6x = 18$$
$$\frac{6x}{6} = \frac{18}{6} \quad \blacktriangleleft \text{ Divide both members by 6.}$$
$$x = 3 \quad \blacktriangleleft \text{ Solution}$$

Check: $4x + 2x - 3 = 10 + 5$

$4(3) + 2(3) - 3$	$10 + 5$
$12 + 6 - 3$	15
15	15 ✓

EXAMPLE 2 Solve:

$$m - \frac{3}{4}m + 3 = 10 - 6$$
$$\frac{1}{4}m + 3 = 4 \quad \blacktriangleleft \text{ Combine terms.}$$
$$\frac{1}{4}m + 3 - 3 = 4 - 3 \quad \blacktriangleleft \text{ Subtract 3 from both members.}$$
$$\frac{1}{4}m = 1$$
$$4\left(\frac{1}{4}m\right) = 4(1) \quad \blacktriangleleft \text{ Multiply both members by 4.}$$
$$m = 4 \quad \blacktriangleleft \text{ Solution}$$

Check: $m - \frac{3}{4}m + 3 = 10 - 6$

$$\begin{array}{r|l} 4 - \frac{3}{4}(4) + 3 & 10 - 6 \\ 4 - 3 + 3 & 4 \\ 4 & 4 \ \checkmark \end{array}$$

Oral EXERCISES

Simplify by combining similar terms. Do not solve the equation.

Sample: $4z + 5z + 1 = 22 - 8$ *What you say:* $9z + 1 = 14$

1. $4a + 5a = 16$

2. $4b - 6 = 10 - 8$

3. $6c + 4c + 1 = 18$

4. $5m + m = 13 + 2$

5. $9n - 5n + 8 = 16$

6. $2p + \frac{1}{2}p = 6 + \frac{1}{2}$

7. $2q - \frac{1}{2}q = 9 - \frac{1}{2}$

8. $m - \frac{1}{2}m = 14 + 1$

9. $n + \frac{1}{3}n = 6 + 1\frac{2}{3}$

10. $b + b - \frac{1}{2}b = (2)(3)(0)$

Written EXERCISES

Solve.

Sample: $4k - k + 2 = 16 - 8$

Solution:

$$\begin{aligned} 4k - k + 2 &= 16 - 8 \\ 3k + 2 &= 8 \\ 3k + 2 - 2 &= 8 - 2 \\ 3k &= 6 \\ \frac{3k}{3} &= \frac{6}{3} \\ k &= 2 \end{aligned}$$

Check: $4k - k + 2 = 16 - 8$

$$\begin{array}{r|l} 4(2) - 2 + 2 & 16 - 8 \\ 8 - 2 + 2 & 8 \\ 8 & 8 \ \checkmark \end{array}$$

A

1. $5p - 2p = 21$

2. $6q + 2q = 32$

3. $4c - c = 36$

4. $9d + d = 80$

5. $2a + 3a = 13 + 12$

6. $8b - 4b = 7 + 21$

7. $8f + f = 20 - 2$

8. $9g - g = 35 + 13$

9. $5z + z - 2 = 28$

10. $16v - v + 10 = 85 - 15$

11. $1.2t + 0.3t = 6 - 1.5$

12. $6r + 3r - 9 = 0$

13. $1\frac{1}{2}s + 2\frac{1}{2}s = 17 + 7$

14. $4\frac{1}{3}m - 1\frac{1}{3}m + 9 = 21$

15. $0.6n + 5.4n - 1 = 35$

16. $1\frac{1}{3}k + \frac{2}{3}k - 1 = 33$

B

17. $\frac{2}{3}m + 1\frac{1}{3}m = 2\frac{1}{2} + 9\frac{1}{2}$

18. $\frac{1}{2}n + 2\frac{1}{2}n = 18\frac{1}{3} - 2\frac{1}{3}$

19. $\frac{2r}{3} + \frac{2r}{3} = 1\frac{1}{4} + 2\frac{3}{4}$

20. $\frac{1}{2}s + \frac{3}{4}s - 4 = 1$

21. $\frac{x}{5} + 8 + \frac{4x}{5} = 10$

22. $3(a + 5) + a = 16$

23. $5(2b - 6) - b = 0$

24. $99 - 62 = 5(2c + 4)$

25. $\frac{3}{5}t - \frac{3}{4} = 3$

26. $\frac{x}{3} - 4 + \frac{5}{3} = 0$

27. $15y + 4\frac{1}{3} - 8y = 11\frac{1}{3}$

28. $\frac{8}{5}z + \frac{3}{5}z - 9\frac{1}{3} = 23\frac{2}{3}$

29. $\frac{3}{8}r - 9 + \frac{1}{8} = 0$

30. $\frac{1}{5}s + \frac{1}{2}s + \frac{2}{4}s = \frac{2}{5}$

31. $6 + 0.2t - 0.1t = 10$

32. $6.2v - 12.8 + 0.3v = 0.2$

C

33. $9.2 + 9m - 4m = 36.7$

34. $10n - 4 - n - 5n = 8.4$

35. $5r + 6.2 - 0.4r = 10.8$

36. $47 + 18 = 5t - 15 - 3t$

Problems

Write and solve an equation to answer the question.

Sample: The sum of four times a number and 21 is 101. Find the number.

Solution: Let n stand for the number.

$$\begin{aligned} 4n + 21 &= 101 \\ 4n + 21 - 21 &= 101 - 21 \\ 4n &= 80 \\ \frac{4n}{4} &= \frac{80}{4} \\ n &= 20 \end{aligned}$$

The number is 20.

1. The sum of three times a number and 7 is 19. What is the number?
2. If six times a number is decreased by 5, the result is equal to 61. Find the number.

3. If four times a number is decreased by 101, the result is equal to 99. Find the number.

4. If 33 is added to seven times a number, the result is equal to 68. Find the number.

5. The sum of a whole number and the next greater whole number is 51. Find the numbers. (*Hint:* call the numbers n and $n + 1$.)

6. When half a number is increased by 9, the result is 32. Find the number.

7. Maria is 5 centimeters taller than Rollie. The sum of their heights is 305 centimeters. How tall is each person?

8. The length of a box lid is three times its width. The perimeter of the box lid is 200 centimeters. How long and how wide is the box lid? (*Hint:* $P = 2l + 2w$)

9. The sum of an even number and the next greater even number is 86. Find the numbers. (*Hint:* if n is an even number, the next greater even number is $n + 2$.)

10. The lengths of the sides of a triangle are shown in the illustration. The perimeter is 108 meters. Find the length of each side.

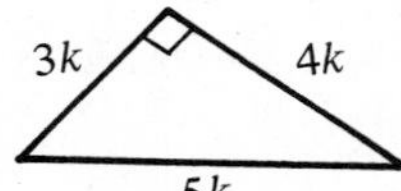

consumer notes

Listing Ingredients

Find a canned product which is a mixture of separate ingredients, such as fruit cocktail or mixed nuts. On the label of the can, read the order in which the ingredients are listed. They should be listed in order by weight, with the ingredient making up the greatest percentage of weight listed first, and so on.

Open the can and sort its contents into separate containers, all of equal weight when empty. Weigh the containers of ingredients. Which weighs the most? Is this ingredient listed first on the label? Are all the other ingredients listed in the correct order?

7-6 *Equations and Problem Solving*

OBJECTIVE

Use equations with one variable to solve problems.

Equations can be useful in solving many kinds of problems. The basic equation-solving strategies are helpful.

EXAMPLE Two cement trucks contain a total of 8.1 cubic meters (m^3) of cement. The large truck holds twice as much as the small truck. How much cement is in each truck?

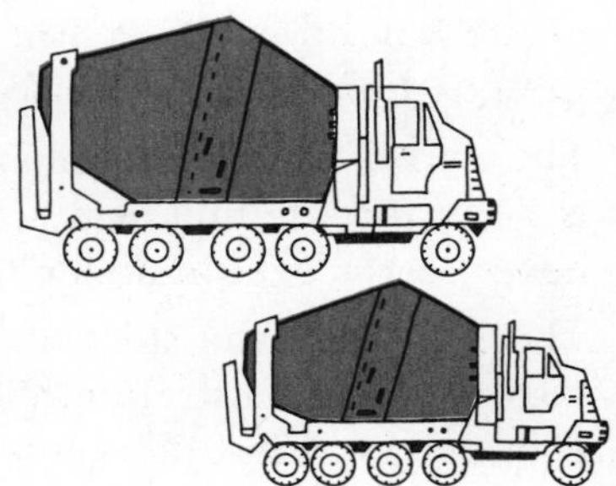

Use a variable to stand for missing information.

Let amount of cement in small truck $= t$.
Then, amount of cement in large truck $= 2t$.
So, total amount of cement $= t + 2t$.

$$\underbrace{\text{cement in small truck}}_{t} + \underbrace{\text{cement in large truck}}_{2t} = \underbrace{\text{total}}_{8.1}$$ ◄ **Equation**

$$3t = 8.1$$ ◄ **Divide each member by 3.**

$$t = 2.7$$

The small truck contains t cubic meters, or $2.7\ m^3$ of cement. The large truck contains $2t$ cubic meters, or $5.4\ m^3$ of cement.

Let's check: $t + 2t = 2.7\ m^3 + 5.4\ m^3$
$= 8.1\ m^3$ ✓

Use the information given to answer the question.

Sample: Swimmer swims m meters Friday; $2m$ meters Saturday; 900 meters total. How far on Friday? On Saturday?

Hint: $\underbrace{\text{Friday meters}}_{m} + \underbrace{\text{Saturday meters}}_{2m} = \underbrace{900}_{900}$

What you say: $3m = 900$; $m = 300$

300 meters on Friday and 600 meters on Saturday.

1. Basketball team record: lost x games; won $3x$ games; played 24 games. How many lost? won?
   Hint: $\underbrace{\text{games lost}}_{x} + \underbrace{\text{games won}}_{3x} = \underbrace{24}_{24}$
2. Sports field: width, w meters; length, $2w$ meters; perimeter, 450 meters. What is the width? length?
   Hint: $\underbrace{2 \cdot \text{width}}_{2 \cdot w} + \underbrace{2 \cdot \text{length}}_{2 \cdot 2w} = \underbrace{\text{perimeter}}_{450}$
3. Two consecutive odd numbers: first number is n; second number is $n + 2$; sum is 36. What are the numbers?
   Hint: $\underbrace{\text{first number}}_{n} + \underbrace{\text{second number}}_{n + 2} = \underbrace{36}_{36}$
4. Three consecutive numbers: first number is m; second number is $m + 1$; third number is $m + 2$; sum is 72. What are the numbers?
   Hint: $\underbrace{\text{first number}}_{m} + \underbrace{\text{second number}}_{m + 1} + \underbrace{\text{third number}}_{m + 2} = \underbrace{72}_{72}$
5. Two consecutive multiples of 5: first multiple is z; second multiple is $z + 5$; their sum is 85. What are the multiples?
   Hint: $\underbrace{\text{first multiple}}_{z} + \underbrace{\text{second multiple}}_{z + 5} = \underbrace{\text{total}}_{85}$

A

Write an equation. Then solve it to answer the question.

1. Alan earned \$6 more on his paper route than Freddie. If Alan earned \$21, how much did Freddie earn?
2. When a swimming pool heater was turned off, the water cooled 3.5° Celsius in one hour. If the cooled water was 22° Celsius, what was the original water temperature?

3. The White Sox beat the Red Sox by 6 runs. If the Red Sox scored 2 runs, how many runs did the White Sox score?
4. LuAnn and Karen have part-time jobs. LuAnn earns 15¢ per hour more than Karen. If Karen earns $1.85 per hour, how much does LuAnn earn?
5. Brand X costs 19¢ more than Brand Y. If Brand X costs 98¢, what is the cost of Brand Y?
6. Betty has 25 new customers on her paper route this month. If she now has 158 customers, how many did she have last month?

B

7. The class had 11 pieces of chicken remaining at the end of the party. If this was one-fifth of the original number of pieces of chicken, how many pieces were eaten?
8. Listo has 4 more record albums than Nathan. Together they have 20 albums. How many does Listo have?
9. The sum of three consecutive numbers is 156. What are the three numbers?
10. The sum of a number and 18.3 is 99. What is the number?
11. The sum of two consecutive even numbers is 74. What are the two numbers?
12. The sum of two consecutive odd numbers is 40. What are the two numbers?

C

13. The length of a rectangle is 6 meters more than the width. If half the perimeter is 48 meters, what are the length and width?
14. The width of a piece of fabric is 25 centimeters less than the length. If the perimeter is 190 centimeters, what are the length and width?
15. Sam is 7 years older than his brother. If the sum of their ages is 11 years, how old is each?
16. Louella is three times as old as her sister. If the difference between their ages is 14 years, how old is each?
17. Priscilla rode her bike half as far this week as last week. If she rode 63 kilometers altogether, how far did she ride last week?
18. The average of 18 and a number is 24. What is the number?
19. The average of two consecutive even numbers is 27. What are the two numbers?

7-7 *Equations with the Variable in Both Members*

OBJECTIVE

Solve equations in which the variable appears in both members.

In the equation $4n = 15 - n$, the variable, n, appears in both members. The properties of equality can be used to make transformations leading to the solution.

EXAMPLE 1 Solve: $4n = 15 - n$

$$4n = 15 - n$$

$$4n + n = 15 - n + n \quad \text{◄ Add } n \text{ to both members.}$$

$$5n = 15$$

$$\frac{5n}{5} = \frac{15}{5} \quad \text{◄ Divide both members by 5.}$$

$$n = 3 \quad \text{◄ Solution}$$

Check: $4n = 15 - n$

$4(3)$	$15 - 3$
12	12 ✓

EXAMPLE 2 Solve: $2x + 3x + 5 = 4 + 9 + x$

$$2x + 3x + 5 = 4 + 9 + x$$

$$5x + 5 = 13 + x \quad \text{◄ Combine terms.}$$

$$5x + 5 - x = 13 + x - x \quad \text{◄ Subtract } x \text{ from both members.}$$

$$4x + 5 = 13$$

$$4x + 5 - 5 = 13 - 5 \quad \text{◄ Subtract 5 from both members.}$$

$$4x = 8$$

$$\frac{4x}{4} = \frac{8}{4} \quad \text{◄ Divide both members by 4.}$$

$$x = 2 \quad \text{◄ Solution}$$

Check: $2x + 3x + 5 = 4 + 9 + x$

$2(2) + 3(2) + 5$	$4 + 9 + 2$
$4 + 6 + 5$	15
15	15 ✓

Written EXERCISES

Solve. Check your answer.

Sample:

$$6k = 28 + 2k$$
$$6k - 2k = 28 + 2k - 2k$$
$$4k = 28$$
$$\frac{4k}{4} = \frac{28}{4}$$
$$k = 7$$

Check: $6k = 28 + 2k$

$6(7)$	$28 + 2(7)$
42	$28 + 14$
42	42 ✓

A

1. $3a = 6 + a$
2. $4b = 35 - b$
3. $7c = 42 + c$
4. $8m = 49 + m$
5. $13n = 19 + 3n$
6. $8r = 16 - 2r$
7. $15s = 9s + 54$
8. $6t + 10 = 7t$
9. $14v + 72 = 17v$
10. $3w + 6 = 12w$
11. $13w = 8 - 3w$
12. $11z + 8 = 15z$
13. $6k - 9 = 3k$
14. $f = 2f - 7$
15. $7g - 21 = 4g$
16. $t = 44 - t$
17. $5r = 43 - 5r$
18. $2 + 3m = 4 + 2m$
19. $b + 6 = 10 - b$
20. $16 - c = 13 + c$
21. $4m - 9 = m + 6$
22. $7n + 5 = 9n - 13$

B

23. $a + 10 = 14a - 16$
24. $14g - g = 10g + 20$
25. $15 - 2m = 16 - 5m$
26. $\frac{1}{2}b + 8 = 1\frac{1}{2}b - 2$
27. $0.25 + c = 3c - 0.75$
28. $16m = 10m$

C

29. $9m - 8 = 6m - 10 + 4m$
30. $3(n - 3) = 4n - 13$
31. $c(8 + 1) + c = 8 + 2c$
32. $5(2n - 4) = 8 + 7n$
33. $\frac{1}{4}(p + 6) = \frac{3}{4}p - 4$
34. $5q - 4 + 5q = 7q + 18$

Problems

1. If a number is increased by 15, the result is the same as two times the number. Find the number.
2. If a number is increased by 36, the result is seven times the number. What is the number?
3. If four times a number is increased by 35, the result is nine times the number. Find the number.

4. If 41 is decreased by three times a number, the result is the same as the number increased by five. Find the number.

5. The length of a rectangle is one meter less than twice the width. The perimeter is 46 meters. Find the length and width.

$2m - 1$

m

6. Four times a number, decreased by ten, is the same as three times the same number increased by three. What is the number?

7. Tony has one more nickel than he has pennies. He has 15 coins. How many nickels does he have?

8. Jolene has two more nickels than pennies, and five more dimes than nickels. She has 21 coins. How many of each coin does she have?

SELF-TEST 2

Solve.

Section 7-5, p. 194

1. $5c + 6c = 22$
2. $4r - 4 = 2.4$
3. $2m = 6 + 10$
4. $3s + 8 + s = 40$

Write and solve an equation to answer the question.

Section 7-6, p. 198

5. The sum of a number and 9 is 25. Find the number.
6. When twice a number is decreased by 1, the result is 21. Find the number.
7. The sum of two consecutive odd numbers is 76. What are the numbers?
8. Rover and Grover are beagles. Rover is 3 years older than Grover. The sum of their ages is 13. How old is Rover?

Solve.

Section 7-7, p. 201

9. $4m + 2 = m + 11$
10. $3n - 6 = 2n + 2$
11. Three times a number, increased by 4, is 8 less than four times the number. Find the number.

Check your answers with those printed at the back of the book.

chapter summary

1. Expressions may be simplified by combining similar terms.

$$3x + 12x = 15x$$

similar terms

2. The addition property of equality: If $r = s$, then $r + t = s + t$.
3. The subtraction property of equality: If $r = s$, then $r - t = s - t$.
4. The division property of equality: If $r = s$, then $\frac{r}{t} = \frac{s}{t}$. $(t \neq 0)$
5. The multiplication property of equality: If $r = s$, then $rt = st$.
6. The process of changing the form of an equation by using a property of equality is called **transforming.** The successive changes are called **transformations.**

chapter test

Solve. Check your answer.

1. $n + 13 = 20$
2. $m - 2 = 19$
3. $6p = 60$
4. $\frac{1}{3}y = 4$
5. $4a - 2 = 10$
6. $b + \frac{1}{2} = 20$
7. $100 = 10x + 30$
8. $30 - \frac{1}{2}x = 20$
9. $16k - 1 = 0$
10. $\frac{c}{5} = \frac{1}{10}$
11. $\frac{3}{4}w = 45$
12. $42 - v = 5v$
13. $26 - 3m = 2m - 14$
14. $\frac{n}{4} + 5 = 7$

Write an equation. Explain what number the variable represents. Do not solve the equation.

15. The sum of a number and 13 is 24. Find the number.
16. If 12 is subtracted from three times a number, the result is equal to the number increased by six. Find the number.
17. The sum of an even number and the next greater even number is 46. Find the number.
18. Each of two sides of a triangle is two-thirds as long as the third side. The perimeter is 168 centimeters. Find the length of the third side.

challenge topics

Puzzles

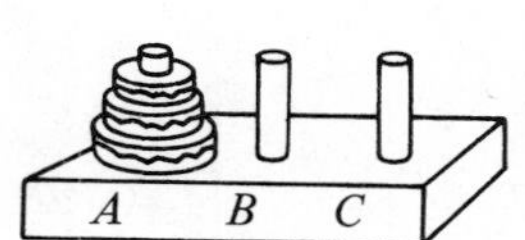

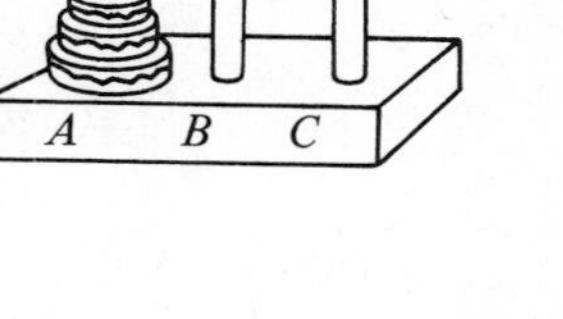

1. Three discs are arranged on peg *A*. The object of the puzzle is to move the discs one at a time so they end up in the same arrangement on peg *B*. You may use all three pegs but a larger disc may *not* be placed on a smaller disc. What is the least number of moves required?

2. A group of campers consists of two children and two adults. They want to cross a river but their canoe will hold only one adult or two children at a time. How can they cross the river? (Hint: two children cross first)
3. A row of ten coins is arranged as illustrated. In this puzzle you are to move any coin over the *two* next to it and onto the coin beyond to make a stack of two coins. You are to finish with five equally spaced stacks of two coins each. (Hint: move only those coins in odd numbered positions or those in even numbered positions.)

cumulative review

Simplify.

1. $\frac{15 + 5}{4}$
2. $3^2 - 3$
3. $16 - (4 \times 4)$

True or false?

4. $\frac{30}{5} = 2 \times 3$
5. $58 = 13 + 35$
6. $5^2 - 5 = 4 \times 5$

Name the value. Let $b = 2$, $l = 6$, $u = 10$.

7. $l + u + b$
8. $\frac{b + u}{l}$
9. $b^2 + u^2$

Write the equation in symbols.

10. The quotient of 42 and 7 is equal to some number.

Solve.

11. $20 = 3 + x$
12. $27 - 5 = y$
13. $13 \times z = 39$
14. $\frac{22}{c} = 2$
15. $28 = 4 \times d$
16. $n^3 = 8$

Name the coordinate.

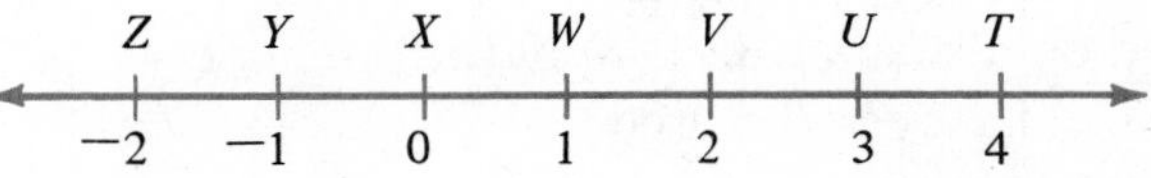

17. U
18. W
19. Y
20. Z

Name the opposite.

21. $^-17$
22. 2
23. 4
24. $\frac{^-3}{8}$

Complete the pattern.

25. 0, ?, ?, 3, ?, 5
26. $^-20$, $^-19$, ?, $^-17$, ?, ?

Graph. Use the number line.

27. The integers less than 0.
28. The numbers between $^-3$ and 2.

Complete. Use $<$ or $>$.

29. $4 \underline{\ ?\ } {}^{-}3$

30. ${}^{-}4 \underline{\ ?\ } 0$

Draw axes and graph.

31. (2, 4), (1, $^{-}$2), (0, 3), ($^{-}$1, 2), and ($^{-}$2, $^{-}$4)

Name the LCM and GCF.

32. 2 and 3

33. 3 and 12

Write each number in the form $2 \times n$ or $(2 \times n) + 1$.

34. 14

35. 21

36. 31

Complete.

37. $\frac{3}{4} = \frac{?}{16}$

38. $\frac{2}{7} = \frac{?}{28}$

Write as a fraction in lowest terms.

39. 5 out of 20

40. 7 out of 21

Write as a decimal and as a percent.

41. $\frac{3}{20}$

42. $\frac{2}{50}$

43. $\frac{99}{100}$

Complete.

44. 10 cm $\leftrightarrow$ _?_ m

45. 10 m $\leftrightarrow$ _?_ cm

Add, subtract, multiply, or divide.

46. $\frac{3}{5} + \frac{1}{5}$

47. $\frac{7}{22} - \frac{4}{22}$

48. $6\frac{2}{3} - 2\frac{1}{3}$

49. $\frac{4}{7} \div \frac{2}{3}$

50. $1\frac{1}{3} \times \frac{3}{4}$

51. $\frac{6}{11} \div \frac{2}{22}$

Find the value when $z = 2$, $y = 3$, and $w = 1$.

52. $\frac{z \cdot y}{w}$

53. $\frac{2}{y} + \frac{w}{y}$

54. $\frac{y}{w} + z$

Solve.

55. $q = 2.3 + 5.4$

56. $r = 11.1 \times 2.34$

57. $s = 54.2 \div 27.1$

58. $t = 15\% \times 50$

Simplify.

59. $(4 + 3)2$

60. $(2 + 5)(4 + 1)$

Find the values of the expression. The replacement set for m is $\{1, 2, 5\}$.

61. $m + 13$

62. $3m - 3$

Complete the factorization of the product.

63. Product: $14\,lm$; $14(\underline{\ ?\ })$, $7(\underline{\ ?\ })$, $2l(\underline{\ ?\ })$

Complete the set of ordered pairs by using the given rule.

64. $2(t + 3)$ $\{(1, 8), (2, \underline{\ ?\ }), (3, 12), (4, \underline{\ ?\ }), (5, \underline{\ ?\ })\}$

Write a number sentence.

65. The product of 2.7 and some number is 7.1.

Find the solution set. The replacement set is given.

66. $3n + 1 = 7$; $\{0, 2, 4, 6\}$

67. $6.07 + t < 10.07$; {the numbers of arithmetic}

To solve, perform the operation as indicated.

68. $6t = 24$; divide by 6

69. $13 + q = 27$; subtract 13

70. $\frac{m}{3} = 21$; multiply by 3

71. $n - 5 = 21$; add 5

Write an equation. Then solve it to answer the question.

72. The sum of a number and 23 is 57. What is the number?

73. A rectangle has width 2 cm and length 6 cm. What is the area?

Solve and graph the solution set. The replacement set is {the numbers of arithmetic}.

74. $g + 2 > 3$

75. $7 - h \leq 4$

Write an inequality. Then write the solution set if the replacement set is {the numbers of arithmetic}.

76. The product of 5 and some number is greater than 20. What can the number be?

Tell which property is illustrated.

77. $(3 + 2) + 5 = 3 + (2 + 5)$

78. $52 = 52$

79. $3 + 2 = 2 + 3$

80. If $ab = c$, then $c = ab$.

81. If $4 + 2 = 6$ and $6 = 3 \cdot 2$, then $4 + 2 = 3 \cdot 2$.

82. Since 2 and 5 are whole numbers, $2 + 5$ is a whole number.

83. Since 2 and 4 are whole numbers, $2 \cdot 4$ is a whole number.

84. $2 + 4 + 5 = 6 + 5$

85. $2 \cdot 4 = 4 \cdot 2$

86. $a(bc) = (ab)c$

87. $2(3 + 5) = 2(3) + 2(5)$

88. $3(5 - 1) = 3(5) - 3(1)$

89. $154 + 0 = 154$

90. $x^2y \cdot 0 = 0$

91. $b \cdot \frac{5}{5} = b$

Write the set of ordered pairs that represents the function. Draw axes and graph the ordered pairs.

92. Rule: $a + 1$
Replacement set: {0, 2, 4}

93. Rule: $2b$
Replacement set: {1, 2, 3}

Solve. Check your answer.

94. $h - 3 = 7$

95. $3 + f = 41$

96. $14t = 56$

97. $7k + 2 = 9$

98. $\frac{4l}{3} = 12$

99. $\frac{7m}{2} - 2 = 12$

100. $3n + 1 = 4n$

101. $2p - 14 = 4$

Review of Skills

Tell what letter on the number line below names the point which represents the number described.

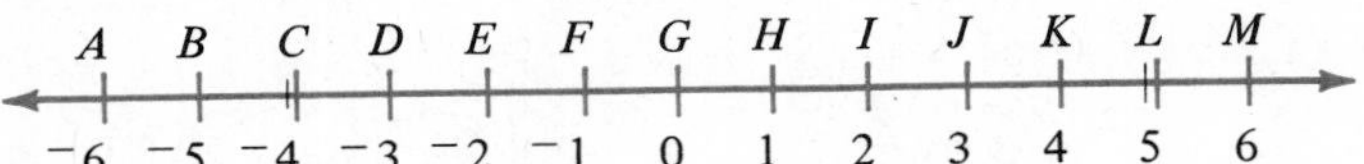

1. One kilometer above sea level

2. One kilometer below sea level

3. Four degrees above zero

4. Five degrees below zero

5. Six points scored

6. A loss of three dollars

Answer the question. Assume that 2 points won is written 2 and 3 points lost is written $^{-}3$.

7. Mario's score was 8, and then he lost 3 points. What was his new score?

8. When Mario's score was $^{-}1$, he won 3 points. What was his new score?

9. If Mario's score was 2, and then he lost 4 points, what was his score then?

Answer the question. Assume that 2 kilometers east is written 2 and 3 kilometers west is written $^{-}3$.

10. Susan walked 3 kilometers west, and then 4 kilometers east. Where was she in relation to her starting point?

11. The next day Susan walked 5 kilometers east, then 8 kilometers west, then 4 kilometers east. Where was she in relation to her starting position?

Answer the question. Assume that a rise of 3 floors is written 3 and a movement down of 2 floors is written $^{-}2$.

12. The elevator rose 3 floors (3) and then moved down 4 floors ($^{-}4$). What was the result of the two moves?

13. The elevator moved down 2 floors and then down 3 more floors. What was the result of the two moves?

Left: Physician performing laboratory tests.

Right: Medical technician operating computer-assisted blood analyzer.

8 Working with Directed Numbers

8-1 *Directed Numbers and the Number Line*

OBJECTIVES

Name the magnitudes of directed numbers.

Use directed numbers in practical situations.

Recall that when we refer to the position of a number on the number line, we mean the position of its graph. Then we can say the following about a horizontal number line:

Numbers to the left of 0 are **negative.**

Numbers to the right of 0 are **positive.**

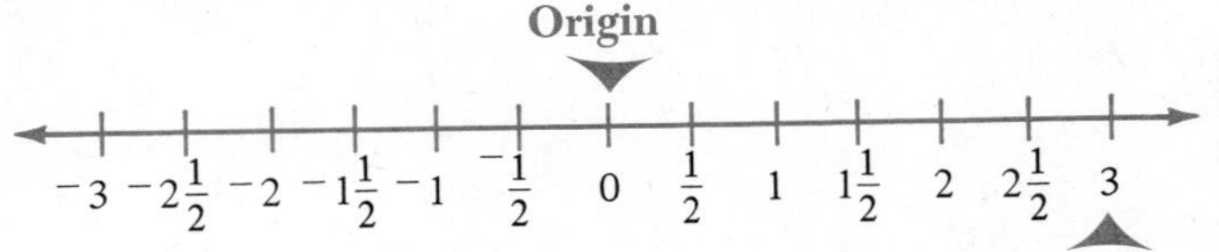

We write 3 instead of $^+3$. $^+3$ is the same as 3.

On a vertical number line, numbers above 0 are **positive.** Numbers below 0 are **negative.**

Pairs of numbers like 3 and $^-3$ are opposites. Note that the point 3 is just as far from 0 as is the point $^-3$. To locate 3 on the horizontal number line, we move 3 units to the right of 0. To locate $^-3$, we move 3 units to the left of 0. The distance between 0 and any number is called the magnitude of the number.

EXAMPLE 1

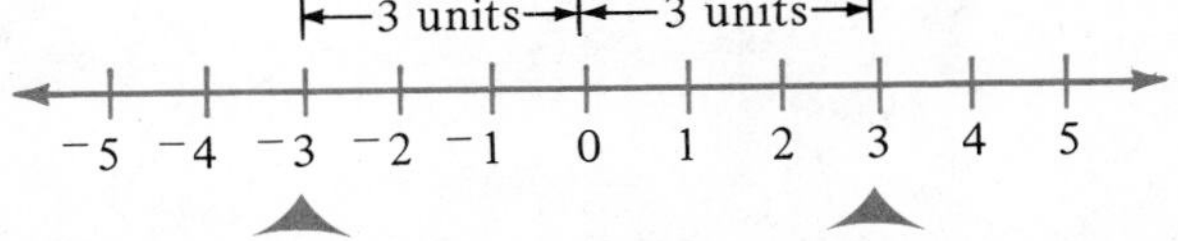

The magnitude of $^-3$ is 3. The magnitude of 3 is 3.

Since direction is important with respect to positive and negative numbers, we often use the term directed numbers. Although 0 is neither positive nor negative, it is called a directed number.

Directed numbers occur in many practical situations.

EXAMPLE 2 To preserve the food, the temperature in the freezer must be kept at 18°C below 0.
We write $^{-}18$°C.

Oral EXERCISES

Tell the meaning in words.

Sample: $^{-}1\frac{1}{3}$ *What you say:* Negative one and one-third

1. $^{-}5$ **2.** $^{-}2.36$ **3.** $^{-}2\frac{2}{3}$ **4.** $^{-}\frac{1}{10}$

Name the directed number described.

Sample: 2 units to the left of zero *What you say:* Negative two

5. 3 units to the right of 0
6. 2 units to the left of 0
7. $5\frac{1}{3}$ units to the right of 0
8. The negative number of magnitude 5
9. The positive number of magnitude $3\frac{3}{4}$
10. The positive number of magnitude 0.03

Use a directed number to express the thermometer reading.

11.

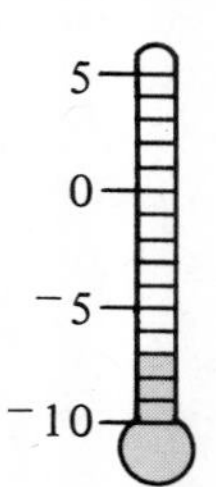

12.

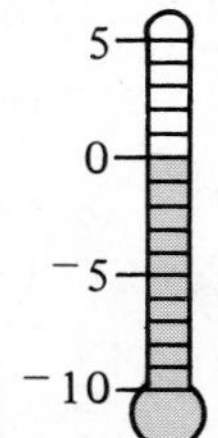

13.

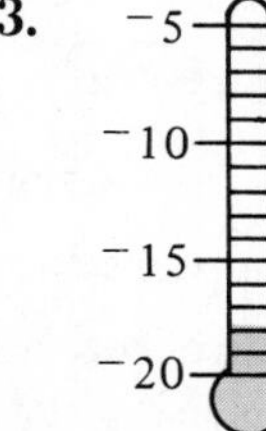

Written EXERCISES

Name the coordinate of the point.

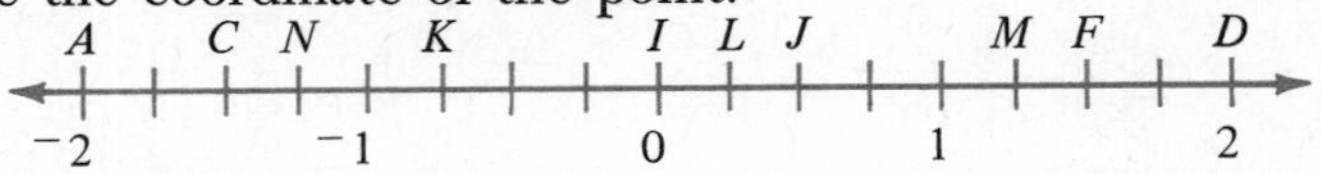

Sample: A *Solution:* $^{-}2$

A

1. D
2. K
3. N
4. F
5. M
6. I
7. C
8. J
9. L

Use a directed number to express the following.

Sample: 20 degrees below zero *Solution:* $^{-}20$

10. 15 degrees above zero
11. 12 degrees below zero
12. 30 meters above sea level
13. 100 meters below sea level
14. 6.8 degrees below zero
15. 22.8 degrees above zero
16. 5.5 degrees above zero
17. 0.1 degree below zero
18. 2.7 degrees below zero
19. 0 degrees

Name the directed number.

Sample: The positive number 4 units from zero *Solution:* 4

20. The negative number 6 units from 0
21. The positive number 5 units from 0
22. The negative number 3.8 units from 0
23. The positive number 20.9 units from 0

B

24. The number that lies the same distance from 0 as $^{-}4$
25. The number that lies the same distance from 0 as 15
26. The number that lies the same distance from 0 as $^{-}6\frac{2}{3}$
27. The number that lies the same distance from 0 as $45\frac{7}{9}$
28. The number that lies the same distance from 0 as $^{-}0.075$
29. Two directed numbers, each 11 units from 0
30. Two directed numbers, each 23 units from 0
31. Two directed numbers, each $5\frac{1}{9}$ units from 0
32. Two directed numbers, each 9.3 units from 0

C

33. Two directed numbers, each 4 units from 5
34. Two directed numbers, each 13 units from $^{-}3$
35. Two directed numbers, each 13 units from 3
36. Two directed numbers, each $4\frac{1}{4}$ units from $^{-}5\frac{3}{4}$

career capsule *Telephone Installer*

Telephone installers deliver, install, and remove telephones in homes and offices. Installers begin their jobs by first inspecting the work area and planning installation procedures. They attach outside wires to a pole or cable and then connect the cable terminals with inside wiring. After installing related inside wiring, they test the telephones to ensure proper working order.

About seven months of classroom and on-the-job training are required to be a telephone installer. Courses in mathematics, physics, and shopwork are helpful. Other qualifications include physical fitness, the ability to work in cramped areas, manual dexterity, good eyesight, normal color vision, and a friendly and patient disposition.

8-2 *Arrows to Represent Directed Numbers*

OBJECTIVE

Use arrows on the number line to represent directed numbers.

We can use positive and negative directed numbers to show gains and losses in football.

EXAMPLE 1 First play ► Gain of 4 yards: 4
Second play ► Loss of 7 yards: $^-7$

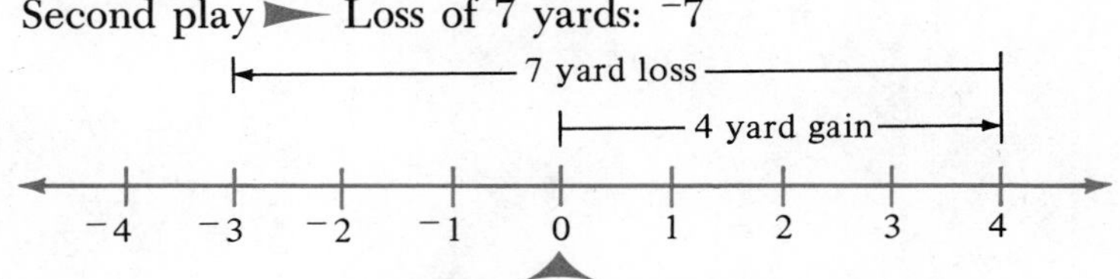

The first play begins here.
Call this point the origin.

Total after two plays ► Loss of 3 yards: $^-3$

In general, we can represent a directed number on the number line by an arrow. The arrow begins at a specified point. Its length corresponds to the magnitude of the directed number. For a positive number, the arrow points to the right. For a negative number, the arrow points to the left.

EXAMPLE 2 5 (Start at the origin.)

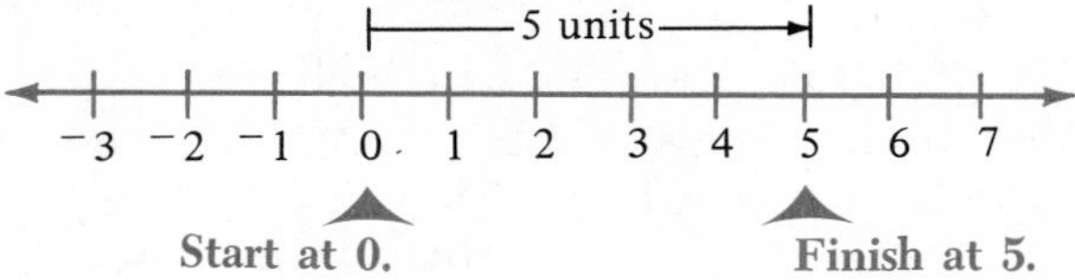

Start at 0. Finish at 5.

EXAMPLE 3 $^-2$ (Start at the origin.)

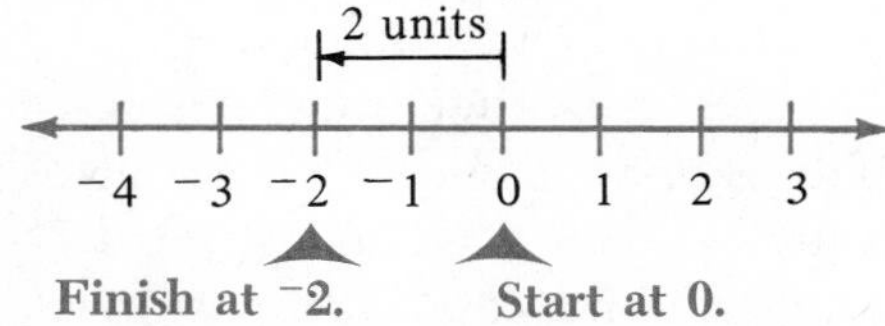

Finish at $^-2$. Start at 0.

EXAMPLE 4 3 (Start at ⁻1.)

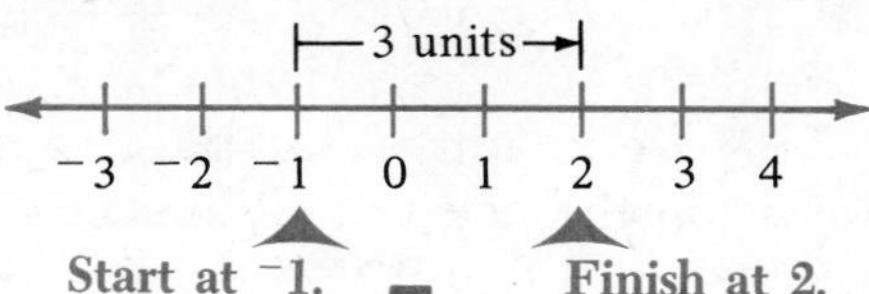

EXAMPLE 5 $1\frac{1}{2}$ (Start at 3.)

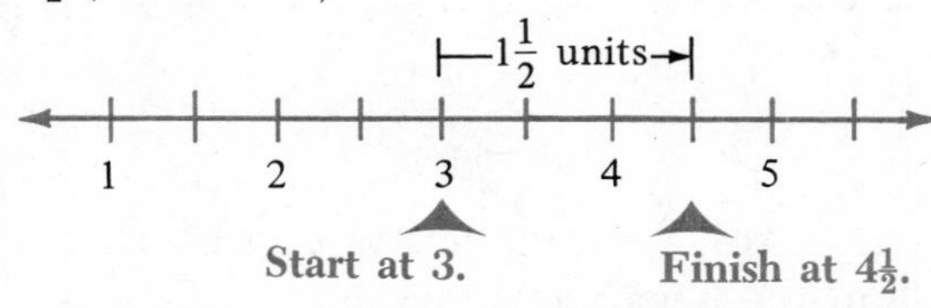

Locate the directed number with respect to 0.

Sample: 30 *What you say:* Thirty units in the positive direction.

1. 6	**2.** ⁻16	**3.** 0.5
4. ⁻$2\frac{1}{2}$	**5.** 8	**6.** ⁻0.7

Use the number line to complete.

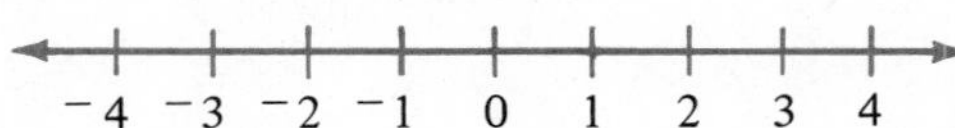

Sample: A move from 0 to 2 is __?__ units to the __?__.
What you say: A move from 0 to 2 is two units to the right.

7. A move from 0 to 1 is __?__ units to the __?__.
8. A move from 0 to ⁻3 is __?__ units to the __?__.
9. A move from 1 to ⁻3 is __?__ units to the __?__.
10. A move from ⁻3 to 1 is __?__ units to the __?__.
11. A move from ⁻$2\frac{1}{2}$ to 0 is __?__ units to the __?__.
12. A move from ⁻4 to 0 is __?__ units to the __?__.

Written EXERCISES

Make a number line sketch to show the moves. Tell where you finish.

Sample: Start at 0. Move 2 units in the positive direction. Then move 3 units in the negative direction.

Solution:

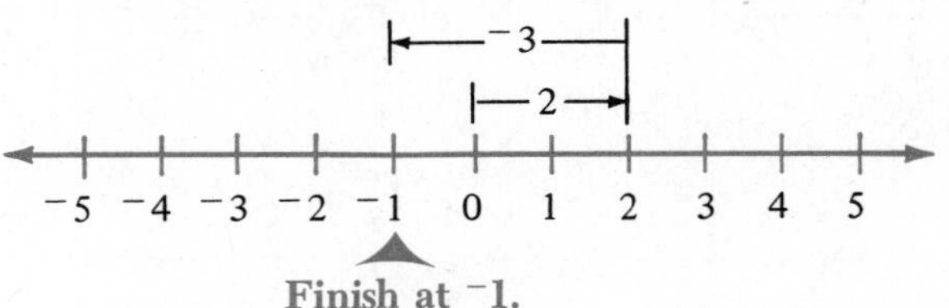

A

1. Start at 0. Move 4 units in the positive direction. Then move 2 units in the negative direction.
2. Start at 0. Move 5 units in the positive direction. Then move 4 units in the negative direction.
3. Start at 0. Move 5 units in the negative direction. Then move 4 units in the positive direction.
4. Start at 0. Move 4 units in the negative direction. Then move 3 units in the positive direction.
5. Start at 0. Move $4\frac{1}{2}$ units in the positive direction. Then move $4\frac{1}{2}$ units in the negative direction.
6. Start at 0. Move $2\frac{1}{3}$ units in the negative direction. Then move $2\frac{1}{3}$ units in the positive direction.

Name the directed number suggested by the arrow.

Sample:

−4 −3 −2 −1 0 1 2 3 4

Solution: −4

7.

−4 −3 −2 −1 0 1 2 3 4

8.

−4 −3 −2 −1 0 1 2 3 4

9.

−4 −3 −2 −1 0 1 2 3 4

10. 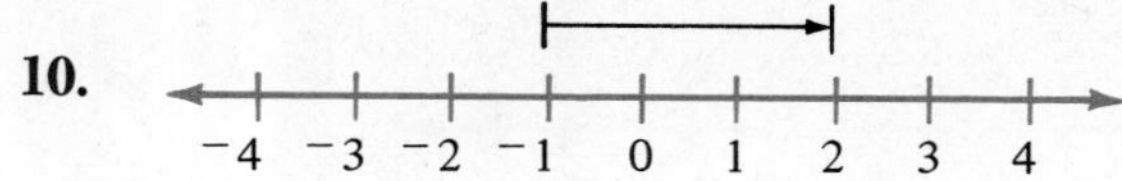

11. 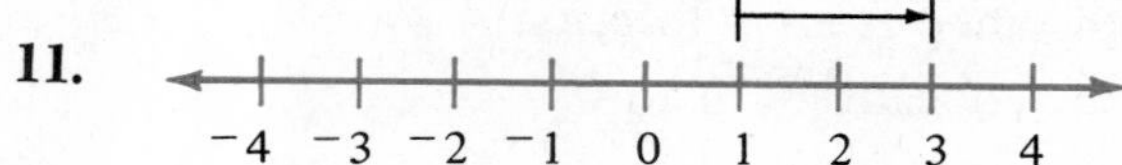

12. ⁻40 ⁻30 ⁻20 ⁻10 0 10 20 30 40

The statement refers to moves on the number line. Make a number line sketch and tell where you finish.

Sample: Start at 4 and move 6 units in the negative direction.

Solution:

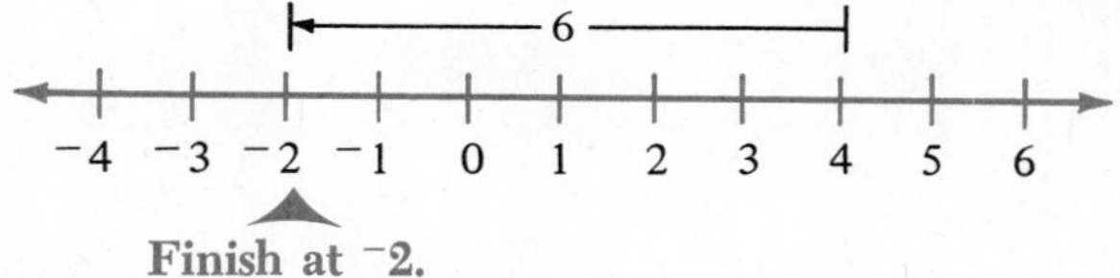

13. Start at 3 and move 4 units in the negative direction.
14. Start at ⁻2 and move 5 units in the positive direction.
15. Start at ⁻3 and move 4 units in the positive direction.
16. Start at 2 and move 5 units in the negative direction.
17. Start at $2\frac{1}{2}$ and move $2\frac{1}{2}$ units in the negative direction.
18. Start at ⁻5 and move 5 units in the positive direction.
19. Start at ⁻3. Move 4 units in the positive direction. Then move 3 units in the negative direction. B
20. Start at 2. Move 3 units in the negative direction. Then move 4 units in the positive direction.

Complete. Use *positive* or *negative*.

21. A move from 4 to 3 is in the __?__ direction.
22. A move from 3 to 5 is in the __?__ direction.
23. A move from ⁻3 to ⁻6 is in the __?__ direction.
24. A move from ⁻5 to ⁻1 is in the __?__ direction.
25. A move from 0 to ⁻4 is in the __?__ direction.
26. A move from 0 to 4 is in the __?__ direction.

C Name the point described.

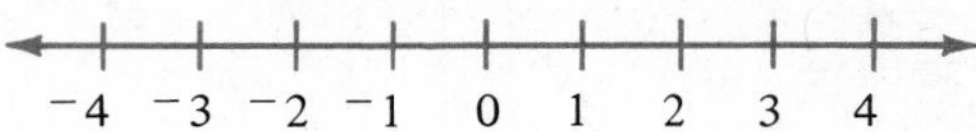

27. The point half the distance from 2 to 4.
28. The point half the distance from $^-4$ to 0.
29. The point half the distance from $^-3$ to 3.
30. The point one-fifth the distance from $^-1$ to 4.
31. The point one-third the distance from $^-2$ to 4.
32. The point one-fourth the distance from 4 to $^-4$.
33. The point half the distance from 2 to $^-2$.
34. The point one-third the distance from 0 to $^-1$.
35. The point one-fourth the distance from $^-4$ to 0.
36. The point half the distance from $^-1$ to $^-2$.

Time out

Do you know how a camera works? Cut off one end of a cracker box and cover it tightly with tissue paper. Center a pinhole in the closed end of the box. Move the box into a dark room. Place a lighted candle one meter before the pinhole. Observe the tissue paper. What image do you see? Can you explain the image with a diagram?

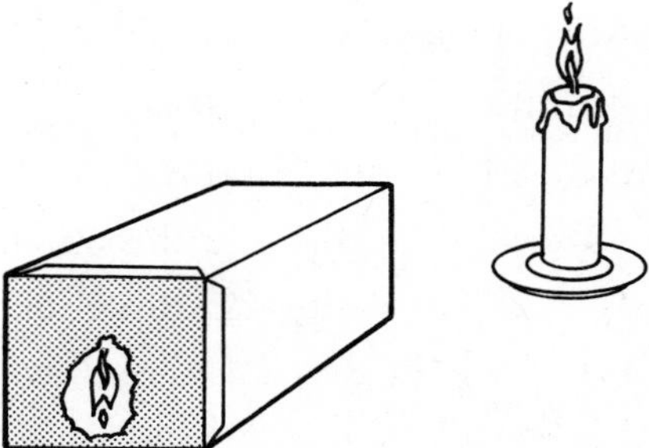

8-3 *Comparing Directed Numbers*

OBJECTIVE
Classify inequality statements as true or false.

We use the symbols $<$, $>$, and $=$, as well as $\leq$, $\geq$, and $\neq$ to compare numbers.

Symbol	*Meaning*	*Symbol*	*Meaning*
$=$	is equal to	$\neq$	is not equal to
$<$	is less than	$\leq$	is less than or equal to
$>$	is greater than	$\geq$	is greater than or equal to

We can use the number line to check the truth of statements that contain these symbols.

EXAMPLE 1 Is $^-2 < 4$ a true statement?

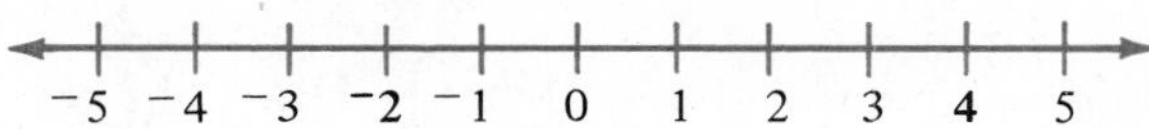

$^-2$ **is to the left** of 4. ► $^-2$ **is less than** 4.
$^-2 < 4$ is a true statement.

EXAMPLE 2 Is $^-1 \geq {^-3}$ a true statement?

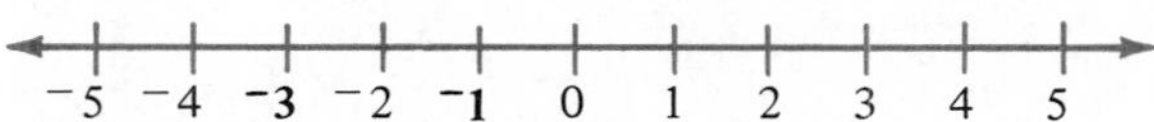

$^-1$ **is to the right of** $^-3$. ► $^-1$ **is greater than** $^-3$.
$^-1 \geq {^-3}$ is a true statement.

EXAMPLE 3 Is $^-3 > 2$ a true statement?

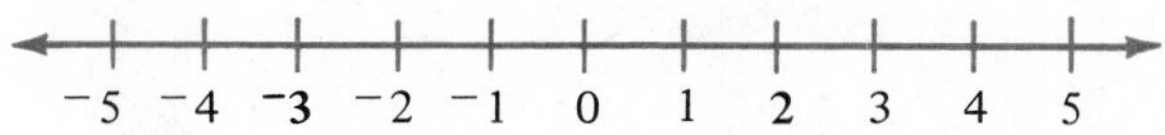

$^-3$ **is to the left of** 2 ► $^-3$ **is less than** 2.
$^-3 > 2$ is a false statement. But these statements are true:

$^-3 < 2$ $\quad$ $^-3 \leq 2$ $\quad$ $^-3 \neq 2$ $\quad$ $2 > {^-3}$

Oral EXERCISES

Complete to make a true statement. Use *right* or *left* and $>$ or $<$.

Sample: 4 is to the __?__ of $^{-}2$; 4 __?__ $^{-}2$.

What you say: 4 is to the right of $^{-}2$; $4 > {}^{-}2$.

1. $1\frac{2}{3}$ is to the __?__ of 0; $1\frac{2}{3}$ __?__ 0.
2. $^{-}8.5$ is to the __?__ of $^{-}8$; $^{-}8.5$ __?__ $^{-}8$.
3. $^{-}5\frac{1}{3}$ is to the __?__ of $^{-}6$; $^{-}5\frac{1}{3}$ __?__ $^{-}6$.
4. 10 is to the __?__ of 0; 10 __?__ 0.
5. 15 is to the __?__ of $^{-}15$; 15 __?__ $^{-}15$.
6. $^{-}12$ is to the __?__ of 2; $^{-}12$ __?__ 2.
7. 5.6 is to the __?__ of 5; 5.6 __?__ 5.
8. $^{-}2$ is to the __?__ of 3; $^{-}2$ __?__ 3.
9. $^{-}2$ is to the __?__ of $^{-}3$; $^{-}2$ __?__ $^{-}3$.
10. $^{-}9.4$ is to the __?__ of 9; $^{-}9.4$ __?__ 9.

Written EXERCISES

Complete to make a true statement. Use right or left and $>$ or $<$.

Sample: $^{-}5$ is to the __?__ of $^{-}4$; so $^{-}5$ __?__ $^{-}4$.

Solution: $^{-}5$ is to the left of $^{-}4$, so $^{-}5 < {}^{-}4$.

A

1. 3 is to the __?__ of $^{-}3$, so 3 __?__ $^{-}3$.
2. $^{-}5$ is to the __?__ of $^{-}6$, so $^{-}5$ __?__ $^{-}6$.
3. $^{-}1$ is to the __?__ of 2; so $^{-}1$ __?__ 2.
4. 2 is to the __?__ of 4, so 2 __?__ 4.
5. $^{-}\frac{1}{2}$ is to the __?__ of 0, so $^{-}\frac{1}{2}$ __?__ 0.
6. $\frac{1}{2}$ is to the __?__ of $^{-}10\frac{1}{2}$, so $\frac{1}{2}$ __?__ $^{-}10\frac{1}{2}$.

Complete to make a true statement. Use $>$ or $<$.

7. 1 __?__ $^{-}1$
8. $^{-}6$ __?__ 6
9. $^{-}6$ __?__ $^{-}5$
10. 4 __?__ 8
11. $^{-}8$ __?__ $^{-}10$
12. 3 __?__ $^{-}4$
13. 0 __?__ $^{-}7$
14. $\frac{1}{2}$ __?__ 0

15. $0 \ \underline{?} \ {}^{-}\frac{1}{5}$

16. ${}^{-}0.02 \ \underline{?} \ 0.002$

17. $4.67 \ \underline{?} \ {}^{-}4.68$

18. ${}^{-}2.32 \ \underline{?} \ {}^{-}2.31$

19. $\frac{1}{3} \ \underline{?} \ {}^{-}\frac{2}{3}$

20. ${}^{-}\frac{3}{4} \ \underline{?} \ \frac{1}{4}$

21. ${}^{-}\frac{5}{6} \ \underline{?} \ 0$

B

True or false?

22. $6 > 12$

23. ${}^{-}2 > {}^{-}5$

24. ${}^{-}6 \leq 6$

25. ${}^{-}0.5 \geq 1.0$

26. ${}^{-}5 \neq 5$

27. $0 > {}^{-}20$

28. ${}^{-}\frac{5}{6} \geq \frac{10}{12}$

29. $5 \leq 6$

30. $1.5 \leq 1.0$

31. ${}^{-}1.5 \leq {}^{-}1.0$

32. $0.0001 < {}^{-}0.0006$

33. ${}^{-}5.003 > {}^{-}5.004$

34. $0 \leq 0.0007$

35. $\pi \leq {}^{-}\pi$

36. $2 < {}^{-}3$

C

Tell which statements are true and which are false, if A, B, C, W, X, Y, and Z are directed numbers. Use the number line below.

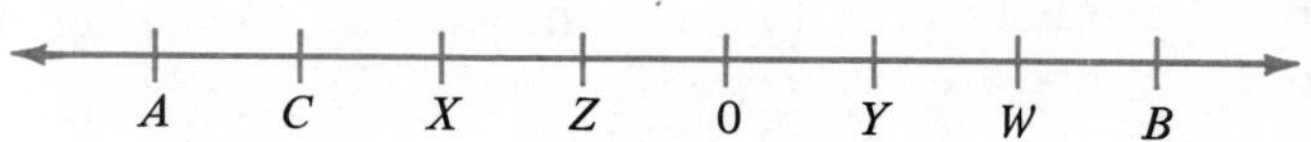

37. Y is a positive number

38. A is a positive number.

39. $Y < B$

40. Z is a negative number.

41. $B \geq A$

42. $Y \geq 0$

calculator corner

Did you know that you can find out someone's age and the amount of change up to \$1 that is in that person's pocket by using a calculator? Hand a calculator to a friend whom you've either just met or haven't seen for a while. Claim that you have a magic calculator that can electronically scan to find unknown facts about people. Give these directions: "Take the number that is double your age. Add 5. Multiply by 50. Add the whole number that represents the amount of change in your pocket, up to \$1. Subtract the number of days in a year. Add 115. Divide by 100." The display will show your friend's age plus the amount of change.

SELF-TEST 1

Be sure that you understand these terms.

origin (p. 212)	opposites (p. 212)
magnitude (p. 212)	directed numbers (p. 212)

Section 8-1, p. 212 Use a directed number to express the following.

1. 2 degrees above zero

2. 5 degrees below zero

3. The positive number 3 units from zero

4. The negative number 5 units from zero

Section 8-2, p. 216 Make a number line sketch to show the moves. Tell where you finish.

5. Start at 0. Move 3 units in the negative direction. Then move 5 units in the positive direction.

6. Start at $^-4$ and move 3 units in the positive direction.

Section 8-3, p. 221 Complete to make a true statement. Use *right* or *left* and $>$ or $<$.

7. 5 is to the __?__ of $^-1$, so 5 __?__ $^-1$.

8. $^-3$ is to the __?__ of $^-4$, so $^-3$ __?__ $^-4$.

True or false?

9. $^-2 < 2$ **10.** $0 < {}^-3$ **11.** $^-1 < {}^-2$

Check your answers with those printed at the back of the book.

8-4 *Integers as Solutions of Inequalities*

OBJECTIVES

Solve an inequality that has a set of integers as its replacement set.

Graph the solution set of an inequality for which the solutions are integers.

Recall that the integers are directed numbers that are either whole numbers or their opposites. Using members of {the integers}, we can now solve an inequality like $x < 1$.

EXAMPLE 1 $x < 1$; replacement set: $\{^-2, ^-1, 0, 1, 2\}$

Replacement	$x < 1$	*True/False*	*Solution?*
$^-2$	$^-2 < 1$	True	YES
$^-1$	$^-1 < 1$	True	YES
0	$0 < 1$	True	YES
1	$1 < 1$	False	No
2	$2 < 1$	False	No

The solutions are $^-2$, $^-1$, and 0. Solution set: $\{^-2, ^-1, 0\}$

Graph:

$^-4$ $^-3$ $^-2$ $^-1$ 0 1 2

EXAMPLE 2 $x \leq 2$; replacement set: $\{^-2, 0, 2, 4\}$

Replacement	$x \leq 2$	*True/False*	*Solution?*
$^-2$	$^-2 \leq 2$	True	YES
0	$0 \leq 2$	True	YES
2	$2 \leq 2$	True	YES
4	$4 \leq 2$	False	No

The solutions are $^-2$, 0, and 2. Solution set: $\{^-2, 0, 2\}$

Graph:

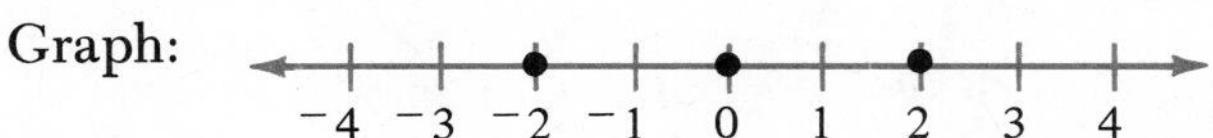

Name the set of directed numbers graphed.

Sample: 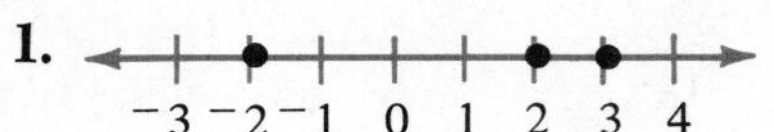

What you say: $\{^{-}1, 0, 1\}$

1. $^{-}3$ $^{-}2$ $^{-}1$ 0 1 2 3 4
2. $^{-}3$ $^{-}2$ $^{-}1$ 0 1 2 3 4
3. $^{-}3$ $^{-}2$ $^{-}1$ 0 1 2 3 4
4. $^{-}3$ $^{-}2$ $^{-}1$ 0 1 2 3 4
5. $^{-}3$ $^{-}2$ $^{-}1$ 0 1 2 3 4
6. $^{-}3$ $^{-}2$ $^{-}1$ 0 1 2 3 4

True, false, or neither?

7. $6 > {^{-}3}$ **8.** ${^{-}6} < {^{-}4}$ **9.** ${^{-}6} > x$

10. $5 \geq {^{-}5}$ **11.** $x < {^{-}5}$ **12.** $k \leq 7$

Written EXERCISES

Show whether a true or a false statement results when the variable in the sentence is replaced by each member of the replacement set. Then state the solution set.

Sample: $n \geq {^{-}4}$: $\{^{-}6, ^{-}8, 0, 2\}$

Solution: ${^{-}6} \geq {^{-}4}$, false; ${^{-}8} \geq {^{-}4}$, false;
$0 \geq {^{-}4}$, true; $2 \geq {^{-}4}$, true
Solution set: $\{0, 2\}$

A

1. $a > {^{-}2}$: $\{^{-}3, ^{-}1, 0\}$ **2.** $z < 3$: $\{0, 1, 3, 4\}$

3. ${^{-}4} < x$: $\{^{-}6, 0, 5\}$ **4.** $y \geq 5$: $\{^{-}5, 0, 5, 6\}$

5. $w \leq 0$: $\{^{-}3, ^{-}2, 0, 1\}$ **6.** ${^{-}7} \geq z$: $\{^{-}8, ^{-}7, 6\}$

7. $k \geq {^{-}\frac{1}{2}}$: $\{^{-}1, ^{-}2, 0\}$ **8.** $m \leq {^{-}2\frac{1}{3}}$: $\{^{-}4, ^{-}3, 0\}$

9. $\frac{1}{2} \geq n$: $\{1, 2, 3\}$ **10.** $7 \geq t$: $\{^{-}3, 0, 9, 12\}$

11. $0 \leq s$: $\{^{-}1, 0, 1, 2\}$ **12.** $c \leq 1$: $\{^{-}4, ^{-}2, 0, 2, 4\}$

Write and graph the solution set. The replacement set is $\{^{-}3, ^{-}2, ^{-}1, 0, 1, 2, 3\}$.

Sample: $x \geq {^{-}2}$ *Solution:* $\{^{-}1, 0, 1, 2, 3\}$

13. $s < 2$ **14.** $y \leq 3$ **15.** $2.5 > s$

16. $n \le {}^{-}3$

17. $r \ge 1$

18. $\frac{1}{2} > a$

19. ${}^{-}2 \ge t$

20. ${}^{-}3.2 < m$

21. $0 \ge w$

22. $0 \le d$

23. $s \ge 0.4$

24. $2 \le v$

B

Write the solution set. Use the designated replacement set.

25. $3.5 > x$: $\{4, 3.6, 3.4, 2.0\}$

26. $y > {}^{-}0.005$: $\{0.002, 0.004, {}^{-}0.002\}$

27. ${}^{-}2.3 > t$: $\{{}^{-}2.1, {}^{-}2.0, {}^{-}3.6\}$

28. ${}^{-}\frac{2}{3} \le p$: $\left\{\frac{2}{3}, {}^{-}\frac{2}{3}, \frac{1}{3}\right\}$

C

29. $w \ge {}^{-}4.8$: $\{5.0, {}^{-}5.3, {}^{-}3.2, 2.0\}$

30. $4.6 < s$: $\{0, 2.4, 4.7, 4.9\}$

31. ${}^{-}\frac{5}{6} < n$: $\left\{{}^{-}1, {}^{-}\frac{4}{6}, \frac{5}{6}, 0\right\}$

32. ${}^{-}\frac{3}{4} \le r$: $\left\{{}^{-}1\frac{1}{2}, {}^{-}1, {}^{-}\frac{1}{4}, 0, \frac{1}{4}, \frac{1}{2}\right\}$

Charlotte Angas Scott 1858–1931

Charlotte Scott studied mathematics at Cambridge University in England. As a woman, she was admitted informally to the examinations, in which she attained the equivalent of eighth place in mathematics. She received a doctorate of science from the University of London in 1885. She was later called to Bryn Mawr, Pennsylvania to help establish the mathematics programs at Bryn Mawr College. She continued to direct these programs for forty years. Charlotte Scott published a mathematical text as well as thirty papers in American and European journals and contributed greatly to the development of algebraic geometry.

8-5 *Graphing Inequalities*

OBJECTIVE
Graph an inequality for which the replacement set is {the directed numbers}

Now let's consider inequalities for which the replacement set is {the directed numbers}. We can graph the solution sets on the number line. The graph of an inequality is the graph of its solution set.

EXAMPLE 1 $x > \frac{1}{2}$; replacement set: {the directed numbers}

The inequality is true when x is any number greater than $\frac{1}{2}$.

Solution set: $\left\{\text{the directed numbers greater than } \frac{1}{2}\right\}$

Graph: 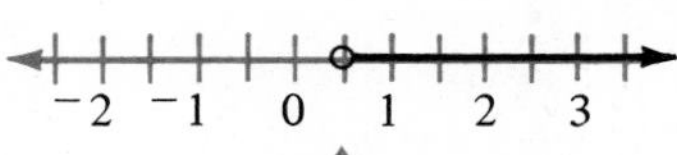

Note the hollow dot.
$\frac{1}{2}$ is not included.

EXAMPLE 2 $m \leq {}^-1$; replacement set: {the directed numbers}
The inequality is true when m is ⁻1 or any number less than ⁻1.

Solution set: {⁻1 and the directed numbers less than ⁻1}

Graph: 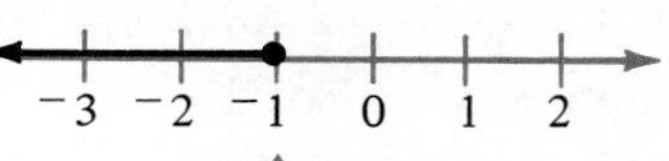

Note the solid dot.
⁻1 is included.

The double inequality ${}^-2 < x < 3$ means that x can be any number between ⁻2 and 3. On the number line:

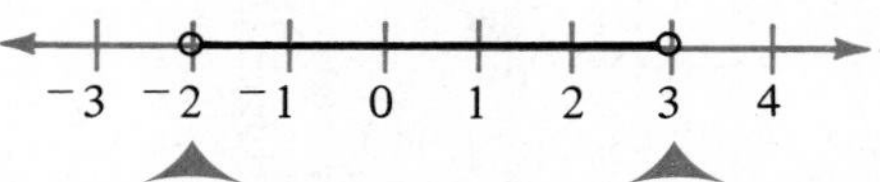

Note the hollow dots at ⁻2 and 3.

EXAMPLE 3 $^-1 < n < 2\frac{1}{2}$; replacement set: {the directed numbers}
The inequality is true when n is any number that is greater than $^-1$ and less than $2\frac{1}{2}$.

Solution set: {the directed numbers between $^-1$ and $2\frac{1}{2}$}.

Graph:

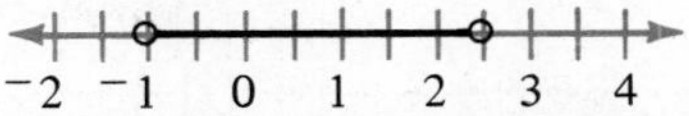

−2 −1 0 1 2 3 4

Oral EXERCISES

Tell what the inequality means.

Sample 1: $t > {}^-6$ *What you say:* t is any number greater than $^-6$.

Sample 2: $^-6 \le x < {}^-4$

What you say: x is either $^-6$ or a number between $^-6$ and $^-4$.

1. $a > 2$
2. $c < {}^-4$
3. $s > {}^-\frac{2}{3}$
4. $t \le \frac{1}{8}$
5. $^-7 \ge z$
6. $4 \le b$
7. $^-4 \le z < {}^-2$
8. $^-\frac{3}{4} < a \le 0$
9. $^-3 \le x < 0$

Match each inequality with its graph. The replacement set is {the directed numbers}.

10. $a > {}^-\frac{1}{4}$
11. $x \le 1$
12. $y > {}^-\frac{2}{3}$
13. $^-2 < r < 2$

A. 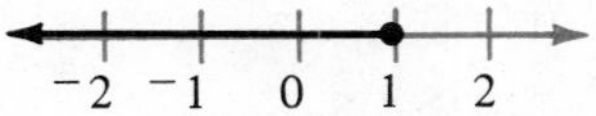 −2 −1 0 1 2

B. 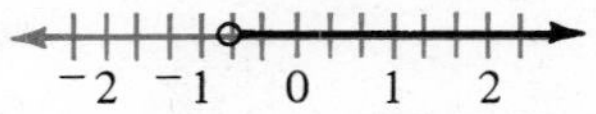 −2 −1 0 1 2

C. 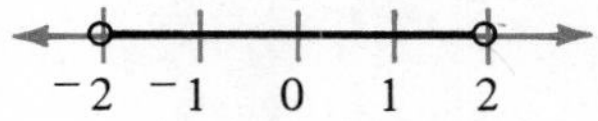 −2 −1 0 1 2

D. 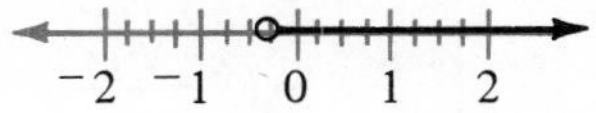 −2 −1 0 1 2

Written EXERCISES

A

Graph.

Sample: {the directed numbers less than 3}

Solution:

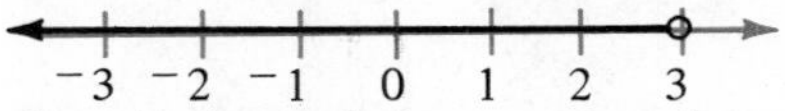

−3 −2 −1 0 1 2 3

1. {the directed numbers greater than $^-3$}
2. {the directed numbers greater than 0}
3. {the directed numbers less than $^-2$}

4. {the directed numbers less than 4}

5. {the directed numbers greater than or equal to $^-3$}

6. {the directed numbers between $^-2$ and 0}

Name the set of directed numbers graphed.

Sample 1: 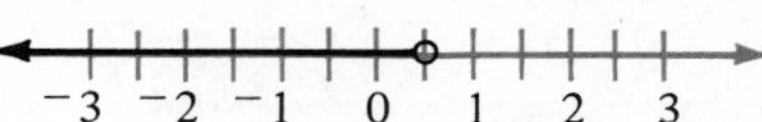

Solution: $\left\{\text{the directed numbers less than } \frac{1}{2}\right\}$

Sample 2: 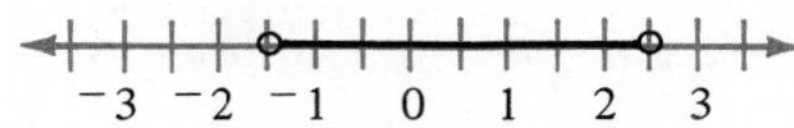

Solution: {the directed numbers between $^-1\frac{1}{2}$ and $2\frac{1}{2}$}

7. −1 0 1 2 3

8. 

9. −2 −1 0 1 2

10. 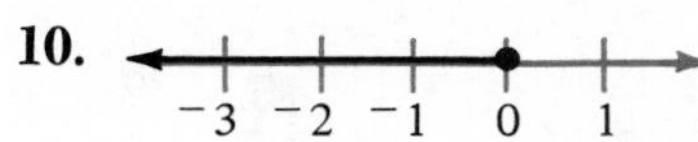

11. −15 −10 −5 0 5

12. −2 0 2 4 6

13. −5 0 5 10 15

14. −3 −2 −1 0 1

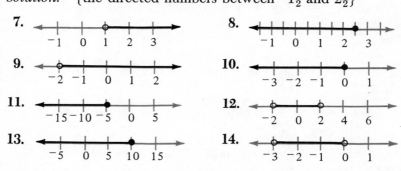

Name and graph the solution set. The replacement set is {the directed numbers}.

B

15. $y > {}^-2$

16. $3 < x$

17. $t \leq 0$

18. $m \geq {}^-1$

19. $b \leq 3$

20. $^-2 < z < 0$

21. $0 \leq x < 1$

22. $^-3 < n \leq 4$

Name the solution set. The replacement set is {the directed numbers}.

C

23. $^-3 > s \geq {}^-8$

24. $0 \leq n \leq 2\frac{1}{3}$

25. $^-5 \geq x > {}^-10$

26. $k \geq \left(\frac{1}{3} + 1\frac{2}{3}\right)$

27. $^-5.6 < p + 1 < {}^-3.2$

28. $^-2.6 < a < 1.2$

29. $y \neq 6\left(\frac{1}{3} + \frac{1}{2}\right)$

30. $^-0.0005 \leq t \leq 0$

31. $0 < z + 2 \leq {}^-6$

32. $^-5(5 - 2) \geq s$

SELF-TEST 2

Be sure that you understand these terms.

integers (p. 225) graph of an inequality (p. 228)

Write the solution set. The replacement set is $\{^{-}1, 0, 1\}$. Section 8-4, p. 225

1. $m > 0$ 2. $n \leq 3$ 3. $^{-}2 \leq t$ 4. $^{-}3 < z$

Name and graph the solution set. The replacement set is {the set of directed numbers}. Section 8-5, p. 228

5. $r < 2$ 6. $b > 1$ 7. $x \geq {^{-}3}$ 8. $^{-}2 < c < {^{-}1}$

Check your answers with those printed at the back of the book.

chapter summary

1. The point to which 0 is assigned on the number line is called the **origin.**
2. The distance between 0 and any number is called the **magnitude** of the number.
3. Arrows may be used with the number line to represent directed numbers.

   For $^{-}3$, the arrow points to the left and is three units in length. For 2, the arrow points to the right and is two units in length.
4. One directed number **is greater than** another if it lies to the **right** of it on the number line. One directed number **is less than** another if it lies to the **left** of it on the number line.
5. The graph of a set of directed numbers like the following can be shown on the number line.

   Graph of $\{^{-}1, 0, 1, 2\}$:

   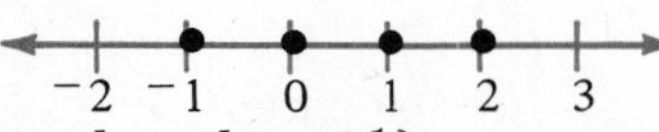

   Graph of {directed numbers less than $1\frac{1}{2}$}:

chapter test

Name the directed number described.

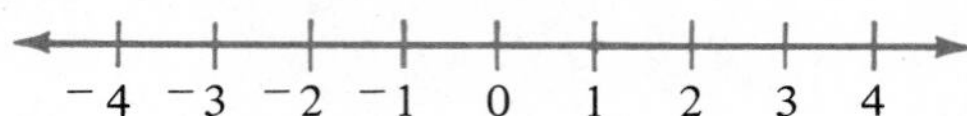

1. 1 unit to the right of 0
2. 2 units to the left of 0
3. the negative number of magnitude 4
4. the positive number 8 units from 0

The statement refers to moves on the number line. Make a sketch and tell where you finish.

5. Start at 0. Move 1 unit in the positive direction. Then move 4 units in the negative direction.
6. Start at 0. Move 3 units in the negative direction. Then move 2 units in the positive direction.
7. Start at $^{-}4$ and move 5 units in the positive direction.

Complete. Use right or left and $>$ or $<$.

8. 3 is to the __?__ of 0, so 3 __?__ 0.
9. $^{-}3$ is to the __?__ of $^{-}4$, so $^{-}3$ __?__ $^{-}4$.

Show whether a true or a false statement results when the variable is replaced by each member of the replacement set. Then state the solution set.

10. $y < {}^{-}2$; $\{{}^{-}3, {}^{-}2, {}^{-}1, 0\}$
11. $x > 5$; $\{4, 5, 6, 7\}$

Graph.

12. {the directed numbers less than 2}
13. {the directed numbers between $^{-}3$ and 1}

Name the solution set. The replacement set is {the directed numbers}.

14. $x < {}^{-}1$
15. $y \geq {}^{-}2$
16. $t > 3$
17. $0 < n < 3$

challenge topics

Logic and Inductive Reasoning

Suppose you observe a pattern that occurs consistently, or see some event take place repeatedly. If you draw some general conclusion from what you have experienced, we say you have used **inductive reasoning.**

Inductive reasoning helps us make "educated guesses" about many things. For example, you might observe mosquitoes biting people. If you could tell that all the mosquitoes were female, you might generalize that "only female mosquitoes bite." Although this generalization seems sensible, we would need to make further observations to be certain. However, if even one male mosquito bites a person, the conclusion is contradicted. Such a contradiction is called a **counterexample.**

Consider the illustration and conclusion. Then either agree with the conclusion or cite at least one counterexample.

1.

Conclusion: All vehicles have at least four wheels.

2. $\begin{array}{r} 15 \\ +\ 7 \\ \hline 22 \end{array}$ $\quad \begin{array}{r} 101 \\ +\ 35 \\ \hline 136 \end{array}$ $\quad \begin{array}{r} 17 \\ 19 \\ \hline 36 \end{array}$

Conclusion: The sum of any two odd numbers is an even number.

3. $\frac{1}{9} = 0.1111\ldots$

$\frac{2}{9} = 0.2222\ldots$

$\frac{3}{9} = 0.3333\ldots$

Conclusion: $\frac{7}{9} = 0.7777\ldots$

4. $1 = 1^2$

$1 + 3 = 2^2$

$1 + 3 + 5 = 3^2$

$1 + 3 + 5 + 7 = 4^2$

Conclusion: The sum of the first ten odd numbers is 10^2.

REVIEW OF SKILLS

Name the opposite of the number or expression.

1. rise **2.** forward **3.** north

4. $^{-}6$ **5.** 0 **6.** 4

Think of moves along a number line. Tell which move you would make to have the indicated result.

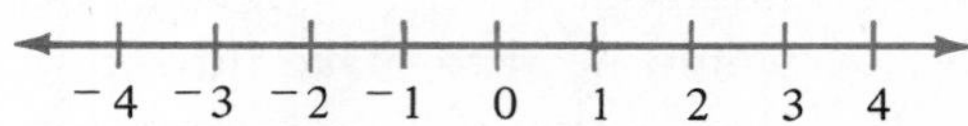

7. What move would you make after a move of $^{-}3$ to have as an end result no change (0)?

8. What move would you make after a move of 6, to have as an end result no change?

9. What move would you make after a move of $^{-}1$, to have as an end result no change?

Simplify.

10. $3 + 6$ **11.** $16 - 6 + 5$ **12.** $x + (5 - 5)$

13. $x + (3 - 2)$ **14.** $(x + 3) - 2$ **15.** $r + 14 - 6$

16. $(6 + 8) - 5$ **17.** $6 + (8 - 5)$ **18.** $6 + 7 - 4 + 5$

Try to determine a value of k that will make the statement true.

19. $k = 3 + 8$ **20.** $5 + k = 3$ **21.** $18 - k = 5$

Complete the set of number pairs according to the given function rule.

22. $f(z) = z + 3$: {(1, 4), (0, 3), (4, __?__), (__?__, 6), (15, __?__)}

23. $f(y) = y - 5$: {(5, 0), (9, 4), (7, __?__), (__?__, 6), (__?__, 8)}

Left: *Weaver using hand loom, 1914.*

Right: *Technician developing pattern by computer. The computer controls the knitting machine shown.*

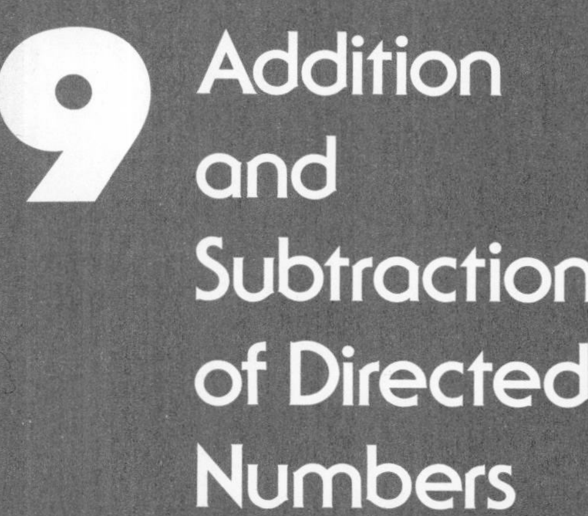

9 Addition and Subtraction of Directed Numbers

9-1 *Adding Directed Numbers on the Number Line*

OBJECTIVE
Use the number line to find sums of directed numbers.

Addition of directed numbers is easy to understand on the number line.

EXAMPLE 1 $4 + 3 = \underline{\ ?\ }$

Begin at 0.

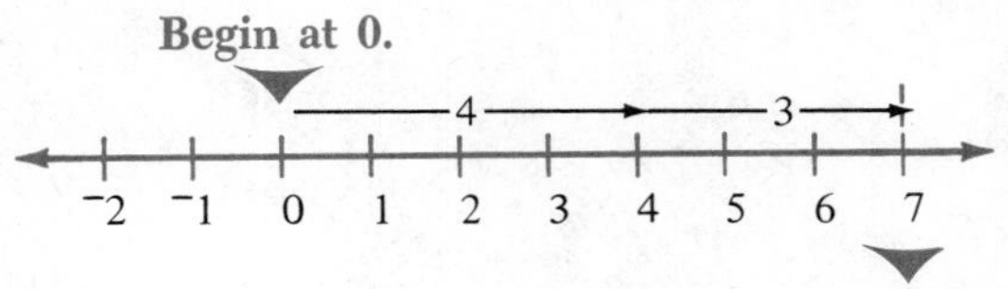

Finish at 7. ► $4 + 3 = 7$

EXAMPLE 2 $^{-}3 + {}^{-}2 = \underline{\ ?\ }$

Begin at 0.

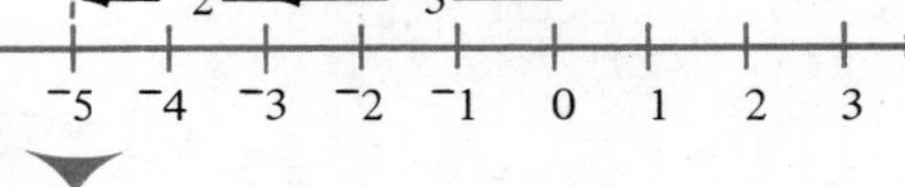

Finish at ⁻5. ► $^{-}3 + {}^{-}2 = {}^{-}5$

EXAMPLE 3 $5 + {}^{-}3 = \underline{\ ?\ }$

Begin at 0.

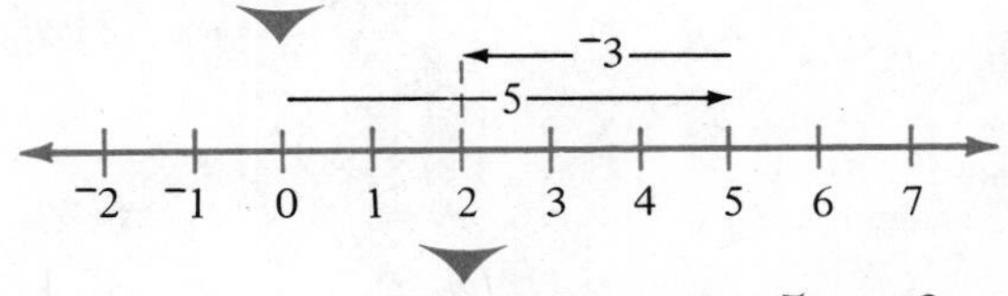

Finish at 2. ► $5 + {}^{-}3 = 2$

EXAMPLE 4 $^{-}3 + 5 = \underline{\ ?\ }$

Begin at 0.

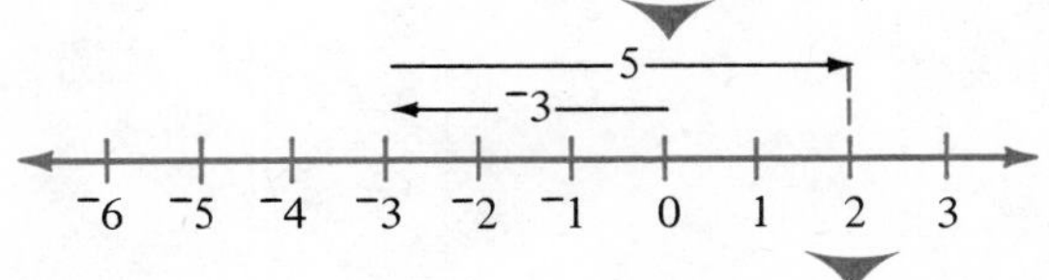

Finish at 2. ► $^{-}3 + 5 = 2$

Name the equation suggested.

Sample:

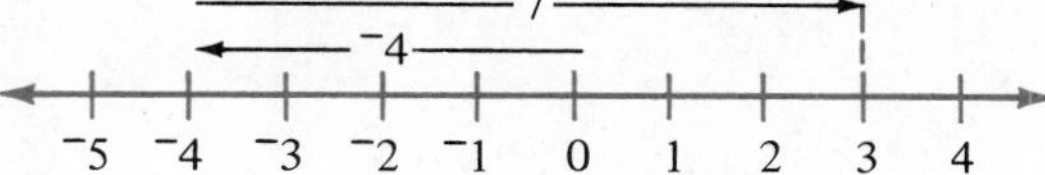

What you say: $^-4 + 7 = 3$

1.

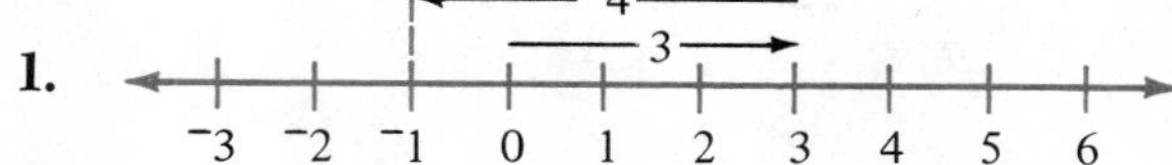

2. $^-30$; 15; $^-20$ $^-15$ $^-10$ $^-5$ 0 5 10 15 20 25

3. $4\frac{1}{2}$; $^-5$; $^-7$ $^-6$ $^-5$ $^-4$ $^-3$ $^-2$ $^-1$ 0 1 2

4. 3; $^-3$; $^-6$ $^-5$ $^-4$ $^-3$ $^-2$ $^-1$ 0 1 2 3

5. $^-2$; 4; $^-3$ $^-2$ $^-1$ 0 1 2 3 4 5 6

Written
EXERCISES

Sketch a number line solution. Complete the equation to make a true statement.

Sample: $^-1 + 2 =$?

Solution:

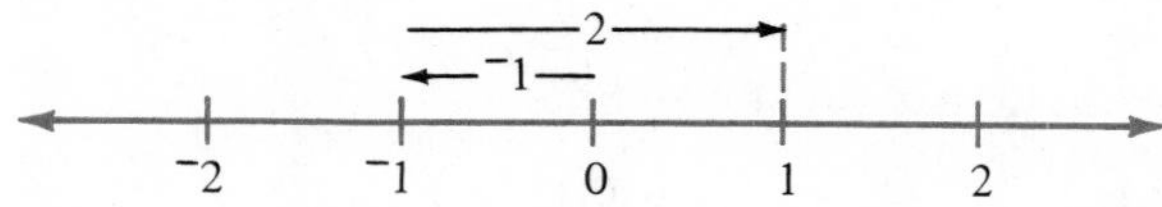

A

1. $^-2 + 4 =$? **2.** $3 + 2 =$?

3. ? $= 6 + {}^-3$ **4.** ? $= 4\frac{1}{2} + {}^-2\frac{1}{2}$

5. $6 + {}^-4 =$? **6.** $7\frac{1}{2} + 3\frac{1}{2} =$?

Tell whether the expression names a positive number, a negative number, or 0. Then simplify. Use the number line for help if necessary.

7. $2 + 3$

8. $1 + 6$

9. $^{-}16 + 6$

10. $15 + {}^{-}9$

11. $15 + {}^{-}25$

12. $^{-}8 + 10$

13. $^{-}12 + 12$

14. $8 + {}^{-}4$

15. $^{-}8 + 4$

16. $^{-}3 + {}^{-}8$

17. $16 + {}^{-}6$

18. $^{-}20 + 21$

Copy and complete the addition table.

19.

+	2	$^{-}4$	6	$^{-}8$
2	?	?	?	?
$^{-}4$	?	?	?	?
6	?	?	?	?
$^{-}8$	?	?	?	?

20.

+	3	$^{-}3$	5	$^{-}7$
3	?	?	?	?
$^{-}3$	?	?	?	?
5	?	?	?	?
$^{-}7$	?	?	?	?

Find the sum.

B **21.** $^{-}2\frac{1}{3} + 2$

22. $5\frac{1}{4} + \dfrac{3}{4}$

23. $^{-}6\frac{1}{2} + 7$

24. $8 + {}^{-}4\frac{1}{2}$

25. $^{-}8 + 4\frac{1}{2}$

26. $104\frac{5}{8} + {}^{-}104\frac{5}{8}$

Find the sum.

27. $\begin{array}{r} 10 \\ \underline{^{-}7} \end{array}$

28. $\begin{array}{r} ^{-}20 \\ \underline{18} \end{array}$

29. $\begin{array}{r} ^{-}17 \\ \underline{20} \end{array}$

30. $\begin{array}{r} 12 \\ \underline{^{-}11} \end{array}$

C **31.** $\begin{array}{r} ^{-}58 \\ \underline{16} \end{array}$

32. $\begin{array}{r} ^{-}63 \\ \underline{98} \end{array}$

33. $\begin{array}{r} 143 \\ \underline{^{-}482} \end{array}$

34. $\begin{array}{r} ^{-}897 \\ \underline{897} \end{array}$

Complete to make a true statement.

Sample: $8 = 10 + \underline{\ ?\ }$ *Solution:* $8 = 10 + {}^{-}2$

35. $16 = 11 + \underline{\ ?\ }$

36. $^{-}8 = 8 + \underline{\ ?\ }$

37. $12 = {}^{-}16 + \underline{\ ?\ }$

38. $7 + \underline{\ ?\ } = {}^{-}2$

39. $6 = 12 + \underline{\ ?\ }$

40. $^{-}9 + \underline{\ ?\ } = 18$

Problems

Express the problem as the sum of two directed numbers. Find the sum and answer the question.

Sample: Twelve students signed up for a cooking class. The first dish they learned to make was coconut-spinach cream puffs. Ten students quit the course. How many are still in the class?

Solution: $12 + {}^{-}10 = \underline{\ ?\ }$

$12 + {}^{-}10 = 2$ ➤ Two students are still in the class.

1. A truck was carrying 31 bales of hay. It hit a pothole in the road and 5 bales fell out. How many bales of hay were left in the truck?
2. Rita had eighty-five cents in change. She put the money in her pocket, which had a small hole in it. A quarter fell out. How much money did she have left?
3. Three hikers are at the top of a cliff 975 meters above sea level. They can see a lake 60 meters directly below them. How many meters above sea level is the lake?

4. Joe won $50 in a public speaking contest. He paid $25 to rent a formal outfit for the award presentation. How much did he have left?
5. An elevator stopped at an insurance company on the twenty-first floor. It then went down sixteen floors, where it stopped at a lawyer's office. On what floor is the lawyer's office?
6. Jack baked 36 chocolate-chip cookies for Marcie's birthday. Marcie ate 5 cookies. How many cookies were left?
7. A pair of denim pants was 90 cm long. It shrank 2 cm when it was washed. How long is it now?
8. A train travels 45 kilometers north. Then it travels 23 kilometers south. How far is the train from its original position?
9. An airplane takes off and climbs to an altitude of 5630 meters. Then it descends 2360 meters. What is the new altitude?

9-2 *Additive Inverses and the Identity Element for Addition*

OBJECTIVES

Simplify expressions like $-(^{-}6)$.

Solve equations like $^{-}8 + 8 = n$, and $0 + {}^{-}10 = x$.

Every directed number has an opposite. Both are the same distance from 0 on the number line, but on opposite sides of 0. Zero is its own opposite. The distance a number is from 0 is called its **magnitude.**

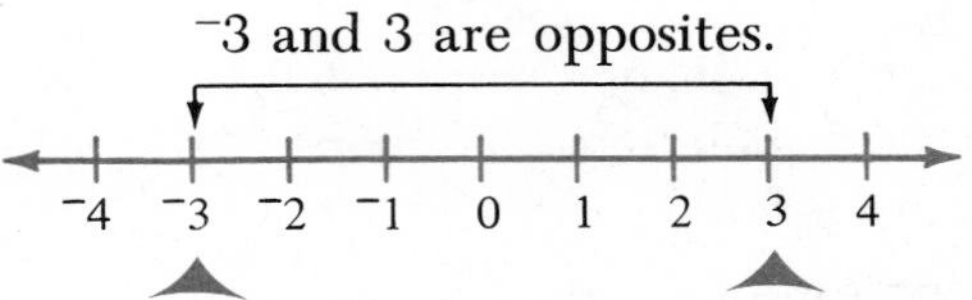

The magnitude of $^{-}3$ is 3. The magnitude of 3 is 3.

You know that the symbol "$-$" in $9 - 7$ means "minus." The same symbol can mean **"the opposite of."** -3 means "the opposite of 3," and $-(^{-}3)$ means "the opposite of $^{-}3$."

EXAMPLE 1 $-(^{-}8)$ means "the opposite of $^{-}8$."
$-(^{-}8) = 8$

EXAMPLE 2 -0.1 means "the opposite of 0.1."
$-0.1 = {}^{-}0.1$

In general, for every directed number m:

If m is positive, then $-m$ is negative;
If m is negative, then $-m$ is positive;
If m is 0, $-m$ is also 0.

The sum of 0 and any directed number is that number.

$$0 + 8 = 8 \qquad {}^{-}3 + 0 = {}^{-}3 \qquad 0 + 0 = 0$$

0 is called the **identity element** for addition.

The sum of any number and its opposite is the identity element, 0.

$$^{-}8 + 8 = 0 \qquad -(^{-}1) + {}^{-}1 = 0$$

The opposite of a number is also called its **additive inverse.**

EXAMPLE 3 $8 + {}^{-}8 = 0$; 8 is the additive inverse of $^{-}8$.
$^{-}8$ is the additive inverse of 8.

Complete to make a true statement.

Sample: 4 is the additive inverse of __?__.

What you say: 4 is the additive inverse of $^{-}4$.

1. $^{-}3$ is the additive inverse of __?__.
2. 3 is the additive inverse of __?__.
3. $10\frac{2}{3}$ is the additive inverse of __?__.
4. 3.4 is the opposite of __?__.
5. __?__ is the additive inverse of $^{-}6\frac{2}{3}$.

Simplify.

Sample: $6 + {}^{-}6$ *What you say:* Zero

6. $40 + {}^{-}40$	**7.** $^{-}32 + 32$	**8.** $\frac{^{-}2}{3} + \frac{2}{3}$
9. $152 + 0$	**10.** $0 + {}^{-}9$	**11.** $\frac{1}{4} + \frac{^{-}1}{4}$

Written EXERCISES

A

Show two ways to express in symbols.

Sample: The opposite of $^{-}2$ *Solution:* $-({}^{-}2)$; 2

1. The opposite of $^{-}4$	**2.** The opposite of $^{-}8$
3. The opposite of 3	**4.** The opposite of 7
5. The opposite of $^{-}16$	**6.** The opposite of $\frac{1}{2}$
7. The opposite of $^{-}3.4$	**8.** The opposite of $\frac{^{-}3}{4}$
9. The opposite of -6.08	**10.** The opposite of $-({}^{-}3)$

Name the two numbers described.

Sample: 2 units from zero on the number line *Solution:* 2, $^{-}2$

11. 5 units from zero on the number line

12. 8 units from zero on the number line

13. 20 units from zero on the number line

14. $3\frac{1}{2}$ units from zero on the number line

15. 5 units from $^{-}5$ on the number line

16. 5 units from 5 on the number line

Tell whether or not the numbers are additive inverses.

17. 8, $^{-}8$ **18.** $^{-}6$, 6 **19.** 0, $^{-}4$

20. 8, 0 **21.** $-(^{-}4)$, 4 **22.** -10, $^{-}10$

23. $-(^{-}7)$, $^{-}7$ **24.** -3.2, 3.2 **25.** $-n$, n

Solve.

Sample: $x = 4 + {^{-}4}$ *Solution:* $x = 4 + {^{-}4}$
$x = 0$

26. $m = {^{-}12} + 12$ **27.** $t = 6 + 0$ **28.** $n = {^{-}3.4} + 3.4$

B **29.** $a + {^{-}3} = 0$ **30.** $4 + b = 0$ **31.** ${^{-}6} + y = {^{-}6}$

32. $8 + x = 8$ **33.** $2\frac{2}{3} + y = 0$ **34.** $s + {^{-}10} = 0$

35. $r + \frac{^{-}2}{3} = 0$ **36.** $t + 0 = \frac{1}{4}$ **37.** $0 = u + {^{-}4}$

38. $c = {^{-}25} + 25$ **39.** $d = {^{-}18} + 18$ **40.** ${^{-}4.8} + m = 0$

Give the meaning. Then write in simplest form.

Sample: -9 *Solution:* The opposite of 9; $^{-}9$

41. $-(^{-}16)$ **42.** -8 **43.** -1.42

44. $-\frac{3}{4}$ **45.** $-(^{-}0.63)$ **46.** -3.4

Simplify.

Sample: $-(-(^{-}1))$ *Solution:* $-(-(^{-}1)) = -(1) = {^{-}1}$

C **47.** $-(^{-}3)$ **48.** $-(-4)$ **49.** $-(-(^{-}3))$

50. $-(^{-}4)$ **51.** $-(-1.3)$ **52.** $-(-(^{-}10))$

9-3 *Simplifying Expressions*

OBJECTIVES

Simplify expressions like $-(3 + 7)$ and $-(-5 + 8)$.

Solve equations like $5 + t = 2$.

The symbol -6 means "the opposite of 6." However, we have seen that $-6 = {}^{-}6$. From now on we will use the symbol -6 for both **negative 6** and **the opposite of 6.** Lowered minus signs will now be used to represent all negative numbers.

Now let's consider the meaning of an expression like $-(3 + 7)$. We will see that the opposite of a sum is the sum of the opposites.

EXAMPLE 1 $-(3 + 7) \stackrel{?}{=} -3 + (-7)$ ◄ $\stackrel{?}{=}$ means "does it equal?"

$$\begin{array}{r|l} -(10) & -10 \\ -10 & -10 \quad \text{Yes} \end{array}$$

EXAMPLE 2 $-(-5 + 8) \stackrel{?}{=} 5 + (-8)$

$$\begin{array}{r|l} -(3) & -3 \\ -3 & -3 \quad \text{Yes} \end{array}$$

EXAMPLE 3 $-[-2 + (-8)] \stackrel{?}{=} 2 + 8$

$$\begin{array}{r|l} -(-10) & 10 \\ 10 & 10 \quad \text{Yes} \end{array}$$

A number line sketch can help us find a solution for an equation like $5 + t = 2$.

EXAMPLE 4 $5 + t = 2$

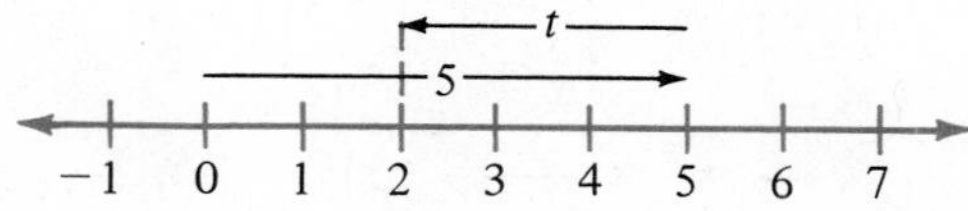

Solution: $t = -3$

EXERCISES

State the expression in two ways.

Sample 1: $-(3 + 6)$ *What you say:* The opposite of 9; the opposite of 3 plus the opposite of 6.

Sample 2: $-(-6 + 3)$ *What you say:* The opposite of -3; the opposite of -6 plus the opposite of 3.

1. $-(4 + 2)$ **2.** $-(6 + 1)$ **3.** $-[4 + (-2)]$

4. $-[5 + (-7)]$ **5.** $-(-8 + 11)$ **6.** $-\left(\frac{1}{2} + \frac{1}{2}\right)$

Name the sum.

7. $\begin{array}{r} -4 \\ \underline{5} \end{array}$ **8.** $\begin{array}{r} 8 \\ \underline{4} \end{array}$ **9.** $\begin{array}{r} 18 \\ \underline{-6} \end{array}$ **10.** $\begin{array}{r} 20 \\ \underline{18} \end{array}$

11. $\begin{array}{r} -8 \\ \underline{-6} \end{array}$ **12.** $\begin{array}{r} -3 \\ \underline{17} \end{array}$ **13.** $\begin{array}{r} -40 \\ \underline{12} \end{array}$ **14.** $\begin{array}{r} -30 \\ \underline{-20} \end{array}$

Written

EXERCISES

Give a simpler name for the expression.

Sample 1: $-(6 + 1)$ *Solution:* $-(6 + 1) = -7$

Sample 2: $-4 + (-2)$ *Solution:* $-4 + (-2) = -6$

A

1. $-(4 + 3)$ **2.** $-(12 + 6)$ **3.** $-(22 + 17)$

4. $-4 + (-8)$ **5.** $-9 + (-7)$ **6.** $-20 + (-1)$

7. $-3.6 + (-4.4)$ **8.** $-\frac{1}{8} + (-2\frac{1}{4})$ **9.** $-(-6 + 7)$

Solve. Use a number line sketch.

Sample: $-4 + t = 1$

Solution:

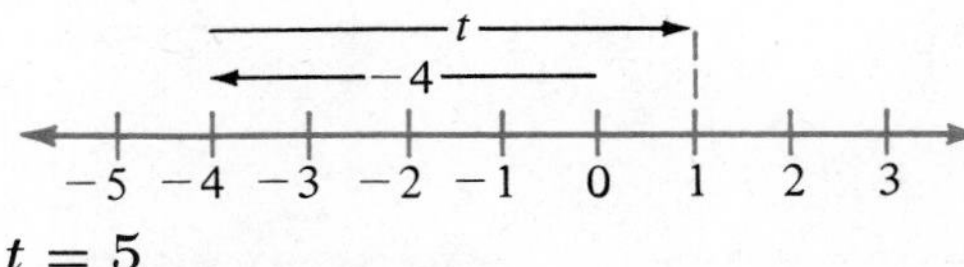

$t = 5$

10. $6 + x = 4$　　11. $-7 + m = -4$　　12. $6 + y = 2$

13. $5 + r = 4$　　14. $-5 + n = 6$　　15. $4 = -5 + s$

Show whether the statement is true or false.

Sample 1: $-(6 + 5) = -6 + (-5)$

Solution: $-(6 + 5) \stackrel{?}{=} -6 + (-5)$

$-(11)$	-11
-11	-11 True

Sample 2: $-(-8 + 2) = -8 + (-2)$

Solution: $-(-8 + 2) \stackrel{?}{=} -8 + (-2)$

$-(-6)$	-10
6	-10 False

16. $-(6 + 8) = -6 + (-8)$
17. $-(8 + 2) = -8 + (-2)$
18. $-16 + 5 = -(16 + 5)$
19. $-7 + (-12) = -(7 + 12)$
20. $-(-5 + 8) = -(-5) + (-8)$
21. $-[20 + (-6)] = -20 + (-6)$

B

22. $-(2\frac{2}{3} + 1\frac{1}{3}) = -2\frac{2}{3} + (-1\frac{1}{3})$
23. $-5\frac{1}{4} + 2\frac{1}{8} = -[5\frac{1}{4} + (-2\frac{1}{8})]$
24. $-[6 + (-9)] = -6 + 9$
25. $-(-0.15 + 1.2) = 0.15 + (-1.2)$

Solve.

26. $-6 = 5 + c$　　27. $5 = -3 + p$

28. $a = -4 + (-4)$　　29. $w + 6 = 7$

30. $-5 = -4 + t$　　31. $11 = t + 7\frac{1}{4}$

32. $-1 = u + 5$　　33. $s = -7 + (-1)$

34. $n + 3.5 = 7$　　35. $-(5 + 9) = s$

36. $-(15 + 3) = t$　　37. $-[7 + (-13)] = r$

38. $-(-15 + 9) = a$　　39. $-(-3 + 7) = b$

40. $-(-7 + 19) = c$　　41. $x = -[15 + (-20)]$

42. $y = -(-25 + 15)$

9-4 *Addition Properties for Directed Numbers*

OBJECTIVES

Apply the properties of addition to directed numbers.

Add directed numbers.

Addition of directed numbers involves use of many of the same properties as addition of positive numbers. Let's restate them and see how we use them to add directed numbers.

The Commutative Property of Addition ▶ **For all directed numbers r and s, $r + s = s + r$.**

The Associative Property of Addition ▶ **For all directed numbers r, s, and t, $(r + s) + t = r + (s + t)$.**

The Additive Property of Zero ▶ **For every directed number r, $r + 0 = 0 + r = r$.**

EXAMPLE 1 $(-2 + 4) + 2 = [4 + (-2)] + 2$ ◀ Commutative Property
$= 4 + (-2 + 2)$ ◀ Associative Property
$= 4 + 0$
$= 4$ ◀ Additive Property of 0

We have seen two more addition properties in this chapter.

▶ **For every directed number r, $-r + r = r + (-r) = 0$.**

▶ **For all directed numbers r and s, $-(r + s) = -r + (-s)$.**

These properties suggest a method for adding two directed numbers without using the number line. We rename the number that has greater magnitude.

EXAMPLE 2 $-8 + 3 = [-5 + (-3)] + 3$ ◀ Rename -8 as a sum, with one addend the opposite of 3.
$= -5 + (-3 + 3)$ ◀ Associative Property
$= -5 + 0$ ◀ Additive Property of Inverses
$= -5$ ◀ Additive Property of 0

EXERCISES

Tell which number has the greater magnitude. Then tell how that number should be renamed to simplify the expression.

Sample: $-15 + 3$ *What you say:* -15 has the greater magnitude. Rename -15 as $-12 + (-3)$.

1. $-23 + 5$ **2.** $-7 + 3$ **3.** $9 + (-5)$

4. $19 + (-9)$ **5.** $9 + (-15)$ **6.** $23 + (-9)$

7. $-7 + 19$ **8.** $-11 + 33$ **9.** $7 + (-20)$

10. $15 + (-29)$ **11.** $19 + (-23)$ **12.** $7\frac{7}{8} + (-7)$

Written EXERCISES

Name the property illustrated.

Sample 1: $5 + (-4) = -4 + 5$

Solution: Commutative Property

Sample 2: $6 + (-6 + 9) = [6 + (-6)] + 9$

Solution: Associative Property

A

1. $8 + (-6) = -6 + 8$ **2.** $-11 + 9 = 9 + (-11)$

3. $-4 + 4 = 0$ **4.** $-2 + (7 + 4) = (-2 + 7) + 4$

5. $0 + (-13) = -13$ **6.** $(-9 + 9) + 4 = -9 + (9 + 4)$

Complete to make a true statement.

Sample 1: $-7 + \underline{\ ?\ } = -7$ *Solution:* $-7 + 0 = -7$

Sample 2: $11 + (-5 + \underline{\ ?\ }) = 11$

Solution: $11 + (-5 + 5) = 11$

7. $\underline{\ ?\ } + (-16) = 0$ **8.** $\underline{\ ?\ } + (-18) = -18 + 9$

9. $7 + \underline{\ ?\ } = 7$ **10.** $20 + (-20) = \underline{\ ?\ }$

11. $22 + \underline{\ ?\ } = 22$ **12.** $33 + (-13) = \underline{\ ?\ } + 33$

13. $(-3 + 3) + \underline{\ ?\ } = 7$ **14.** $(-15 + 15) + 5 = \underline{\ ?\ }$

15. $9 + (-17 + \underline{\ ?\ }) = 9$ **16.** $-9 = (-2 + 2) + \underline{\ ?\ }$

17. $(-15 + 17) + 5 = 5 + (17 + \underline{\ ?\ })$

18. $(-7 + 7) + \underline{\ ?\ } = 15$

Add. Use the additive property of inverses.

19. $7 + 13 + (-13)$ **20.** $-7 + 7 + 16$

21. $3 + (-3) + (-27)$

22. $-15 + (-17) + 17$

23. $23 + 11 + (-11) + 17 + (-17)$

24. $-4 + 20 + (-20)$

25. $3\frac{1}{4} + 5\frac{2}{3} + (-5\frac{2}{3})$

26. $-3\frac{2}{5} + 5 + 19 + 3\frac{2}{5}$

Add.

27. $\begin{array}{r} -5 \\ 3 \\ \underline{-3} \end{array}$

28. $\begin{array}{r} 27 \\ -9 \\ \underline{9} \end{array}$

29. $\begin{array}{r} 13 \\ -13 \\ \underline{33} \end{array}$

30. $\begin{array}{r} 43 \\ -27 \\ \underline{-43} \end{array}$

Show that the statement is true.

Sample: $-7 + 15 = 28 + (-20)$

Solution: $-7 + 15 \stackrel{?}{=} 28 + (-20)$

$-7 + (7 + 8)$	$(8 + 20) + (-20)$
$(-7 + 7) + 8$	$8 + [20 + (-20)]$
$0 + 8$	$8 + 0$
8	8

B

31. $-5 + 15 = -7 + 17$

32. $-11 + 21 = -9 + 19$

33. $-13\frac{1}{3} + 5 = 3\frac{1}{3} + (-11\frac{2}{3})$

34. $25 + (-15) = (-37) + 47$

35. $-13 + 21 + 13 = 35 + (-14)$

36. $-12 + (-3) + 7 = -16\frac{1}{3} + 8\frac{1}{3}$

Simplify.

Sample: $-13 + 5 + 3 + (-17)$

Solution:
$$\begin{aligned} -13 + 5 + 3 + (-17) &= [-13 + (-17)] + (5 + 3) \\ &= -30 + 8 \\ &= -22 + (-8) + 8 \\ &= -22 + 0 \\ &= -22 \end{aligned}$$

37. $5 + 11 + 3 + (-17)$

38. $-11 + (-5) + 5 + 19$

39. $-11 + (-7) + 25$

40. $19 + (-19) + 3 + 31$

C

41. $-31 + 69 + 25 + 11$

42. $19 + (-15) + (-11) + 5 + (-3)$

43. $-43 + (-33) + 15 + (-17) + 7$

44. $-5.8 + 8.8 + 1.4 + (-4.6)$
45. $-6.4 + 16.6 + (-12.9) + 8.4$
46. $48 + (-43) + 18 + 34 + 28 + (-2)$

SELF-TEST 1

Be sure that you understand these terms.

magnitude (p. 240)
additive inverse (p. 241)
identity element (p. 240)
$\stackrel{?}{=}$ (p. 243)

Sketch a number line solution. **Section 9-1, p. 236**

1. $2 + {}^{-}1 = \underline{\ ?\ }$
2. $3 + {}^{-}5 = \underline{\ ?\ }$
3. $4 + {}^{-}3 = \underline{\ ?\ }$
4. ${}^{-}1 + 4 = \underline{\ ?\ }$

Give the meaning. Then write in simplest form. **Section 9-2, p. 240**

5. ${}^{-}5$
6. $-({}^{-}6)$

Solve.

7. $z = {}^{-}17 + 17$
8. $12 + {}^{-}12 = n$
9. $0 + {}^{-}7 = b$
10. $y + {}^{-}4 = 0$

Give a simpler name for the expression. **Section 9-3, p. 243**

11. $-(7 + 2)$
12. $-4 + (-3)$

Solve. Use the number line for help if necessary.

13. $-2 + x = 1$
14. $3 + t = -2$

Show that the statement is true. Name the property illustrated. **Section 9-4, p. 246**

15. $-2 + 2 = 0$
16. $(-3 + 7) + 4 = -3 + (7 + 4)$
17. $-(-9 + 2) = 9 + (-2)$
18. $-12 + 10 = 10 + (-12)$

Check your answers with those printed at the back of the book.

9-5 *Subtracting Directed Numbers*

OBJECTIVE
Subtract a directed number by adding the opposite of the number.

We can use the number line to subtract directed numbers, such as $7 - 5$. It seems reasonable to show "Subtract 5" by an arrow much like the one for "Add 5." However, the arrow should point in the opposite direction.

EXAMPLE 1 $7 - 5 = \underline{\ ?\ }$

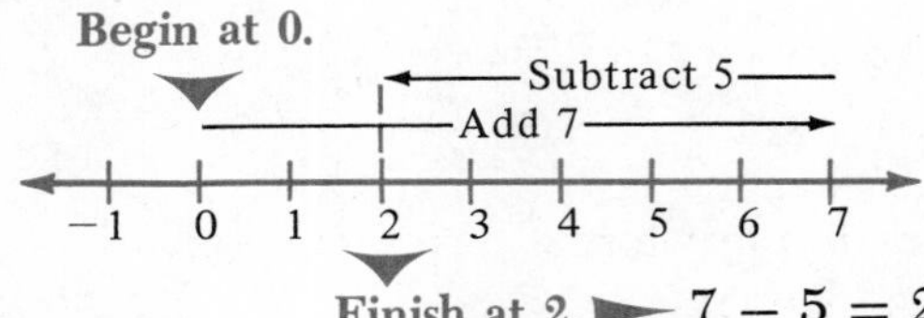

$7 - 5 = 2$

Look at the sketch in Example 1. It is just like the number line sketch for the equation $7 + (-5) = 2$. In fact, subtracting a directed number gives the same result as adding its opposite.

$$7 - 5 = 2 \qquad 7 + (-5) = 2$$

The equations $7 - 5 = 2$ and $7 + (-5) = 2$ are equivalent equations.

EXAMPLE 2 $10 - (-6) = \underline{\ ?\ }$

$10 - (-6) = 10 + 6$ ◄ To subtract −6, add its opposite.

$= 16$

EXAMPLE 3 $2 - 8 = \underline{\ ?\ }$

$2 - 8 = 2 + (-8)$ ◄ To subtract 8, add its opposite.

$= -6$

EXAMPLE 4 $-5 - (-4) = \underline{\ ?\ }$

$-5 - (-4) = -5 + 4$ ◄ To subtract −4, add its opposite.

$= -1$

► **For all directed numbers a and b, $a - b = a + (-b)$.**

Oral EXERCISES

State the subtraction equation indicated and the equivalent addition equation.

Sample:

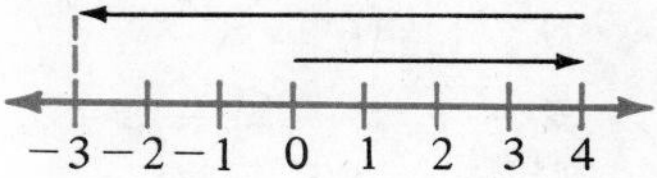

What you say: $4 - 7 = -3$
$4 + (-7) = -3$

1.

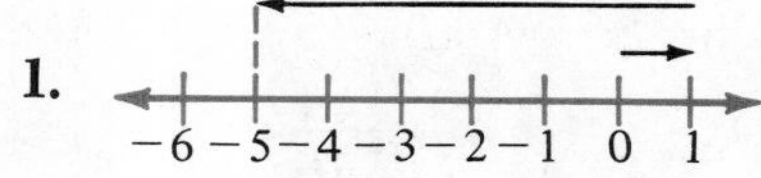

2.

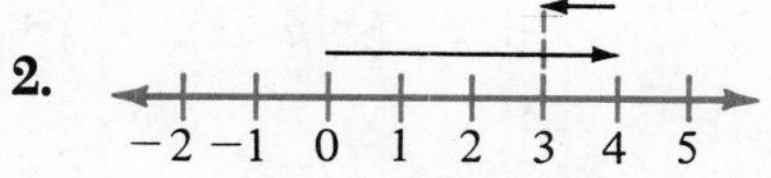

3. −3 −2 −1 0 1 2 3 4

4. −20 −10 0 10

State the equivalent addition equation.

Sample 1: $6 - (-3) = 9$ *What you say:* $6 + 3 = 9$

Sample 2: $-8 - (-3) = -5$ *What you say:* $-8 + 3 = -5$

5. $5 - (-2) = 7$ **6.** $12 - (-6) = 18$ **7.** $5 - (-9) = 14$

8. $16 - (-8) = 24$ **9.** $26 - (-6) = 32$ **10.** $33 = 24 - (-9)$

11. $-8 - 2 = -10$

12. $-12 - (-4) = -8$

13. $-3 - (-9) = 6$

Written EXERCISES

Solve. Begin by writing the equivalent addition equation.

Sample 1: $14 - 6 = m$ *Solution:* $14 + (-6) = m$
$8 = m$

Sample 2: $2 - 9 = r$ *Solution:* $2 + (-9) = r$
$-7 = r$

A

1. $14 - 2 = b$ **2.** $22 - 6 = x$ **3.** $1 - 12 = s$

4. $4 - 17 = x$ **5.** $15 - (-2) = c$ **6.** $19 - (-3) = y$

7. $9 - (-24) = p$ **8.** $6 - 13 = t$ **9.** $21 - 7 = d$

10. $6 - 16 = k$ **11.** $n = 2 - (-12)$ **12.** $s = 6 - (-4)$

13. $-1 - (-9) = k$

14. $-20 - (-10) = z$

15. $r = 17 - 8$

16. $p = 2 - 13$

17. $w = 11 - 16$

18. $-16 - 4 = m$

19. $-4 - 21 = r$

20. $t = -5\frac{1}{2} - 1$

21. $-6\frac{3}{4} - (-2\frac{1}{4}) = k$

Subtract. Add to check.

Sample: $\begin{array}{r} 16 \\ \underline{-8} \end{array}$ *Solution:* $\begin{array}{r} 16 \\ \underline{-8} \\ 24 \end{array}$ Check: (Add) $\begin{array}{r} -8 \\ \underline{24} \\ 16 \end{array}$

22. $\begin{array}{r} 18 \\ \underline{-8} \end{array}$ **23.** $\begin{array}{r} -2 \\ \underline{8} \end{array}$ **24.** $\begin{array}{r} 57 \\ \underline{-14} \end{array}$ **25.** $\begin{array}{r} -32 \\ \underline{-15} \end{array}$

26. $\begin{array}{r} 14 \\ \underline{-7} \end{array}$ **27.** $\begin{array}{r} -2 \\ \underline{-9} \end{array}$ **28.** $\begin{array}{r} 20 \\ \underline{-3} \end{array}$ **29.** $\begin{array}{r} -5 \\ \underline{-19} \end{array}$

Subtract.

Sample 1: $-4 - 7$ *Solution:* $-4 - 7 = -4 + (-7)$
$= -11$

Sample 2: $-15 - (-19)$

Solution: $-15 - (-19) = -15 + 19$
$= 4$

B

30. $7 - 19$ **31.** $-22 - 4$ **32.** $15 - (-16)$

33. $2 - (-9)$ **34.** $-4 - 12$ **35.** $-10 - 32$

36. $-10 - (-40)$ **37.** $-0.6 - 0.4$ **38.** $-0.50 - (-0.20)$

Sample 3: $12 - [-(5 + 3)]$ *Solution:* $12 - [-(5 + 3)] =$
$12 - (-8) = 12 + 8 = 20$

C

39. $4 - [-(15 + 1)]$

40. $11 - (1 + 4)$

41. $-20 - (2 + 3)$

42. $(6 + 1) - (-5)$

43. $-(3 + 13) - 6$

44. $(2 + 10) - 16$

45. $-5 - (12 - 2)$

46. $-17 - [-(4 - 1)]$

47. $-(2 + 4) - [-(8 + 4)]$

48. $-(3 - 5) - (2 + 3)$

49. $2 - [-(1 - 3)]$

50. $[-1 - (-1)] - [1 + (-1)]$

career capsule

Plumber

Plumbers install water, gas, and waste disposal systems in homes, factories, schools and other buildings. They lay out pipe systems as a building is being built. In the final stages of construction, they install air conditioning units and connect systems of radiators, water heaters, plumbing fixtures and sprinkler systems.

The usual training for a plumber is a five year apprenticeship program. Courses in mathematics, physics and chemistry are helpful.

9-6 *Functions and Directed Numbers*

OBJECTIVE

Solve function equations that involve adding and subtracting directed numbers.

A function "machine" may accept directed numbers as inputs and give them as outputs. Recall that inputs are values for x. The outputs are values for $f(x)$.

EXAMPLE 1 $f(x) = x + 4$; replacement set: $\{-3, -2, -1, 0, 1\}$

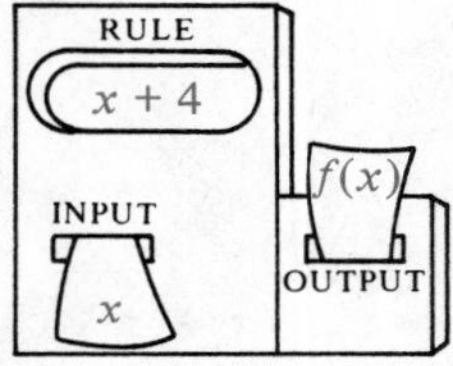

x	$f(x)$	$(x, f(x))$
-3	1	$(-3, 1)$
-2	2	$(-2, 2)$
-1	3	$(-1, 3)$
0	4	$(0, 4)$
1	5	$(1, 5)$

Function: $\{(-3, 1), (-2, 2), (-1, 3), (0, 4), (1, 5)\}$

EXAMPLE 2 $f(x) = x - 5$; replacement set: $\{2, 1, 0, -1, -2\}$

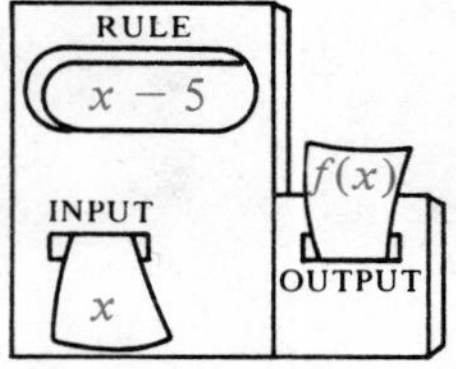

x	$f(x)$	$(x, f(x))$
2	-3	$(2, -3)$
1	-4	$(1, -4)$
0	-5	$(0, -5)$
-1	-6	$(-1, -6)$
-2	-7	$(-2, -7)$

Function: $\{(2, -3), (1, -4), (0, -5), (-1, -6), (-2, -7)\}$

Graph:

EXAMPLE 3 $f(x) = 3 - x$; replacement set: $\{4, 3, 2, 1, 0, -1, -2, \ldots\}$

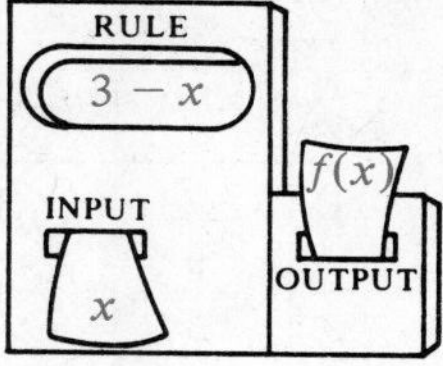

x	$f(x)$	$(x, f(x))$
4	-1	$(4, -1)$
3	0	$(3, 0)$
2	1	$(2, 1)$
1	2	$(1, 2)$
0	3	$(0, 3)$
-1	4	$(-1, 4)$
-2	5	$(-2, 5)$
.	.	.
.	.	.
.	.	.

Function: $\{(4, -1), (3, 0), (2, 1), (1, 2), (0, 3), (-1, 4), (-2, 5), \ldots\}$

Tell how to complete.

$f(x) = x + 5$

	x	$f(x)$	$(x, f(x))$
Sample:	1	6	$(1, 6)$
1.	2	?	?
2.	3	?	?
3.	-1	?	?
4.	-2	?	?
5.	-3	?	?

$f(x) = x - 2$

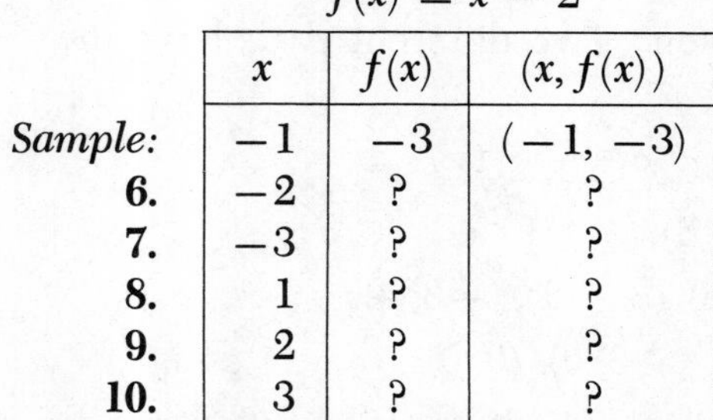

	x	$f(x)$	$(x, f(x))$
Sample:	-1	-3	$(-1, -3)$
6.	-2	?	?
7.	-3	?	?
8.	1	?	?
9.	2	?	?
10.	3	?	?

Written EXERCISES

Complete the table according to the function machine. Then graph the function. Can you give a simpler rule that gives the same result?

RULE $x-(-x)$ INPUT x OUTPUT $f(x)$

A

	x	$f(x)$	$(x, f(x))$
Sample:	3	6	(3, 6)
1.	2	?	?
2.	1	?	?
3.	0	?	?
4.	-1	?	?
5.	-2	?	?
6.	-3	?	?

Complete according to the given function equation.

Sample: $f(t) = t + (-1)$: $\{(0, \underline{?}), (-1, \underline{?}), (2, \underline{?})\}$

Solution: $\{(0, -1), (-1, -2), (2, 1)\}$

7. $f(y) = y + 3$: $\{(-6, -3), (-3, \underline{?}), (0, \underline{?}), (3, \underline{?}), (6, \underline{?}), (9, \underline{?})\}$

8. $f(m) = m + (-2)$: $\{(-1, -3), (-2, -4), (-3, \underline{?}), (-4, \underline{?})\}$

9. $f(k) = k - 1$: $\{(0, -1), (2, \underline{?}), (4, \underline{?}), (6, \underline{?}), (8, \underline{?})\}$

10. $f(t) = t - (-5)$: $\{(12, 17), (10, \underline{?}), (8, \underline{?}), (6, \underline{?}), (4, \underline{?})\}$

11. $f(n) = n + (-10)$: $\{(10, 0), (8, -2), (6, \underline{?}), (4, \underline{?}), (2, \underline{?})\}$

12. $f(k) = -9 + k$: $\{(-1, -10), (-3, \underline{?}), (-5, \underline{?}), (1, \underline{?}), (3, \underline{?})\}$

13. $f(t) = t - 0$: $\{(4, 4), (\underline{?}, 6), (\underline{?}, 8), (\underline{?}, -4), (\underline{?}, -6)\}$

Tell whether or not the set of number pairs is a function.

Sample: $\{(1, -1), (2, -2), (2, -3), (4, -3)\}$

Solution: The set is not a function. Two different pairs have the same first member.

14. $\{(10, 2), (9, 2), (7, 2), (5, 2), (3, 2), (1, 2)\}$

15. $\{(2, 5), (3, 7), (1, 4), (2, 6), (8, 8), (3, 1)\}$

16. $\{(1, 0), (-1, 4), (2, 4), (-2, 5), (3, -1), (-3, 4)\}$

17. $\{(3, 3), (4, 4), (-1, 2), (2, 5), (-3, 6), (0, 0)\}$

18. $\{(-50, 2), (-40, 2), (-30, 2), (-20, 2), (-10, 2), (0, 2), \ldots\}$

Match each set of number pairs in Column 1 with its function equation in Column 2.

COLUMN 1

B

19. $\{(2, -1), (3, 0), (4, 1), (5, 2), (6, 3)\}$
20. $\{(6, 4), (4, 2), (2, 0), (0, -2), (-2, -4)\}$
21. $\left\{(7, 7), (-4, -4), \left(\frac{1}{2}, \frac{1}{2}\right), (0, 0), (5, 5)\right\}$
22. $\{(-1, 4), (-2, 3), (-3, 2), (-4, 1), (-5, 0), (0, 5)\}$
23. $\{(-6, -3), (-2, 1), (2, 5), (6, 9), (10, 13)\}$

COLUMN 2

A. $f(t) = t + 0$
B. $f(x) = x - 3$
C. $f(s) = s - (-3)$
D. $f(y) = y + (-2)$
E. $f(n) = n - (-5)$

Use the function equation and the given replacement set to write a function.

Sample: $y - (-3) = f(y);\ \{-2, 0, 2, 4, 6\}$
Solution: $\{(-2, 1), (0, 3), (2, 5), (4, 7), (6, 9)\}$

24. $f(k) = k - 4;\ \{12, 14, 16, 18, 20\}$
25. $t + 2 = f(t);\ \{5, 10, 15, 20, 25\}$
26. $f(h) = h - (-8);\ \{6, 3, 0, -3, -6, -8\}$
27. $f(m) = m + (-7);\ \{-21, -14, -7, 0, 7, 14, 21\}$
28. $f(z) = 5 - (-z);\ \{-3, -2, -1, 0, 1, 2, 3\}$
29. $f(n) = -n;\ \left\{\frac{1}{2}, 1, 1\frac{1}{2}, 2\frac{3}{4}\right\}$ C
30. $f(x) = x - 1.5;\ \{-1.5, 3, 3.5, 7\}$
31. $f(t) = t - (-1);\left\{-\frac{1}{2}, -\frac{1}{4}, 0, \frac{1}{4}\right\}$
32. $f(z) = z + 0.2;\ \{-1, 0, 1, 2\}$
33. $b - 2 = f(b);\ \left\{-1, -\frac{1}{2}, \frac{1}{2}, 1\right\}$
34. $0.5 + (-n) = f(n);\ \{-0.5, 0.5, 1, 1.5\}$

SELF-TEST 2

Solve. Begin by writing the equivalent addition equation.

Section 9-5, p. 250

1. $8 - 3 = x$ **2.** $5 - 7 = y$

3. $m = -2 - 7$ **4.** $n = -3 - (-4)$

Subtract.

5. $\begin{array}{r} 20 \\ -12 \\ \hline \end{array}$ **6.** $\begin{array}{r} 4 \\ -5 \\ \hline \end{array}$

7. $\begin{array}{r} 10 \\ -10 \\ \hline \end{array}$ **8.** $\begin{array}{r} 7 \\ -3 \\ \hline \end{array}$

Section 9-6, p. 254 Complete according to the given function equation.

9. $f(x) = x + (-2)$: $\{(3, \underline{?}), (2, \underline{?}), (-2, \underline{?}), (0, \underline{?})\}$

10. $f(x) = x - 4$: $\{(4, \underline{?}), (3, \underline{?}), (-1, \underline{?}), (\underline{?}, 0)\}$

Check your answers with those printed at the back of the book.

calculator corner

When you use your calculator, you must remember to follow the rules of algebra. To solve a problem such as $(65 \times 2) + (75 \times 3)$ you must first multiply 65×2 and write down the answer, multiply 75×3 and write down the answer, and finally add the two answers. What is $(65 \times 2) + (75 \times 3)$?

Here is a formula which shows a quicker way to calculate a problem like $(65 \times 2) + (75 \times 3)$ without any writing: $(A \times B) + (C \times D) = [((A \times B) \div D) + C] \times D$. Let $A = 65$, $B = 2$, $C = 75$

and $D = 3$. Find $[((A \times B) \div D) + C] \times D$ with your calculator. Does $(65 \times 2) + (75 \times 3) = [((65 \times 2) \div 3) + 75] \times 3$? Multiply $13 \times 2 + 14 \times 5$ with your calculator, using the formula and $A = 13$, $B = 2$, $C = 14$, $D = 5$. Have a friend multiply $(13 \times 2) + (14 \times 5)$ with a calculator, without any formulas. Which method is faster?

Of course, your calculator may have a feature which enables it to calculate $(65 \times 2) + (75 \times 3)$ directly. If so, try both methods. You'll see what a time-saver that feature is.

chapter summary

1. Addition of directed numbers can be shown on the number line.

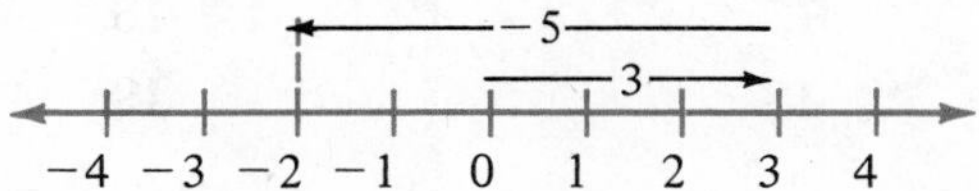

2. Every directed number has an **opposite.** Its opposite is also called its **additive inverse.**

3. The sum of any directed number and its opposite is 0.

4. The opposite of every positive number is negative.
The opposite of every negative number is positive.
The opposite of 0 is 0.

5. The sum of any directed number and 0 is that number. That is, 0 is the **identity element** for addition.

6. Subtraction of directed numbers can be shown on the number line.

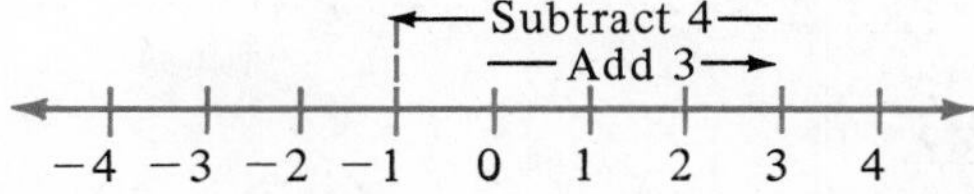

7. Subtracting one directed number from another is the same as adding the opposite. In general, we say $r - s = r + (-s)$.

chapter test

Name the opposite.

1. 5 **2.** -3 **3.** ${}^{-}2$

Solve.

4. $n + {}^{-}4 = 0$ **5.** $-7 + 7 = t$ **6.** $-12 + x = 0$

7. $6 + n = 5$ **8.** $3 = -2 + m$ **9.** $4 + a = -2$

Name the property illustrated.

10. $-12 + 12 = 0$

11. $2 + [-3 + (-2)] = [2 + (-3)] + (-2)$

12. $7 + (-12) = -12 + 7$

13. $-5 + [-(-5)] = 0$

Solve. Begin by writing an equivalent addition equation.

14. $x = 4 - 5$ **15.** $n = 8 - 12$ **16.** $-2 - 5 = x$

17. $2 - (-9) = b$ **18.** $z = -5 - (-6)$ **19.** $4 - (-2) = c$

Complete according to the function equation.

20. $f(t) = t + (-2)$; $\{(0, \underline{\ ?\ }), (-1, \underline{\ ?\ })\}$

21. $f(z) = z - (-8)$; $\{(-5, \underline{\ ?\ }), (2, \underline{\ ?\ })\}$

22. $f(c) = -1 - c$; $\{(8, \underline{\ ?\ }), (-6, \underline{\ ?\ })\}$

Complete the table according to the given function rule. Then write the set of ordered pairs and graph the function.

$$f(a) = -a + 1$$

	a	$f(a)$	$(a, f(a))$
Sample:	-1	2	$(-1, 2)$
23.	-2	?	?
	-3	?	?
	0	?	?
	1	?	?
	2	?	?
	3	?	?

challenge topics

Absolute Value

Study the number line pictured below. How many units from 0 is 4? How many units from 0 is -4? Do you see that each number is 4 units from 0? The distance from 0 of a number on the number line is called the **absolute value** of the number.

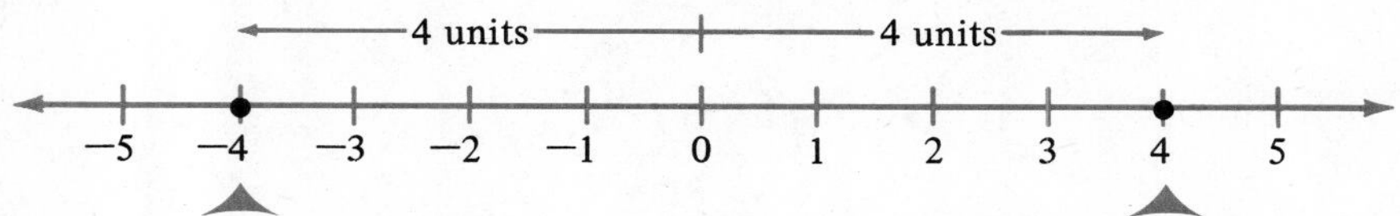

The absolute value of -4 is 4. **The absolute value of 4 is 4.**

The symbol $|x|$ stands for the absolute value of the directed number x. The symbol is read "the absolute value of x."

$$|10| = 10; \quad \left|\frac{2}{3}\right| = \frac{2}{3}; \quad |35| = 35$$

$$|-10| = 10; \quad \left|-\frac{2}{3}\right| = \frac{2}{3}; \quad |-35| = 35$$

We define absolute value for directed numbers as follows:

When $r \geq 0$, $|r| = r$. When $r < 0$, $|r| = -r$.

Note that the absolute value of *any* directed number is *always* a **positive** number or **zero.**

True or false?

1. $|-3| = 3$ **2.** $|2| = |-2|$ **3.** $|-1| > |0|$
4. $|-1| \neq |1|$ **5.** $|0| < |-1|$ **6.** $|4| > |-4|$

Solve.

7. $|x| = 2$ **8.** $-|y| = -2$ **9.** $-|t| + 2 = 0$
10. $|t| = 0$ **11.** $|a| + 1 = 3$ **12.** $|y| - 2 = 4$

Find the value.

13. $|2 + 3|$ **14.** $|8 - 7|$ **15.** $-|3| + |3|$
16. $|8 - 7| - |1|$ **17.** $|6 - 9|$ **18.** $|-3 + 2| - |1|$

Review of Skills

Perform the operation indicated.

1. $1\frac{1}{4} \times \frac{1}{2}$
2. $1\frac{5}{9} \div 4\frac{2}{3}$
3. $3\frac{1}{8} \div 1\frac{1}{4}$
4. 0.02×7.1
5. $\frac{12.3}{0.3}$
6. 0.66×0.5

Complete.

7. $-4 + (-4) + (-4) = \underline{\ ?\ }$
   $3 \cdot (-4) = \underline{\ ?\ }$
8. $-2 + (-2) + (-2) + (-2) = \underline{\ ?\ }$
   $4 \cdot (-2) = \underline{\ ?\ }$

Complete the pattern.

9. $3 \cdot 4 = 12$
   $2 \cdot 4 = 8$
   $1 \cdot 4 = 4$
   $0 \cdot 4 = \underline{\ ?\ }$
   $-1 \cdot 4 = \underline{\ ?\ }$
   $-2 \cdot 4 = \underline{\ ?\ }$
10. $3 \cdot 7 = 21$
   $2 \cdot 7 = 14$
   $1 \cdot 7 = \underline{\ ?\ }$
   $0 \cdot 7 = \underline{\ ?\ }$
   $-1 \cdot 7 = \underline{\ ?\ }$
   $-2 \cdot 7 = \underline{\ ?\ }$

True or false? (a and b are directed numbers.)

11. $a \cdot b = b \cdot a$
12. $a + b = b + a$
13. $a + (b + c) = (a + b) + c$
14. $a \cdot (b \cdot c) = (a \cdot b) \cdot c$
15. $a \cdot (b + c) = (a + b) + (a \cdot c)$
16. $a \cdot (b + c) = a \cdot b + a \cdot c$

Simplify. Use the distributive property.

17. $7y + 9y$
18. $2z + 3z$
19. $4t + 2n + 3n + t$
20. $14m + m + 2b$

Left: Machine which produced eight mail bags per minute.

Right: Press which can print one hundred million stamps per day.

10

Multiplication and Division of Directed Numbers

10-1 *Multiplication by a Positive Number or by Zero*

OBJECTIVES

Multiply a directed number by a positive number.

Apply the multiplication properties of 0 and 1.

Multiplication by a positive integer can be thought of as repeated addition.

EXAMPLE 1 $3 \cdot 5 = 5 + 5 + 5 = 15$
$3 \cdot 5 = 15$

EXAMPLE 2 $2(-7) = -7 + (-7) = -14$
$2(-7) = -14$

It is not clear how to interpret $-9 \cdot 3$ as repeated addition. The commutative property, which we assume to be true for directed numbers, makes it easier.

EXAMPLE 3 $-9 \cdot 3 = 3(-9) = -9 + (-9) + (-9)$
$-9 \cdot 3 = -27$

We also assume the multiplicative properties of 0 and 1 for directed numbers.

EXAMPLE 4 $5 \cdot 0 = 0 \cdot 5 = 0$ $\quad -4 \cdot 0 = 0(-4) = 0$

EXAMPLE 5 $1 \cdot 8 = 8 \cdot 1 = 8$ $\quad 1(-7) = -7 \cdot 1 = -7$

Look closely at Examples 1–5. Notice the following patterns.

The product of two **positive** numbers is **positive.**
The product of a **positive** number and a **negative** number is **negative.**
The product of 0 and any directed number is 0.
The product of 1 and any directed number is that directed number.

Tell how to complete each of the following to make a true statement.

Sample: $-7 + (-7) + (-7) + (-7) = \underline{\ ?\ }$
$4(-7) = \underline{\ ?\ }$

What you say: $-7 + (-7) + (-7) + (-7) = -28$
$4(-7) = -28$

1. $5 + 5 + 5 = \underline{\ ?\ }$
$3 \cdot 5 = \underline{\ ?\ }$

2. $3 + 3 + 3 + 3 = \underline{\ ?\ }$
$4 \cdot 3 = \underline{\ ?\ }$

3. $-8 + (-8) + (-8) = \underline{\ ?\ }$
$3(-8) = \underline{\ ?\ }$

4. $-12 + (-12) = \underline{\ ?\ }$
$2(-12) = \underline{\ ?\ }$

5. $0 + 0 + 0 + 0 = \underline{\ ?\ }$
$4 \cdot 0 = \underline{\ ?\ }$

6. $-11 + (-11) = \underline{\ ?\ }$
$2(-11) = \underline{\ ?\ }$

Written
EXERCISES

Simplify. Assume that the variable represents a positive number.

Sample 1: $-16 \cdot 3$ *Solution:* $-16 \cdot 3 = -48$

Sample 2: $n\left(-\frac{2}{3}\right)$ *Solution:* $n\left(-\frac{2}{3}\right) = -\frac{2}{3} \cdot n = -\frac{2n}{3}$

A

1. $4(-6)$ **2.** $5(-8)$ **3.** $11 \cdot 13$

4. $3 \cdot 7m$ **5.** $4(-9)$ **6.** $6(-7)$

7. $-5 \cdot w$ **8.** $-8 \cdot 7$ **9.** $p\left(-\frac{1}{5}\right)$

10. $-4 \cdot \frac{1}{3}$ **11.** $-0.15(2)$ **12.** $\left(-\frac{1}{5}\right)\left(\frac{3}{4}\right)$

13. $-3(0.321)$ **14.** $\frac{2}{7}\left(-\frac{2}{5}\right)$ **15.** $\left(\frac{1}{6}\right)(5)$

Complete.

16.

×	0	1	3	6	9
0	?	?	?	?	?
−1	?	?	?	?	?
−3	?	?	?	−18	?
−6	?	?	?	?	?
−9	?	?	−27	?	?

17.

×	−1	−3	−5	−7
1	?	?	?	?
3	?	?	?	−21
5	?	−15	?	?
7	?	?	?	?
9	?	?	?	?

Simplify.

Sample: $2(-6) + 2(-4)$

Solution: $2(-6) + 2(-4) = -12 + (-8) = -20$

18. $3(-9) + 3 \cdot 4$

19. $(-2 \cdot 7) + (-2 \cdot 5)$

20. $2(-6) + 2(-4)$

21. $8 + (-2 \cdot 7)$

22. $(-1 \cdot 8) + 19$

23. $(-7 \cdot 1) + 8$

24. $(-3 \cdot 5) + (-3 \cdot 5)$

25. $9(-3) + 9(-3)$

Solve.

Sample: $3 \cdot m = 21$ *Solution:* $3 \cdot m = 21$

$3 \cdot 7 = 21$

So, $m = 7$.

B **26.** $4(-8) = h$

27. $2(m) = -36$

28. $6(-11) = h$

29. $3 \cdot m = -45$

30. $-8 \cdot \frac{3}{4} = x$

31. $-4\frac{1}{5}x = -4\frac{1}{5}$

32. $p(-6) = -48$

33. $5(-12) = a$

34. $-12 \cdot 0 = n$

35. $-1 \cdot 17 = x$

36. $-1 \cdot 39 = a$

37. $-5\frac{1}{3} = 5\frac{1}{3}m$

C **38.** $a + 2(-3) = -10$

39. $-13 \cdot b = -3 \cdot 13$

40. $5 + 3(-4) = m$

41. $(-6 \cdot 3) + p = 15$

42. $-5 \cdot 11 = -5 \cdot m$

43. $(-7 \cdot 4) + m = -31$

Kotaro Honda 1870–1954

Kotaro Honda was one of Japan's leading metallurgists. (A metallurgist is a scientist who experiments with metals.) In 1916 he found that the addition of cobalt to tungsten steel produced a more powerful magnet than steel. Nothing more advanced in the field of magnetics was discovered until the mid 20th century. In 1937 Honda was awarded the Cultural Order of the Rising Sun, Japan's equivalent of the Nobel Prize.

10-2 *Multiplication Properties for Directed Numbers*

OBJECTIVES

Apply the associative property of multiplication to directed numbers.

Apply the distributive property to directed numbers.

We assume that multiplication of directed numbers is **associative.** That is, the way that factors are grouped does not affect the product.

EXAMPLE 1 $(4 \cdot 2)(-3) = 8(-3) = -24;$

$$4 \cdot [2(-3)] = 4(-6) = -24$$

We also assume that the **distributive** property holds for multiplication of directed numbers.

EXAMPLE 2 $4[5 + (-2)] = 4 \cdot 5 + 4(-2)$

$4 \cdot 3$	$20 + (-8)$
12	12 ✓

EXAMPLE 3 $-3(1 + 6) = -3 \cdot 1 + (-3 \cdot 6)$

$-3 \cdot 7$	$-3 + (-18)$
-21	-21 ✓

Let's review the properties of multiplication which we will assume to be true for directed numbers. For all directed numbers r, s, and t:

1. $r \cdot s = s \cdot r$ ◀ The Commutative Property
2. $(r \cdot s) \cdot t = r \cdot (s \cdot t)$ ◀ The Associative Property
3. $r(s + t) = r \cdot s + r \cdot t$ ◀ The Distributive Property
4. $r \cdot 0 = 0 \cdot r = 0$ ◀ The Multiplicative Property of Zero
5. $r \cdot 1 = 1 \cdot r = r$ ◀ The Multiplicative Property of One

Oral EXERCISES

Name the property illustrated.

Sample: $5(-8) = -8 \cdot 5$ *What you say:* Commutative property.

1. $8(-5 + 4) = 8(-5) + 8 \cdot 4$
2. $17(-14) = -14 \cdot 17$
3. $12 \cdot 0 = 0$
4. $-1 \cdot 25 = 25(-1)$
5. $2(-9) + 5(-9) = (2 + 5)(-9)$
6. $-2\frac{1}{5} = -2\frac{1}{5} \cdot 1$
7. $(5 \cdot 4)3 = 3(5 \cdot 4)$

True or false?

8. $-8(3) = -8[5 + (-2)]$
9. $7(-2) > 6(-2)$
10. $8(-4)3 = 8 \cdot 4(-3)$
11. $[-7 + (-5)]2 = (-7 \cdot 2) + (-5 \cdot 2)$
12. $0(-3) > 2 \cdot 5$
13. $[-5 + (-4)]3 = -5 \cdot 3 + (-4)3$
14. $-4 \cdot 5 \neq -5 \cdot 4$
15. $(-2\frac{3}{5})(4) = (4)(-2\frac{3}{5})$

Written EXERCISES

Write the expression as a sum of two products. Then simplify the expressions to show that they are equal.

Sample 1: $7[6 + (-9)]$

Solution: $7[6 + (-9)] = 7(6) + 7(-9)$

$7(-3)$	$42 + (-63)$
-21	-21

A

1. $3(4 + 1)$
2. $4(-5 + 2)$
3. $7[-8 + (-1)]$
4. $-1(3 + 5)$
5. $-8(1 + 6)$
6. $10[-10 + (-10)]$
7. $[3 + (-6)]8$
8. $[-4 + (-2)]3$
9. $(-8 + 6)\frac{1}{2}$
10. $[9 + (-12)]\frac{1}{3}$
11. $-\frac{1}{4}(12 + 16)$
12. $-0.8(6 + 0.1)$

Show that the statement is true.

Sample: $-4(3 + 5) = (-4 \cdot 3) + (-4 \cdot 5)$

Solution:
$$\begin{array}{r|l} -4(3 + 5) & = (-4 \cdot 3) + (-4 \cdot 5) \\ \hline -4(8) & -12 + (-20) \\ -32 & -32 \checkmark \end{array}$$

13. $(4)[5(-2)] = (4 \cdot 5)(-2)$
14. $(4 - 7)3 = (4 \cdot 3) - (7 \cdot 3)$
15. $[2 + (-5)]3 = (2 \cdot 3) + (-5 \cdot 3)$
16. $-4(6 + 4) = (-4 \cdot 6) + (-4 \cdot 4)$
17. $-3(8 + 2) = (-3 \cdot 8) + (-3 \cdot 2)$
18. $-4(2 + 3 + 1) = (-4 \cdot 2) + (-4 \cdot 3) + (-4 \cdot 1)$
19. $(5 - 8)(3) = 5 \cdot 3 - 8 \cdot 3$
20. $(-7 + 5)4 = (-7 \cdot 4) + (5 \cdot 4)$
21. $[-4 + 1 + (-2)]3 = (-4 \cdot 3) + (1 \cdot 3) + (-2 \cdot 3)$
22. $-3\left(\frac{1}{4} + \frac{1}{2}\right) = \left(-3 \cdot \frac{1}{4}\right) + (-3)\left(\frac{1}{2}\right)$
23. $5[-3 + (-4)] = 5(-3) + 5(-4)$
24. $(-7 \cdot 2) + (-6 \cdot 2) = [-7 + (-6)]2$

Let $w = 3$, $x = 5$, $y = \frac{1}{4}$, $z = -8$. Show that the resulting statement is true.

B

25. $w(x + z) = wx + wz$
26. $x \cdot z = z \cdot x$
27. $y(w + z) = (w + z)y$
28. $(xz)y = x(zy)$
29. $-1 \cdot x = x(-1)$
30. $2(w + z) = 2w + 2z$
31. $-3(x - w) = (-3x) - (-3w)$
32. $4z + 4x = 4(z + x)$
33. $w \cdot 0 = 0 \cdot w$
34. $w(x + z) = wz + wx$

Multiply.

Sample: $3(-47)$ *Solution:*
$$\begin{array}{r} -50 + 3 \\ 3 \\ \hline -150 + 9 = -141 \end{array}$$

C

35. $3(-216)$
36. $-2(321)$
37. $4(-28)$
38. $10(-327)$
39. $-5(149)$
40. $2(-607)$
41. $-4(48)$
42. $9(-118)$
43. $6(-248)$

10-3 *Multiplication of Negative Numbers*

OBJECTIVES

Find the product of two negative numbers.

Find the product of three or more directed numbers.

We have seen the following pattern for the product of two directed numbers:

positive × positive = positive
positive × negative = negative
negative × positive = negative

We can use the distributive property to show:

negative × negative = positive

EXAMPLE 1
$$\begin{aligned} -2(-3+7) &= -2(-3) + (-2\cdot 7) \\ -2\cdot 4 &= -2(-3) + (-2\cdot 7) \\ -8 &= -2(-3) + (-14) \\ -8 &= 6 + (-14) \end{aligned}$$
Then it must be true that $-2(-3) = 6$.

EXAMPLE 2
$$\begin{aligned} -5[10+(-6)] &= -5\cdot 10 + [-5(-6)] \\ -5\cdot 4 &= -50 + [-5(-6)] \\ -20 &= -50 + 30 \quad \blacktriangleleft -5(-6) \text{ must equal } 30. \\ -20 &= -20 \end{aligned}$$

EXAMPLE 3
$$\begin{aligned} -1(-2+9) &= -1(-2) + (-1\cdot 9) \\ -1\cdot 7 &= 2 + (-9) \quad \blacktriangleleft -1(-2) = 2 \\ -7 &= -7 \end{aligned}$$

Here's a simple way to remember the sign of the product of two directed numbers.

► If the two signs are **alike**, the product is **positive**.
If the two signs are **unlike**, the product is **negative**.

We use these same rules to determine the sign of a product when more than two factors are multiplied.

$$3 \cdot 4(-1) \blacktriangleright (3 \cdot 4) \cdot (-1) = -12$$

$(3 \cdot 4)$: positive; (-1): negative

► The product of two or more directed numbers is positive if there is an even number of negative factors. The product is negative if there is an odd number of negative factors.

Tell whether the expression represents a positive number or a negative number. Do not simplify.

1. $-4 \cdot 2$
2. $-4(-5)(-7)$
3. $\frac{1}{2}(-2)5$
4. $-2(-3)4$
5. $\frac{1}{2}(-2)\left(-\frac{1}{3}\right)$
6. $-3 \cdot 9(-1)(-2)$
7. $\frac{1}{5}\left(-\frac{1}{8}\right)(-2)$
8. $-7\left(-\frac{1}{2}\right)(-2)$
9. $-4(-4)$
10. $-1 \cdot 3\left(-\frac{1}{2}\right)$
11. $-6(-6)(-6)$
12. $-5 \cdot 5(-5)$

Written EXERCISES

Tell whether the expression represented is positive, negative, or zero. Then simplify.

Sample: $-4 \cdot 3 \cdot 2$ *Solution:* negative; -24

A

1. $-3 \cdot 6$
2. $-5 \cdot 1(-4)$
3. $-3(-2)(-5)$
4. $-\frac{1}{2} \cdot 0(-5)$
5. $-3(-5)2$
6. $\frac{1}{3}(-2)$
7. $-3(-2)2(-1)$
8. $(-2)^3$
9. $-7(-3)1$
10. $-5(-2)2$
11. $(-5)^2$
12. $-6 \cdot 2 \cdot 0 \cdot \frac{1}{2}$

Rewrite the expression as a sum of two products. Then simplify both expressions to show that they are equal.

Sample 1: $5[2 + (-4)]$

Solution: $5[2 + (-4)] = 5(2) + 5(-4)$

$5(-2)$	$10 + (-20)$
-10	-10 ✓

Sample 2: $-3(-2 + 4)$

Solution: $-3(-2 + 4) = -3(-2) + (-3)(4)$

$-3(2)$	$6 + (-12)$
-6	-6 ✓

13. $-3[5 + (-3)]$ **14.** $5[-3 + (-2)]$ **15.** $-2(7 + 5)$

16. $3(-8 + 5)$ **17.** $(-6 + 3)(-2)$ **18.** $(-8 + 2)(-2)$

19. $-\frac{1}{2}(5 + 0)$ **20.** $2[8 - (-2)]$

21. $-5[-3 + (-4)]$ **22.** $-2(-5 + 5)$

23. $-6\left[\frac{1}{2} + (-1)\right]$ **24.** $-3[-2 + (-1)]$

Evaluate. Let $a = 3$, $b = -2$, $c = 1$, $d = 5$, $f = -3$.

Sample: $a \cdot b \cdot f$

Solution: $3(-2)(-3) = 18$

B

25. $-a \cdot b$ **26.** $b \cdot c(-2)$ **27.** $(a)(-d)(-1)$

28. $-3(a)(-c)$ **29.** $f \cdot a - 2c$ **30.** $3 \cdot a \cdot c \cdot f$

31. $ab + cf$ **32.** $(-c) + df$ **33.** $(-2)f + a$

Simplify.

C

34. $-3 + [-6 + (2 \cdot 4)]$

35. $[-3 + (-2)] + [-4(-1 + 5)]$

36. $-3[4(-6 + 4)]$

37. $5[-1(2 \cdot 3) + (-2 \cdot 0)]$

Evaluate.

38. $(-1)^2$ **39.** $(-1)^3$ **40.** $(-3)^2$

41. $(-3)^3$ **42.** $(-8)^2$ **43.** $(-8)^3$

10-4 *The Distributive Property in Simplifying Expressions*

OBJECTIVE
Simplify algebraic expressions by combining similar terms.

We use the distributive property to simplify expressions.

EXAMPLE 1 $7x + 3x = (7 + 3)x = 10x$

EXAMPLE 2
$$\begin{aligned} 7m - 3a + 2m + a &= 7m + 2m + (-3a) + a && \leftarrow \text{Group like terms.} \\ &= (7 + 2)m + (-3 + 1)a && \leftarrow \text{Distributive property} \\ &= 9m + (-2)a \\ &= 9m - 2a \end{aligned}$$

EXAMPLE 3
$$\begin{aligned} 7n + 6n + n - 3 &= (7n + 6n + n) - 3 \\ &= (7 + 6 + 1)n - 3 \\ &= 14n - 3 \end{aligned}$$

EXAMPLE 4
$$\begin{aligned} 15t + 9s + 3t - 7s &= 15t + 3t + 9s + (-7s) \\ &= (15 + 3)t + [9 + (-7)]s \\ &= 18t + 2s \end{aligned}$$

EXAMPLE 5
$$\begin{aligned} -5x + y + 3y - x &= -5x + (-x) + y + 3y \\ &= -5x + (-1x) + 1y + 3y && \leftarrow -x = -1x \\ &= [-5 + (-1)]x + (1 + 3)y \\ &= -6x + 4y \end{aligned}$$

As soon as you understand this, you will probably do much of it in your head.

EXERCISES

Simplify by combining similar terms.

Sample: $5w - 2w + 4$ *What you say:* $3w + 4$

1. $3p + 4p + 2p$
2. $10a - 6 + 4a$
3. $8n + (-3n)$
4. $4x - 2 + (-2x)$
5. $3w - 3n + 5w$
6. $6x + 3y + (-4x) + 3$

7. $\frac{2}{3}x + 3y + \frac{1}{3}x$

8. $-7a + 3b + 5a$

9. $3m + 2n + (-5m) + (-2n)$

10. $3c + 4a + (-5c) + (-2)$

Written EXERCISES

Simplify by combining similar terms.

Sample 1: $5x + 3m - 2x + m$

Solution: $5x + 3m - 2x + m = [5x + (-2x)] + (3m + m)$
$= 3x + 4m$

Sample 2: $3a + 2(-4a - 6b)$

Solution: $3a + 2(-4a - 6b) = 3a + (-8a) + (-12b)$
$= -5a + (-12b) = -5a - 12b$

A

1. $3b + (-4a) + b + a$
2. $-a + 5b + 2a - 3b$
3. $-2xy - 3p + (-7xy)$
4. $2r - 5s - 6r + 3s$
5. $-m - 7x - 2 + 4m + x$
6. $\frac{2}{3}y - \frac{1}{2}x + \left(-\frac{1}{3}y\right) + \frac{2}{3}x$
7. $4a + 3c + (-2a) + 6 - c$
8. $3w + y + (-w) - 2 + (-y)$
9. $2ab + (-6) + (-ab) + 1$
10. $-3a^2 + 2a + a^2 - 1$
11. $4c^2 + 7c + (-6c^2)$
12. $-2r^2 + 3 + (-5r^2) + (-2)$

B

13. $x(3x - 2) + (x^2 + 5)$
14. $-5(a + 4) + (-3a)$
15. $3(ab + c) + (-2ab) + 1$
16. $-3(mn + 2) - mn + 4$
17. $-7s + 3(-2s + 2)$
18. $13a + [-7(a - 1)]$
19. $\frac{2}{5}m + \frac{1}{3}m^2 + \frac{1}{5}m + \left(-\frac{2}{3}m^2\right)$
20. $10y - 12w + 2(-8y + 3w)$

C

21. $2[x(3x - 2)] + (x^2 + 5)$
22. $-3y[(2y - 1)2 + (-y)]$
23. $-5a(6a + 4) + [-4(20a^2 + 15a)]$
24. $[-5 + (-3c) + (-4c^2)]10 + c^2$

Find the value of the expression, if $a = -2$, $b = 7$, $c = -1$, and $d = 5$.

25. $6 + (b + d)^2$
26. $5(a + b) + d$

27. $\frac{1}{2}(ab) + 1$

28. $a(3c - d)$

29. $a^2 \cdot c$

30. $-2(cd + a) - 1$

31. $(d + c)^2 + a$

32. $(a + c)^2 + cd$

33. $\left(\frac{1}{5}d + c\right)\frac{1}{2}$

34. $cab - 2c^2$

35. $0.3cd + (7a)^2$

36. $0.2c + 0.3ac^2$

SELF-TEST 1

Multiply.

Section 10-1, p. 264

1. $3(-4)$
2. $-8 \cdot 5$
3. $-9 \cdot 0$

Solve.

4. $-4 \cdot n = -4$
5. $-2 \cdot 5 = m$
6. $3x = -6$

Name the property illustrated.

Section 10-2, p. 267

7. $-3 \cdot 4 = 4(-3)$
8. $(-6 \cdot 4)8 = 8(-6 \cdot 4)$
9. $4[-6 + (-2)] = 4(-6) + 4(-2)$

Tell whether the product is positive, negative, or zero. Then simplify.

Section 10-3, p. 270

10. $-2(-3) \cdot 4$
11. $-4(-6)(-5)$

Use the distributive property to rewrite the expression as a sum of two products. Then simplify both expressions to show they are equal.

12. $-4(-6 + 2)$
13. $-8[-9 + (-14)]$

Simplify by combining similar terms.

Section 10-4, p. 273

14. $-3m + 4n - 5m$
15. $-13k - 3 + 5 - 8k$

Check your answers with those printed at the back of the book.

10-5 *Division of Directed Numbers*

OBJECTIVES

Divide directed numbers.

Write the decimal equivalent of a fraction like $-\frac{2}{5}$.

Multiplication and division are **inverse operations.** Given a division sentence we can write a related multiplication sentence.

$$32 \div 8 = 4 \blacktriangleright 8 \cdot 4 = 32 \text{ (or } 4 \cdot 8 = 32)$$

We can use this relationship to form a pattern of signs for dividing directed numbers.

EXAMPLE 1 $-32 \div 8 = \underline{\ ?\ } \blacktriangleright$ Since $-4 \cdot 8 = -32$, $-32 \div 8 = -4$.

EXAMPLE 2 $\frac{-35}{-5} = \underline{\ ?\ } \blacktriangleright$ Since $7(-5) = -35$, $\frac{-35}{-5} = 7$.

EXAMPLE 3 $\frac{18}{-9} = \underline{\ ?\ } \blacktriangleright$ Since $-2(-9) = 18$, $\frac{18}{-9} = -2$.

If you look closely at the examples, you'll note that the pattern is the same as for multiplication. When dividing directed numbers:

► If the two signs are **alike,** the answer is **positive.**
If the two signs are **unlike,** the answer is **negative.**

Example 3 names the fraction $\frac{18}{-9}$. $\frac{-18}{9}$ names the same number.

Look at these other examples:

$$\frac{-4}{2} = \frac{4}{-2} = -\frac{4}{2} = -2 \qquad \frac{-15}{-3} = \frac{15}{3} = 5$$

A number expressed as a fraction can be changed to decimal form by doing the indicated division.

EXAMPLE 4 $\frac{-3}{5} \blacktriangleright 5\overline{)-3.0}$ with quotient -0.6 $\blacktriangleright \frac{-3}{5} = -0.6$

Complete to make a true statement.

1. Because $6 \cdot 8 = 48$, we know $\frac{48}{6} = \underline{\ ?\ }$.
2. Because $9(-4) = -36$, we know $-36 \div 9 = \underline{\ ?\ }$.
3. Because $-7 \cdot 8 = -56$, we know $\frac{-56}{-7} = \underline{\ ?\ }$.
4. Because $-5(-6) = 30$, we know $\frac{30}{-5} = \underline{\ ?\ }$.
5. Because $\underline{\ ?\ }(-10) = -60$, we know $-60 \div 6 = -10$.

Written EXERCISES

A

Simplify.

1. $-45 \div 9$
2. $50 \div 5$
3. $-60 \div 5$
4. $-48 \div 2$
5. $-24 \div 4$
6. $-5\overline{)55}$
7. $\frac{-36}{5 + 4}$
8. $\frac{-8 + (-2)}{5}$
9. $\frac{-56}{-8}$
10. $\frac{-54}{6}$
11. $\frac{-32}{-6 + (-2)}$
12. $\frac{40}{-8}$
13. $\frac{-12}{7 + (-3)}$
14. $\frac{-25}{8 + (-3)}$
15. $\frac{-7 + (-8)}{-3}$
16. $\frac{-35}{-2 + (-5)}$
17. $\frac{-28}{8 + (-4)}$
18. $\frac{-36}{-12}$

Write the decimal equivalent.

19. $-\frac{3}{5}$
20. $\frac{15}{-100}$
21. $\frac{6}{-10}$
22. $\frac{4}{5}$
23. $\frac{-4}{-20}$
24. $\frac{-9}{20}$
25. $\frac{3}{25}$
26. $\frac{-7}{8}$
27. $\frac{-6}{-8}$
28. $\frac{-7}{5}$
29. $\frac{-3}{4}$
30. $\frac{-1}{-5}$

B

True or false?

31. $-\frac{3}{4} = \frac{-3}{-4}$
32. $\frac{-4}{10} = -0.4$
33. $\frac{-4}{-7} = \frac{4}{7}$
34. $\frac{7}{8} = \frac{-7}{-8}$
35. $\frac{2}{-4} = \frac{-2}{4}$
36. $-\frac{1}{8} = \frac{8}{-1}$

10-6 *Reciprocals of Directed Numbers*

OBJECTIVES

Name the reciprocal of a directed number.

Divide by a number by multiplying by its reciprocal.

Use reciprocals to solve equations like $3c = -18$.

Two numbers are **reciprocals** of each other if their product is 1. A number and its reciprocal have like signs.

EXAMPLE 1

$\frac{1}{2} \cdot 2 = 1$ ► $\frac{1}{2}$ and 2 are reciprocals.

$-\frac{1}{2}(-2) = 1$ ► $-\frac{1}{2}$ and -2 are reciprocals.

$-0.25(-4) = 1$ ► -0.25 and -4 are reciprocals.

The Reciprocal Property ► **For every directed number r except 0,**

$$r \cdot \frac{1}{r} = \frac{1}{r} \cdot r = 1.$$

When we are dividing by a number, it is often easier to multiply by its reciprocal.

EXAMPLE 2 $-8 \div 4 = -2$ $\quad -8 \cdot \frac{1}{4} = -2$ ◄ 4 and $\frac{1}{4}$ are reciprocals.

$3 \div \frac{1}{5} = 15$ $\quad 3 \times 5 = 15$ ◄ $\frac{1}{5}$ and 5 are reciprocals.

► **For every directed number r, and every directed number s except 0,**

$$r \div s = r \cdot \frac{1}{s}.$$

We can use reciprocals to solve equations. First we identify the coefficient of the variable. Then we multiply both members of the equation by the reciprocal of the coefficient of the variable.

EXAMPLE 3 Solve $\frac{3n}{5} = -6$.

$$\frac{3}{5} \cdot n = -6 \quad \text{◀ The coefficient of } n \text{ is } \frac{3}{5}.$$

$$\frac{5}{3} \cdot \frac{3}{5} \cdot n = \frac{5}{3}(-6) \quad \text{◀ The reciprocal of } \frac{3}{5} \text{ is } \frac{5}{3}.$$

$$1 \cdot n = -10$$

$$n = -10$$

EXAMPLE 4 Solve $-6s = 42$.

$$-6 \cdot s = 42 \quad \text{◀ The coefficient of } s \text{ is } -6.$$

$$-\frac{1}{6} \cdot -6 \cdot s = -\frac{1}{6} \cdot 42 \quad \text{◀ The reciprocal of } -6 \text{ is } -\frac{1}{6}.$$

$$1 \cdot s = -7$$

$$s = -7$$

Oral EXERCISES

Name the reciprocal.

Sample 1: $\frac{2}{-3}$ *What you say:* $\frac{-3}{2}$

Sample 2: -0.5 *What you say:* $-2 \left(\text{Note: } -0.5 = -\frac{1}{2}\right)$

1. $\frac{3}{4}$
2. $\frac{1}{-3}$
3. $-\frac{3}{5}$
4. $\frac{5}{-8}$
5. $1\frac{1}{2}$
6. $-1\frac{3}{4}$
7. -0.2
8. 0.25
9. 8

Tell how to complete to make a true statement.

10. $\frac{2}{5} \div \frac{1}{4} = \frac{2}{5} \cdot$?
11. $\frac{1}{-5} \div 4 = \frac{1}{-5} \cdot$?
12. $-\frac{2}{3} \div$? $= -\frac{2}{3} \cdot \frac{4}{5}$
13. $\frac{1}{-4} \div$? $= \frac{1}{-4} \cdot 5$
14. $\frac{-7}{8} \div 1\frac{1}{3} = \frac{-7}{8} \cdot$?
15. $0.5 \div 0.2 = 0.5 \cdot$?

Written EXERCISES

Complete to make a true statement.

Sample: $\frac{3}{-10} \cdot \frac{-10}{3} = \underline{\ ?\ }$. *Solution:* $\frac{3}{-10} \cdot \frac{-10}{3} = \frac{-30}{-30} = 1$

A

1. $\frac{7}{8} \cdot \frac{8}{7} = \underline{\ ?\ }$
2. $-\frac{3}{5}\left(-\frac{5}{3}\right) = \underline{\ ?\ }$
3. $\frac{1}{-3} \cdot \underline{\ ?\ } = 1$
4. $-\frac{4}{9} \cdot \underline{\ ?\ } = 1$
5. $\underline{\ ?\ }(-1) = 1$
6. $\frac{9}{-5}\left(-\frac{5}{9}\right) = \underline{\ ?\ }$

Simplify. Use reciprocals.

Sample 1: $\frac{-2}{3} \div 4$ *Solution:* $\frac{-2}{3} \div 4 = \frac{-2}{3} \cdot \frac{1}{4} = \frac{-2}{12}$

$= \frac{-1}{6} = -\frac{1}{6}$

Sample 2: $\frac{1}{-6} \div \frac{2}{-3}$ *Solution:* $\frac{1}{-6} \div \frac{2}{-3} = \frac{1}{-6} \cdot \frac{-3}{2}$

$= \frac{-3}{-12} = \frac{1}{4}$

7. $\frac{1}{-3} \div \frac{2}{3}$
8. $\frac{-5}{6} \div 2$
9. $\frac{1}{5} \div \frac{2}{-5}$
10. $10 \div \frac{1}{-3}$
11. $7 \div \frac{1}{-4}$
12. $\frac{7}{-10} \div 3$
13. $\frac{2}{-5} \div \frac{2}{-5}$
14. $\frac{1}{-8} \div \frac{1}{-2}$
15. $-14 \div \frac{2}{7}$
16. $\frac{1}{2} \div \frac{1}{-3}$
17. $\frac{5}{-6} \div \frac{6}{-5}$
18. $\frac{1}{7} \div \frac{1}{-6}$

Solve.

Sample: $-3w = 21$ *Solution:*

$$-3w = 21$$
$$-\frac{1}{3}(-3)w = -\frac{1}{3} \cdot 21$$
$$1 \cdot w = -\frac{21}{3}$$
$$w = -7$$

19. $8b = -16$
20. $-x = -9$
21. $-4a = 28$
22. $10 = -4a$
23. $-3x = 15$
24. $-24 = 2x$
25. $-11x = -11$
26. $-12y = -4$
27. $-2a = -20$

28. $-9m = 72$ 29. $-6y = -3$ 30. $-21 = -3y$

Solve. No variable is 0.

Sample: $\frac{2}{m} = 6$ *Solution:*

$$\frac{2}{m} = 6$$
$$m \cdot \frac{2}{m} = m \cdot 6$$
$$2 = 6m$$
$$\frac{1}{6} \cdot 2 = \frac{1}{6} \cdot 6m$$
$$\frac{2}{6} = m \text{ or } m = \frac{1}{3}$$

31. $\frac{1}{x} = -6$ 32. $-\frac{3}{m} = 5$ 33. $\frac{2}{5}a = -10$ B

34. $\frac{5}{-4c} = 8$ 35. $\frac{1}{3c} = 7$ 36. $\frac{5}{-a} = 10$

Divide.

Sample: $4a \div \frac{1}{3}$ *Solution:* $4a \div \frac{1}{3} = 4a \cdot \frac{3}{1} = 12a$

37. $-3a \div \frac{1}{5}$ 38. $(-2d + 5d) \div \frac{1}{2}$ 39. $\frac{m}{5} \div 3$

40. $-6w \div 5$ 41. $\frac{-t}{10} \div \frac{-1}{5}$ 42. $4k \div (-3)$

Problems

Find the unknown number.

1. 7 divided by some number is equal to -14. What is the number?
2. The product of -15 and some number is -6. Find the number.
3. The product of $\frac{5}{-7}$ and some number is 1. What is the number?
4. The reciprocal of some number is -9. Find the number.
5. The reciprocal of some number is $-\frac{5}{7}$. Find the number.
6. The reciprocal of some number is -8. Find the number.
7. When -16 is divided by a number the result is -2. What is the number?

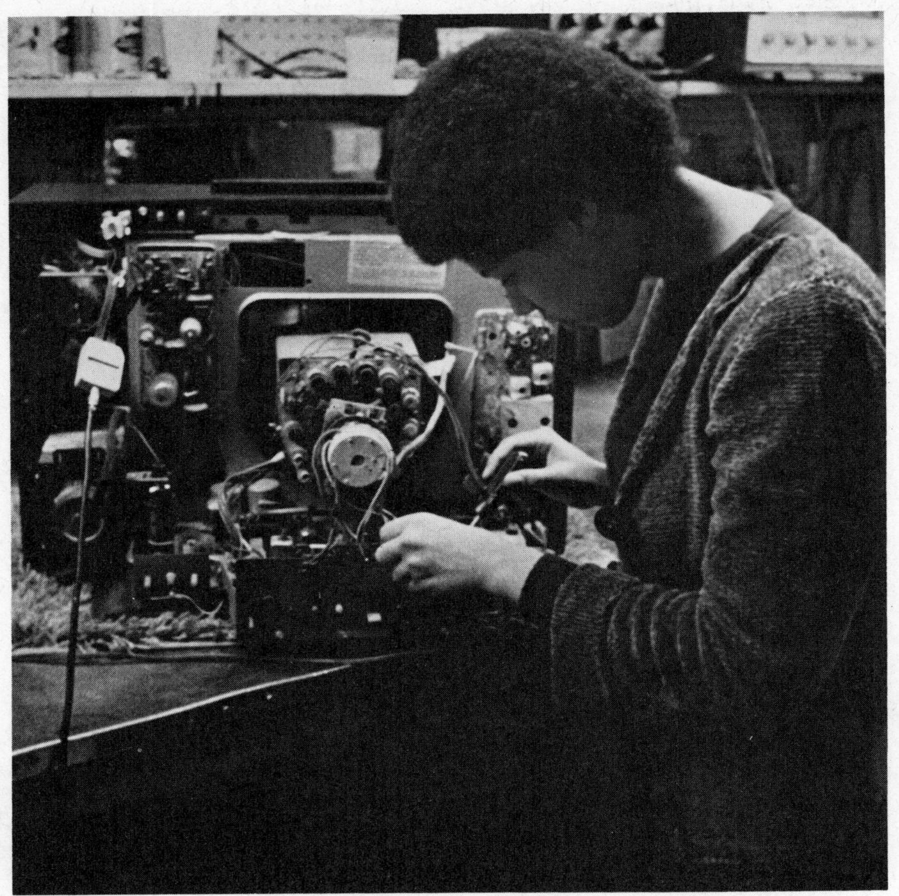

career capsule

Television and Radio Service Technician

Television and radio service technicians repair electronic products, television sets, radios, stereo components, tape recorders, intercoms and public address systems. Using voltmeters and signal generators they check suspected circuits for loose or broken connections and other probable causes of trouble. Technicians refer to wiring diagrams which show connections and contain information on repair.

Becoming a qualified service technician requires two to four years on-the-job experience. High school training should include courses in mathematics, electronics and physics.

10-7 *Functions and Directed Numbers*

OBJECTIVE

Use function equations that involve multiplying and dividing directed numbers.

The work of a function machine may involve multiplying or dividing directed numbers.

EXAMPLE 1 $f(t) = \frac{2t}{3}$; replacement set: $\{-3, -2, -1, 0, 1\}$

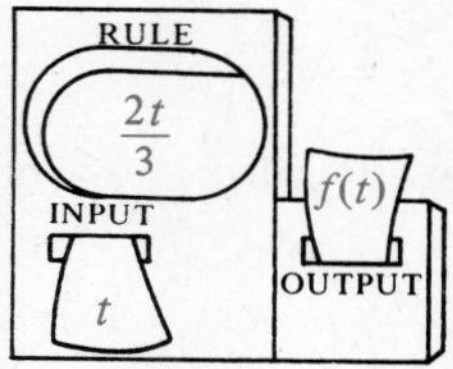

t	$f(t)$	$(t, f(t))$
-3	-2	$(-3, -2)$
-2	$-1\frac{1}{3}$	$(-2, -1\frac{1}{3})$
-1	$-\frac{2}{3}$	$\left(-1, -\frac{2}{3}\right)$
0	0	$(0, 0)$
1	$\frac{2}{3}$	$\left(1, \frac{2}{3}\right)$

Function: $\left\{(-3, -2), (-2, -1\frac{1}{3}), \left(-1, -\frac{2}{3}\right), (0, 0), \left(1, \frac{2}{3}\right)\right\}$

EXAMPLE 2 $f(x) = -\frac{1}{2}x$; replacement set: $\{-2, -1, 0, 1, 2\}$

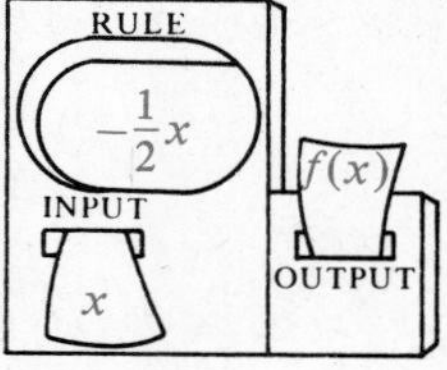

x	$f(x)$	$(x, f(x))$
-2	1	$(-2, 1)$
-1	$\frac{1}{2}$	$\left(-1, \frac{1}{2}\right)$
0	0	$(0, 0)$
1	$-\frac{1}{2}$	$\left(1, -\frac{1}{2}\right)$
2	-1	$(2, -1)$

Function: $\left\{(-2, 1), \left(-1, \frac{1}{2}\right), (0, 0), \left(1, -\frac{1}{2}\right), (2, -1)\right\}$

Graph:

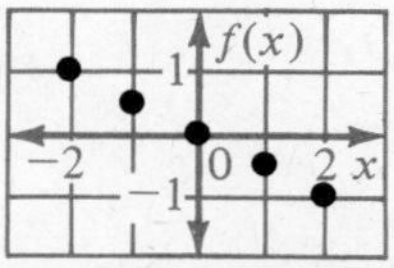

Match each function equation in Column 1 with the correct function from Column 2. The replacement set for each is $\{-2, -1\}$.

COLUMN 1	COLUMN 2
1. $f(a) = -a(-a)$	**A.** $\{(-2, 3), (-1, 6)\}$
2. $f(b) = -\frac{1}{2} \cdot b$	**B.** $\{(-2, -10), (-1, -5)\}$
3. $f(y) = -3 \cdot y$	**C.** $\{(-2, 4), (-1, 0)\}$
4. $f(c) = \frac{6}{-c}$	**D.** $\{(-2, 4), (-1, 1)\}$
5. $f(m) = m \div \frac{1}{5}$	**E.** $\{(-2, 6), (-1, 3)\}$
	F. $\left\{(-2, 1), \left(-1, \frac{1}{2}\right)\right\}$

Tell whether or not the set of ordered number pairs is a function.

6. $\{(-1, 2), (-2, 4), (3, -6)\}$

7. $\{(-3, 4), (5, 2), (-3, 1), (7, -1)\}$

8. $\{(-2, -3), (1, 3), (0, 1), (5, 9)\}$

9. $\left\{(3, -1), \left(1, -\frac{1}{3}\right), \left(-2, \frac{2}{3}\right), \left(-1, \frac{1}{3}\right)\right\}$

10. $\{(6, -3), (5, 2), (-2, 1), (-2, 3)\}$

Written EXERCISES

A

Complete the table according to the rule shown on the function machine. The replacement set is $\{-2, -1, 0, 2, 3\}$. Draw the graph of the function.

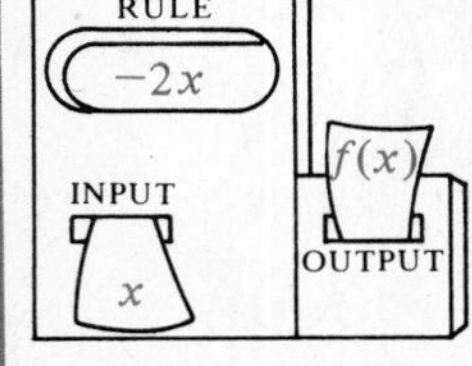

	x	$f(x)$	$(x, f(x))$
Sample:	-2	4	$(-2, 4)$
1.	-1	?	?
2.	0	?	?
3.	2	?	?
4.	3	?	?

Use the replacement set $\{2, 1, 0, -1, -2, -3\}$ to complete the table for each function machine. Compare the completed tables and comment.

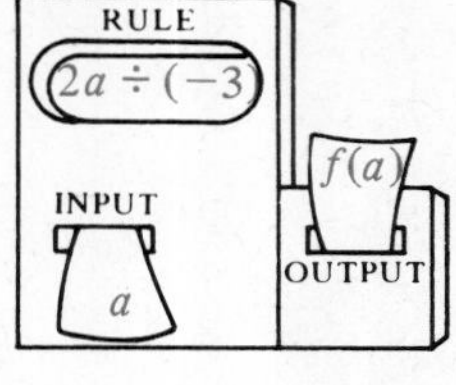

	a	$f(a)$	$(a, f(a))$
Sample:	2	$-\frac{4}{3}$	$\left(2, -\frac{4}{3}\right)$
5.	1	?	?
6.	0	?	?
7.	-1	?	?
8.	-2	?	?
9.	-3	?	?

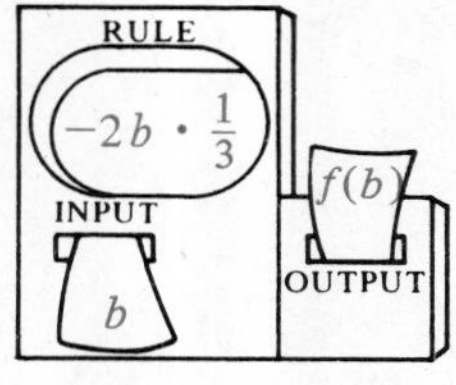

	b	$f(b)$	$(b, f(b))$
Sample:	2	$-\frac{4}{3}$	$\left(2, -\frac{4}{3}\right)$
10.	1	?	?
11.	0	?	?
12.	-1	?	?
13.	-2	?	?
14.	-3	?	?

Complete the set of number pairs by using the given function equation. The replacement set is $\{-3, -2, 0, 1\}$.

Sample: $f(x) = -\frac{x}{4}$: $\left\{\left(-3, \frac{3}{4}\right), \left(-2, \frac{1}{2}\right), (0, \underline{\ ?\ }), (1, \underline{\ ?\ })\right\}$

Solution: $\left\{\left(-3, \frac{3}{4}\right), \left(-2, \frac{1}{2}\right), (0, 0), \left(1, -\frac{1}{4}\right)\right\}$

15. $f(a) = \frac{a}{3}$: $\left\{(-3, -1), \left(-2, -\frac{2}{3}\right), (0, \underline{\ ?\ }), (1, \underline{\ ?\ })\right\}$

16. $f(x) = -2x + 1$: $\{(-3, 7), (-2, 5), (0, \underline{\ ?\ }), (1, \underline{\ ?\ })\}$

17. $f(w) = -w \cdot \frac{1}{5}$: $\left\{\left(-3, \frac{3}{5}\right), \left(-2, \frac{2}{5}\right), (0, \underline{\ ?\ }), (1, \underline{\ ?\ })\right\}$

18. $f(y) = 3y - 2$: $\{(-3, -11), (-2, \underline{\ ?\ }), (0, -2), (1, \underline{\ ?\ })\}$

19. $f(t) = \frac{-2t}{5}$: $\left\{\left(-3, \frac{6}{5}\right), (-2, \underline{\ ?\ }), (0, \underline{\ ?\ }), (1, \underline{\ ?\ })\right\}$

20. $f(c) = 4c \div 2$: $\{(-3, \underline{\ ?\ }), (-2, \underline{\ ?\ }), (0, 0), (1, \underline{\ ?\ })\}$

Write the number pairs indicated by the given function equation and replacement set.

B

21. $f(n) = -3n + 2$: $\{-2, -1, 0, 2, 3, 4\}$

22. $f(a) = \frac{3}{4}(a) - 1$: $\{-4, -2, 0, 2, 8\}$

23. $f(y) = \frac{y}{2} + 1$: $\{-2, -1, 0, 6\}$

24. $f(b) = (-b)(-b)$: $\{-3, -2, 4, 5\}$

25. $f(m) = \frac{6}{m}$: $\{-5, -4, -3, -2, -1\}$

26. $f(w) = -2 \cdot 3w$: $\left\{-\frac{1}{2}, -\frac{1}{3}, -2, 3\right\}$

27. $f(c) = \frac{7}{-c}$: $\{-4, -3, -2, 3\}$

28. $f(h) = -3 \div h$: $\left\{-9, -3, 6, \frac{1}{3}, \frac{1}{2}\right\}$

29. $f(n) = 5n^2$: $\{-2, -1, 0, 2\}$

30. $f(d) = d \cdot \frac{2}{d}$: $\{-5, -3, -1, 2, 4\}$

SELF-TEST 2

Be sure that you understand the term *reciprocal* (p. 278).

Simplify if necessary. Then divide.

Section 10-5, p. 276

1. $\frac{-36}{4}$

2. $\frac{-15}{-5}$

3. $\frac{-7 + (-5)}{3}$

4. $\frac{-1 + (-6)}{-3}$

Section 10-6, p. 278 Simplify. Use reciprocals.

5. $\frac{-9}{16} \div \frac{-9}{16}$

6. $-21 \div \frac{-3}{7}$

7. $-18 \div \frac{3}{4}$

8. $-\frac{4}{3} \div \frac{3}{4}$

Solve.

9. $2x = -18$

10. $-3y = -24$

11. $4z = 28$

12. $8m = -16$

Complete.

Section 10-7, p. 283

13. $f(x) = -\frac{1}{2}x$; $\{(0, \underline{\ ?\ }), (-4, \underline{\ ?\ }), (4, \underline{\ ?\ }), (-5, \underline{\ ?\ })\}$

Check your answers with those printed at the back of the book.

chapter summary

1. The product of any directed number and 0 is 0.
2. The product of any directed number and 1 is that directed number.
3. Multiplication of directed numbers is commutative and associative. Also, the distributive property holds true for directed numbers.

$$r \cdot s = s \cdot r$$ ◄ The commutative property

$$r \cdot (st) = (rs) \cdot t$$ ◄ The associative property

$$r(s + t) = rs + rt$$ ◄ The distributive property

4. In multiplying two directed numbers, if the two signs are **alike,** the product is **positive.** If the two signs are **unlike,** the product is **negative.**
5. In dividing two directed numbers, if the two signs are **alike,** the quotient is **positive.** If the two signs are **unlike,** the quotient is **negative.**
6. The distributive property can be used to simplify expressions which involve directed numbers.
7. Two numbers are **reciprocals** of each other if their product is 1.
8. Dividing by a directed number is the same as multiplying by its reciprocal. That is, for every directed number r, and every directed number s except 0, $r \div s = r \cdot \frac{1}{s}$.

challenge topics *Probability*

Suppose you toss a penny and a nickel at the same time. What combinations of heads and tails might come up? Study the chart.

Nickel

Penny		H	T
	h	h,H	h,T
	t	t,H	t,T

The chart shows that there are four possible **outcomes,** that is, four ways for the coins to come up heads and tails. A coin is **honest** if after many tosses it comes up heads very nearly the same number of times it comes up tails. Assuming the two coins are honest, each of the four outcomes is said to be **equally likely.** From the chart we see that the probability of an outcome of two heads (h,H) is 1 out of 4 or $\frac{1}{4}$. We write: $P(h,H) = \frac{1}{4}$.

What are the possible outcomes when two dice are tossed? The sum of the number of dots on the upper faces is considered the outcome.

	1	**2**	**3**	**4**	**5**	**6**
1	2	3	4	5	6	**7**
2	3	4	5	6	7	8
3	4	5	6	7	8	9
4	5	6	7	8	9	10
5	6	7	8	9	10	11
6	7	8	9	10	11	12

◄ **1 + 6 = 7**

The table shows that there are 36 possible outcomes. If the dice are honest, each of the outcomes is equally likely. The probability of any one is $\frac{1}{36}$. The table shows that an outcome of 6 may occur in 5 different ways. $P(6) = 5 \times \frac{1}{36} = \frac{5}{36}$

1. Two coins are tossed. What is the probability of getting two tails?

2. Two coins are tossed. What is the probability of getting a head and a tail?
3. A single coin is tossed 100 times. It comes up heads 52 times and tails 48 times. Is the coin honest? Explain.
4. Two dice are tossed. Assuming equally likely outcomes, what is the probability of an outcome of 4? of 6? of 8?
5. Two dice are tossed. What is the probability of getting an 8 by having both dice come up with a 4?

chapter test

Simplify.

1. $6(-8)$
2. $-9 \cdot 5$
3. $\frac{36}{-4}$
4. $\frac{-54}{6}$
5. $-3(-3)(-3)$
6. $-2(-2)(-2)$
7. $-1 \cdot 1(-8)$
8. $-2 \cdot 4(-5)$
9. $\frac{5 + (-17)}{4}$
10. $\frac{-28}{-4}$
11. $2m + 3t - 6m$
12. $4z - 3b + 2b - 6z$

Name the reciprocal.

13. $-\frac{1}{2}$
14. $1\frac{2}{3}$
15. -0.75

Solve.

16. $4y + (-2) = 22$
17. $\frac{x}{3} = -7$
18. $5k + (-k) = 20$
19. $5a - 2 = 13$
20. $-4m = -3 \cdot 8$
21. $\frac{2}{3}x = -8$

Complete using the given function equation.

22. $f(m) = 5m + 2$: {(0, __?__), (1, __?__), (3, __?__)}
23. $f(a) = 3a - 4$: {(0, __?__), (−1, __?__), (5, __?__), (−2, __?__)}

Review of Skills

Simplify.

1. $3 + (-8)$
2. $\frac{3}{4} \cdot \frac{2}{5}$
3. $-4 \cdot 3$
4. $\frac{2}{3} \cdot \frac{1}{2}$
5. $-7 \cdot 2$
6. $-6 + (-2)$
7. $-6 + 6$
8. $-1.8 \cdot \frac{1}{2}$
9. $5(-3)$

Name the additive inverse.

10. -7
11. 10
12. $-\frac{5}{7}$
13. 5

Solve.

14. $x + 4 = 17$
15. $-3x = 27$
16. $5x = 21$
17. $21 = 6 + x$
18. $\frac{2}{5} \cdot x = -6$
19. $32 = 4x$
20. $x + 9 = 6$
21. $\frac{1}{3} \cdot x = 11$
22. $7x = -56$

Use the distributive property to simplify.

23. $8m - 3m$
24. $\frac{5}{6}x + \frac{2}{3}x$
25. $5y + 4y$

Complete to make a true statement. Use $<$ or $>$.

26. $7 \underline{\ ?\ } 9$
27. $-8 \underline{\ ?\ } -5$
28. $-7 \underline{\ ?\ } 4$
29. $3 \cdot 2 \underline{\ ?\ } 5$
30. $-\frac{1}{3} \underline{\ ?\ } -\frac{4}{5}$
31. $4(-1) \underline{\ ?\ } -3$
32. $-6 \underline{\ ?\ } -9$
33. $10 \underline{\ ?\ } 12$
34. $3 + 4 \underline{\ ?\ } 9$

True or false?

35. $6 > 5$ and $5 > 6$.
36. $4 < 7$ and $4 + 3 < 7 + 3$.
37. $5 > 4$ and $5 \cdot 3 > 4 \cdot 3$.
38. $4 < 6$ and $4(-2) < 6(-2)$.

Left: Early aerial weather observers.

Right: Console of all-electronic weather forecasting system.

Solving Equations and Inequalities

11-1 *Equations of Type* $x + a = b$

OBJECTIVE
Solve equations like $x + 7 = 15$.

The equation $x + 7 = 15$ is of the type $x + a = b$, where x is the variable, and a and b are directed numbers.

These equations are also of type $x + a = b$, although they may look different.

$m - 3 = 7$	$15 = x + 3.5$	$-6 = 2 + h$
$m + (-3) = 7$	$x + 3.5 = 15$	$h + 2 = -6$

We solve equations of the type $x + a = b$ by using the addition property of equality.

EXAMPLE 1

$$x + 7 = 15$$
$$x + 7 + (-7) = 15 + (-7) \quad \text{Add } -7 \text{ to both members.}$$
$$x + 0 = 15 + (-7) \quad 7 + (-7) = 0$$
$$x = 8$$

EXAMPLE 2

$$3 = -10 + n$$
$$10 + 3 = 10 + (-10) + n \quad \text{Add 10 to both members.}$$
$$10 + 3 = 0 + n \quad 10 + (-10) = 0$$
$$13 = n$$

EXAMPLE 3

$$t - 7 = -10$$
$$t + (-7) = -10 \quad \text{To subtract 7, add its opposite.}$$
$$t + (-7) + 7 = -10 + 7 \quad \text{Add 7 to both members.}$$
$$t + 0 = -10 + 7 \quad -7 + 7 = 0$$
$$t = -3$$

EXERCISES

State in the form $x + a = b$.

Sample: $m - 3 = -5$ *What you say:* $m + (-3) = -5$

1. $-13 + k = 20$
2. $-4 + y = -3$
3. $-6 = x + 3$
4. $w - (-9) = 20$

5. $z + (-2) = -7$

6. $u - 10 = 52$

7. $-\frac{3}{4} + t = 1$

8. $-\frac{1}{3} + z = -6$

9. $(-3 + 2) + y = 10$

10. $q - (3 + 6) = -9$

11. $14 = r + 2$

12. $16 = -4 + y$

Written EXERCISES

Complete.

Sample:

$$\begin{aligned} y + 3 &= 12 \\ y + 3 + (-3) &= 12 + (-3) \\ y + \underline{\ ?\ } &= 12 + (-3) \\ y &= \underline{\ ?\ } \end{aligned}$$

Solution:

$$\begin{aligned} y + 3 &= 12 \\ y + 3 + (-3) &= 12 + (-3) \\ y + 0 &= 12 + (-3) \\ y &= 9 \end{aligned}$$

A

1. $$\begin{aligned} m - 6 &= 19 \\ m + (-6) + 6 &= 19 + 6 \\ m + \underline{\ ?\ } &= 19 + 6 \\ m &= \underline{\ ?\ } \end{aligned}$$

2. $$\begin{aligned} k + 14 &= 7 \\ k + 14 + \underline{\ ?\ } &= 7 + (-14) \\ k + \underline{\ ?\ } &= 7 + (-14) \\ k &= \underline{\ ?\ } \end{aligned}$$

3. $$\begin{aligned} 5\tfrac{1}{4} + v &= 8 \\ -5\tfrac{1}{4} + 5\tfrac{1}{4} + v &= 8 + \underline{\ ?\ } \\ \underline{\ ?\ } + v &= 8 + (-5\tfrac{1}{4}) \\ v &= \underline{\ ?\ } \end{aligned}$$

4. $$\begin{aligned} -6 + x &= 12 \\ 6 + (-6) + x &= 12 + \underline{\ ?\ } \\ \underline{\ ?\ } + x &= 12 + 6 \\ x &= \underline{\ ?\ } \end{aligned}$$

Solve and check.

Sample: $t + (-8) = 24$

Solution:

$$\begin{aligned} t + (-8) &= 24 \\ t + (-8) + 8 &= 24 + 8 \\ t &= 32 \end{aligned}$$

Check: $t + (-8) \stackrel{?}{=} 24$

$32 + (-8)$	24
24	24 ✓

5. $-2 + r = 20$

6. $x + 4 = -13$

7. $z + (-13) = 9$

8. $-5 + w = 15$

9. $-16 + n = 25$

10. $-44 = u + 5$

11. $b + \frac{2}{3} = -5$

12. $s + \frac{1}{5} = 2\frac{3}{10}$

13. $-6 = m + (-9)$

14. $n + (-51) = 0$

15. $x + 14 = 0$

16. $\frac{5}{6} + z = 5$

17. $m + 1.8 = 6.9$

18. $-18.5 + k = 26.3$

19. $y - 4 = -2\frac{1}{2}$

20. $a + \left(-\frac{2}{3}\right) = 6$

B

21. $n - \left(-\frac{1}{3}\right) = \frac{1}{6}$

22. $y + \frac{3}{8} = \frac{3}{4}$

23. $-\frac{1}{6} + t = -\frac{1}{12}$

24. $-\frac{3}{5} = -\frac{10}{2} + p$

25. $-0.6 = -3.2 + v$

26. $-0.06 = -6.2 + s$

Solve for y.

27. $y + s = z$

28. $-n + y = h$

29. $d = b + y$

30. $k = y - w$

31. $r + y = -t$

32. $y + (-a) = -b$

Solve for z.

C

33. $z - r = s$

34. $z + (-p) = q$

35. $m = z + q$

36. $z - (-x) = y$

37. $z - g = -h$

38. $d + z = f$

Williamina Fleming 1857–1911

Williamina Fleming entered the field of astronomy as a clerk at the Harvard College Observatory in 1881. Demonstrating an obvious talent for astronomy, she became assistant to Professor Edward Pickering and soon excelled in the field. Her chief work dealt with classification of stars based on patterns photographed when their light was scattered through a prism. In 1890 Fleming published the *Draper Catalogue of Stella Spectra*, classifying 10,351 stars. She was admitted to the Royal Astronomical Society in 1906.

11-2 *Equations of Type* $ax = b$

OBJECTIVE

Solve equations like $3x = 45$.

The equation $3x = 45$ is of the type $ax = b$. x is a variable. a and b are directed numbers.

Here are some other equations of this type.

$$0.3 = -2n \blacktriangleright -2n = 0.3 \qquad \frac{3}{7} = -3b \blacktriangleright -3b = \frac{3}{7}$$

We solve equations of the type $ax = b$ by using the multiplication property of equality. We multiply by the reciprocal of a, the coefficient of x.

EXAMPLE 1

$$4m = 3$$

$$\frac{1}{4} \cdot 4m = \frac{1}{4} \cdot 3 \quad \blacktriangleleft \text{ Multiply both members by the reciprocal of 4.}$$

$$1 \cdot m = \frac{1}{4} \cdot 3 \quad \blacktriangleleft \frac{1}{4} \cdot 4 = 1$$

$$m = \frac{3}{4}$$

EXAMPLE 2

$$-\frac{3t}{2} = 9$$

$$-\frac{3}{2} \cdot t = 9 \quad \blacktriangleleft \text{ The coefficient of } t \text{ is } -\frac{3}{2}.$$

$$-\frac{2}{3}\left(-\frac{3}{2}\right)t = -\frac{2}{3} \cdot 9 \quad \blacktriangleleft \text{ Multiply both members by } -\frac{2}{3}.$$

$$1 \cdot t = -\frac{2}{3} \cdot 9 \quad \blacktriangleleft -\frac{2}{3}\left(-\frac{3}{2}\right) = 1$$

$$t = -6$$

EXAMPLE 3

Solve $\frac{x}{m} = t$ for x. $\blacktriangleleft$ $m \neq 0$. Otherwise, $\frac{1}{m}$ has no meaning.

$$m \cdot \frac{1}{m} \cdot x = m \cdot t \quad \blacktriangleleft \text{ Multiply both members by } m.$$

$$1 \cdot x = m \cdot t \quad \blacktriangleleft m \cdot \frac{1}{m} = 1 \text{ if } m \neq 0.$$

$$x = mt$$

EXERCISES

Name the reciprocal of the coefficient of the variable.

Sample: $4x = 20$ *What you say:* $\frac{1}{4}$

1. $3y = 12$
2. $-6m = 36$
3. $-7t = 49$
4. $8y = \frac{1}{4}$
5. $\frac{k}{6} = 3$
6. $\frac{s}{-5} = -2$
7. $\frac{1}{4}q = 6\frac{1}{4}$
8. $\frac{2}{5}b = -10$
9. $\frac{-z}{4} = 7$

Tell what number should replace the question mark to complete the equation.

Sample: $\underline{\ ?\ } \cdot \frac{3}{2}y = y$

What you say: $\frac{2}{3}$, since $\frac{2}{3} \cdot \frac{3}{2} \cdot y = 1y = y$.

10. $\underline{\ ?\ } \cdot 5s = s$
11. $\underline{\ ?\ }(-8z) = z$
12. $-\frac{1}{2}p \cdot \underline{\ ?\ } = p$
13. $\underline{\ ?\ }\left(-\frac{7g}{9}\right) = g$
14. $\underline{\ ?\ } \cdot \frac{2}{3}x = x$
15. $\frac{-6m}{-5} \cdot \underline{\ ?\ } = m$

Written EXERCISES

Solve and check.

Sample: $\frac{4}{5}c = 20$

Solution:

$$\frac{4}{5}c = 20$$
$$\frac{5}{4} \cdot \frac{4}{5} \cdot c = 20 \cdot \frac{5}{4}$$
$$c = 25$$

Check: $\frac{4}{5}c \stackrel{?}{=} 20$

$\frac{4}{5} \cdot 25$	20
20	20 ✓

A

1. $3x = 39$
2. $-y = 56$
3. $-18 = 5q$
4. $-7a = 63$
5. $\frac{-3u}{5} = -21$
6. $\frac{1}{4}b = 3$
7. $w(-4) = -23$
8. $16s = 64$
9. $7d = -9$
10. $\frac{-1}{6}v = 10$

Solve for the underlined variable. Assume that no divisor has the value 0.

11. $g\underline{d} = v$ **12.** $\underline{g}d = v$ **13.** $a = l\underline{w}$

14. $a = \underline{l}w$ **15.** $i = p\underline{r}$ **16.** $i = \underline{p}r$

17. $\pi\underline{d} = c$ **18.** $\pi\underline{c} = s$ **19.** $s = \underline{c}t$

Solve.

20. $15 = 7v$ **21.** $8y = -40$ B

22. $-3j = -5$ **23.** $\frac{n}{7} = 2$

24. $\frac{2z}{3} = 4$ **25.** $\frac{7}{-5}q = 25$

26. $0.3s = 18$ **27.** $-0.02 = -0.05x$

28. $-2.3a = 46$ **29.** $2.5h = -0.5$

Solve the formula for the indicated variable.

30. Distance:
$d = rt$
Solve for t.

31. Circumference of a circle:
$c = 2\pi r$
Solve for r.

32. Volume of a cone:
$v = \frac{1}{3}bh$
Solve for b.

33. Volume of a cylinder:
$v = bh$
Solve for h.

Solve for the underlined variable. Then let $r = -\frac{4}{5}$, $t = \frac{1}{5}$, $s = 4$, and $u = 8$, and find the value of that variable.

Sample: $s\underline{x} = r$

Solution: $\frac{1}{s} \cdot sx = \frac{1}{s} \cdot r \blacktriangleright x = \frac{r}{s}$

If $r = -\frac{4}{5}$ and $s = 4$, $x = -\frac{4}{5} \div 4 = -\frac{4}{5} \cdot \frac{1}{4} = -\frac{1}{5}$

34. $\underline{b}r = t$ **35.** $u\underline{n} = s$ **36.** $\underline{a}t = u$ C

37. $-r = u\underline{m}$ **38.** $-st = -r\underline{k}$ **39.** $-t\underline{p} = t$

40. $\frac{1}{s} \cdot \underline{b} = u$ **41.** $t\underline{c} = -s$ **42.** $ut = \underline{d}s$

11-3 *Equations of Type* $ax + bx = c$

OBJECTIVE
Solve equations like $5x + 6x = 14$ and $-w = -8w + 14$.

The equation $5x + 6x = 14$ is of the type $ax + bx = c$.

$ax + bx = c$ ◄ x is a variable.
a, b, and c are directed numbers.
ax and bx are similar terms.

These equations are also of this type.

$$\frac{1}{4}t + \frac{1}{2}t = 5 \qquad y = 12 - 3y \qquad 7 + 5n = 3n$$

$$1y + 3y = 12 \qquad 3n + (-5n) = 7$$

To solve equations in which the variable appears in more than one term, we first combine similar terms. Then we use the properties of equality.

EXAMPLE 1 $3r + 7r = 40$

$10r = 40$ ◄ Add $3r + 7r$.

$\frac{1}{10} \cdot 10r = \frac{1}{10} \cdot 40$ ◄ Multiply both members by $\frac{1}{10}$.

$1 \cdot r = \frac{1}{10} \cdot 40$ ◄ $\frac{1}{10} \cdot 10 = 1$

$r = 4$

EXAMPLE 2 $\frac{3}{5}x + \frac{4}{5}x = -21$

$\frac{7}{5}x = -21$ ◄ Add $\frac{3}{5}x + \frac{4}{5}x$.

$\frac{5}{7} \cdot \frac{7}{5}x = \frac{5}{7}(-21)$ ◄ Multiply both members by $\frac{5}{7}$.

$1 \cdot x = \frac{5}{7}(-21)$ ◄ $\frac{5}{7} \cdot \frac{7}{5} = 1$

$x = -15$

EXAMPLE 3

$$-w = -8w + 14$$
$$8w + (-w) = 8w + (-8w) + 14 \quad \blacktriangleleft \text{ Add } 8w \text{ to both members.}$$
$$8w + (-w) = 0 + 14 \quad \blacktriangleleft -8w + 8w = 0$$
$$7w = 14 \quad \blacktriangleleft \text{ Combine similar terms.}$$
$$\frac{1}{7} \cdot 7w = \frac{1}{7} \cdot 14 \quad \blacktriangleleft \text{ Multiply both members by } \frac{1}{7}.$$
$$1 \cdot w = \frac{1}{7} \cdot 14 \quad \blacktriangleleft \frac{1}{7} \cdot 7 = 1$$
$$w = 2$$

EXAMPLE 4

$$3x + 6 = 2x - 4$$
$$-2x + 3x + 6 = -2x + 2x - 4 \quad \blacktriangleleft \text{ Add } -2x \text{ to both members.}$$
$$x + 6 = 0 - 4$$
$$x + 6 + (-6) = 0 - 4 + (-6) \quad \blacktriangleleft \text{ Add } -6 \text{ to both members.}$$
$$x + 0 = -10 \quad \blacktriangleleft 6 + (-6) = 0$$
$$x = -10$$

EXAMPLE 5

$$rx + tx = k, \text{ and } r + t \neq 0$$
$$x(r + t) = k \quad \blacktriangleleft \text{ Distributive property}$$
$$x(r + t)\frac{1}{r + t} = k \cdot \frac{1}{r + t} \quad \blacktriangleleft \text{ Multiply both members by } \frac{1}{r + t}.$$
$$x \cdot 1 = k \cdot \frac{1}{r + t} \quad \blacktriangleleft (r + t) \cdot \frac{1}{r + t} = 1$$
$$x = \frac{k}{r + t}$$

Combine similar terms to give a simpler name.

1. $3x + 5x$
2. $2y + (-3y)$
3. $\frac{1}{7}a + \frac{2}{7}a$
4. $\frac{3}{2}q + \left(-\frac{1}{2}q\right)$
5. $3k + 7k + 4k$
6. $2s + (-3s) + 5s$
7. $10m + 2n - 3m$
8. $-25p + 12g + 13p$
9. $-7t + (-3t)$
10. $15r + r + (-1)$

True or false?

11. $\frac{2z}{5} + \frac{z}{5}$ is the same as $\frac{3z}{5}$.

12. $\frac{c}{8} + \frac{c}{4}$ is the same as $\frac{3c}{4}$.

13. $5f + \frac{1}{5}f$ is the same as $\frac{6}{5}f$.

14. $-17b + 3b$ is the same as $-14b$.

Written EXERCISES

Complete.

Sample:

$$3n + (-5n) = 12$$
$$\underline{\ ?\ } \cdot n = 12$$
$$\underline{\ ?\ }(-2n) = 12 \cdot \underline{\ ?\ }$$
$$n = \underline{\ ?\ }$$

Solution:

$$3n + (-5n) = 12$$
$$-2n = 12$$
$$-\frac{1}{2}(-2n) = 12\left(-\frac{1}{2}\right)$$
$$n = -6$$

A

1. $$6a - 2a = 12$$
$$\underline{\ ?\ } \cdot a = 12$$
$$\underline{\ ?\ } \cdot 4a = 12 \cdot \underline{\ ?\ }$$
$$a = \underline{\ ?\ }$$

2. $$-7b + (-b) = -16$$
$$\underline{\ ?\ } \cdot b = -16$$
$$\underline{\ ?\ }(-8b) = -16 \cdot \underline{\ ?\ }$$
$$b = \underline{\ ?\ }$$

3. $$\frac{1}{4}x = \frac{3}{4}x + 5$$
$$-\frac{3}{4}x + \frac{1}{4}x = \frac{3}{4}x - \frac{3}{4}x + 5$$
$$\underline{\ ?\ } \cdot x = \underline{\ ?\ } + 5$$
$$x = \underline{\ ?\ }$$

4. $$\frac{n}{2} + \frac{2n}{5} = 18$$
$$\underline{\ ?\ } \cdot n = 18$$
$$\underline{\ ?\ } \cdot \frac{9}{10} \cdot n = 18 \cdot \underline{\ ?\ }$$
$$n = \underline{\ ?\ }$$

5. $$-13m + (-5m) = 36$$
$$\underline{\ ?\ } \cdot m = 36$$
$$\underline{\ ?\ }(-18)m = 36 \cdot \underline{\ ?\ }$$
$$m = \underline{\ ?\ }$$

6. $$-\frac{2}{3}s = \frac{1}{3}s + (-8)$$
$$-\frac{1}{3}s + \left(-\frac{2}{3}s\right) = -\frac{1}{3}s + \frac{1}{3}s + (-8)$$
$$\underline{\ ?\ } \cdot s = -8$$
$$s = \underline{\ ?\ }$$

Solve for the variable indicated. Assume that no divisor has the value 0.

Sample: Solve $tm + km = s$ for m. *Solution:*

$$tm + km = s$$
$$m(t + k) = s$$
$$m = \frac{s}{t + k}$$

7. Solve $cz + dz = b$ for z.
8. Solve $2d - kd = u$ for d.
9. Solve $g = vq + rq$ for q.
10. Solve $-wt - ft = 20$ for t.
11. Solve $3h + jh = -3$ for h.
12. Solve $ds + ps = -a$ for s.

Solve and check.

13. $2x + 5x = 13$
14. $-2z + (-4z) = -18$
15. $3y + (-2y) = -7$
16. $4 = -5w + (-4w)$
17. $-38 = 15b + (-34b)$
18. $2.22 = 0.4m - 0.03m$
19. $-0.25 = -1.3q - 1.2q$
20. $44h - 9h = 70$
21. $\frac{7m}{9} + \frac{2m}{9} = -\frac{1}{9}$
22. $\frac{r}{6} + \frac{5r}{6} = 2$

Sample: $7r = 2r + 10$

Solution:

$$7r = 2r + 10$$
$$7r - 2r = 2r - 2r + 10$$
$$5r = 10$$
$$\frac{1}{5} \cdot 5r = 10 \cdot \frac{1}{5}$$
$$r = 2$$

Check: $7r \stackrel{?}{=} 2r + 10$

$7(2)$	$2(2) + 10$
14	$4 + 10$
14	14 ✓

23. $12a = 19a - 35$
24. $-8t = 2t + 5$
25. $3x = -2x + 30$
26. $-10k = 3k + 39$
27. $-1 + (-5n) = -6n$
28. $6c = 5c + 5$

B

29. $9y = 73 + y - 1$
30. $-8 + 3x + (-2) = 2x + 8$
31. $3p + 5 = 2p + 8$
32. $c = 6.3 - 0.05c$
33. $-\frac{5}{8}x + 3 = -\frac{3}{8}x + 7$
34. $\frac{2m}{3} - \frac{5m}{6} = 24$
35. $0.6z = 0.2z + 1.6$
36. $11a - 4a = -2a + 45$

C

37. $-3[x + (-2)] = 11 - 5x$
38. $3(z + 1) = 2(z - 2)$
39. $7y - 2(y - 5) = 25$
40. $4(h + 5) + h = 35$
41. $p - \frac{1}{2}(p + 4p) + 4 = 30$
42. $\frac{1}{3}(9w - 18) + 2w = 14$

11-4 *Applying Formulas*

OBJECTIVE

Use basic formulas to solve practical problems.

EXAMPLE 1 Find the volume.

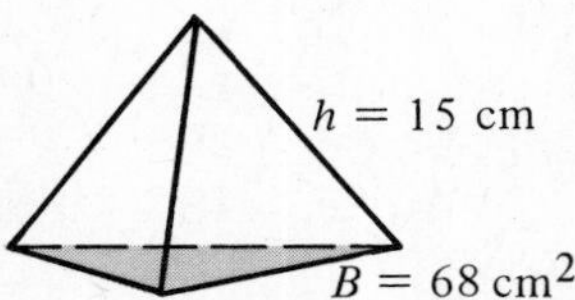

Formula: $V = \frac{1}{3}Bh$

$B = 68,\ h = 15$

$V = \frac{1}{3} \cdot 68 \cdot 15$

$= 340$

The volume is 340 cm^3.

EXAMPLE 2 Find the height.

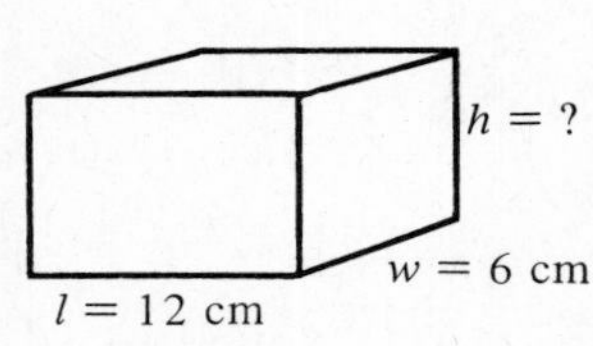

Volume: 576 cm^3

Formula: $V = lwh$

$$\frac{1}{lw} \cdot V = \frac{1}{lw} \cdot lwh$$

$$\frac{V}{lw} = h$$

Formula for h: $h = \frac{V}{lw}$

$$h = \frac{576}{12 \times 6} = 8$$

The height of the box is 8 cm.

EXAMPLE 3 A bank makes a one-year loan of $25,000 to a business. If the interest for the year is $1750, what is the rate of interest? Formula: Interest = principal × rate × time or, $I = prt$.

$$\frac{1}{pt} \cdot I = \frac{1}{pt} \cdot prt$$

$$\frac{I}{pt} = r$$

► Formula for r: $r = \frac{I}{pt}$.

$$r = \frac{1750}{25{,}000} = 0.07 = 7\%$$

The rate of interest is 7%.

In Examples 1–3 we simplified the arithmetic by first solving for the variable. Of course, we could have substituted first, and then solved the resulting equation.

Problems

Solve. Use the formula $A = lw$ (Area = length × width).

1. The length of a rectangular swimming pool is 19 meters. The area of the pool is 133 square meters. Find the width.
2. The dimensions of a rectangular picture are 12 cm by 18 cm. What is the area of the picture?

Solve. Use the formula $I = prt$ (Interest = principal × rate × time).

3. Sheila borrowed \$2700.00 from the bank at a rate of $9\frac{1}{4}\%$. She paid \$499.50 in interest. How long did she keep the loan?
4. Rudy borrowed \$1000 for a period of 9 months $\left(\frac{3}{4}\text{ year}\right)$. He paid \$30.00 interest. What was the rate of interest?
5. A homeowner borrowed money at the rate of $8\frac{1}{2}\%$ for a period of 2 years. The interest charged was \$255. What was the amount of the loan?
6. A couple borrowed \$4000 for 2 years at 7% interest. How much interest did they pay?

Solve. Use the formula Area $= \frac{1}{2} \times$ altitude × sum of bases,

$A = \frac{1}{2}as$.

7. The area of a trapezoid is 640 square centimeters. The sum of the bases is 80 cm. Find the altitude.

base
altitude
base

8. What is the area of this trapezoid?

28.3 m
5 m
52.5 m

9. The area of this trapezoid is 18 square centimeters. What is the altitude?

5 cm
?
7 cm

10. The area of this trapezoid is 540 square meters. What is the sum of the lengths of the bases?

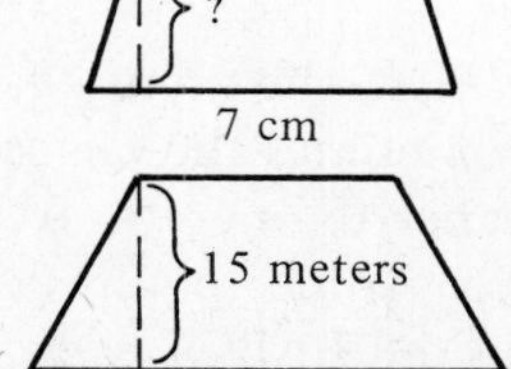

SELF-TEST 1

Solve and check.

Section 11-1, p. 292 1. $r + 3 = 8$ 2. $-7 = t - 2$

Section 11-2, p. 295 Solve and check.

3. $2t = -10$ 4. $-7a = 21$

Section 11-3, p. 298 Solve and check.

5. $8k - 4k = -2$ 6. $2b = 3b - 4$

Section 11-4, p. 302 Solve. Use $A = lw$.

7. The area of a rectangle is 26 square meters. The width is 4 meters. What is the length?
8. A plot of land is 13 meters long and has an area of 143 square meters. What is the width?

Check your answers with those printed at the back of the book.

consumer notes *Energy Guide*

The Energy Efficiency Ratio, EER, is used to determine the efficiency of room air conditioners. The EER is computed by using the air conditioner's cooling capacity, which is measured in British thermal units (Btu's) and the electrical power it requires, which is measured in watts. To obtain the EER, divide $\frac{\text{Btu's}}{\text{watts}}$. The greater the EER, the more efficient the machine is.

Sometimes the air conditioner which is more expensive to buy is cheaper to operate. Would you rather buy an 8,000 Btu air conditioner which requires 900 watts or one which requires 1300 watts? Find the EER of each.

11-5 *The Addition Property of Inequality*

OBJECTIVES
Solve inequalities like $x + 5 > -1$ and $x + 6 \leq 3$.
Graph solution sets of inequalities.

Let's see if it seems reasonable to assume an addition property for inequality like the one for equality.

Add 3 to both members.	Add -2 to both members.
$5 < 9$ ◄ True	$-8 \geq -10$ ◄ True
$8 < 12$ ◄ True	$-10 \geq -12$ ◄ True

The Addition Property of Inequality ► **For all directed numbers r, s, and t,**
if $r < s$, then $r + t < s + t$;
if $r > s$, then $r + t > s + t$.

Recall that subtracting a directed number is the same as adding its opposite. Then if $r < s$, $r - t < s - t$ because $r + (-t) < s + (-t)$.

Now let's use the addition property to solve inequalities.

EXAMPLE 1

$$x + 5 < 8$$
$$x + 5 + (-5) < 8 + (-5) \quad \blacktriangleleft \text{ Add } -5 \text{ to both members.}$$
$$x + 0 < 8 + (-5) \quad \blacktriangleleft \; 5 + (-5) = 0$$
$$x < 3$$

Graph:
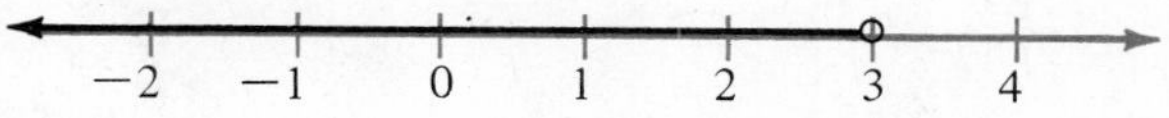

3 is not included.

EXAMPLE 2

$$3 + m \leq 2$$
$$-3 + 3 + m \leq -3 + 2 \quad \blacktriangleleft \text{ Add } -3 \text{ to both members.}$$
$$0 + m \leq -3 + 2 \quad \blacktriangleleft \; -3 + 3 = 0$$
$$m \leq -1$$

Graph:
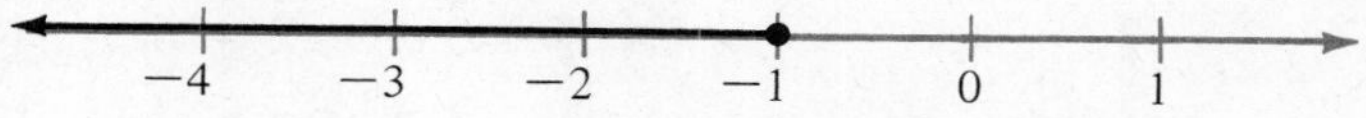

-1 is included

Tell whether the statement is true or false. Explain your answer in terms of the number line.

Sample: $-5 < 3$ *What you say:* True; -5 is to the left of 3 on the number line.

1. $7 > -6$
2. $0 > -2$
3. $0 < -5$
4. $-6 > -7$
5. $\frac{2}{3} > \frac{5}{6}$
6. $-\frac{1}{4} < \frac{1}{5}$

Tell why the statement is true.

Sample: If $7 < b$, then $7 + (-3) < b + (-3)$.

What you say: -3 is added to both members.

7. If $2 > m$, then $2 - 3 > m - 3$.
8. If $d > -6$, then $5 + d > 5 - 6$.
9. If $20 > y$, then $20 + 4 > y + 4$.
10. If $13 < r$, then $-9 + 13 < -9 + r$.

Written EXERCISES

Match each inequality in Column 1 with an equivalent inequality in Column 2.

A

COLUMN 1	COLUMN 2
1. $3 + x \leq 5$	**A.** $x \leq 21$
2. $x + 7 > 16$	**B.** $x \geq -3$
3. $x - 9 \leq 12$	**C.** $x > 9$
4. $x + 4 \leq -10$	**D.** $x < 5$
5. $x - 2 < 3$	**E.** $x \leq 2$
6. $x + (-5) \geq -8$	**F.** $x \leq -14$

Complete. Then graph the solution set.

Sample:

$$y + (-5) < -2$$
$$y + (-5) + \underline{\ ?\ } < -2 + \underline{\ ?\ }$$
$$y < \underline{\ ?\ }$$

Solution:

$$y + (-5) < -2$$
$$y + (-5) + 5 < -2 + 5$$
$$y < 3$$

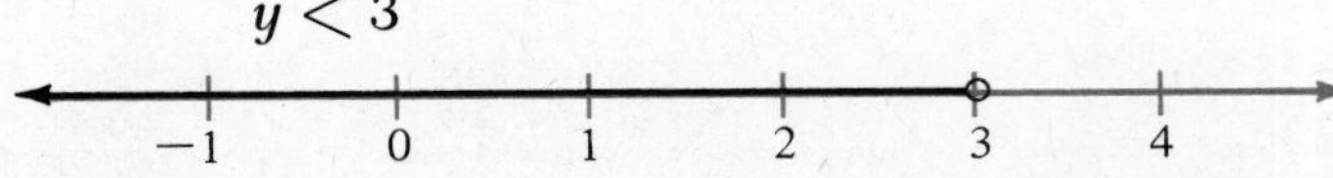

7. $x + 11 > 3$
$x + 11 + \underline{\ ?\ } > 3 + \underline{\ ?\ }$
$x > \underline{\ ?\ }$

8. $k + 8 \le 7$
$k + 8 + \underline{\ ?\ } \le 7 + \underline{\ ?\ }$
$k \le \underline{\ ?\ }$

9. $-6 \ge t + (-4)$
$-6 + \underline{\ ?\ } \ge t + (-4) + \underline{\ ?\ }$
$\underline{\ ?\ } \ge t$

10. $a + 1 \ge -5$
$a + 1 + \underline{\ ?\ } \ge -5 + \underline{\ ?\ }$
$a \ge \underline{\ ?\ }$

11. $9 + p < 4$
$\underline{\ ?\ } + 9 + p < \underline{\ ?\ } + 4$
$p < \underline{\ ?\ }$

12. $s - 10 < -5$
$s - 10 + \underline{\ ?\ } < -5 + \underline{\ ?\ }$
$s < \underline{\ ?\ }$

Solve the inequality and write its solution set.

Sample: $m + 2 > 5$

Solution:
$$m + 2 > 5$$
$$m + 2 + (-2) > 5 + (-2)$$
$$m > 3$$
{the directed numbers greater than 3}

13. $z + (-7) \ge 3$
14. $v + 4 < -5$
15. $14 < n + 2$
16. $x - 15 > -22$
17. $5 < g + 18$
18. $10 + q > 5$
19. $-4 + w \ge -9$
20. $m + 6 < 8\frac{1}{2}$
21. $2 + u < -2$
22. $10 + r \ge -20$
23. $-5 \le k + (-5)$
24. $s + 16 > -9$

B

25. $-32 \ge -16 + b$
26. $0 > -12 + d$
27. $4\left(-1 + \frac{a}{4}\right) \le 0$
28. $\frac{1}{3}(3z - 12) < -3$
29. $\frac{5m - 10}{5} \ge -15$
30. $6\left(2 + \frac{b}{6}\right) < -10$
31. $(-24 + 2r)\frac{1}{2} \ge -20$
32. $0.1(10w - 30) < 5$
33. $5y - 12 > 4y$
34. $0.5(8 + 2k) < -2$

C

35. $3(x - 1) \ge 2(x + 2)$
36. $\frac{4}{5}\left(\frac{5}{4}j + 15\right) > 9$
37. $8(-2n + n) + 9n \le -\frac{1}{4}$
38. $\frac{18 + 4h}{3} < \frac{h}{3} + (-1)$
39. $7(m - 2) < 6m + (-10)$
40. $\frac{-18 + 6a}{3} \ge -5a + (-3.2)$

11-6 *The Multiplication Property of Inequality*

OBJECTIVES
Solve inequalities like $4y > 12$ and $-5x + (-2) \leq 8$, and graph the solution sets.

Let's look at some inequalities where both members are multiplied by the same directed number.

The multiplier can be positive:

$4 < 9$ ◄ True
$2(4) < 2(9)$
$8 < 18$ ◄ True

The multiplier can be negative:

$6 > 4$ ◄ True
$-3(6) > -3(4)$
$-18 > -12$ ◄ False. $-18 < -12$

When the multiplier is negative, the sense of the inequality is reversed. The multiplier can also be 0. Then, of course, both members would be 0.

The Multiplication Property of Inequality ► For all directed numbers, r, s, and t:

(1) If t is positive and $r < s$, $rt < st$.
If t is positive and $r > s$, $rt > st$.

(2) If t is negative and $r < s$, $rt > st$.
If t is negative and $r > s$, $rt < st$.

(3) If $t = 0$ and $r < s$ or $r > s$, then $rt = st = 0$.

EXAMPLE 1

$$4y > 12$$
$$\frac{1}{4} \cdot 4y > \frac{1}{4} \cdot 12 \quad \text{◄ Multiply both members by } \frac{1}{4}.$$
$$y > 3$$

Graph:

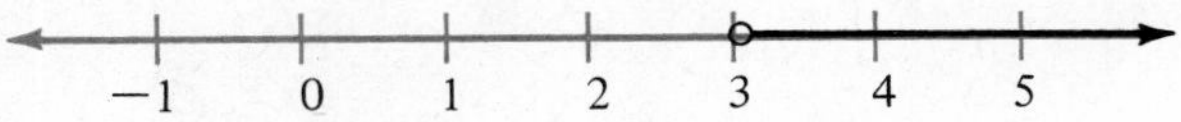

EXAMPLE 2

$$-5x + (-2) \leq 8$$
$$-5x + (-2) + 2 \leq 8 + 2 \quad \text{◄ Add 2 to both members.}$$
$$-5x \leq 10$$
$$-\frac{1}{5}(-5x) \geq -\frac{1}{5} \cdot 10 \quad \text{◄ Multiply both members by } -\frac{1}{5}. \text{ Change } \leq \text{ to } \geq.$$
$$x \geq -2$$

Graph:

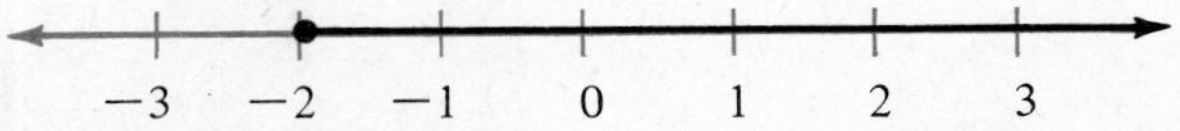

EXAMPLE 3

$$-3x + 1 < 5$$
$$-3x + 1 + (-1) < 5 + (-1) \quad \blacktriangleleft \text{Add } -1 \text{ to both members.}$$
$$-3x < 4$$
$$-\frac{1}{3}(-3)x > -\frac{1}{3} \cdot 4 \quad \blacktriangleleft \text{Multiply both members by } -\frac{1}{3}. \text{ Change } < \text{ to } >.$$
$$x > -\frac{4}{3}$$

Graph:

Number line with points $-\frac{5}{3}$, $-\frac{4}{3}$, $-\frac{3}{3}$, $-\frac{2}{3}$, $-\frac{1}{3}$, 0, $\frac{1}{3}$; open circle at $-\frac{4}{3}$, ray extending right.

Tell whether the symbol $>$, $<$, or $=$ should replace each question mark to make a true statement.

1. $15 \underline{\ ?\ } 10$ and $15 \cdot 2 \underline{\ ?\ } 10 \cdot 2$
2. $-8 \underline{\ ?\ } 5$ and $-8(-3) \underline{\ ?\ } 5(-3)$
3. $2 \underline{\ ?\ } 3$ and $2 \cdot 0 \underline{\ ?\ } 3 \cdot 0$
4. $-14 \underline{\ ?\ } 7$ and $-14 \cdot 3 \underline{\ ?\ } 7 \cdot 3$
5. $-4 \underline{\ ?\ } -7$ and $-4(-1) \underline{\ ?\ } -7(-1)$
6. $5 \underline{\ ?\ } 0$ and $5 \cdot 2 \underline{\ ?\ } 0 \cdot 2$
7. $-6 \underline{\ ?\ } 15$ and $-6 \cdot 0 \underline{\ ?\ } 15 \cdot 0$

Written EXERCISES

Use the multiplication property of inequality to change the first inequality into the second.

Sample: $12 < 25$; $48 < 100$ *Solution:*
$$12 < 25$$
$$12 \cdot 4 < 25 \cdot 4$$
$$48 < 100$$

A

1. $-6 < -5$; $30 > 25$
2. $9 > -3$; $27 > -9$
3. $26 \geq 13$; $2 \geq 1$
4. $-30 \leq 45$; $6 \geq -9$
5. $-4 > -10$; $-16 > -40$
6. $8 < 9$; $16 < 18$
7. $-2 \geq -5$; $6 \leq 15$
8. $3m > 24$; $m > 8$
9. $-\frac{d}{3} \geq 7$; $d \leq -21$
10. $5z \leq 10$; $z \leq 2$

Solve. Then graph the solution set.

Sample: $3x > 9$ *Solution:*

$$3x > 9$$
$$\frac{1}{3} \cdot 3x > \frac{1}{3} \cdot 9$$
$$x > 3$$

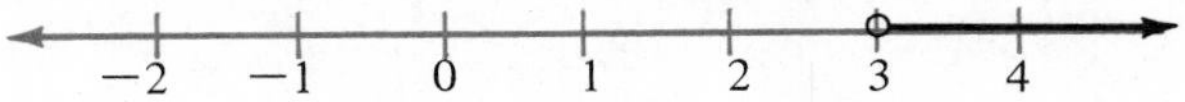

11. $14m \geq 42$ **12.** $18r < 12$ **13.** $\frac{4}{5}w \leq 16$

14. $-5 < 10n$ **15.** $8d \leq -16$ **16.** $-18 < 9v$

17. $\frac{1}{5}s > -1$ **18.** $100 < 10p$ **19.** $-15 < 5b$

Solve each inequality and write the solution set. Remember that multiplying both members of an inequality by a negative number reverses the sense of the inequality.

Sample: $-2b < 10$

Solution:

$$-2b < 10$$
$$-\frac{1}{2}(-2b) > 10\left(-\frac{1}{2}\right)$$
$$b > -5$$

Solution set: {the directed numbers greater than -5}.

20. $-t > 29$ **21.** $-7y \geq -9$ **22.** $27 < -3m$

23. $-\frac{1}{6} > \frac{1}{3}u$ **24.** $-14 > -z$ **25.** $-\frac{n}{5} \leq 3$

26. $2m - 1 < 11$ **27.** $3 - 2s \geq 13$ **28.** $-8b + 1 < -15$

B **29.** $\frac{n}{4} < 7$ **30.** $-\frac{4}{5}z \geq 40$ **31.** $24 > -\frac{3}{4}x$

32. $\frac{m}{3} + 2 \leq 0$ **33.** $-(5r + 2) < 18$ **34.** $-0.50x < -2$

35. $-7a + 4 - a < -5 + a$ **36.** $-2[3t + (-6)] \geq 2t$

37. $c + 3[-9 + (-c)] < -c + 3$ **38.** $\frac{1}{5}u - 8 > -2$

39. $5d - 3(4 - d) \geq 20$ **40.** $-w + 5 < -4w - 7$

C **41.** $10\left(\frac{9}{2} - \frac{1}{5}\right) > 2q$ **42.** $12\left(\frac{1}{4} - \frac{w}{6}\right) \leq -3w$

SELF-TEST 2

Be sure that you understand these terms.

Addition Property of Inequality (p. 305)
Multiplication Property of Inequality (p. 308)

Solve. Graph the solution set. **Section 11-5, p. 305**

1. $x + 4 > 7$
2. $t - 3 \leq -4$
3. $-2 \leq t + 1$
4. $-2 - m > -5$

Section 11-6, p. 308

5. $7n \leq 21$
6. $-\frac{1}{2}y < 8$
7. $-3b + 3 > 12$
8. $2c - 2 \geq -2$

Check your answers with those printed at the back of the book.

chapter summary

1. Equations of the type $\boldsymbol{x + a = b}$ are solved for x by applying the addition property of equality.
2. Equations of the type $\boldsymbol{ax = b}$ are solved for x by applying the multiplication property of equality.
3. Equations of the type $\boldsymbol{ax + bx = c}$ are solved for x by first combining similar terms and then applying the properties of equality.
4. The **addition property of inequality** can be stated as follows. For all directed numbers r, s, and t: If $r < s$, then $r + t < s + t$;
   If $r > s$, then $r + t > s + t$.
5. The **multiplication property of inequality** can be stated as follows. For all directed numbers r, s, and t:
   (1) If t is a positive number, if $r < s$, then $rt < st$;
   if $r > s$, then $rt > st$.
   (2) If t is a negative number, if $r < s$, then $rt > st$;
   if $r > s$, then $rt < st$.
   (3) If t is 0 and $r < s$ or $r > s$, then $rt = st = 0$.

challenge topics

Exponential Notation

As we have seen, exponential notation is very useful in expressing, in a simple way, a product consisting of repeating factors. For example:

$$8 \cdot 8 \cdot 8 \cdot 8 \cdot 8 \cdot 8 = 8^6$$

Study the pattern below:

$$\begin{aligned} \mathbf{3 \cdot 3 \cdot 3 \cdot 3} &= \mathbf{3^4} \\ \mathbf{3 \cdot 3 \cdot 3} &= \mathbf{3^3} \\ \mathbf{3 \cdot 3} &= \mathbf{3^2} \\ \mathbf{3} &= \mathbf{3^1} \end{aligned}$$

Do you see why $3 = 3^1$? In a similar manner $y^1 = y$ and $k^1 = k$. We read k^1 as "k to the first power."

Often a large number can be expressed as the product of two numbers of which one is a power of **10.**

For example, here are two ways of writing **3800** as a product involving a power of 10:

$$\begin{aligned} \mathbf{3800} &= \mathbf{38 \times 100} \\ &= \mathbf{38 \times 10^2} \end{aligned} \qquad \begin{aligned} \mathbf{3800} &= \mathbf{3.8 \times 1000} \\ &= \mathbf{3.8 \times 10^3} \end{aligned}$$

A number is said to be in **scientific notation** when it is written as the product of a number between 1 and 10 and a power of 10 expressed in exponential notation. Which of the methods shown above expresses **3800** in **scientific notation?** To write **21,500** in scientific notation, we note that **2.15** is a number between 1 and 10.

$$\begin{aligned} \mathbf{21{,}500} &= \mathbf{2.15 \times 10{,}000} \\ &= \mathbf{2.15 \times 10^4} \end{aligned}$$

What power of 10 should replace n to make the statement true?

1. $2000 = 2 \times \text{n}$

2. $94000 = 9.4 \times \text{n}$

3. $1000 = 1 \times \text{n}$

4. $19{,}800 = 1.98 \times \text{n}$

5. $30{,}500 = 3.05 \times \text{n}$

6. $2{,}190{,}000 = 2.19 \times \text{n}$

Express as a regular decimal numeral.

7. 1.02×10^2

8. 6.6×10^2

9. 2.07×10^3

10. 6.02×10^5

Write in scientific notation.

11. 1200	12. 6000	13. 250
14. 75,000	15. 1,900,000	16. 2,870
17. two thousand	18. five hundred	19. two million
20. nine million	21. five thousand	22. four billion

chapter test

Solve.

1. $x - 5 = -7$
2. $6t + 2t = 4$
3. $-8k = 56$
4. $25 = -14 + x$
5. $5x = 30$
6. $2x - 5x = 15$
7. $\frac{x}{6} + 5 = 7$
8. $-\frac{2}{7}t + \frac{1}{7}t = 5$
9. $-\frac{3x}{4} = 9$
10. $-1.5x + 0.5 = -1$

Solve for y. Assume that no divisor has the value 0.

11. $y + c = d$
12. $yb = c$
13. $cy - d = -b$
14. $dy - by = c$

Solve. Graph the solution set.

15. $4x < -16$
16. $-\frac{1}{2}x > 2$
17. $-4 + x > -1$
18. $3x + 4x \leq 49$
19. $x + 5 > -1$
20. $-3x + 6 \geq 0$
21. The figure has volume 78 cubic centimeters. Use the formula $V = lwh$ and solve for l. Then substitute and find the value of l.

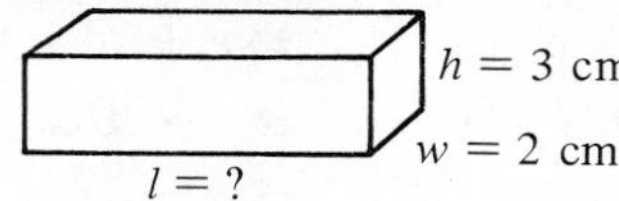

22. A garden plot is to be 15 meters wide. How long will you make it if you want its total area to be 75 square meters?

REVIEW OF SKILLS

Write as a power of 10.

Sample: 100 *Solution:* $100 = 10 \cdot 10 = 10^2$

1. 1000 **2.** 10 **3.** 10,000,000 **4.** 100,000

Write in expanded form.

Sample: 543

Solution: $500 + 40 + 3 = 5 \cdot 10^2 + 4 \cdot 10 + 3$

5. 6325 **6.** 157 **7.** 80,491 **8.** 674

Simplify.

9. $9x + 2x$ **10.** $10y - 8y$ **11.** $-6q - 8q$

12. $4 \cdot 5 + 4 \cdot 2$ **13.** $4(5 + 2)$ **14.** $11 \cdot 3 + 11 \cdot 7$

15. $31 \cdot 2 + 31 \cdot 8$ **16.** $14 \cdot 14 + 14 \cdot 6$ **17.** $12 + (-5)$

18. $12 - 5$ **19.** $18 + (-18)$ **20.** $18 - 18$

21. $53 + 32$ **22.** $42 + 34$ **23.** $34 + 42$

24. $(19 + 3) + 7$ **25.** $19 + (3 + 7)$ **26.** $29 + (1 + 15)$

27. $11(3 + 7)$ **28.** $31(2 + 8)$ **29.** $-14 + 14$

Name the additive inverse.

30. 72 **31.** -10 **32.** -61

33. $\frac{1}{5}$ **34.** 2 **35.** $-\frac{4}{3}$

Solve.

36. $-6 = -16 + 2m$ **37.** $2m + 6 = 6 - 3m$

38. $3m + 7 = -2$ **39.** $5m - 13m = -24$

40. $4m = 2m - 4$ **41.** $-21 + m = -8m + 12$

Left: Public transportation in Seattle, about 1889.

Right: Modern public transportation in San Francisco.

12 Addition and Subtraction of Polynomials

Adding Polynomials

12-1 *Polynomials*

OBJECTIVE
Identify types of polynomials.

Expressions like $12t$, $m + 3$, and $x^2y^2 + 3x + y + 2$ are called **polynomials.** A polynomial in one variable takes the form

$$ax^m + bx^n + cx^p + \cdots + d$$

where a, b, c, and d are directed numbers and m, n, and p are positive integers.

EXAMPLE 1 $3x + 2$ ◄ $a = 3, m = 1$
$d = 2$

EXAMPLE 2 $5x^2 + x + 3$ ◄ $a = 5, m = 2$
$b = 1, n = 1$
$d = 3$

Some polynomials have names that indicate the number of terms.

$12t$	► one term	► **monomial**
$m + 3$	► two terms	► **binomial**
$x^2 + 3x + 2$	► three terms	► **trinomial**

A polynomial which has more than three terms, such as $x^2y^2 + 3x + y + 2$, has no special name. It is simply called a polynomial.

Here are more examples of polynomials.

Monomials ► $5k^2$ $\quad s^3$ $\quad \frac{2b}{3}$ $\quad 7$

Binomials ► $n + 8$ $\quad 2 + x^2$ $\quad ab - c$

Trinomials ► $2x^2 + 3x + 1$ $\quad a + 2b - c$

Polynomials ► $m^2 + m + n + 3$ $\quad b^3 + c^2 + c + 2$

Tell whether the polynomial is a monomial, a binomial, or a trinomial.

1. $-4a^2$
2. $2n + 6 + 7m$
3. $-4rst - 5rs$
4. $-2xy$
5. $-14cd + c + 15$
6. $15rst^2$
7. $10x^2yz^3$
8. $\frac{1}{4}ab^2c^3$
9. $x - y$
10. $3^2 + 4^2$
11. $12wxyz$
12. $6 + 3x + x^2$

Written EXERCISES A

Tell whether the right member is a monomial, a binomial, or a trinomial.

1. $V = \frac{1}{3}Bh$
2. $A = lw$
3. $A = p + prt$
4. $a = s^2$
5. $q = 4D + 5$
6. $n = 10t + u$
7. $P = a + b + c$
8. $I = 0.03PT$
9. $V = 6 + c^2 + b$

Use the symbols 3, c^2, b, and b^5 to write an expression.

10. A monomial
11. A polynomial with four terms
12. A binomial
13. A trinomial
14. A polynomial with five terms
15. A polynomial with six terms

Nikolai Ivanovich Lobachevski

In 1829 Nikolai Ivanovich Lobachevski developed a new geometry which revolutionized mathematics. For centuries geometry had been based on the axioms of Euclid. One of these states that parallel lines never intersect. Lobachevski invented a geometry in which parallel lines *can* intersect. Nearly eighty years later non-Euclidean geometry would have a profound effect on the development of Albert Einstein's theory of relativity.

12-2 *Standard Form*

OBJECTIVE

Express polynomials in standard form.

A polynomial in one variable is in **standard form** when the terms are ordered so that the variable in the first term has the greatest exponent, the variable in the second term has the next greatest exponent, and so on. The greatest exponent names the **degree** of the polynomial.

EXAMPLE 1 $3x + 10x^2 + 5 = \mathbf{10x^2 + 3x + 5}$ ◄ standard form

The degree is 2.

EXAMPLE 2 $x + x^4 - 2 = \mathbf{x^4 + x - 2}$ ◄ standard form

The degree is 4.

Notice in Example 2, there are no terms of degree two or three. But we can insert "missing" terms to complete the polynomial.

EXAMPLE 3 $x + x^4 - 2 = x^4 + 0x^3 + 0x^2 + x - 2$

0 0

The meaning of the polynomial is unchanged.

Some polynomials have more than one variable. We write these polynomials in standard form by ordering the terms according to values of exponents of one of the variables.

EXAMPLE 4 $5m^2n - m^3 + 4mn^2 = -m^3 + 5m^2n + 4mn^2$

Terms ordered according to exponents of m.

$= 4mn^2 + 5m^2n - m^3$

Terms ordered according to exponents of n.

Name the degree of the polynomial.

1. $x^2 + 2$
2. $b - 7$
3. $3c^2 + c + 1$
4. $x^5 - 2$
5. $2y^2 + y + 1$
6. m^3
7. $t^5 - 2$
8. $2n^2 - n + 1$
9. $y + 5$
10. $x^8 - x^2 + 1$

Written EXERCISES

A

Write in standard form.

Sample: $x^3 - 3 + 7x^5 + x$ *Solution:* $7x^5 + x^3 + x - 3$

1. $c - 7c^5$
2. $-4 + 2x^2$
3. $9k^2 - 5 + 3k^5 - k^3$
4. $12t^2 + 10 - 9t^4$
5. $3n^5 - 4n + n^2$
6. $2a^2 - 4a^3 + a - 1$
7. $14a^5 - 8a^7 + a^3$
8. $d^2 - 5 + d$
9. $5r^4 - 2r^2 + r^9$
10. $2x^3 - 3x^5 + 4 - 7x^7$

Write in standard form.

Sample: $2mn - 5m^2n^2 + 6m^3 - 1$

Solution: $6m^3 - 5m^2n^2 + 2mn - 1$
(or $-5m^2n^2 + 2mn + 6m^3 - 1$)

B

11. $4xy - 3x^2$
12. $n^2 + m^3 - m^2n$
13. $2a^2b^2 - 6a^3b + 7a^6$
14. $r^3 - 3s^2 - 2rs^3 + 4$
15. $2a^2 + 2b^2 + ab$
16. $7 + 3p^4 + q^4 - 6p^2q^2$
17. $m^3n^2 + n^3 + m^4n^2 + m^2$
18. $13z^2 + 2x^5 - 7x + 4x^3$

Write in standard form. Insert any "missing" terms.

Sample: $2x^5 + x - 2$

Solution: $2x^5 + 0x^4 + 0x^3 + 0x^2 + x - 2$

19. $3m^4 - 1$
20. $3n^2 + 8 + n^6$
21. $s^5 - 3s^2 + 2$
22. $5 - y^3 + 2y^5$
23. $x^7 + x^4$
24. $12 - p^2 + 7p^3$
25. $k - 2k^5 + k^7 - 19$
26. $1 + 6d^5$

12-3 *Polynomials and Function Machines*

OBJECTIVE
Evaluate polynomials used as function rules.

As you have seen, the rule for finding values of $f(x)$ with a function machine is often a polynomial.

EXAMPLE 1 $f(x) = 3x - 1$; replacement set: $\{-3, -1, 0, 1, 3, 5\}$

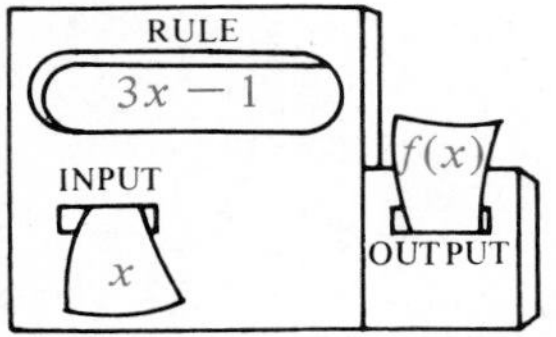

x	$f(x)$	$(x, f(x))$
-3	-10	$(-3, -10)$
-1	-4	$(-1, -4)$
0	-1	$(0, -1)$
1	2	$(1, 2)$
3	8	$(3, 8)$
5	14	$(5, 14)$

Function: $\{(-3, -10), (-1, -4), (0, -1), (1, 2), (3, 8), (5, 14)\}$

EXAMPLE 2 $f(x) = 2x^2 - 2$; replacement set: $\{2, 0, -1, -2, -3\}$

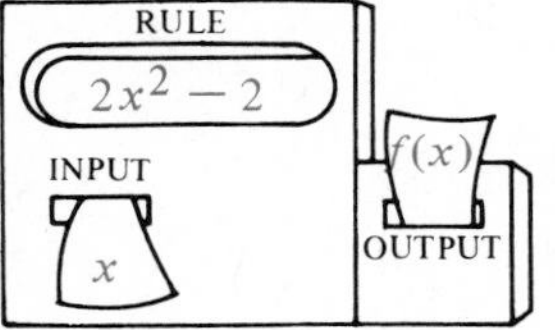

x	$f(x)$	$(x, f(x))$
2	6	$(2, 6)$
0	-2	$(0, -2)$
-1	0	$(-1, 0)$
-2	6	$(-2, 6)$
-3	16	$(-3, 16)$

Function: $\{(2, 6), (0, -2), (-1, 0), (-2, 6), (-3, 16)\}$

calculator corner

You can use your calculator as a function machine. Let the polynomial $x^2 + x + 4$ be the rule. Choose five input values for x which are between $^-5$ and 5. Find the corresponding output values, make a list of ordered pairs, and graph them. Now choose five input values between -10 and -5 and five between 5 and 10. Find the output values and graph the ordered pairs. Can you determine what the graph looks like? The more ordered pairs you find, the more exact your graph will be. Try to graph other polynomials with your function machine.

Tell how to complete the table.

$f(x) = x^2 + 1$

	x	$f(x)$	$(x, f(x))$
	5	26	(5, 26)
1.	0	?	?
2.	2	?	?
3.	4	?	?
4.	-1	?	?
5.	-3	?	?

$f(x) = x^2 + x + 1$

	x	$f(x)$	$(x, f(x))$
	-5	21	$(-5, 21)$
6.	0	?	?
7.	-1	?	?
8.	1	?	?
9.	-2	?	?
10.	2	?	?

Written EXERCISES

Find the value of $f(a)$. Use the given replacement for a.

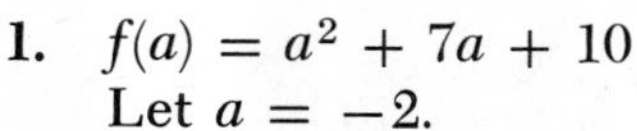

Sample: $f(a) = 4 - 3a + 2a^2$ Let $a = -1$.

Solution: $4 - 3(-1) + 2(-1)^2$
$4 + 3 + 2$
9

A

1. $f(a) = a^2 + 7a + 10$ Let $a = -2$.

2. $f(a) = a^2 - 8a - 15$ Let $a = 0$.

3. $f(a) = a^2 - 14a + 33$ Let $a = 3$.

4. $f(a) = 7a^2 - 15a + 2$ Let $a = 1$.

5. $f(a) = 5 + 9a - 18a^2$ Let $a = \frac{1}{3}$.

6. $45 - 70a + 25a^2 = f(a)$ Let $a = \frac{1}{5}$.

7. $f(a) = 14 - (-6a + 5) - 21$ Let $a = -2$.

8. $f(a) = -(-7a + 12)$ Let $a = 0.3$.

9. $f(a) = (a^2 - 12) + 3$
Let $a = -4$.

10. $f(a) = 2a - (a + 3)$
Let $a = 5$.

11. $f(a) = -(5 - 4a)$
Let $a = 2$.

12. $a^2 + 100a + 20 = f(a)$
Let $a = 10$.

13. $f(a) = (2 - 3a) - 4a$
Let $a = 2$.

14. $f(a) = (3a + 6) - (4a - 7)$
Let $a = 0.2$.

Use the function machine and the rule to complete the table.

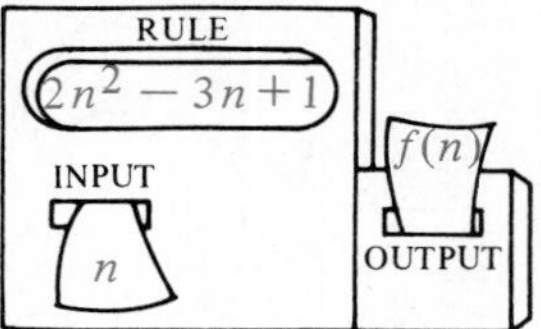

	n	$f(n)$	$(n, f(n))$
15.	-7	120	?
16.	-3	28	?
17.	-1	?	?
18.	0	?	?
19.	4	?	?
20.	6	?	?
21.	8	?	?

Use the function equation and replacement set to write the function.

Sample: $f(c) = 4c^2 - 2c + 4$; $\{-2, -1, 0, 1, 2\}$

Solution: $\{(-2, 24), (-1, 10), (0, 4), (1, 6), (2, 16)\}$

B

22. $f(b) = (2b^2 + 3) + b$; $\{-3, -1, 0, 1, 3\}$
23. $f(d) = 6d - (3d - 5)$; $\{-6, -4, -2, 0, 2, 4, 6\}$
24. $f(h) = 7 - 2h + h^2$; $\left\{-1, -\frac{1}{2}, 0, \frac{1}{2}, 1\right\}$
25. $f(a) = a^3 - 2a + 4$; $\{-3, -2, 0, 2, 3\}$
26. $f(m) = 5m^2 - 10m - 15$; $\left\{-\frac{1}{10}, -\frac{1}{5}, 0, \frac{1}{5}, \frac{1}{10}\right\}$
27. $f(x) = 12 + x - 3x^2$; $\{-4, -2, 0, 2, 4\}$
28. $f(y) = y^2 + y + 3$; $\{-6, -4, -2, 0, 2, 4, 6\}$
29. $f(t) = t^3 - 1$; $\{-2, -1, 0, 1, 2\}$

C

30. $f(x) = (3x + 5) - 4x + 7$; $\{-10, -5, 0, 5, 10\}$
31. $f(y) = 2 + y^2 - (3y - 1)$; $\{-0.1, 0, 0.1\}$
32. $f(s) = 4 - (-5s - 1) - 2s^2 + 3$; $\{-5, -3, -1, 0, 1, 3, 5\}$

12-4 *Addition of Polynomials*

OBJECTIVES

Find the sum of polynomials, such as $4x + 8$ and $x + 6$, or $3x^2 - x + 1$ and $5x + 7x^2$.

To **add** polynomials, we combine **similar** terms. We can arrange the work either vertically or horizontally:

EXAMPLE 1 Add $4x + 1$ and $x + 3$.

Vertical

$$\begin{array}{r} 4x + 1 \\ x + 3 \\ \hline 5x + 4 \end{array}$$

Horizontal

$$\begin{aligned} (4x + 1) + (x + 3) &= 4x + x + 1 + 3 \\ &= 5x + 4 \end{aligned}$$

EXAMPLE 2 Add $5y - 7$ and $3y + 2$.

Vertical

$$\begin{array}{l} 5y + (-7) \\ 3y + \quad 2 \\ \hline 8y + (-5) = 8y - 5 \end{array}$$

Horizontal

$$\begin{aligned} [5y + (-7) + (3y + 2)] &= 5y + 3y + (-7) + 2 \\ &= 8y + (-5) \\ &= 8y - 5 \end{aligned}$$

If the polynomials are not in standard form, we usually express each in standard form before adding.

EXAMPLE 3 Add $5m^2 - 4 + 5m$ and $3 - 5m - m^2$.

$$\begin{array}{rcrcrcr} 5m^2 - 4 + 5m & \blacktriangleright & 5m^2 + & & 5m & + (-4) & \\ 3 - 5m - m^2 & \blacktriangleright & -1m^2 + & & (-5m) & + \quad 3 & \\ \hline & & 4m^2 + & & 0m & + (-1) & = 4m^2 - 1 \end{array}$$

We can check the result by substituting for m. Let's use $m = 1$ and check Example 3.

$$\begin{array}{c} \begin{array}{r} 5m^2 + \quad 5m + (-4) \\ -1m^2 + (-5m) + \quad 3 \\ \hline \end{array} \blacktriangleright \begin{array}{r} 5 + \quad 5 + (-4) \\ -1 + (-5) + \quad 3 \\ \hline \end{array} \blacktriangleright \begin{array}{r} 6 \\ -3 \\ \hline 3 \end{array} \end{array}$$

$$4m^2 - 1 = 4 - 1 = 3 \quad \checkmark$$

EXERCISES

Simplify.

Sample: $(4r - 2t) + 3t$ What you say: $4r + t$

1. $(3a + 6) + 2a$

2. $12n + (2m - 6n)$

3. $(4c + 3) - 6c$

4. $(2k^2 - 5h) + 11h$

5. $\frac{1}{2}b + (c + 4b)$

6. $2x + \left(5y + \frac{1}{2}x\right)$

7. $(2r - 5s) - 2s$

8. $(2s + t) + (s - t)$

9. $(2a^3 - 5b^2) - 8b^2$

10. $7.3m + (4.8n + 2.1m)$

11. $0.7t + (3.1r - 0.9t)$

12. $(0.4w + 0.7z) - 0.2w$

Written

EXERCISES

Add.

Sample 1: $\begin{array}{r} 2t + 7 \\ 4t + 3 \\ \hline \end{array}$ *Sample 2:* $\begin{array}{r} r^2 \qquad + 1 \\ 3r^2 + 7s + 5 \\ \hline \end{array}$

Solution: $6t + 10$ *Solution:* $4r^2 + 7s + 6$

A

1. $\begin{array}{r} 6w + 4 \\ 8w + 5 \\ \hline \end{array}$

2. $\begin{array}{r} 3k + h \\ 4k + 7h \\ \hline \end{array}$

3. $\begin{array}{r} 2a + 4a^3 \\ a + 5a^3 \\ \hline \end{array}$

4. $\begin{array}{l} 12x - 2y \\ \ \ 7x \\ \hline \end{array}$

5. $\begin{array}{r} m^3 + 5n^2 \\ -m^3 - 3n^2 \\ \hline \end{array}$

6. $\begin{array}{r} 2t + 12 \\ 6t - 7 \\ \hline \end{array}$

7. $\begin{array}{r} x^2 + 2y \\ x^2 - 2y \\ \hline \end{array}$

8. $\begin{array}{r} 3r^2 + 2s^2 + t^2 \\ 4r^2 + 5s^2 + 3t^2 \\ \hline \end{array}$

9. $\begin{array}{r} -7x^2 + 5xy + 4y^2 \\ -3x^2 - 2xy - 6y^2 \\ \hline \end{array}$

10. $\begin{array}{r} 6a + 9 \\ 2a - 4 \\ \hline \end{array}$

11. $\begin{array}{r} m^2 - n^2 + p^2 \\ 4m^2 - 3n^2 - 5p^2 \\ \hline \end{array}$

12. $\begin{array}{r} 9z^2 \qquad + 5w^2 \\ 4z + 7w^2 \\ \hline \end{array}$

13. $\begin{array}{r} 7c + 4 \\ 3c - 12 \\ \hline \end{array}$

14. $\begin{array}{r} 5x - 7 \\ 2x - 2 \\ \hline \end{array}$

15. $\begin{array}{r} 4a - b \\ -5a - b \\ \hline \end{array}$

16. $\begin{array}{r} 3x + y \\ -3x - y \\ \hline \end{array}$

17. $\begin{array}{r} 3x^2 - 4y + 9 \\ x^2 - y - 12 \\ \hline \end{array}$

18. $\begin{array}{r} 3r^2 + 8d + 4 \\ r^2 + 3d + 1 \\ \hline \end{array}$

19. $\begin{array}{r} y^2 + z \\ y^2 - z \\ \hline \end{array}$

20. $\begin{array}{r} 4n^2 - 7n + 9 \\ 2n^2 \qquad - 1 \\ \hline \end{array}$

21. $\begin{array}{r} 7.6a + 2.4b + 5 \\ 1.8a - 1.7b + 3 \\ \hline \end{array}$

22. $(12s^2 + 24) + (3s^4 - 12s^2)$

23. $(m^2 + 4m - 8) + (2m^2 - 9m + 5)$

24. $(8k - 5h^2) + (13k - h^2)$

25. $(k^4 - 5k^2 + 4) + (-3k^3 + 6k - 1)$

26. $(7z^2 - 3z + 6) + (4z^2 + 9z - 11)$

27. $(2x^2 + 4xy + 2y^2) + (2x^2 - 4xy + 2y^2)$

Add. Check by using $a = -1$, $b = 2$, $c = 3$, $d = 4$.

Sample:
$$\begin{array}{r} 3a - 5 \\ a + 3 \\ 2a - 1 \\ \hline 6a - 3 \end{array}$$
Solution: $6a - 3$

Check:
$$\begin{array}{r} 3(-1) - 5 = -8 \\ 1(-1) + 3 = 2 \\ 2(-1) - 1 = -3 \\ \hline 6(-1) - 3 = -9 \end{array} \checkmark$$

B

28. $\begin{array}{r} 2d - 8 \\ 4d + 1 \\ \hline \end{array}$

29. $\begin{array}{r} 2b + 5 \\ 5b - 10 \\ \hline \end{array}$

30. $\begin{array}{r} c^2 + 4c - 6 \\ 2c^2 - c + 6 \\ \hline \end{array}$

31. $\begin{array}{r} 8a + 2b - 12 \\ a - b - 7 \\ 4a - 3b + 4 \\ \hline \end{array}$

32. $\begin{array}{r} 3c - d + 5 \\ c + d + 4 \\ 5c - 2d \\ \hline \end{array}$

33. $\begin{array}{r} 2a + 8 - 2d \\ 4a - 13 - d \\ -6a + 2d \\ \hline \end{array}$

34. $\begin{array}{r} 5c + 6d \\ 7c - 2d \\ \hline \end{array}$

35. $\begin{array}{r} d^3 - 5d^2 + 7d \\ 3d^3 - 3d^2 - 7d \\ \hline \end{array}$

36. $\begin{array}{r} a^2 - 4a - 1 \\ -6a^2 - 8 \\ \hline \end{array}$

Add.

37. $\begin{array}{r} \frac{1}{2}s^3 + t^3 \\ s^3 - t^3 \\ \hline \end{array}$

38. $\begin{array}{r} 2\frac{1}{3}k^2 - m^2 \\ \frac{1}{3}k^2 + \frac{1}{2}m^2 \\ \hline \end{array}$

39. $\begin{array}{r} \frac{3}{5}a - 2b \\ \frac{2}{5}a - 2b \\ \hline \end{array}$

40. $\begin{array}{r} 0.2rs - 0.61 \\ 0.5rs + 0.26 \\ 4.6rs + 0.54 \\ \hline \end{array}$

41. $\begin{array}{r} 4.6 + 5ab \\ 7.0 + 3ab \\ -9.2 - 3ab \\ \hline \end{array}$

42. $\begin{array}{r} 2c - 15 \\ 6c + 30 \\ -9c - 9 \\ \hline \end{array}$

43. $\begin{array}{r} 13x^4 - 4.2x^2y^2 + 5y^4 \\ 7x^4 - 8x^2y^2 - 7.2y^4 \\ \hline \end{array}$

44. $\begin{array}{r} 4h^3 - 5k^2 - 3 \\ 2h^3 - 3k^2 - 6k \\ \hline \end{array}$

45. $(21x^3 + 4x^2 - 7x + 16) + (7x - 9 - 2x^2 - 8x^3) + (x - 4)$

46. $(-4k^2) + (2k^2 - 5k^4 - 1 + k) + (7k + 2k^2 + k^5 - 9)$

12-5 *Addition Properties*

OBJECTIVE
Use the commutative and associative properties in adding polynomials.

We assume that addition of polynomials is both commutative and associative.

EXAMPLE 1 The Commutative Property of Addition:

$$\begin{aligned}(3x + 9) + (x - 4) &= 3x + 9 + x + (-4)\\ &= 3x + x + 9 + (-4)\\ &= \mathbf{4x + 5}\\ (x - 4) + (3x + 9) &= x + (-4) + 3x + 9\\ &= x + 3x + (-4) + 9\\ &= \mathbf{4x + 5}\end{aligned}$$

EXAMPLE 2 The Associative Property of Addition:

$$\begin{aligned}[(4m^2 + 3) + (m^2 - 10)] + 4m^2 &= [4m^2 + 3 + m^2 + (-10)] + 4m^2\\ &= (5m^2 - 7) + 4m^2\\ &= \mathbf{9m^2 - 7}\\ (4m^2 + 3) + [(m^2 - 10) + 4m^2] &= (4m^2 + 3) + (m^2 - 10 + 4m^2)\\ &= 4m^2 + 3 + (5m^2 - 10)\\ &= \mathbf{9m^2 - 7}\end{aligned}$$

If you think of a polynomial as a way of representing a number, it seems logical that polynomials have the same properties as numbers.

EXERCISES

Tell which property of addition justifies the statement.

1. $(7 + x) + 4x^2 = 4x^2 + (7 + x)$
2. $(y^3 - 6) + (y^3 + 7) = (y^3 + 7) + (y^3 - 6)$
3. $(2a + 5) + (4a - 6) = (4a - 6) + (2a + 5)$
4. $[4n + (1 + 3n^2)] + n = 4n + [(1 + 3n^2) + n]$
5. $9s + (2s^2 - 5) = (2s^2 - 5) + 9s$
6. $[(3d + 2) + d] + 4d^2 = (3d + 2) + [(d + 4d^2)]$

7. $[(x^2 + y) + (xy - 2)] + (x - y) = (x^2 + y) + [(xy - 2) + (x - y)]$

8. $(k + 1) + [(k^2 - 4) + (5k - 2)] = [(k^2 - 4) + (5k - 2)] + (k + 1)$

9. $(2t + s) + [(t - s) + (s - 3)] = (2t + s) + [(s - 3) + (t - s)]$

10. $[3r + (r + 5)] + (r + 2) = 3r + [(r + 5) + (r + 2)]$

Written EXERCISES

Simplify both members to show that they are equal.

Sample: $(5a - 3) + (4 + a) = (4 + a) + (5a - 3)$

Solution:

$5a - 3 + 4 + a$	$4 + a + 5a - 3$
$5a + a - 3 + 4$	$a + 5a + 4 - 3$
$6a + 1$	$6a + 1$ ✓

A

1. $(12 - 4b) + (4 + 2b) = (4 + 2b) + (12 - 4b)$
2. $-5k + (k^2 - 2k + 4) = (k^2 - 2k + 4) + (-5k)$
3. $(2b - 7) + (2b - 3) = 2b + [-7 + (2b - 3)]$
4. $(6a - b) + (a + b) = (a + b) + (6a - b)$
5. $(10z^2 - 8z + 3) + (6z - 5z^2) = (6z - 5z^2) + (10z^2 - 8z + 3)$
6. $[(2x - 4y - 12) + (x + 2y + 9)] + (y - 3) = (2x - 4y - 12) + [(x + 2y + 9) + (y - 3)]$
7. $(m - 2) + [(2m^2 + m - 7) + (3m + 1)] = [(m - 2) + (3m + 1)] + (2m^2 + m - 7)$
8. $(7x^2 + 10xy + 6y^2) + (-2x^2 - y^2) = (-2x^2 - y^2) + (7x^2 + 10xy + 6y^2)$
9. $(-a^3 + 2a^2 - 5a) + (a^4 - 4a) = (a^4 - 4a) + (-a^3 + 2a^2 - 5a)$

Find both sums. Compare.

10.
$$\begin{array}{r} 3k - 5 \\ k + 8 \\ \hline \end{array} \qquad \begin{array}{r} k + 8 \\ 3k - 5 \\ \hline \end{array}$$

11.
$$\begin{array}{r} 5y - 12 \\ -3y + 10 \\ \hline \end{array} \qquad \begin{array}{r} -3y + 10 \\ 5y - 12 \\ \hline \end{array}$$

12.
$$\begin{array}{r} 6x - 2 \\ 3x + 10 \\ -x - 11 \\ \hline \end{array} \qquad \begin{array}{r} -x - 11 \\ 3x + 10 \\ 6x - 2 \\ \hline \end{array}$$

13.
$$\begin{array}{r} -3x + 5y \\ -4x + y \\ -x \\ \hline \end{array} \qquad \begin{array}{r} -3x + 5y \\ -x \\ -4x + y \\ \hline \end{array}$$

14. $\begin{array}{r} 2t - 2s - 10 \\ 5t - 3s + 1 \\ \hline \end{array}$ $\quad \begin{array}{r} 5t - 3s + 1 \\ 2t - 2s - 10 \\ \hline \end{array}$

15. $\begin{array}{r} x^2 + 2y^2 \\ x^2 - y^2 \\ -x^2 \quad\quad \\ \hline \end{array}$ $\quad \begin{array}{r} -x^2 \quad\quad \\ x^2 - y^2 \\ x^2 + 2y^2 \\ \hline \end{array}$

Find the value. Use $a = -2$, $b = 3$, $x = 0$, $y = 1$.

Sample 1: $8b^2 + 3x - 2$

Solution: $8(9) + 3(0) - 2 = 72 - 2 = 70$

Sample 2: $3a^2 + 6a - 10$

Solution: $3(4) + 6(-2) - 10 = 12 - 12 - 10 = -10$

16. $-7x^2 - 4x + 9$
17. $y^3 + 5y^2 - 8y$
18. $2a^2 - 4ax + x^2$
19. $a^2 + b^2 + x^2$
20. $a^3 - a^2 + 2a$
21. $by + ab + bx$
22. $2.1b^2 + 1.3b - 1$
23. $xy + bx + ax$
24. $(2a + b) + (-2a - b)$
25. $0.5y + 2.5b + 3$
26. $2ab + 3a + 2b$
27. $x^4 + x^3 + x^2 + x + 1$

Show that a true statement results when the variable is replaced by the suggested value.

Sample: $(2a + 5) + (4a - 6) = (4a - 6) + (2a + 5)$; $a = 3$

Solution: $(2a + 5) + (4a - 6) \stackrel{?}{=} (4a - 6) + (2a + 5)$

$(2 \cdot 3 + 5) + (4 \cdot 3 - 6)$	$(4 \cdot 3 - 6) + (2 \cdot 3 + 5)$
$11 + 6$	$6 + 11$
17	17 ✓

B

28. $4r + (3r - 2) = (4r + 3r) - 2$; $r = 2$
29. $(p^2 - 3p) + 5p = 5p + (p^2 - 3p)$; $p = 4$
30. $(3y + 4) + (6y^2 + 11y - 4) = (6y^2 + 11y - 4) + (3y + 4)$; $y = 5$
31. $2a + [4a + (8a - 3)] = (2a + 4a) + (8a - 3)$; $a = 10$
32. $(y^2 - 2y^3 + y^2) + (-4y + 5) = (-4y + 5) + (y^2 - 2y^3 + y^2)$; $y = 3$
33. $(3x - 2) + (5x - 4) = (5x - 4) + (3x - 2)$; $x = -2$
34. $(k^3 - 2k^2 - 20) + (k^3 - k) = (k^3 - k) + (k^3 - 2k^2 - 20)$; $k = 0$
35. $4r^2 + (5 - 10r + 2r^2) = (4r^2 + 5) + (-10r + 2r^2)$; $r = \frac{1}{2}$

SELF-TEST 1

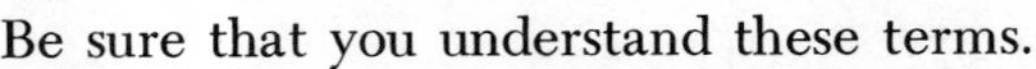

Be sure that you understand these terms.

polynomial (p. 316)	monomial (p. 316)
binomial (p. 316)	trinomial (p. 316)
standard form (p. 318)	degree (p. 318)

Tell whether the polynomial is a monomial, a binomial, or a trinomial. **Section 12-1, p. 316**

1. $6q - r$ **2.** $2abc + 4$

3. $6x + 4ab + 5d$ **4.** $6ab$

Write in standard form. **Section 12-2, p. 318**

5. $2x + 5 + 9x^2$ **6.** $m^2 + 2 + m^3$

7. $1 + x^2y + xy^2$ **8.** $2y + y^5 + 1$

Find the value of $f(a)$. Use the given replacement for a. **Section 12-3, p. 320**

9. $f(a) = 2a^2 + a + 3;\ a = -1$

10. $f(a) = a^2 - 4a - 4;\ a = 0$

Add. Check by using $a = 1$, $b = 2$. **Section 12-4, p. 323**

11. $\begin{array}{r} 4a + 5 \\ \underline{8a - 14} \end{array}$ **12.** $\begin{array}{rrr} -4a^2 & & +\ 6b^2 \\ \underline{9a^2} & \underline{+\ ab} & \underline{-\ 5b^2} \end{array}$

Tell which property of addition justifies the statement. **Section 12-5, p. 326**

13. $[(2y + 3) + (8y^2 + y + 2)] + y^3 = (2y + 3) + [(8y^2 + y + 2) + y^3]$

14. $(12z^2 + z + 1) + (z^2 - 5) = (z^2 - 5) + (12z^2 + z + 1)$

Check your answers with those printed at the back of the book.

Subtracting Polynomials

12-6 *Polynomials and Their Opposites*

OBJECTIVES

Apply the addition property of zero to polynomials.

Give the opposite of a polynomial.

When you add zero to any polynomial, the polynomial is unchanged. Zero is called the **identity element** for addition of polynomials.

EXAMPLE 1 $(3t + 7) + 0 = 0 + (3t + 7) = 3t + 7$

EXAMPLE 2 $(-x^3 + 3x + 1) + 0 = 0 + (-x^3 + 3x + 1) = -x^3 + 3x + 1$

Recall that every number has an **opposite** (or **additive inverse**) and that the sum of a number and its opposite is 0. This is also true for polynomials.

EXAMPLE 3 The opposite of $x + 3$ is written $-(x + 3)$.
$(x + 3) + [-(x + 3)] = 0$

EXAMPLE 4 The opposite of $-x^2 + 1$ is written $-(-x^2 + 1)$.
$(-x^2 + 1) + [-(-x^2 + 1)] = 0$

You will also recall that the opposite of an addition expression such as $x + 3$ is the sum of the opposites of the terms. We use this property to write the opposite of a polynomial without using parentheses.

EXAMPLE 5 $-(x + 3) = -x + (-3) = -x - 3$

EXAMPLE 6 $-(2x^3 - 7x^2 + 22) = -2x^3 + 7x^2 - 22$

EXERCISES

Give the sum of the two polynomials. Justify your answer.

Sample 1: $-(8b - c + 9)$ and $(8b - c + 9)$

What you say: 0; the sum of any polynomial and its opposite is 0.

Sample 2: $(4k - 4k)$ and $(5x^3 + 2x - 1)$

What you say: $5x^3 + 2x - 1$; $4k - 4k = 0$ and 0 is the identity element for addition of polynomials.

1. $(9x^2 - 8x)$ and $-(9x^2 - 8x)$
2. $-(2st - t)$ and $(2st - t)$
3. $(12a^3b^3 - a^2b^2 + b)$ and $(-12a^3b^3 + a^2b^2 - b)$
4. $(20xy^2 - 20xy^2)$ and $(3c^2 - 13cd + 7d^2)$
5. $-(r^3 - r^2 + r - 5)$ and $(r^3 - r^2 + r^2 - 5)$
6. $(27k^4 - 1)$ and $(7h^3 - 7h^3)$

Match each polynomial in Column 1 with its additive inverse in Column 2.

COLUMN 1	COLUMN 2
7. $5x^2 + 11x + 2$	A. $a^2b^2 + 12ab - 20$
8. $a^2b^2 - 12ab - 20$	B. $-5x^2 + 11x - 2$
9. $-a^2b^2 - 12ab + 20$	C. $-a^2b^2 + 12ab + 20$
10. $5x^2 - 11x + 2$	D. $-5x^2 - 11x - 2$

Written EXERCISES

A

Give the opposite. Write your answer in standard form.

Sample: $-k^2 + 5k - 6$

Solution: $-(-k^2 + 5k - 6) = k^2 - 5k + 6$

1. $2m^2 - 3m + 15$
2. $-w^2 + 3w - 40$
3. $\frac{m^2}{10} - \frac{2n^2}{7} + \frac{4mn}{2}$
4. $2 + \frac{a}{5} - \frac{a^2}{12}$
5. $12x^9 + 6x^7 + 3x^5 + x + 1$
6. $-2a^2 - a^3 + 5a - 7$
7. $-(-5x^2 - 3x + 7)$
8. $3x^4 + 5x^3 - 2x^2 - x - 6$
9. $-2k + 1 - 7k^2 - 4k^3 + k^6$
10. $-[(-4b^2 + 6b - 1)] + 2b$

Write in standard form without using parentheses.

Sample: $-(3x^6 - 8x^2 + 5x^4 - 1)$

Solution: $-3x^6 - 5x^4 + 8x^2 + 1$

11. $-(3y^2 + 13y + 5)$
12. $-(y^2 - 8y + 5)$
13. $-(-10 + 4x - x^2)$
14. $-\left(-\frac{a}{3} - \frac{a^2}{4} + 18\right)$

15. $-(-2x^3 + 25x^2 - 10)$

16. $-(-12a^3 - 4ab^2 + 6b^3 + 12a^2b)$

17. $-(1.8x^5 - 6.2x^3 - 0.7x + 15)$

18. $-\left(-\frac{k^5}{6} - \frac{k^4}{2} - \frac{k^3}{5} - 1\right)$

19. $-(-y^7 + 2y^5 - 6y^3 + y - 2)$

20. $-(8.1r^3 + 1.2r^4 - 0.3r - 1.8)$

Add. First arrange your work in vertical form.

Sample: $-(8k^2 - 5k + 10)$ and $-(3k^2 - k + 4)$

Solution:

$$\begin{array}{rcr} -(8k^2 - 5k + 10) & = & -8k^2 + 5k - 10 \\ \underline{-(3k^2 - k + 4)} & = & \underline{-3k^2 + k - 4} \\ & & -11k^2 + 6k - 14 \end{array}$$

B

21. $(5x^2 + 5x)$ and $-(x^2 + x)$

22. $-(5x + y)$ and $-(5x - y)$

23. $(3c + 10)$ and $-(3c + 10)$

24. $-(2x + 4)$ and $(3x - 10)$

25. $(a^2 + b^2)$ and $-(a^2 + b^2)$

26. $-(2x^2 - 4x)$ and $(4x - 2x^2)$

27. $-(3r^2 - 5s + 2t - 4)$ and $(-5r^2 - 4t - 12)$

28. $-(2.3a^2 + 6.8ab - 3.6b^2)$ and $(3.2a^2 + 4.6ab + 3.6b^2)$

29. $\left(\frac{1}{3}x^3 + \frac{1}{3}x^2 + \frac{3}{2}\right)$ and $-\left(\frac{1}{3}x^3 - \frac{1}{2}x^2 + \frac{1}{2}\right)$

30. $(5x^5 + 7x^3 - x^2 + 4)$ and $-(6x^5 - 2x^3 + 3x^2 + 4)$

Write in standard form without using grouping symbols.

Sample: $-[2x^4 - (x + 5x^2 - 6)]$

Solution:

$$\begin{aligned} -[2x^4 - (x + 5x^2 - 6)] &= -[2x^4 - x - 5x^2 + 6] \\ &= -2x^4 + 5x^2 + x - 6 \end{aligned}$$

C

31. $5s^2 - (s^3 + 4s + 8)$

32. $(x^5 - 7) + (4x^2 + 9)$

33. $-[(5a - 10) + (a^5 - 2a^2 + a)]$

34. $7 - (4x - 2x^2) + 5x^3$

35. $-(15y^2 - 3y) + (-7 + 2y^3)$

36. $-[-(2a^4 - 8) + (7a + a^2)]$

37. $-[(-x^2 - 5x + 8) - (x^3 + 2x^4)]$

38. $-[-(2k^5) + (k^3 - 1) - (k^4 + k)]$

12-7 *Subtraction with Polynomials*

OBJECTIVE
Subtract a polynomial by adding its opposite.

We can subtract polynomials by applying the same ideas used earlier to do subtraction.

EXAMPLE 1 $10 - 4 = 10 + (-4) = 6$
$5a - (-4b) = 5a + 4b$

EXAMPLE 2 $(8t - 3) - (t + 3) = (8t - 3) + \underbrace{(-t - 3)}_{\text{opposite of } t + 3} = 7t - 6$

EXAMPLE 3 Subtract:

$$\begin{array}{r} 10a^2 + 8a + 5 \\ \underline{3a^2 - a + 1} \end{array}$$

► Add:

$$\begin{array}{r} 10a^2 + 8a + 5 \\ \underline{-3a^2 + a - 1} \\ 7a^2 + 9a + 4 \end{array}$$

Recall that we can add to check subtraction. We add the answer to the number subtracted.

EXAMPLE 4 Subtract:

$$\begin{array}{r} 12s + 7 \\ \underline{5s - 3} \end{array}$$

► Add:

$$\begin{array}{r} 12s + 7 \\ \underline{-5s + 3} \\ 7s + 10 \end{array}$$

Check:

$$\begin{array}{r} 7s + 10 \\ \underline{5s - 3} \\ 12s + 7 \end{array} \checkmark$$

Name the opposite.

Sample: $4 - 2t$ *What you say:* $-4 + 2t$

1. $-2k$
2. $4x^5$
3. $z + 2$
4. $4c - d$
5. $-5 - 6x^2$
6. $2 - 4a + b$
7. $-3a^2 + 2a - 6$
8. $-\frac{1}{2}a - \frac{1}{3}b - \frac{1}{4}c$

Subtract the second polynomial from the first.

Sample: $\begin{array}{r} 2a \\ -5a \\ \hline \end{array}$ *What you say:* $2a$ plus $5a$, or $7a$

9. $\begin{array}{r} -15c \\ 10c \\ \hline \end{array}$

10. $\begin{array}{r} 3ab \\ 8ab \\ \hline \end{array}$

11. $\begin{array}{r} \frac{1}{2}k \\ -\frac{1}{4}k \\ \hline \end{array}$

12. $\begin{array}{r} 12b \\ 5b \\ \hline \end{array}$

Written EXERCISES

Subtract the second polynomial from the first. Check by addition.

Sample: $\begin{array}{l} 3x + 4y \\ 2x - 3y - 1 \\ \hline \end{array}$

Solution: $\begin{array}{r} 3x + 4y \\ 2x - 3y - 1 \\ \hline x + 7y + 1 \end{array}$ *Check:* $\begin{array}{r} x + 7y + 1 \\ 2x - 3y - 1 \\ \hline 3x + 4y \end{array}$ ✓

A

1. $\begin{array}{l} 4r + 7s \\ 3r - 2s \\ \hline \end{array}$

2. $\begin{array}{l} 8 + c \\ 3 - 2c \\ \hline \end{array}$

3. $\begin{array}{r} 5p + 2 \\ -2p + 2 \\ \hline \end{array}$

4. $\begin{array}{r} 10k^2 + 3 \\ 5k^2 + 8 \\ \hline \end{array}$

5. $\begin{array}{r} 5x^2 + 20 \\ x^2 + 15 \\ \hline \end{array}$

6. $\begin{array}{r} 5 + 4c \\ 15 - c \\ \hline \end{array}$

7. $\begin{array}{r} 3b^2 + 5c \\ b^2 - 8c + 5 \\ \hline \end{array}$

8. $\begin{array}{l} 8x - 4y \\ 5x - 2y \\ \hline \end{array}$

9. $\begin{array}{lr} 2m^2 & + 4 \\ m^2 - 7m & \\ \hline \end{array}$

10. $\begin{array}{r} 10x + 4y + 9 \\ 2x - y + 8 \\ \hline \end{array}$

11. $\begin{array}{r} -2k + 5h^2 \\ - 4h^2 \\ \hline \end{array}$

12. $\begin{array}{lr} 2x^3 + 13x^2 & \\ -x^3 & - 10 \\ \hline \end{array}$

Write the expression without parentheses. Do not combine similar terms.

Sample: $(8x - 9) - (6 - x)$ *Solution:* $8x - 9 - 6 + x$

13. $(k - 10) - (2k + 15)$
14. $(4 - 2s) - (-6 + 9s)$

15. $(-2y^2 - 4y) - (y^2 - 3y)$
16. $(3y^2 + 5y) - (-y^2 - 8y)$
17. $(2x - y + 8) - (13x + 4y + 9)$
18. $(-10 - 3a - 5b) - (-7b + 2a - 8)$

Simplify. Write the answer in standard form.

Sample: $(2 + 7b) - (-3 + 5b)$
Solution: $(2 + 7b) - (-3 + 5b) = 2 + 7b + 3 - 5b = 2b + 5$

19. $(3w - 5) - (4w + 7)$
20. $(a + 3b) - (a - 8b)$
21. $(2t^2 + 5) - (9 - 4t^2)$
22. $(3 - 7d) - (1 - d)$
23. $(2r + 3s) - (2r + 3s)$
24. $(4x - 9y) - (-5x + 10)$
25. $(1 - 2w) - (1 - 3w)$ B
26. $(3.5a + 0.5) - (2.1a + 0.2)$
27. $(-2d + 4c) - (-5d + 7c)$
28. $(2a - b) - (2a - b)$
29. $(3 - 10d + 7d^2) - (4 + 3d^2)$
30. $(2.7s^3 - 0.7s^2) - (-1.3s^2 - 0.9)$

Subtract the second polynomial from the first. Check by addition.

Sample:

$$\begin{array}{r} x^2 + 14x - 49 \\ \underline{6x^2 + 5x - 1} \end{array}$$

Solution:

$$\begin{array}{r} x^2 + 14x - 49 \\ \underline{6x^2 + 5x - 1} \\ -5x^2 + 9x - 48 \end{array}$$

Check:

$$\begin{array}{r} 6x^2 + 5x - 1 \\ \underline{-5x^2 + 9x - 48} \\ x^2 + 14x - 49 \end{array} \checkmark$$

31. $$\begin{array}{r} 6r^2 + 13r + 7 \\ \underline{2r^2 + 10r - 4} \end{array}$$

32. $$\begin{array}{r} 12w^2 + w - 2 \\ \underline{4w^2 + 7w - 3} \end{array}$$

33. $$\begin{array}{r} 2h^2 - 15h - 8 \\ \underline{h^2 + 6h + 5} \end{array}$$

34. $$\begin{array}{r} 5x^2 - 11x + 2 \\ \underline{-2x^2 - 3x - 1} \end{array}$$

35. $$\begin{array}{r} -3b^2 + 6b + 1 \\ \underline{-4b^2 \qquad + 3} \end{array}$$

36. $$\begin{array}{r} x^2 \qquad + 9 \\ \underline{-3x^2 - 4x + 13} \end{array}$$

37. $\begin{array}{r} 7x^2 - 12x \\ 20x - 7 \\ \hline \end{array}$

38. $\begin{array}{r} 8b^3 - 2b^2 + 5b \\ 6b^3 - 4b^2 + b \\ \hline \end{array}$

39. $\begin{array}{r} k^2 + 2k \\ - 3k + 5 \\ \hline \end{array}$

Simplify. Remove all grouping symbols and combine similar terms. Write the answer in standard form.

C

40. $2c - [c - (4c + 6) + 10 - 3c^2] + 6c^2$
41. $(6k - 4) - [(3k + 1) + 7 - (-2k - 6)]$
42. $-(15b + 10) - [-3b - (2 + b) + 8]$
43. $[(8 + 4x) - (3x - 2)] - [2 - (x - 3 + x^2)]$
44. $-[y - (3 + y)] - [-8y + (9y - y^2) + 4] + y$

SELF-TEST 2

Be sure you understand the term *identity element for addition of polynomials.* (p. 330)

Section 12-6, p. 330 Add. Justify your answer.

1. $-(2c^2 + c + 7) + (2c^2 + c + 7)$
2. $(2x - 2x) + (7x^2 - 1)$

Give the opposite. Write your answer in standard form.

3. $-(2y^3 - y + 3y^2)$
4. $12z + z^3 - z$

Section 12-7, p. 333 Subtract the second polynomial from the first.

5. $\begin{array}{r} 4m - 3 \\ -2m - 2 \\ \hline \end{array}$

6. $\begin{array}{r} 2t + 4 \\ t + 1 \\ \hline \end{array}$

Simplify.

7. $(2x^2 + 3x) - (4x^2 + 5x)$
8. $(3n^2 + 5) - (2n^2 - 8)$

Check your answers with those printed at the back of the book.

12-8 *Polynomials and Problem Solving*

OBJECTIVE
Solve problems with information expressed in polynomial form.

The information given in a word problem may be expressed in polynomial form.

EXAMPLE 1 Find the area of the shaded part of the figure. The area of the square is $4m^2 + 4m + 1$. The area of the circle is $4m + 6$.

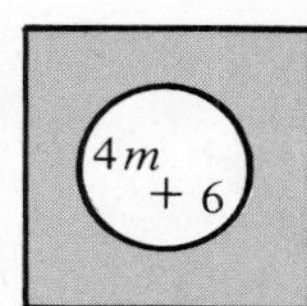

Subtract:

$$\begin{array}{r} 4m^2 + 4m + 1 \\ 4m + 6 \\ \hline 4m^2 \quad\quad - 5 \end{array}$$

◄ Area of square
◄ Area of circle
◄ Area of shaded region

EXAMPLE 2 Find the distance from R to T.

Add:

$$\begin{array}{l} a^2 + 3ab - 2 \\ 4a^2 - ab \\ \hline 5a^2 + 2ab - 2 \end{array}$$

◄ distance from R to S
◄ distance from S to T
◄ distance from R to T

Problems

Write the answer as a polynomial in standard form.

1. Find the perimeter of the figure at the right.

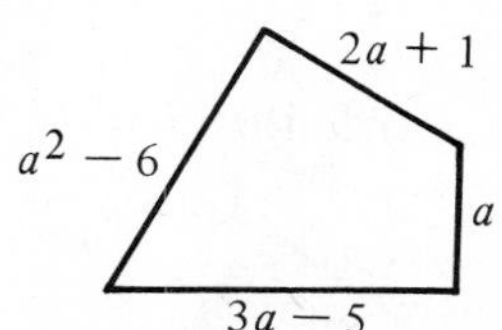

2. A square has sides of length $7 - 12t$. Find the perimeter.

3. One plot of land has area $\frac{1}{2}a - 9$. A connecting plot has area $a^2 + \frac{1}{3}a + 5$. Find the combined area.

4. The length XZ is $2x^3 + 6x^2 + 7$. The length XY is $4x^2 + 6$. Find the length YZ.

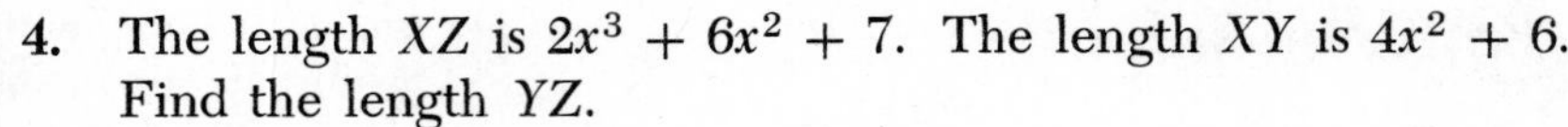

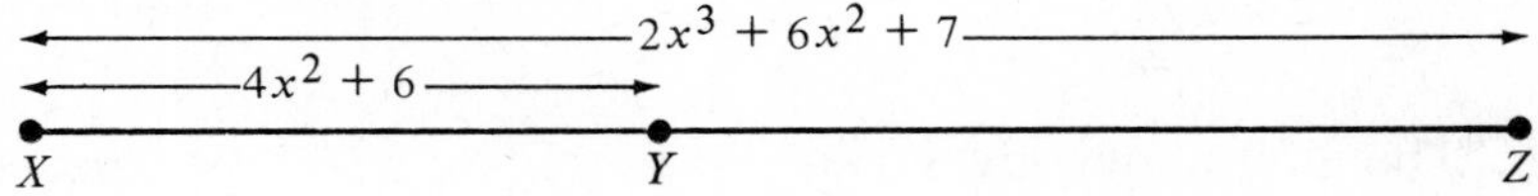

5. The area of $ABDE$ is $4z^2 - 3z + 8$. The area of $ABCE$ is $3z^2 + 5$. Find the area of CDE.

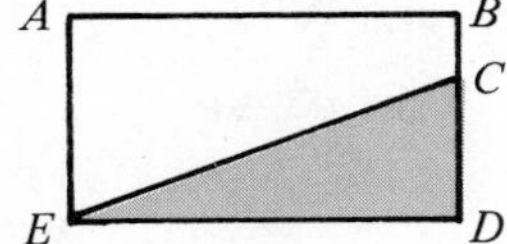

6. The area of the square is $4r^4 + 8r^2 + 16$. The area of the shaded region is $3r^3 + 2r^2$. Find the area of the circle.

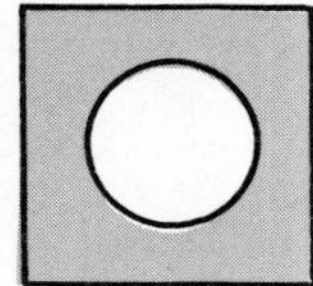

7. A board had length $1 - 5a - 6a^2$. A carpenter sawed a piece of length $4 - 2a^2$ from the end. How long is the remaining piece?

8. Two planes flew different routes from London to San Francisco. Plane 1 flew a distance of $\frac{1}{2}x^2 + \frac{2}{3}x - 4$. Plane 2 flew a distance of $\frac{3}{4}x^2 - \frac{1}{6}x + 9$. How much farther did Plane 2 travel?

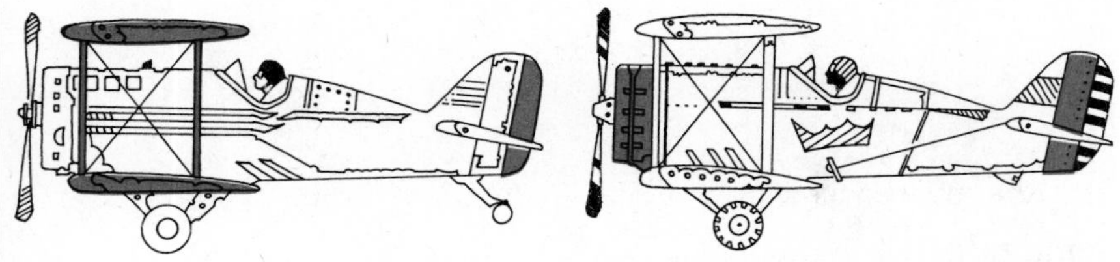

9. Fairfield Farms owned land with combined area $\frac{2}{3}x^3 + \frac{1}{4}x^2 + 5$. They purchased another piece of land with area $\frac{1}{4}x^3 + 2x^2 + x$. Find the total area of their land.

12-9 *Polynomials and Solving Equations*

OBJECTIVE
Solve and check equations like $2t + (4 - t) = 10$ and $5y - (2y + 4) = 12$.

We may need to simplify polynomial expressions as the first step in solving an equation.

EXAMPLE 1 Solve:

$$\begin{aligned} 3x + (2x + 4) &= 14 \\ 3x + 2x + 4 &= 14 \\ 5x + 4 &= 14 \\ 5x &= 10 \\ x &= 2 \end{aligned}$$

Check:

$$\begin{aligned} 3(2) + [2(2) + 4] &\stackrel{?}{=} 14 \\ 6 + (4 + 4) &\stackrel{?}{=} 14 \\ 6 + 8 &\stackrel{?}{=} 14 \\ 14 &= 14 \ \checkmark \end{aligned}$$

EXAMPLE 2 Solve:

$$\begin{aligned} 3m - (5 - 2m) &= 40 \\ 3m - 5 + 2m &= 40 \\ 5m - 5 &= 40 \\ 5m &= 45 \\ m &= 9 \end{aligned}$$

Check:

$$\begin{aligned} 3(9) - [5 - 2(9)] &\stackrel{?}{=} 40 \\ 27 - (5 - 18) &\stackrel{?}{=} 40 \\ 27 - (-13) &\stackrel{?}{=} 40 \\ 40 &= 40 \ \checkmark \end{aligned}$$

EXAMPLE 3 Solve:

$$\begin{aligned} 14 &= (3n + 4) - (n + 2) \\ 14 &= 3n + 4 - n - 2 \\ 14 &= 2n + 2 \\ 12 &= 2n \\ 6 &= n \end{aligned}$$

Check:

$$\begin{aligned} 14 &\stackrel{?}{=} [3(6) + 4] - (6 + 2) \\ 14 &\stackrel{?}{=} (18 + 4) - 8 \\ 14 &\stackrel{?}{=} 22 - 8 \\ 14 &= 14 \ \checkmark \end{aligned}$$

Written EXERCISES

A

Solve. Check your solution.

1. $(2n + 4) + (3n - 7) = 2$
2. $k + (k - 3) + (2k - 4) = 1$
3. $(9x - 42) - 3x = -6$
4. $-4z + (11z + 3) = 24$
5. $8 + (2x - 10) = 14$
6. $(2y - 28) + 5y = 42$
7. $(3n + 6) - n = 40$
8. $6y - (2y - 16) = 0$
9. $20 + (16 - 8k) = 44$
10. $(2z + 1) - (12z + 6) = 30$
11. $(0.2x + 1) - 4 = 6$
12. $-37 = -(5n + 1) + 11n$
13. $24 = (4s + 1) - (2s + 1)$
14. $-(x^2 - 5) + x^2 + 3x = 35$

Solve.

B

15. $-3n - (4n^2 - 2n + 5) = 12 - 4n^2$
16. $(4k - 5) + 7 = (9k - 6) + 3$
17. $2 + (3x - 5) + (4x + 6) = (4x + 1) - 15$
18. $(4x - 1.2) - 8 = (2x + 5) - (1 + 2x)$
19. $(4k + 8) - (2k - 14) = (8 - 6k) + (6k + 2)$
20. $(3t - 1) + (4t + 5) - 12 = 7 - (2t + 3)$
21. $(a^2 + 5) - (a^2 - 6) - 3a = 5a - 21$
22. $(x - 3) - (4x + 2) = -x - 12$
23. $16b - (6b - 13) = 3b - (b + 3) + (7b + 2)$
24. $(0.5x - 3) + (0.5x + 1) = 0.7x - (4 - 0.3x) + 2x$
25. $(2x - 1) - (x - 1) + (5x - 6) = 7x - 5$

C

26. $[4a - (5a + 6)] + 2a = 12$
27. $-(n^2 + 2n - 5) + (n^2 - 6n) = -4n + 21$
28. $-[-6t + (9 - 5t)] + (4t - 7) = 8t - 30$
29. $6b - [(3b + 1) - 2b] = 19 + b$
30. $(t^2 + 1) + [(1 - t^2) + (4 + 2t)] = (5t + 3)$

SELF-TEST 3

Write as a polynomial in standard form.

Section 12-8, p. 337

1. A triangle has sides of length $2ab + 1$, $3ab - 4$, and $4ab + 2$. Find the perimeter.
2. A square has sides of length $4x + 2$. Find the perimeter.
3. One box of soap has volume $3x^2 - 5$. A smaller box has volume $x^2 + 4$. Find the difference.

Section 12-9, p. 339

Solve.

4. $6 + (3x + 1) = 19$
5. $-(x + 1) + (2x + 4) = 9$
6. $(y - 3) + (3y + 1) = 10$
7. $(4n + 3) + (n + 5) = 23$

Check your answers with those printed at the back of the book.

---

chapter summary

1. Polynomial expressions are sometimes classified by the number of terms. **Monomials** contain one term. **Binomials** contain two terms. **Trinomials** contain three terms.
2. A polynomial in one variable is in **standard form** when the terms are ordered so that the variable in the first term has the greatest exponent, the variable in the second term has the next greatest exponent, and so on.
3. The sum of polynomials is found by combining similar terms.
4. The commutative and associative properties of addition apply to polynomials.
5. Zero is the **identity element** for addition of polynomials. Every polynomial has an opposite. The sum of a polynomial and its opposite is 0.
6. The **opposite** (additive inverse) of a polynomial expression is the sum of the opposites of the terms of the polynomial.
7. Subtracting a polynomial is the same as adding its opposite.

chapter test

Tell whether the polynomial is a monomial, a binomial, or a trinomial.

1. -3 **2.** $\frac{1}{2}t$ **3.** $\frac{2}{3}x^2 + x + 1$

4. $6 - c^2$ **5.** $7abc$ **6.** $2z^2 + z$

Write in standard form.

7. $a^3 - 8 + 2a^5$ **8.** $12 - 3a^2b$ **9.** $5x^2 - 4x^3 + x$

Add.

10. $\begin{array}{r} 7y^2 - 4y + 15 \\ \underline{13y^2 - 9y + 18} \end{array}$ **11.** $\begin{array}{r} 11t^2 + 5 \\ \underline{-2t^2 - 1} \end{array}$

Add.

12. $(2b + 7) + (4b - 5)$

13. $(-9m - 4) + (9m + 8)$

Subtract the second polynomial from the first.

14. $\begin{array}{r} 5a^2 + a - 1 \\ \underline{2a^2 - 3a + 4} \end{array}$

15. $\begin{array}{r} 4x^2 - 2x + 3 \\ \underline{2x - 7} \end{array}$

Simplify.

16. $(2z^2 - 5) - (z^2 - 1)$

17. $(5b + 5) - (-3b - 2)$

Simplify. Remove grouping symbols and combine similar terms.

18. $(4t - 6) + (3t - 1)$

19. $(5s - 7r) - (7r - 5s)$

20. $(4x + 5) - (2x - 6)$

21. $(a^2 - 2a) + (2a - 3)$

Write as a polynomial in standard form.

22. The perimeter of a square with sides of length $4t - 3$.

23. The perimeter of a rectangle with length $\frac{1}{2}z + 4$ and width $z - 3$.

Solve and check.

24. $(5a - 7) + 4a = 11$

25. $k + (k - 4) = 0$

26. $p - (4 - 2p) = 5$

27. $(-3n + 1) + (2n - 1) = 5$

challenge topics *Slope*

The slope of roads, sidewalks, or roof tops may be described by a ratio that compares **rise** and **run** in the form of a fraction, whole number, or percent.

EXAMPLE

$$\text{Slope} = \frac{\text{rise}}{\text{run}} = \frac{40}{1000} = 4\%$$

The idea of slope is important in mathematics. It is used to describe a line graphed on coordinate axes. A line that slopes upward from left to right is said to have **positive slope.** A line that slopes downward from left to right is said to have **negative slope.**

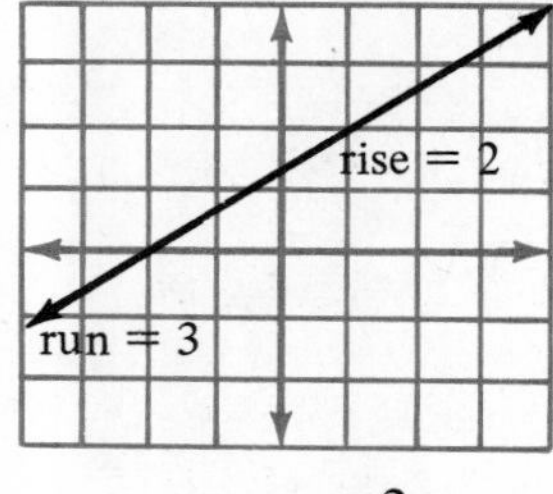

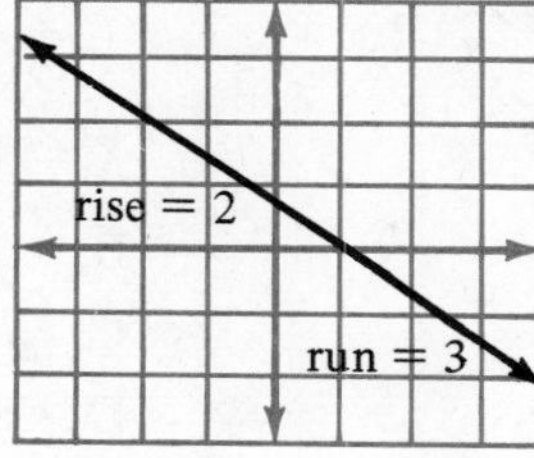

$$\text{Slope} = \frac{2}{3} \qquad\qquad \text{Slope} = -\frac{2}{3}$$

If the coordinates of two points on a line are known, the slope may be found in this way:

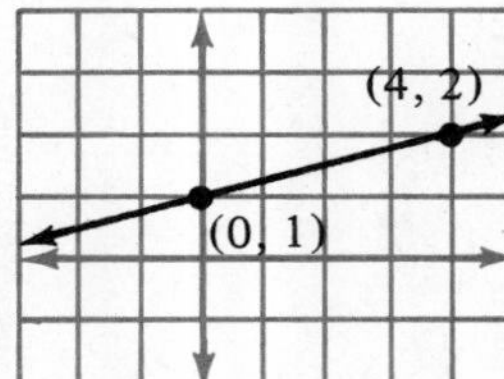

$$\text{Slope} = \frac{\text{difference in second coordinates}}{\text{difference in first coordinates}}$$

$$\text{Slope} = \frac{2-1}{4-0}$$

$$\text{Slope} = \frac{1}{4}$$

Tell whether the slope of the line is positive or negative. Then find the slope.

1.

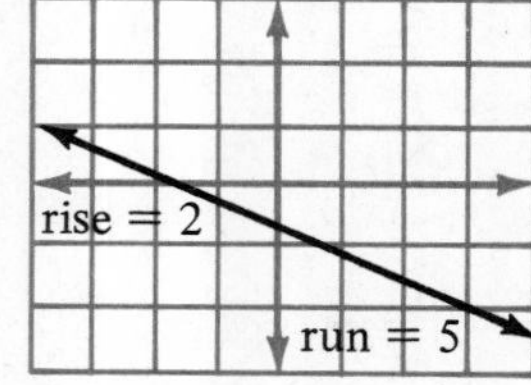

2.

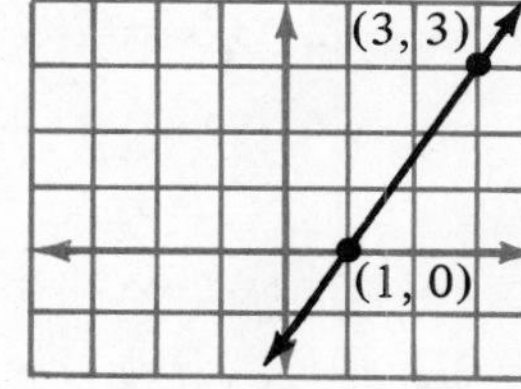

3.

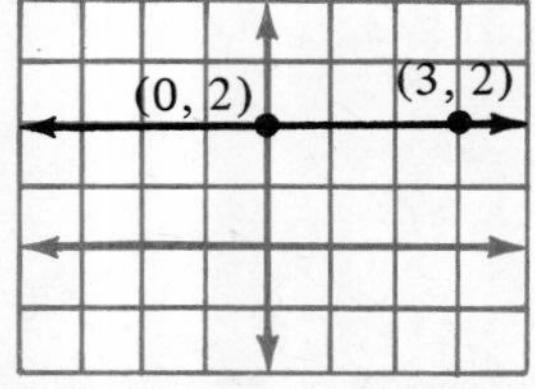

4.

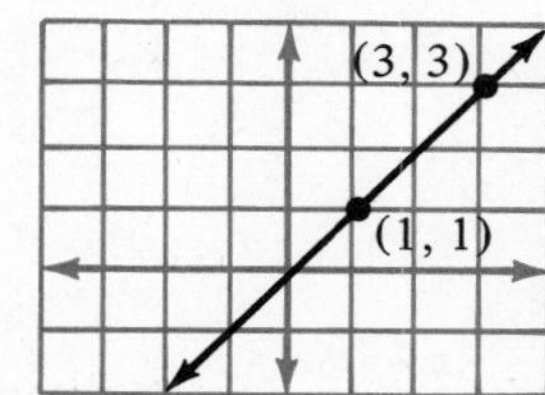

review of skills

Match each expression in Column 1 with a corresponding expression in Column 2.

COLUMN 1	COLUMN 2
1. $4 + 4 + 4$	**A.** 3^4
2. $3 \cdot 3 \cdot 3 \cdot 3$	**B.** $(4 \cdot 5) + 4$
3. $k \cdot h \cdot h$	**C.** kh^2
4. $6 \cdot 6 \cdot 5 \cdot 5$	**D.** $2b + 3c$
5. $5 + 5 + 5 + 5 + 4$	**E.** $6^2 \cdot 5^2$
6. $b + b + c + c + c$	**F.** $3 \cdot 4$

Simplify.

7. 4^2 **8.** $4 \cdot 5$ **9.** 6^3

10. $(a)(-5)$ **11.** $5 \cdot 5^2$ **12.** $-7 \cdot 2$

Simplify. Use the distributive property.

13. $(4 - t)3$ **14.** $(c + d)b$ **15.** $r(s - t)$

16. $-4(2 - x)$ **17.** $2m(n + p)$ **18.** $2a(b - c)$

Tell which of the following properties is illustrated: Commutative Property, Associative Property, Multiplicative Property of One, Property of Reciprocals.

19. $3 = 3 \cdot 1$ **20.** $4 \cdot 3 = 3 \cdot 4$ **21.** $a \cdot b = b \cdot a$

22. $k \cdot 1 = k$ **23.** $(2 \cdot 3)5 = 2(3 \cdot 5)$ **24.** $6 \cdot \frac{1}{6} = 1$

Solve.

25. $t \cdot 7 = 42$ **26.** $t \cdot 2 = 2^3$ **27.** $2^2 \cdot t = 2^3$

28. $t \cdot 6^2 = 6^3$ **29.** $7 \cdot t = 7^2$ **30.** $7^2 \cdot t = 7^3$

Simplify.

31. $\frac{22 \cdot 8 - 13 \cdot 8}{8}$ **32.** $\frac{20 \cdot 5 - 12 \cdot 7}{4}$

Left: Road builders, near Eighty Eight, Kentucky.

Right: Construction crew on modern highway.

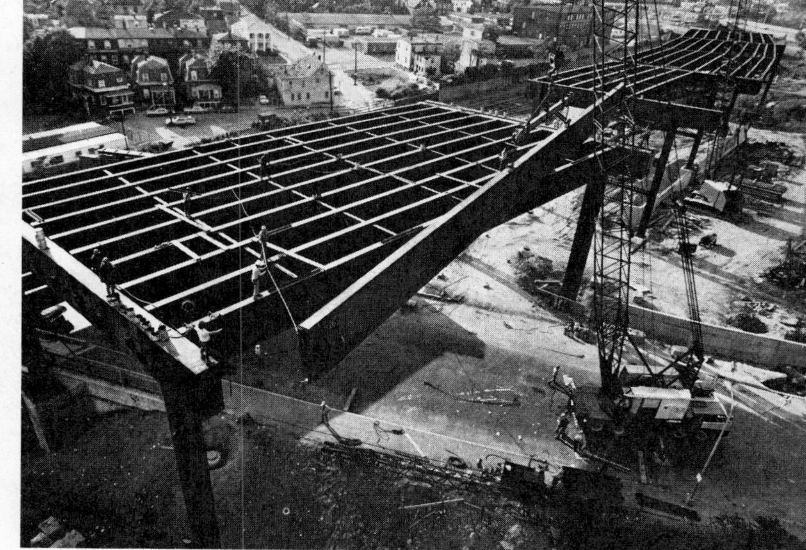

13 Multiplication and Division of Polynomials

Multiplication by a Monomial

13-1 *Repeating Factors and Exponents*

OBJECTIVE

Apply a rule of exponents to simplify expressions: $m \cdot m \cdot m = m^3$; $\frac{a}{b} \cdot \frac{a}{b} = \left(\frac{a}{b}\right)^2$

Recall that a multiplication expression involving a repeating factor may be written with an **exponent.** The repeating factor is called the **base.**

$7 \cdot 7 \cdot 7 \cdot 7 = 7^4$ (4: exponent; 7: base)

$m \cdot m \cdot m = m^3$ (3: exponent; m: base)

We read 7^4 as "seven to the fourth power." We read m^3 as either "m to the third power," or "m cubed."

EXAMPLE 1 $t \cdot t^3 = t(t \cdot t \cdot t)$ ◄ The factor t four times
$= t^4$

EXAMPLE 2 $rs \cdot rs \cdot rs \cdot rs \cdot rs = (rs)^5$ ◄ The factor rs five times

EXAMPLE 3 $rs \cdot s \cdot s \cdot s \cdot s = r(s \cdot s \cdot s \cdot s \cdot s)$ ◄ The factor r once
$= rs^5$ The factor s five times

Compare Examples 2 and 3. In Example 2 we need the parentheses to show that the exponent applies to rs, not just to s.

Here is a rule for simplifying when a factor is repeated in a multiplication expression.

► For any directed number a, and all positive integers p and q:

$$a^p \cdot a^q = a^{p+q}$$

EXAMPLE 4 $n^4 \cdot n^3 = n^{4+3} = n^7$

EXAMPLE 5 $(ab)^2(ab) = (ab)^{2+1} = (ab)^3$

Oral EXERCISES

Simplify. Use exponents.

1. $m \cdot m \cdot m \cdot m \cdot m$
2. $6 \cdot x \cdot x^5 \cdot x$
3. $n \cdot n \cdot n^4$
4. $2^3 \cdot 2$
5. $(ab)^5 \cdot (ab)^4$
6. $w \cdot w \cdot z \cdot z \cdot z$
7. $5 \cdot r \cdot r \cdot s \cdot s \cdot s$
8. $(ef)^3 \cdot (ef)^4$
9. $(x \cdot x)(y \cdot y \cdot y)$
10. $p \cdot p^3 \cdot p$

Written EXERCISES

A

Give the value. Use $x = 3$ and $z = 2$.

1. z^2
2. $10z^2$
3. $(x \cdot x)(z \cdot z \cdot z)$
4. x^3
5. $x \cdot x \cdot x \cdot z$
6. $3 \cdot z \cdot z$
7. $4 \cdot x \cdot x$
8. $(x \cdot z)^2$
9. $(3z)(xz)$
10. $5z^4$
11. $8x^3$
12. x^3x^2

Simplify.

13. $(3 \cdot 4)(x \cdot x)$
14. $(6 \cdot 12)(a \cdot a)$
15. $(x + y + z)(x + y + z)$
16. $(z + 1)(1 + z)$
17. $-5 \cdot 3(h \cdot h)$
18. $(-4)(x \cdot x \cdot x)$
19. $-7(z \cdot z \cdot z \cdot z)(2)$
20. $5 \cdot 3 \cdot 2(r \cdot r)$
21. $7(-12)(y \cdot y \cdot y \cdot y)$
22. $12 \cdot 5(z \cdot z^2)$
23. $3(x)(-2)(x)$
24. $9 \cdot 4 \cdot x^3 \cdot x^2$
25. $(8 \cdot 3)(m^2 \cdot m^3 \cdot m)$
26. $-3 \cdot 4(n \cdot n^2)$
27. $6(-7)t \cdot t$
28. $m \cdot m(-m) \cdot m$

Sample: $8^3 \cdot 8^4$ *Solution:* $8^3 \cdot 8^4 = 8^{3+4} = 8^7$

29. $2^2 \cdot 2^1$
30. $6^3 \cdot 6^4$
31. $x^5 \cdot x^2$
32. $m \cdot m \cdot m^2$
33. $p \cdot p^4$
34. $-3 \cdot t \cdot t^3$
35. $(a^2)(a^3)(-1)$
36. $m^4 \cdot m^5$
37. $y \cdot y^2 \cdot y^3$

B

Find the correct replacement for x.

Sample: $3^6 = 3^x \cdot 3^2$ *Solution:* $3^6 = 3^4 \cdot 3^2$; $x = 4$

38. $2^2 \cdot 2^4 = 2^x$
39. $(y \cdot y)(y \cdot y) = y^x$
40. $b^7 = b^2 \cdot b^x$
41. $r^2 \cdot r^x \cdot r^4 = r^{12}$
42. $(s + t)^x = (s + t)(s + t)^3$
43. $(m - n)^6 = (m - n)^4(m - n)^x$

13-2 *Products of Monomials*

OBJECTIVE
Use exponents to simplify expressions.

Our rule of exponents allows us to simplify expressions such as $(3xy)(8x^2y)$.

EXAMPLE 1 $(3xy)(8x^2y) = (3 \cdot 8)(x \cdot x^2)(y \cdot y)$
$= (24)(x^{1+2})(y^{1+1})$
$= 24x^3y^2$

EXAMPLE 2 $(a^3)(-3ab)(2b) = (-3 \cdot 2)(a^3 \cdot a)(b \cdot b)$
$= (-6)(a^{3+1})(b^{1+1})$
$= -6a^4b^2$

EXAMPLE 3 $\left(\frac{1}{2}mn\right)\left(\frac{1}{3}m^3\right) = \left(\frac{1}{2} \cdot \frac{1}{3}\right)(m^{1+3})(n)$
$= \frac{1}{6}m^4n$ or $\frac{m^4n}{6}$

EXERCISES

Simplify.

Sample 1: $2(-6y)$ *What you say:* $-12y$

Sample 2: $(-7)(-2)(a^2 \cdot a)(b \cdot b^2)$ *What you say:* $14a^3b^3$

1. $-7(5a)$
2. $(-t^2)(t)$
3. $(k)(k^2)$
4. $(m^3)(m^4)$
5. $(m)^3(m)^2$
6. $(4t^2)(t)^2$
7. $5(m^3 \cdot m^4)(n \cdot n^2)$
8. $7(x^4 \cdot x^5)(y^3 \cdot y^4)$
9. $a(x \cdot x^3)(d^3 \cdot d^3)$
10. $-4(a \cdot a^2)(b^3 \cdot b^5)$
11. $-3(b^3 \cdot b^4)$
12. $2(r \cdot r^2)(n \cdot n \cdot n)$

Written EXERCISES

Simplify.

Sample: $(-5xy)(3xy^2)$ *Solution:* $(-5xy)(3xy^2)$
$= (-5 \cdot 3)(x \cdot x)(y \cdot y^2)$
$= -15x^2y^3$

A

1. $(4xy)(7xy^2)$
2. $(6ab)(8a^2b)$
3. $(-4b)(-4b)(3b)$
4. $(9xy^2)(y^3)(-3xy)$
5. $(5mn)(3m)(-4m)$
6. $(11s^2)(-7s^3)$
7. $(x)(-6x)(5y)$
8. $(5a)(2ab)(-4b)$
9. $(-a)(-3ab)(-b)$
10. $m^2(-5mn)(2n)$
11. $6s(rs)(-s^2)$
12. $(-4ab)(2bc)(-2b)$
13. $(-12)(c)(-b)(-3c)$
14. $\left(\frac{1}{3}mn\right)\left(\frac{1}{5}mn\right)$
15. $(3xy)(-x)(-xy)$
16. $-x^2y(xy)(-xy)$

B

17. $(-7y)(3x^3y^2)(-x^3y^5)$
18. $-0.8x(20x^2y^5)(-x^2y)$
19. $-5a(0.2a^3b^5)(0.4ab^2)$
20. $(3^3ab^3)(-a^2b^5)$
21. $(-ab)(-7a^2b^2)(-5c^8)$
22. $(x^4)(x^2y)(y^3)$
23. $(3n)^2(mn)(3m)^2$
24. $(a^2d)(-2a^2)(d^2)$

Sample: $(7x^2)(3y)(-2y) + (5xy)(-3xy)$
Solution: $(7x^2)(3y)(-2y) + (5xy)(-3xy)$
$= (-42x^2y^2) + (-15x^2y^2) = -57x^2y^2$

C

25. $(6x^2)(3y) + (7xy)(x)$
26. $(-3pq)(4p^2q) - (6q^2)(-p^3)$
27. $(5a^2b^3)(-3ab) + (ab^2)(a^2b^2)$
28. $(-2xy^2)(5x^2)(-4y) - (8xy^3)(5xy)$
29. $(-2m^2)(-6mn)(mn) - (2m^2n^2)(-4m)(m)$
30. $(-2a^2bc^3)(-ab^2c) + (5c^2)(-6a^3b^3)(ac^2)$
31. $\left(\frac{1}{2}xy^2\right)\left(\frac{2}{3}x\right) + \left(\frac{1}{3}y^2\right)\left(\frac{1}{2}x^2\right)$
32. $(0.3t)(-0.2t^2) + (0.2t^2)(0.2t)$
33. $\left(\frac{1}{4}mn\right)(2m^2) - (4m^3)\left(\frac{1}{4}n\right)$
34. $\left(\frac{3}{5}xyz\right)\left(\frac{1}{2}x\right) - \left(\frac{2}{3}x^2\right)(3yz)$
35. $(1.2a^2b)(2.7bc^2) - (6ab^2)(0.2ac^2)$

13-3 *A Power of a Product*

OBJECTIVES

Simplify expressions such as $(3ab)^3$ and $(-2xy)^2$.

Find the value of such expressions as $(4^3)^2$ and $[(-2)^2]^3$.

When a product is raised to a power, each factor of the product is raised to that power.

EXAMPLE 1 $(3ab)^3 = 3ab \cdot 3ab \cdot 3ab = 3 \cdot 3 \cdot 3 \cdot a \cdot a \cdot a \cdot b \cdot b \cdot b$
$= 3^3a^3b^3 = 27a^3b^3$

EXAMPLE 2 $(-2xy)^2 = (-2)(-2)x \cdot x \cdot y \cdot y = 4x^2y^2$

For all directed numbers a and b and any positive integer p:

$$(ab)^p = a^pb^p$$

An expression such as $(4^2)^3$ is described as a **power of a power.**

EXAMPLE 3 $(4^2)^3 = 4^2 \cdot 4^2 \cdot 4^2 = 4^{2+2+2} = 4^{3 \cdot 2} = 4^6$

EXAMPLE 4 $(m^5)^2 = m^5 \cdot m^5 = m^{5+5}$ ◄ $m^{5+5} = m^{2 \cdot 5} = m^{5 \cdot 2}$
$= m^{10}$

For every directed number a, and all positive integers p and q:

$$(a^p)^q = a^{p \cdot q}$$

EXERCISES

Answer *Yes* or *No*.

1. Is $(7a)^3$ always the same as $7a^3$?
2. Is $4a^2$ always the same as 4^2a^2?
3. Is $(2x^2)^2$ always the same as $4x^4$?
4. Is $9y^2$ always the same as $(3y)^2$?
5. Is $27t^3$ always the same as $(27t)^3$?
6. Is $(x^2)^3$ always the same as x^5?

Simplify.

Written EXERCISES

A

1. $(3ab)^4$ **2.** $(4xy)^3$ **3.** $(3xyz)^4$
4. $(-3xyz)^4$ **5.** $(-8mn)^2$ **6.** $(-10xy)^3$
7. $(10x^2y^2)^2$ **8.** $(-5mn^2)^3$ **9.** $(-ab)^3$
10. $(-2y^5)^3$ **11.** $(-r^2s^2)^4$ **12.** $(3mnp)^2$
13. $(n^4)^4$ **14.** $(-a^5)^3$ **15.** $(0 \cdot m^2n)^2$

Find the value. For a variable, use the given value.

Sample: $(5x^3)^2;\ x = 2$ *Solution:* $5^2x^{3 \cdot 2} = 5^2x^6 = 5^2 \cdot 2^6 = 25 \cdot 64 = 1600$

16. $(4^2)^2$ **17.** $(10^2)^3$ **18.** $(-2^3)^2$
19. $(2y^3)^2;\ y = 2$ **20.** $(n^3)^5;\ n = 1$ **21.** $(-3a^2)^2;\ a = 3$
22. $(5x)^4;\ x = 2$ **23.** $(-5y^3)^2;\ y = 10$
24. $(5n^3)^2;\ n = -2$ **25.** $(-5a^4)^3;\ a = 1$
26. $(75y^3)^4;\ y = 0$ **27.** $(0.5a^2)^2;\ a = 10$
28. $(8x^4)^2;\ x = \frac{1}{2}$ **29.** $(-8a^2b)^2;\ a = \frac{1}{2},\ b = 10$

Square the monomial.

30. $5x$ **31.** $-5xy^2$ **32.** $-0.4xy^3$
33. $0.2ab^2c^3$ **34.** $-3x^3y^2z$ **35.** $-12abc$

Simplify.

Sample: $(3ab)^3 + (4a)(-5ab)(ab^2)$
Solution: $(3ab)^3 + (4a)(-5ab)(ab^2) = 27a^3b^3 - 20a^3b^3 = 7a^3b^3$

B

36. $(3xy)^4 + (3x)^3(5xy^2)(y)^2$
37. $(5a)^2(-2ab^2)^2 + (3a)^2(ab)^2(b)^2$
38. $(2x^2)(-5x^3) + (-4x)(2x^2)^2 + 10x^5$
39. $(m^2)m + (2m^2)(-2m) + (2m)^3$
40. $(-2c)(-3cd)^3 + (3c)^2(cd)^2(-6d)$
41. $(rs)^6(-6rs^3) + r(r^2s^3)^3 + (2r^2)^2(r^3s^9)$

C

42. $(3x)^2(-16x^4) + (-4x^4)(-x)^2 + (-10x^3)^2$
43. $(-at)^3(0.2a^2t) + (t^2a)^2(0.3a^3) + (t^2a)(ta^2)^2$
44. $(-0.1xy)^5(0.2xy^2) + (x^2y)^3(0.2y^2)^2 + (-x^3y)^2(-y)^4y$

13-4 *A Monomial Times a Polynomial*

OBJECTIVE

Complete multiplications such as $x(x^2 - 2xy + y)$ and $-3w^3(w^2 - 4w + 10)$.

We use the distributive property to complete ordinary multiplications such as 3×45. We use the same property to complete multiplications involving monomials and polynomials.

Compare Examples 1 and 2.

EXAMPLE 1 $3 \times 45 = 3(40 + 5)$ ► or ►

$$\begin{aligned} 3 \times 45 &= 3(40 + 5) \\ &= 3(40) + 3(5) \\ &= 120 + 15 \\ &= 135 \end{aligned}$$

$$\begin{array}{r} 45 \\ 3 \\ \hline 15 \\ 120 \\ \hline 135 \end{array}$$

EXAMPLE 2 ► or ►

$$\begin{aligned} 3s(7s + 5) &= 3s(7s) + 3s(5) \\ &= 21s^2 + 15s \end{aligned}$$

$$\begin{array}{r} 7s + 5 \\ 3s \\ \hline 21s^2 + 15s \end{array}$$

EXAMPLE 3 ► or ►

$$\begin{aligned} &x(x^2 - 2xy + y) \\ &= x \cdot x^2 + x(-2xy) + x \cdot y \\ &= x^3 - 2x^2y + xy \end{aligned}$$

$$\begin{array}{r} x^2 - 2xy + y \\ x \\ \hline x^3 - 2x^2y + xy \end{array}$$

EXAMPLE 4

$$\begin{aligned} &-3w^3(w^2 - 4w + 10) \\ &= -3w^3 \cdot w^2 + (-3w^3)(-4w) + (-3w^3)(10) \\ &= -3w^5 + 12w^4 - 30w^3 \end{aligned}$$

EXERCISES

Simplify.

Sample: $5(x - 3)$ *What you say:* $5x - 15$

1. $3(2 + x)$	**2.** $10(2x - 3y)$	**3.** $-5(5 - x^2)$
4. $(8 - y)(-y)$	**5.** $-8x^5(3 + x)$	**6.** $-1(k - 4b)$
7. $(x - y)16$	**8.** $(3x - 2)8$	**9.** $21y(x + y)$
10. $-2y(5y - 5)$	**11.** $xy(4x + 7)$	**12.** $12a(3a + 5)$

Written EXERCISES

A

Multiply.

1. $-x(x^2 + 6x - 7)$
2. $-6(2k^2 - 2k + 4)$
3. $-5(-d^2 + 2ad - c^2)$
4. $-y(y^2 - 12xy + x^2)$
5. $d^2(a - b - d)$
6. $2t^2(3 - t^2 - 2t)$
7. $(7 - 3x - x^3)(-x^2)$
8. $-p^2(5p^3 - p^2 + 2p - 3)$
9. $-y^3(y^2 - y^3 + 1)$
10. $ab(3ab - 4a + 2b)$
11. $\begin{array}{r} 5 + 2x - x^2 \\ 5x \\ \hline \end{array}$
12. $\begin{array}{r} 9y - 1 - 3y^3 \\ -4y \\ \hline \end{array}$
13. $\begin{array}{r} 3k^2 - 4k - 10 \\ -0.2k \\ \hline \end{array}$
14. $\begin{array}{r} 6a + 4b - 2c^2 \\ a^2 \\ \hline \end{array}$
15. $\begin{array}{r} -4m^2 + mn - 2n^2 \\ -m^2 \\ \hline \end{array}$
16. $\begin{array}{r} 4a^2 + 5b^2 + 6c^2 \\ 1.5a \\ \hline \end{array}$

Simplify.

17. $x(2x + 3y) + 6(-xy)$
18. $a(b - a) + 3a(b - a)$
19. $7m(-m - n) + m(m - n)$
20. $x(2y - 3x) + 3x(y + 2x)$
21. $3a(a + b) + 5a(a + b)$
22. $6a(3a - 2b) + a(a + b)$
23. $-2y(5x + y) + 4y(5y + x)$
24. $4ab(a - 3b) - 8a(2ab + 8b^2)$
25. $2x^2(3w - 4x) + (wx + x^2)(2x)$
26. $(a + 3b)(ab) - a(-3b^2 - 2ab)$
27. $xy(x^2 - xy^2) + (3y)(2x^3 + x^2y^2)$
28. $(3m^2n)(m^2 - 2n) + m^2n(m^2 - n)$

B

Multiply.

29. $6a^2b(10 - 4ab^4 + 6a^6b^4 - b^{10})$
30. $10ab^2(16 + 12a^{10}b^2 - 4a^6b^8 - 14a^2b^{10})$
31. $-a^3b\left(\frac{1}{2}a^2b - \frac{1}{2}a^3b^2 + ab^2 - b^3\right)$
32. $-1.5a^2b(0.5ab^2 + 4a^2b^2 - 5a^2b - b^3)$
33. $21x^4y^4(-3x^2 + 4xy - 5y^2)$

Solve.

34. $-3x + 4(x - 2) = 11$
35. $4y + 3(-y - 1) = 8$
36. $2 = (10n + 6) - 6(n - 2)$
37. $22 = (4k + 3.5) - 2.5(k - 8)$
38. $0.8(7 - x) + 7x = 18$
39. $34 = (-1)(10 - x) - 12x$
40. $7 - 3(a + 1) = 3a - 2$
41. $-10(2 + 2x) + 312 = 3.5(8 - x)$

C

42. $y - (y + 21) = 1.5y - 1.5(7 - y)$
43. $10a - 2(a - 8) = 28a - 14(2a + 8)$
44. $0.1(3x - 12) - (3x - 2.5) = 6.5 + 0.25(3x - 7)$
45. $6(4k - 5) = -5(2 - 5k) - 7$

Problems

Express the answer as a polynomial in simplest form.

A

1. Find the area of the triangle.
$\left(Hint\text{: } A = \frac{1}{2}bh\right)$

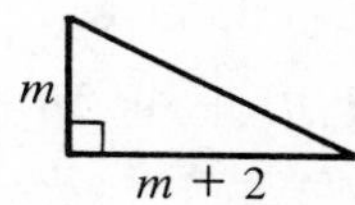

2. Find the area of a square with sides of length $5t$. Find the perimeter.
3. Find the area of a rectangle with length $2x^2 + 5$ and width $3x$.
4. Find the perimeter of a pentagon if each of the five sides has length $2x^2 + 3x + 1$.

B

5. A cylinder has radius 5 centimeters and height $2t + 9$. The volume is given by the formula $V = \pi r^2 h$. Find the volume. (You don't have to substitute a value for π.)
6. Find the volume of the box.
(*Hint:* $V = lwh$)

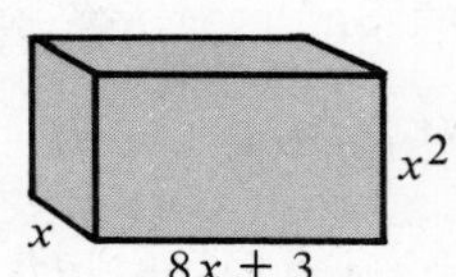

7. Find the area of the bottom of the box in Problem 6.

8. A rectangular piece of sheet metal has four circular holes punched in it. The area of each circle is $c^2 + 1$. Find the area of the remaining piece of metal.

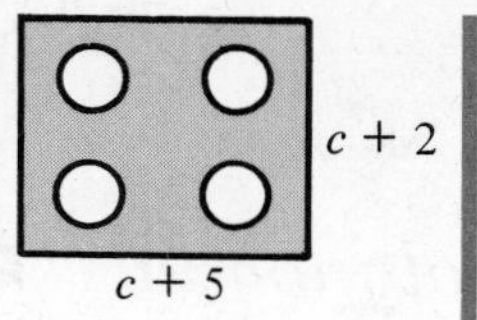

C

9. A cube has edges of length y^2. (a) Find its volume. (b) Find its surface area.

10. (a) Find the area of the figure.
(b) Find its perimeter.

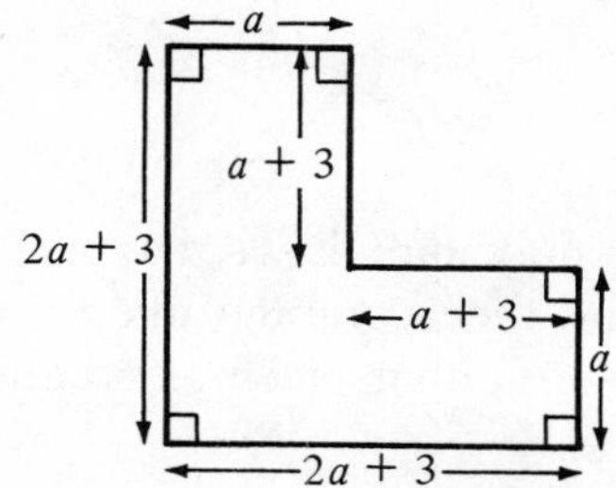

SELF-TEST 1

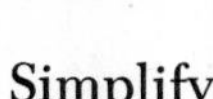

Be sure that you understand these terms.

exponent (p. 346) base (p. 346)

Simplify.

Section 13-1, p. 346

1. $(-2 \cdot 5)(x \cdot x \cdot x)$
2. $3 \cdot n(-n)n$
3. $4^2 \cdot 4^3$
4. $z^5 \cdot z^6$
5. $(3ts)(-2t^2s^2)$
6. $(-4m)(2m^2n)$

Section 13-2, p. 348

7. $(2xy)^3$
8. $(-a^2)^2$

Section 13-3, p. 350

Find the value.

9. $(2^4)^2$
10. $(3^3)^2$

Simplify.

Section 13-4, p. 352

11. $-x(3x^2 + x - 5)$
12. $4a(a + 2b) + b(4a + b)$

Check your answers with those printed at the back of the book.

13-5 *A Polynomial Times a Polynomial*

OBJECTIVE
Multiply polynomials, such as $(3x - 4)(x + 2)$ and $(n^2 + 2n - 3)(n + 4)$.

To multiply two polynomials we may need to use the distributive property more than once and then combine like terms. This is the same method we use to multiply two numbers such as 45 and 23.

EXAMPLE 1

$$\begin{array}{r} 45 \\ \times 23 \\ \hline \end{array} \quad \rightarrow \quad \begin{array}{rrrl} & 40 + 5 & & \\ & 20 + 3 & & \\ \hline & 120 + 15 & & \leftarrow 3(40 + 5) \\ 800 + 100 & & & \leftarrow 20(40 + 5) \\ \hline 800 + 220 + 15 = 1035 & & & \end{array}$$

If we arrange the work horizontally the steps are in different order.

$$\begin{aligned} (23)(45) &= (20 + 3)(40 + 5) \\ &= 20(40 + 5) + 3(40 + 5) \\ &= [(20 \cdot 40) + (20 \cdot 5)] + [(3 \cdot 40) + (3 \cdot 5)] \\ &= 800 + 100 + 120 + 15 \\ &= 1035 \end{aligned}$$

EXAMPLE 2 $(3x - 4)(x + 2)$ →

$$\begin{array}{rrl} & 3x - 4 & \\ & x + 2 & \\ \hline & 6x - 8 & \leftarrow 2(3x - 4) \\ 3x^2 - 4x & & \leftarrow x(3x - 4) \\ \hline 3x^2 + 2x - 8 & & \end{array}$$

Horizontally:

$$\begin{aligned} (3x - 4)(x + 2) &= 3x(x + 2) - 4(x + 2) \\ &= 3x^2 + 6x - 4x - 8 \\ &= 3x^2 + 2x - 8 \end{aligned}$$

When one of the polynomials is a trinomial, it is usually easier to arrange the work in vertical form.

EXAMPLE 3 $(n^2 + 2n - 3)(n + 4)$ ►

$$\begin{array}{r} n^2 + 2n - 3 \\ n + 4 \\ \hline 4n^2 + 8n - 12 \\ n^3 + 2n^2 - 3n \phantom{{}- 12} \\ \hline n^3 + 6n^2 + 5n - 12 \end{array}$$

Oral EXERCISES

Use the distributive property to name the expression as the sum or difference of two products. Do not multiply.

Sample: $(n - 2)(3n + 7)$

What you say: $n(3n + 7) - 2(3n + 7)$

1. $(3a - 9)(5a + 2)$
2. $(3a + 2)(2a + 3)$
3. $(3x + 5)(3x + 5)$
4. $(7b - 3)(b + 4)$
5. $(4c + 14)(c - 3)$
6. $(6t + 5)(t - 4)$
7. $(a + 7b)(2ab + 3a - b)$
8. $(3n + 5)(3n - 5)$

Multiply in two ways. Use both the vertical and the horizontal form.

Sample: $(5x + 3)(2x + 4)$

Solution:

$$\begin{array}{r} 5x + 3 \\ 2x + 4 \\ \hline 20x + 12 \\ 10x^2 + 6x \phantom{{}+ 12} \\ \hline 10x^2 + 26x + 12 \end{array}$$

$$\begin{aligned} &(5x + 3)(2x + 4) \\ &= [5x(2x + 4)] + [3(2x + 4)] \\ &= (10x^2 + 20x) + (6x + 12) \\ &= 10x^2 + 26x + 12 \end{aligned}$$

A

1. $(a + 5)(a + 4)$
2. $(m + 2)(m + 7)$
3. $(6m + 4)(2m + 13)$
4. $(4a - 8)(a + 8)$
5. $(x + 1.5)(x + 1.5)$
6. $(2b - 9)(b + 10)$

Multiply. Use either form.

7. $(x - 9)(x + 9)$
8. $(m - 4)(m - 6)$
9. $(x + 2)(x - 2)$
10. $(5m - 1)(4m - 2)$
11. $(3 + 4n)(8 + 9n)$
12. $(5x + 2)(7x - 3)$
13. $(6 - 4y)(3 - 4y)$
14. $(2x + 7)(2x + 7)$
15. $(4n + 3)(3 - 5n)$
16. $(2 - 3n)(3 - 2n)$
17. $(5t + 1)(5t - 1)$
18. $(z - 12)(2z + 1)$

Multiply. Do it mentally if you can. Then substitute to check your answer. Use $x = 1$ and $y = 1$.

Sample: $(3x + y)(x + 2y)$
Solution: $3x^2 + 7xy + 2y^2$

Check: $[3(1) + 1][1 + 2(1)] = 4 \cdot 3$
$= 12$
$3(1^2) + 7(1 \cdot 1) + 2(1^2) = 3 + 7 + 2$
$= 12$ √

19. $(8x + 2)(2x + 5)$
20. $(y + 3)(y + 1)$
21. $(2x + 3)(x + 1)$
22. $(2a - 5)(2a + 5)$
23. $(1 - 2b)(2 + b)$
24. $(p + 8)(p - 20)$
25. $(2s + 3)(s + 4)$
26. $(m + n)(m + n)$
27. $(8q - 2)(q - 10)$
28. $(2x - 2y)(x + y)$
29. $(1.5w - 2.5)(w + 1)$
30. $(s + t)(2s + 2t)$

Multiply.

B

31. $(8 + 8m)(1 - 5m)$
32. $(y + x)(8y + x)$
33. $(2n - m)(2n + m)$
34. $(2a - 0.5b)(a + 8b)$
35. $(3m + n)(0.5n + 2m)$
36. $(4m^2 + 3m + 4)(m - 5)$
37. $(x - 3)(x^2 - 6x + 7)$
38. $(x + y)(x^2 - xy - y^2)$
39. $(s^2 + st + t^2)(s - t)$
40. $(a^2 - 6a - 7)(a - 1)$
41. $(9 + x^2)(4 + x^2)$
42. $(x^2 - 10)(x^2 - 7)$
43. $(a^2b^2 + 1)(a^2b^2 + 1)$
44. $(k^4 - 2)(k^4 - 3)$
45. $(6 + r)(7 - 3r - 2r^2)$
46. $(m^2 + 3m + 4)(m^2 - 4m + 5)$
47. $(x - 2y + 1.5z)(2x + 2y - 2.5z)$
48. $(y - 1)(y^4 - y^3 - y^2 - y - 1)$

Problems

A

Express the answer as a polynomial in simplest form.

1. A rectangle has length $2x + 1$ and width $x + 4$. (a) Find the area. (b) Find the perimeter.

2. The height of a triangle is 3 centimeters more than the length of the base. Find the area. $\left(\textit{Hint: } A = \frac{1}{2}bh\right.$. Express the answer in terms of b.$\left.\right)$

3. A square has sides of length t. A rectangle has length 6 meters more than t and width 5 meters less than t. Find the area of the rectangle.

B

4. Find the area of each small rectangle. Find the area of the entire region by finding the product of two binomials. Check by comparing the result with the sum of the areas of the four small rectangles.

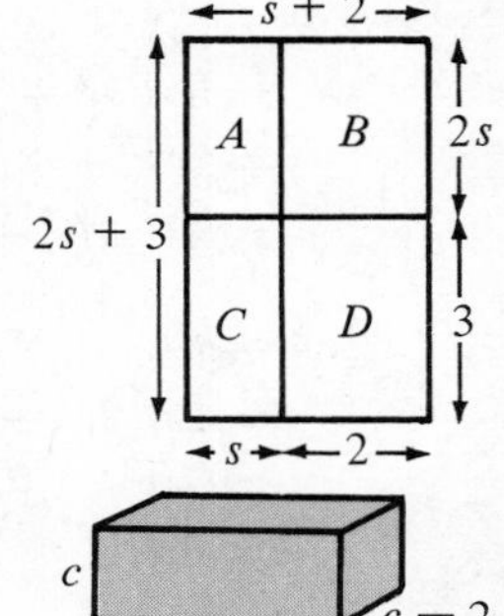

5. Find the volume of the box. Find the area of the bottom of the box.

C

Write an equation representing the given information. Express each member of the equation as a polynomial in simplest form.

6. The length of a rectangle is 8 meters more than its width. If each dimension were 1 meter more, the area would be 35 square meters greater.

7. The length of a rectangle is 4 centimeters more than its width. If the length and width were each 2 centimeters shorter, the area would be 40 square centimeters less.

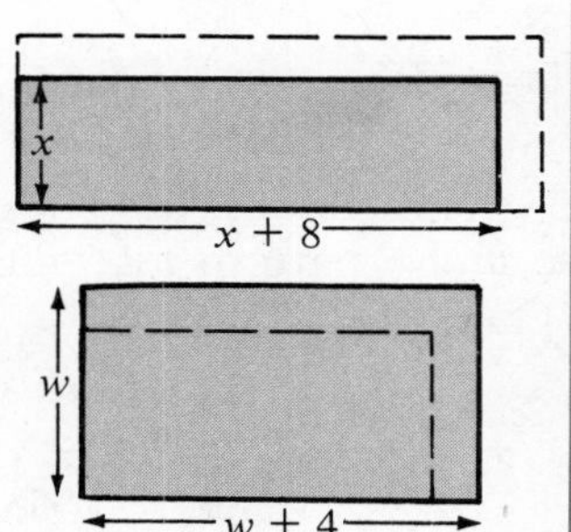

8. Jill has some pennies, nickels, and dimes. In all, she has \$3.92. The number of nickels is two less than the number of pennies. She has 13 more dimes than pennies. (*Hint*: the value of the nickels is $5(p - 2)$ cents.)

13-6 *Special Polynomial Products*

OBJECTIVE

Complete multiplications such as $(3x + 2)^2$ and $(m + 5)(m - 5)$.

The exponent in an expression like $(3x + 2)^2$ tells us how many times the polynomial is to be used as a factor. We **expand** the expression by finding the product of the factors.

EXAMPLE 1
$$\begin{aligned}(3x + 2)^2 &= (3x + 2)(3x + 2)\\ &= 3x(3x + 2) + 2(3x + 2)\\ &= 9x^2 + 6x + 6x + 4\\ &= 9x^2 + 12x + 4\end{aligned}$$

EXAMPLE 2
$$\begin{aligned}(2n - 3)^2 &= (2n - 3)(2n - 3)\\ &= 2n(2n - 3) - 3(2n - 3)\\ &= 4n^2 - 6n - 6n + 9\\ &= 4n^2 - 12n + 9\end{aligned}$$

Examples 1 and 2 demonstrate a pattern for expanding the square of *any* binomial:

$$(\text{first term})^2 + (\text{twice product of terms}) + (\text{second term})^2$$

► **For all directed numbers a and b, $(a + b)^2 = a^2 + 2ab + b^2$.**

EXAMPLE 3
$$\begin{aligned}(5t + 3)^2 &= (5t)^2 + 2(5t)(3) + 3^2\\ &= 25t^2 + 30t + 9\end{aligned}$$

We can also find a pattern for products of pairs of binomials like $(x + 7)(x - 7)$ and $(2n - 3)(2n + 3)$.

EXAMPLE 4
$$\begin{aligned}(x + 7)(x - 7) &= x(x - 7) + 7(x - 7)\\ &= x^2 - 7x + 7x - 49\\ &= x^2 - 49 \blacktriangleleft x^2 - 7^2\end{aligned}$$

EXAMPLE 5
$$\begin{aligned}(2n - 3)(2n + 3) &= 2n(2n + 3) - 3(2n + 3)\\ &= 4n^2 + 6n - 6n - 9\\ &= 4n^2 - 9 \blacktriangleleft (2n)^2 - 3^2\end{aligned}$$

In Examples 4 and 5 notice that the **terms are the same** in each pair of expressions but the **signs are different.** The product in each case is the difference of two squares.

► **For all directed numbers a and b, $(a - b)(a + b) = a^2 - b^2$.**

EXAMPLE 6 $(3m - 5)(3m + 5) = (3m)^2 - 5^2$
$= 9m^2 - 25$

EXERCISES

Name the missing terms.

1. $(a + 3)^2 = (a + 3)(a + 3) = a^2 + \underline{\ ?\ } + 9$
2. $(3x + 2y)^2 = (3x + 2y)(3x + 2y) = 9x^2 + 12xy + \underline{\ ?\ }$
3. $(3 - 2x)^2 = (3 - 2x)(3 - 2x) = \underline{\ ?\ } - \underline{\ ?\ } + 4x^2$
4. $(2k + 3)^2 = (2k + 3)(2k + 3) = 4k^2 + \underline{\ ?\ } + \underline{\ ?\ }$
5. $(c + 5d)^2 = (c + 5d)(c + 5d) = c^2 + \underline{\ ?\ } + \underline{\ ?\ }$
6. $(1 - 5z)^2 = (1 - 5z)(1 - 5z) = \underline{\ ?\ } - \underline{\ ?\ } + 25z^2$
7. $(3x + 1)(3x - 1) = \underline{\ ?\ } - \underline{\ ?\ }$
8. $(a - 5b)(a + 5b) = \underline{\ ?\ } - \underline{\ ?\ }$

Written
EXERCISES

Multiply mentally. Then check your work on paper.

Sample: $(5a + 2b)^2$

Solution: $25a^2 + 20ab + 4b^2$ Check:

$$\begin{array}{r} 5a + 2b \\ 5a + 2b \\ \hline 10ab + 4b^2 \\ 25a^2 + 10ab \quad\quad \\ \hline 25a^2 + 20ab + 4b^2 \end{array}$$

A

1. $(b + 4)^2$
2. $(x + y)^2$
3. $(x - a)^2$
4. $(y + 3b)^2$
5. $(3x - 2c)^2$
6. $(2a - 5)^2$
7. $(x + y)(x - y)$
8. $(4m - 3)(4m + 3)$
9. $(3k - q)(3k + q)$
10. $(ax + 2by)(ax - 2by)$
11. $(ac + bc)^2$
12. $(ac + bc)(ac - bc)$

Expand.

B

13. $(k^2 + 6)^2$
14. $(16 - 3ab)^2$
15. $(3x - 5wy)^2$
16. $(2m^2 - 11)^2$
17. $(3 + xy^2)^2$
18. $\left(5p - \frac{1}{5}\right)^2$
19. $(4m + 10)^2$
20. $(x^2 + 8y^2)^2$
21. $(3bc + 10ab)^2$
22. $(mn^2 - 5)^2$
23. $(4m + 7b)^2$
24. $(0.8 - a)^2$
25. $(18 + 2ab)^2$
26. $(2x^2 + y^2)^2$
27. $(-st^2 + 2)^2$
28. $(3x^2 + 4z^2)^2$
29. $(0.4m^2 + 0.9n)^2$
30. $(4c - 0.1d)^2$

C

31. $(2y^3 - 1)^2$
32. $(z^2 - y^3)^2$
33. $(z^3 - x^3)^2$
34. $(p + 0.3q^2)^2$
35. $(0.2 + 0.5m^2)^2$
36. $(0.7 + 3x)^2$
37. $\left(4k - \frac{1}{8}\right)^2$
38. $\left(a + \frac{1}{2}b\right)^2$
39. $\left(2\frac{1}{2}p - \frac{1}{5}\right)^2$

Problems

Write the answer as a polynomial in simplest form.

1. What is the area of a square if the length of one side is $3x + 8$?
2. The length of a box is four meters longer than its width. The height is 3 meters shorter than the width. If the width is $2v$ meters, what is the volume?

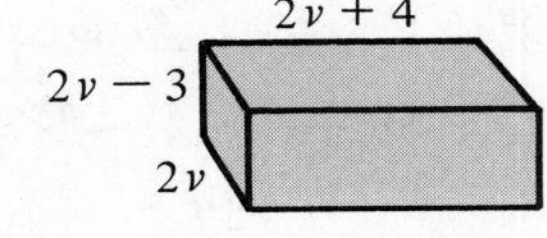

3. A square was cut from a rectangular piece of wood. The L-shaped scrap which was left has an area of 176 cm². The width of the scrap is 8 cm. How wide was the original piece of wood? (*Hint:* $x^2 = (x - 8)^2 + 176$)

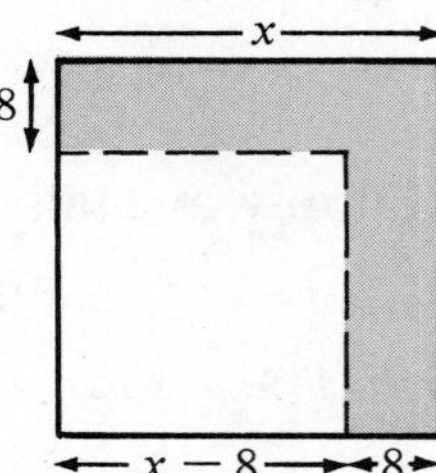

4. The difference between the square of a whole number and the square of the next greater whole number is 15. What are the numbers?
5. The square of a whole number is 41 less than the square of the next greater whole number. What are the numbers?
6. The product of an integer and the next greater integer exceeds the square of the lesser integer by 13. Find the integers.
7. The product of an integer and the next greater integer is 36 less than the square of the greater integer. What are the integers?

career capsule

Sheet-Metal Worker

Sheet-metal workers put together, install, and repair products made of sheet-metal such as drainpipes and furnace casings. They begin their jobs by reading blueprints to learn the dimensions of the product part and the type of metal needed. By putting measurement marks on the metal parts, they set up reference lines for cutting, straightening, or bending parts by machine. Workers then hand-hammer parts into shape, weld the parts together and finish the job by smoothing the joints with files or grinders.

A sheet-metal worker needs a background in mathematics, drafting, and sheet-metal working. Apprenticeship programs are available or skills can be acquired from on-the-job training. Applicants should have good health, balance, and manual dexterity.

13-7 *Multiplication Properties for Polynomials*

OBJECTIVE

Apply the properties of multiplication to polynomials.

Changing the order in which two polynomials are multiplied does not change the result. Multiplication of polynomials is **commutative.**

EXAMPLE 1 $(4a^2b)(3ac) = 12a^3bc$
$(3ac)(4a^2b) = 12a^3bc$

EXAMPLE 2 $(2x + 1)(x - 8) = 2x^2 - 15x - 8$
$(x - 8)(2x + 1) = 2x^2 - 15x - 8$

When more than two polynomials are multiplied, changing the way in which they are grouped does not change the result. Multiplication of polynomials is **associative.**

EXAMPLE 3 $[(2xy)(4x^2)](3y) = (8x^3y)(3y) = 24x^3y^2$
$(2xy)[(4x^2)(3y)] = (2xy)(12x^2y) = 24x^3y^2$

We have already used the **distributive** property to multiply polynomials.

EXAMPLE 4 $(x + 3)(x - 7) = x(x - 7) + 3(x - 7)$
$= x^2 - 4x - 21$

1 is the **identity element** for multiplication of polynomials.

EXAMPLE 5 $(3m^2 + 5) \cdot 1 = 1 \cdot (3m^2 + 5) = 3m^2 + 5$

Recall that if the product of two numbers is 1, the numbers are **reciprocals** or **multiplicative inverses** of each other. Polynomials have multiplicative inverses.

EXAMPLE 6 $2y \cdot \frac{1}{2y} = 1$ ◄ Assume $y \neq 0$.

$2y$ and $\frac{1}{2y}$ are **reciprocals** if $y \neq 0$.

EXAMPLE 7 $-\frac{3xy^2}{2}\left(-\frac{2}{3xy^2}\right) = 1$ ◀ Assume $x \neq 0$ and $y \neq 0$.

$-\frac{3xy^2}{2}$ and $-\frac{2}{3xy^2}$ are **reciprocals** if $x \neq 0$ and $y \neq 0$.

Match each expression in Column 1 with its reciprocal in Column 2. Assume that no denominator is zero.

COLUMN 1	COLUMN 2
1. $\frac{1}{2a - b}$	**A.** $\frac{3a + 2}{3a^2b}$
2. $\frac{1}{2}a^2b^2$	**B.** a^3
3. $\frac{3a^2b}{3a + 2}$	**C.** $\frac{a + b}{a - b}$
4. $\frac{1}{a^3}$	**D.** $2a - b$
5. $\frac{a - b}{a + b}$	**E.** $a + b$
6. $\frac{1}{a + b}$	**F.** $\frac{2}{a^2b^2}$

Tell which property of multiplication justifies the sentence.

Sample: $(ax + b)(2xy) = (2xy)(ax + b)$

What you say: The commutative property

7. $(2x + y)(3x - 4) = 2x(3x - 4) + y(3x - 4)$

8. $\left(\frac{5x^2y^3}{z}\right)\left[(4az)\left(\frac{5x}{2y}\right)\right] = \left[\left(\frac{5x^2y^3}{z}\right)(4az)\right]\left(\frac{5x}{2y}\right)$

9. $[(3at^2)(2s^2t^3)](2s^2t) = [(2s^2t^3)(3at^2)](2s^2t)$

10. $[(3x^2)(5 + a)]\left(\frac{1}{y^4}\right) = \left(\frac{1}{y^4}\right)[(3x^2)(5 + a)]$

11. $(d^2 - 1)(d^2 + 1) = (d^2 + 1)(d^2 - 1)$

12. $(x^3 + 1)(x^3 - 1) = (x^3 + 1)x^3 - (x^3 + 1) \cdot 1$

Written EXERCISES

Name the reciprocal. Assume that no numerator or denominator is zero.

A

1. $\dfrac{bm}{a - b}$ 2. $\dfrac{b - ac}{ab}$ 3. $\dfrac{m - b}{a - b}$ 4. $\dfrac{1 - y}{1 + y}$

5. $\dfrac{x^2 + 2x + 1}{(x + 1)^2}$ 6. $\dfrac{x^3 - y^3}{x - y}$ 7. $\dfrac{3}{4}(a + b^2)$ 8. $\dfrac{-5x}{7(y^2 + 1)}$

Show that the sentence is correct.

Sample: $3x[(x + y)y^2] = [(3x)(x + y)]y^2$

Solution: $3x[(x + y)y^2] \stackrel{?}{=} [3x(x + y)]y^2$

$3x[xy^2 + y^3]$	$[3x^2 + 3xy]y^2$
$3x^2y^2 + 3xy^3$	$3x^2y^2 + 3xy^3$ ✓

9. $ab[(a + b)(a - b)] = (a^2b + ab^2)(a - b)$
10. $4x^2(14z + 7y) = (14z + 7y) \cdot 4x^2$
11. $8mn(5x + 4y) = 40mnx + 32mny$
12. $[(x + y)(x - y)](x + y) = (x - y)(x + y)^2$

B

13. $(0.5a + b)(b - 0.5a)x = b^2x - (0.5a)^2x$
14. $[(a^2b^2)(ab^2)](ab) = (ab^2)[(a^2b^2)(ab)]$
15. $(3x^2 + 5x + 2)(x - 1) = (x^2 - 1)(3x + 2)$
16. $[(3m + 2n)(3m - 2n)](6m + 2n) =$ $(3m + 2n)[(3m - 2n)(6m + 2n)]$

Multiply. Tell which property of multiplication justifies each step.

Sample: $(4x^4)(9x^2)$

Solution:
$$\begin{aligned}(4x^4)(9x^2) &= 4(x^4 \cdot 9)x^2 && \text{◄ The Associative Property}\\ &= 4(9 \cdot x^4)x^2 && \text{◄ The Commutative Property}\\ &= (4 \cdot 9)(x^4 \cdot x^2) && \text{◄ The Associative Property}\\ &= 36x^6\end{aligned}$$

C

17. $4y^3(y^4 - 1)$
18. $(mn)(mn + 1)$
19. $(x^2 + xy + y^2)(xy)$
20. $(12a^2b)(4ab)$
21. $\left(\dfrac{1}{2}mnp\right)\left(\dfrac{1}{4}m^2np^2\right)$
22. $(0.5a^2 - b)(b + 0.5a)$
23. $2.3x^2(2x^3 + 0.5x)$
24. $\dfrac{2}{3}m\left(\dfrac{1}{2}mn - \dfrac{n^2}{4}\right)$

25. $\left(\frac{5n}{2} - \frac{1}{3}\right)\left(\frac{5n}{2} + \frac{1}{3}\right)$

26. $3.7y(2y + 0.3y - 1.2)$

27. $(0.1t + t^2)(3t - 0.5)$

28. $\frac{1}{4}x\left(x^3 - \frac{1}{3}x^2 + \frac{1}{2}\right)$

29. $\left(\frac{3}{5}rs - r\right)\left(\frac{5s}{r}\right)$

30. $\left(\frac{xy}{3}\right)\left(\frac{3x}{y}\right)$

SELF-TEST 2

Be sure you understand these terms.

expand (p. 360) multiplicative inverse (p. 364)

Multiply. **Section 13-5, p. 356**

1. $(b - 3)(b + 2)$
2. $(n + 1)(n - 5)$
3. $(2t + 7)(3t - 1)$
4. $(4x^2 + x + 2)(x + 1)$

Expand. **Section 13-6, p. 360**

5. $(n - 4)^2$
6. $(2b + 6)^2$

Multiply.

7. $(n - 4)(n + 4)$
8. $(2b + 6)(2b - 6)$

Tell which property justifies each step. Assume $y \neq 0$. **Section 13-7, p. 364**

9. $$3y^2\left(8y + \frac{1}{3y^2}\right) = (3y^2)(8y) + 3y^2\left(\frac{1}{3y^2}\right)$$
$$= 3(y^2 8)y + 3y^2\left(\frac{1}{3y^2}\right)$$
$$= 3(8y^2)y + 3y^2\left(\frac{1}{3y^2}\right)$$
$$= 24y^3 + 1$$

Check your answers with those printed at the back of the book.

13-8 *Dividing Monomials*

OBJECTIVE
Simplify expressions such as $\frac{14a^3b}{-2a}$ by division.

To divide one monomial by another we need to understand and use factors, exponents, and division.

Example 1 shows two methods of dividing. We can use either to divide monomials.

EXAMPLE 1 $4^5 \div 4^2 = \underline{\ ?\ }$

(1) $\frac{4^5}{4^2} = \frac{4 \cdot 4 \cdot 4 \cdot 4 \cdot 4}{4 \cdot 4} = \left(\frac{4}{4} \cdot \frac{4}{4}\right) 4 \cdot 4 \cdot 4$
$= (1 \cdot 1) 4 \cdot 4 \cdot 4 = \mathbf{4^3}$

(2) $\frac{4^5}{4^2} = \frac{4^2 \cdot 4^3}{4^2} = \frac{4^2}{4^2} \cdot 4^3 = 1 \cdot 4^3 = \mathbf{4^3}$

EXAMPLE 2 $t^6 \div t^2 = \underline{\ ?\ }$

(1) $\frac{t^6}{t^2} = \frac{t \cdot t \cdot t \cdot t \cdot t \cdot t}{t \cdot t} = \left(\frac{t}{t} \cdot \frac{t}{t}\right) t \cdot t \cdot t \cdot t$
$= (1 \cdot 1) t \cdot t \cdot t \cdot t = \mathbf{t^4}$

(2) $\frac{t^6}{t^2} = \frac{t^2 \cdot t^4}{t^2} = \left(\frac{t^2}{t^2}\right) t^4 = 1 \cdot t^4 = \mathbf{t^4}$

Examples 1 and 2 demonstrate a general rule of exponents that applies when the greater exponent appears in the **numerator.**

For any directed number a, except 0, and all positive integers p and q such that $p > q$:

$$\frac{a^p}{a^q} = a^{p-q}$$

Now let's consider situations where the greater exponent appears in the **denominator.**

EXAMPLE 3 $\frac{8^2}{8^5} = \frac{8^2 \cdot 1}{8^2 \cdot 8^3} = \left(\frac{8^2}{8^2}\right) \cdot \frac{1}{8^3} = 1 \cdot \frac{1}{8^3} = \mathbf{\frac{1}{8^3}}$

EXAMPLE 4 $\frac{x^3}{x^5} = \frac{x^3 \cdot 1}{x^3 \cdot x^2} = \left(\frac{x^3}{x^3}\right) \cdot \frac{1}{x^2} = 1 \cdot \frac{1}{x^2} = \mathbf{\frac{1}{x^2}}$

For any directed number a, except 0, and for all positive integers p and q such that $p < q$:

$$\frac{a^p}{a^q} = \frac{1}{a^{q-p}}$$

You already know that any number divided by itself equals 1. This leads us to the following property.

For any directed number a, except 0, and for all positive integers p:

$$\frac{a^p}{a^p} = 1.$$

Now let's use these rules of exponents to divide.

EXAMPLE 5 $\frac{15a^3b^4}{-3ab^2} = \frac{15}{-3} \cdot \frac{a^3}{a} \cdot \frac{b^4}{b^2} = -5a^{3-1}b^{4-2} = \mathbf{-5a^2b^2}$

EXAMPLE 6 $\frac{-9abc}{3b^3c} = \frac{-9}{3} \cdot a \cdot \frac{b}{b^3} \cdot \frac{c}{c} = -3a \cdot \frac{1}{b^{3-1}} \cdot 1 = \mathbf{\frac{-3a}{b^2}}$

EXERCISES

Name the missing factor.

Sample 1: $p^{10} = p^7 \cdot$ ___?___ *What you say:* p^3

Sample 2: $\frac{m^5}{m^4} = \frac{m^2}{m} \cdot$ ___?___ *What you say:* $\frac{m^3}{m^3}$ or 1

1. $5^8 = 5^5 \cdot$ ___?___ **2.** $x^5 = x \cdot$ ___?___ **3.** $a^3 \cdot$ ___?___ $= a^7$

4. $\frac{n^4}{n^3} = \frac{n^3}{n^2} \cdot$ ___?___ **5.** $\frac{7^5}{7^2} = \frac{7}{7} \cdot$ ___?___ **6.** $\frac{b^3}{b^2} = \frac{b}{b} \cdot$ ___?___

Simplify.

7. $\frac{3x \cdot 3x \cdot 3y}{3 \cdot 3 \cdot y}$

8. $\frac{m \cdot n \cdot m}{m \cdot m \cdot m \cdot m \cdot n \cdot n}$

9. $\frac{x \cdot y \cdot y \cdot y \cdot y}{x \cdot y \cdot y}$

10. $\frac{3 \cdot 3 \cdot a \cdot a \cdot a}{3 \cdot a \cdot a}$

11. $\frac{2 \cdot 2 \cdot 3}{2 \cdot 2 \cdot 2 \cdot 2 \cdot 2 \cdot 3}$

12. $\frac{x \cdot x \cdot y}{x \cdot x \cdot y \cdot y \cdot y}$

Written EXERCISES

Simplify. Assume no denominator is 0.

Sample 1: $\dfrac{15a^4b^3}{-3ab}$

Solution: $\dfrac{15a^4b^3}{-3ab} = \dfrac{15}{-3}\cdot\dfrac{a^4}{a}\cdot\dfrac{b^3}{b} = -5a^3b^2$

Sample 2: $\dfrac{-10xy}{-5x^5}$ *Solution:* $\dfrac{-10xy}{-5x^5} = \dfrac{-10}{-5}\cdot\dfrac{x}{x^5}\cdot y = \dfrac{2y}{x^4}$

A

1. $\dfrac{x^9}{x^5}$ **2.** $\dfrac{m^7}{m^2}$ **3.** $\dfrac{(rs)^6}{(rs)^{11}}$

4. $\dfrac{8x^9}{4x^5}$ **5.** $\dfrac{6m^7}{-12m^{12}}$ **6.** $\dfrac{-x^{12}}{x^4}$

7. $\dfrac{3q^6}{15q^4}$ **8.** $\dfrac{-6b^6}{-2b^2}$ **9.** $\dfrac{12z^2}{9x^2z^3}$

10. $\dfrac{42a^2b}{49ab^2}$ **11.** $\dfrac{30mn^3}{18m^2n^2}$ **12.** $\dfrac{34xy^3}{51x^2y}$

13. $\dfrac{6xy^2}{9x^2y}$ **14.** $\dfrac{3mn^2}{15m^2n^2}$ **15.** $\dfrac{26a^2b^3}{39ab^5}$

B

16. $\dfrac{10x^4y^2}{-2xy}$ **17.** $\dfrac{64x^2y^2z^2}{(-4xyz)^3}$ **18.** $\dfrac{-25ab^2}{-10a^2b}$

19. $\dfrac{21xyz}{7x^2y^2z^2}$ **20.** $\dfrac{-x^7}{-2xy}$ **21.** $\dfrac{-27x^2y^3}{-9xyz}$

22. $\dfrac{2ab^4}{(2b^2)^2}$ **23.** $\dfrac{30bd^3}{(3d^2)^2}$ **24.** $\dfrac{-24a^2b^5}{-8ab^3}$

25. $\dfrac{21x^7y^9}{(-x^2y^4)^2}$ **26.** $\dfrac{(-0.6m^4n^5)^2}{6m^3n}$ **27.** $\dfrac{14r^4s^2}{-7s^2}$

28. $\dfrac{35x^6y^4z^2}{5x^3y^3z}$ **29.** $\dfrac{58mn^2p^3}{87m^4n^3p^2}$ **30.** $\dfrac{38a^2b^3c^4}{57a^3b^2c^2}$

C

31. $\dfrac{3(ab)^3}{2.7ab^2}$ **32.** $\dfrac{(-3)^4x^9y^2}{27x^8y^4}$ **33.** $\dfrac{-0.8x^2y^7}{-0.56x^{12}y^3}$

34. $\dfrac{5m^p}{5m}, p > 1$ **35.** $\dfrac{(-2)^3x^py^q}{x^qy^p}, p > q$

36. $\dfrac{2^6x^py^{p-1}}{16x^2y^{p-2}}, p > 2$ **37.** $\dfrac{(-69ab)^r}{(23ab)^r}$

13-9 *Dividing a Polynomial by a Monomial*

OBJECTIVE
Simplify expressions such as $\frac{18r^2 - 6s}{3r}$ by division.

Recall that division is distributive over addition. We use this fact to divide a polynomial by a monomial. We divide each term of the polynomial by the monomial, then add the quotients.

Example 1 shows two ways to divide.

EXAMPLE 1 $(6x^2 + 18x) \div 3$

(1) $3\overline{)6x^2 + 18x}$ with quotient $2x^2 + 6x$

(2) $$\frac{6x^2 + 18x}{3} = \frac{6x^2}{3} + \frac{18x}{3} = 2x^2 + 6x$$

EXAMPLE 2 $$\frac{21x^2 - 14y^2}{7} = \frac{21x^2}{7} - \frac{14y^2}{7} = 3x^2 - 2y^2$$

EXAMPLE 3 $$\frac{4c^3 + 20bc}{4c} = \frac{4c^3}{4c} + \frac{20bc}{4c} \quad \blacktriangleleft c \neq 0$$
$$= c^2 + 5b$$

EXAMPLE 4 $$\frac{18r^2 - 6s}{3r} = \frac{18r^2}{3r} - \frac{6s}{3r} \quad \blacktriangleleft r \neq 0$$
$$= 6r - \frac{2s}{r}$$

EXAMPLE 5 $$\frac{12ac^2 + 9a^2c}{3ac} = \frac{12ac^2}{3ac} + \frac{9a^2c}{3ac} \quad \blacktriangleleft a \neq 0, \ \blacktriangleleft c \neq 0$$
$$= 4c + 3a$$

EXERCISES

Match each expression in Column 1 with an equivalent expression in Column 2.

COLUMN 1	COLUMN 2
1. $\frac{ab^3}{b^2}$	A. $\frac{14a + 15b}{3}$
2. $\frac{x^3a^2b}{x^3a^3b^2}$	B. $\frac{b^2}{b} + \frac{ab}{b}$
3. $\frac{6a + 3b}{3}$	C. $\frac{63a}{9} + \frac{5b}{9}$
4. $\frac{14a}{3} + \frac{15}{3}b$	D. $\frac{6a}{3} + \frac{3b}{3}$
5. $\frac{b^2 + ab}{b}$	E. $\frac{1}{ab}$
6. $\frac{63a + 5b}{9}$	F. ab

Written
EXERCISES

Simplify. Assume no denominator is 0.

Sample: $\frac{1}{7}(14x + 21y)$ *Solution:* $\frac{1}{7}(14x + 21y) = \frac{14x}{7} + \frac{21y}{7}$
$= 2x + 3y$

A

1. $\frac{1}{6}(24x - 18)$
2. $\frac{-2}{3}(18a + 9)$
3. $\frac{1}{2}(-14b - 8)$
4. $\frac{1}{r}(rs^2 - r^2)$
5. $(-54x^2 - 108)\frac{1}{9}$
6. $(ab^2 + b^3)\frac{1}{b^2}$
7. $\left(\frac{-1}{3}\right)(6a^2 + 6a + 9)$
8. $\left(\frac{-1}{6}\right)(36x^2 + 12x - 42)$

Divide. Assume no denominator is 0.

9. $\frac{6y - 12}{6}$
10. $\frac{7m + 28}{14}$
11. $\frac{7k + 63a}{7}$
12. $\frac{9p^2 + 6p}{3p}$
13. $\frac{16q + 72q^2}{8}$
14. $\frac{3a^5 + 7a^7}{a^4}$

15. $\dfrac{48b^2 + 64b^4}{16b^2}$

16. $\dfrac{30x^6 + 7x^4}{3x^3}$

17. $\dfrac{9m^3 + 21}{-3}$

18. $\dfrac{4y^2 + 6y}{2y}$

19. $\dfrac{4b^2 - 8b}{2b}$

20. $\dfrac{64k^3 - 24k}{-8k}$

B

21. $\dfrac{t^3 + s^2t^2 + t}{st}$

22. $\dfrac{9a^2b + 12ab - 15ab^2}{3ab}$

23. $\dfrac{xy^2 - x^2y + x^3}{x}$

24. $\dfrac{18t^2 + 15t - 33}{3}$

25. $\dfrac{14t^3 - 56t^2 - 35t}{7t}$

26. $\dfrac{ax^5 - bx^4 + cx^3 - x^2}{-x}$

27. $\dfrac{-s^3 + s^2 - 27s}{-s}$

28. $\dfrac{14a^3b^3 - 12a^2b^2 + 10ab}{2ab}$

29. $\dfrac{mx^3 + nx^2 + ax^4}{x^2}$

30. $\dfrac{xyp + xyq}{xy}$

31. $\dfrac{4x^2y^4 + 8xy^3}{x^3y}$

32. $\dfrac{st^4 + 2s^3t^2 + s^2t^2}{s^2t^2}$

consumer notes *Recycling*

Recycling refuse is one way consumers can fight pollution. Recycling is sometimes done with the aid of a conveyor belt. Large chunks of waste are placed on a belt where a machine shreds them. Some metal items are sorted out by a magnet. Paper and cloth are separated by a column of air. Glass is sorted into colors by an optical scanner. Aluminum is separated by an electrostatic field. The combustibles left, such as food, rubber, and rags can be burned as fuel. The noncombustibles can be reused by companies. Efforts are being made to encourage consumers to deposit waste in containers, lessening the cost of refuse collection and the cost of environmental pollution. Can you think of other ways to recycle waste?

13-10 *Dividing by a Binomial*

OBJECTIVE
Simplify expressions like $\frac{x^2 - 8x - 9}{x + 1}$ by division.

Division by a binomial is a process similar to "long division." Read each step of Example 1 carefully and be sure you follow it.

EXAMPLE 1 $\frac{x^2 + 7x + 12}{x + 3}$ ► $x + 3\overline{)x^2 + 7x + 12}$

$$\begin{array}{rl} & \quad x + 4 \\ \text{Think: } x \cdot \underline{?} = x^2. \blacktriangleright & x + 3\overline{)x^2 + 7x + 12} \\ \text{Multiply } x(x + 3). \blacktriangleright & \quad \underline{x^2 + 3x} \\ \text{Subtract } x^2 + 3 \text{ from } x^2 + 7x + 12. \blacktriangleright & \qquad\quad 4x + 12 \\ \text{Think: } x \cdot \underline{?} = 4x. \blacktriangleright & \qquad\quad \underline{4x + 12} \\ \text{Multiply } 4(x + 3) \text{ and subtract.} \blacktriangleright & \qquad\qquad\quad 0 \end{array}$$

Check: $(x + 3)(x + 4) = x^2 + 7x + 12$ ✓

EXAMPLE 2 $\frac{10m^2 - 19m - 15}{2m - 5} = \underline{?}$ ►

$$\begin{array}{r} 5m + 3 \quad\quad \\ 2m - 5\overline{)10m^2 - 19m - 15} \\ \underline{10m^2 - 25m} \qquad \\ 6m - 15 \\ \underline{6m - 15} \\ 0 \end{array}$$

Check: $(2m - 5)(5m + 3) = 10m^2 - 19m - 15$ ✓

EXAMPLE 3 $\frac{4x^2 - 9}{2x - 3} = \underline{?}$

$$\begin{array}{r} 2x \qquad + 3 \\ 2x - 3\overline{)4x^2 \qquad\quad - 9} \\ \underline{4x^2 - 6x} \qquad \\ 6x - 9 \\ \underline{6x - 9} \\ 0 \end{array}$$ ◄ Leave space for $0 \cdot x$.

Check: $(2x - 3)(2x + 3) = 4x^2 - 9$

Divide and check.

Written EXERCISES

A

1. $\frac{x^2 + 7x + 12}{x + 4}$
2. $\frac{a^2 + 5a + 6}{a + 2}$
3. $\frac{b^2 - 5b + 6}{b - 3}$
4. $\frac{t^2 + 3t - 10}{t - 2}$
5. $\frac{y^2 + 3y - 10}{y + 5}$
6. $\frac{m^2 + 12m + 27}{m + 9}$
7. $\frac{m^2 + 8m + 15}{m + 3}$
8. $\frac{n^2 - 10n + 24}{n - 4}$
9. $\frac{p^2 + 7p - 18}{p - 2}$
10. $\frac{4a^2 + 12a + 9}{2a + 3}$
11. $\frac{3x^2 - 4x - 4}{x - 2}$
12. $\frac{x^2 - 8x + 15}{x - 3}$
13. $\frac{6c^2 - 12c + 6}{2c - 2}$
14. $\frac{9z^2 + 24z + 16}{3z + 4}$

B

15. $\frac{a^2 - 2ab + b^2}{a - b}$
16. $\frac{s^2 + 2st + t^2}{s + t}$
17. $\frac{4b^2 + 4bc - 3c^2}{2b + 3c}$
18. $\frac{8m^2 - 10am - 3a^2}{4m + a}$
19. $\frac{s^2 - 4}{s - 2}$
20. $\frac{p^4 - 16}{p^2 + 4}$
21. $\frac{6t^2 - 6}{2t - 2}$
22. $\frac{y^4 + y^2 - 2}{y^2 - 1}$

Divide. First rewrite the polynomial in standard form if necessary.

23. $\frac{6a^2 + 2 + 7a}{3a + 2}$
24. $\frac{12k^2 - 32k + 5}{6k - 1}$
25. $\frac{12b^2 - 1 - b}{4b + 1}$
26. $\frac{10a^2 + 48a + 54}{5a + 9}$
27. $\frac{x^2 - 4ax - 5a^2}{x - 5a}$
28. $\frac{y^2 + 14by + 45b^2}{9b + y}$
29. $\frac{15a^2 - 8b^2 - 2ab}{3a + 2b}$
30. $\frac{20p^2 - 43pq + 21q^2}{-3q + 4p}$

C

Divide.

31. $\frac{y^3 - y^2 + 2y - 2}{y - 1}$

32. $\frac{x^3 + 5x^2 + 2x + 10}{x + 5}$

33. $\frac{3t^3 + 6t^2 - t - 2}{3t^2 - 1}$

34. $\frac{t^3 - 6t^2 + 12t - 8}{t - 2}$

35. $\frac{3b^2 + b - 2}{b + 1}$

36. $\frac{m^3 + 2m^2 - 2m - 4}{m + 2}$

37. $\frac{x^3 - x^2 + x - 1}{x - 1}$

38. $\frac{2r^2t^2 + r^3t + 2t^2 + rt}{2t + r}$

SELF-TEST 3

Section 13-8, p. 368

Simplify. Assume no denominator is 0.

1. $\frac{x^6}{x^2}$

2. $\frac{2mn^2}{m}$

3. $\frac{-3zx}{z^2x^3}$

4. $\frac{15xy}{3x^2y}$

Section 13-9, p. 371

Divide. Assume no denominator is 0.

5. $\frac{4z + 8}{2}$

6. $\frac{9b^2 - 18}{3b}$

7. $\frac{-8n^2 + 4n}{2n}$

8. $\frac{c^2d + cd^2}{cd}$

Section 13-10, p. 374

9. $\frac{m^2 + 6m + 9}{m + 3}$

10. $\frac{4n^2 - 4n - 15}{2n + 3}$

Check your answers with those printed at the back of the book.

chapter summary

1. **Exponents** are used to simplify multiplication expressions that contain repeating factors.

2. For all directed numbers a and b, and positive integers p and q:

$$a^p \cdot a^q = a^{p+q}$$
$$(ab)^p = a^p \cdot b^p$$
$$(a^p)^q = a^{pq}$$

3. For all directed numbers a and b:

$$(a + b)^2 = a^2 + 2ab + b^2$$
$$(a - b)(a + b) = a^2 - b^2$$

4. Multiplication of polynomials is **commutative** and **associative.** Also, multiplication of polynomials is distributive over addition.

5. The product of a polynomial and 1 is that polynomial. 1 is the **identity element** for multiplication of polynomials.

6. An expression is the **multiplicative inverse (reciprocal)** of a polynomial if its product with the polynomial is 1.

7. For all directed numbers a and b, and positive integers p and q.

$$\text{If } p > q\text{: } \frac{a^p}{a^q} = a^{p-q}$$

$$\text{If } p < q\text{: } \frac{a^p}{a^q} = \frac{1}{a^{q-p}}$$

$$\text{If } p = q\text{: } \frac{a^p}{a^q} = 1$$

8. To divide a polynomial by a monomial we divide each term of the polynomial by the monomial, then add the quotients.

9. To divide a polynomial by a binomial, we use a process similar to long division.

challenge topics

Know Your Angles

Use heavy paper or cardboard to make a 30–60–90 triangle and a 45–90–45 triangle.

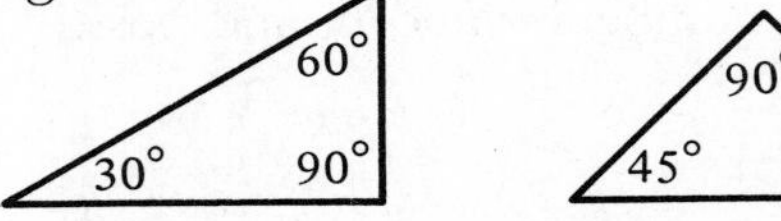

By using both triangles at the same time you can draw many figures quickly and accurately.

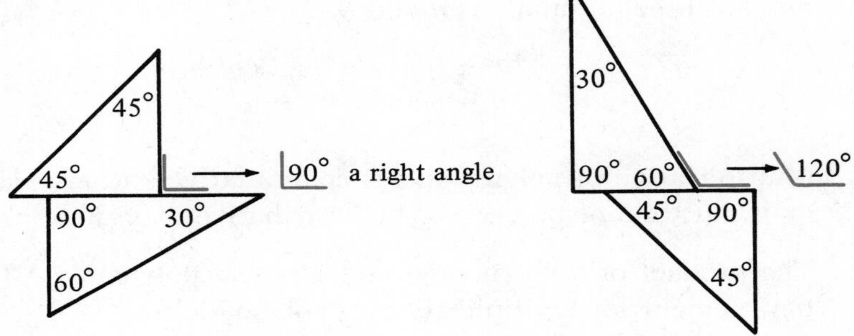

Use the triangles to duplicate each figure.

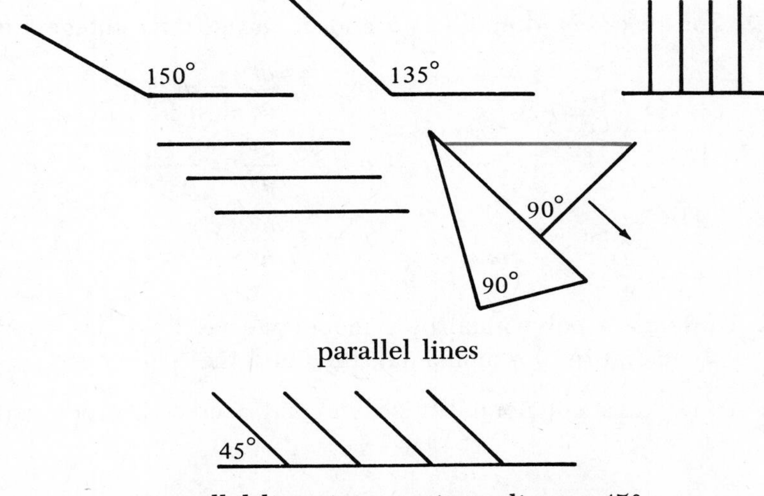

parallel lines

45°

parallel lines intersecting a line at 45°

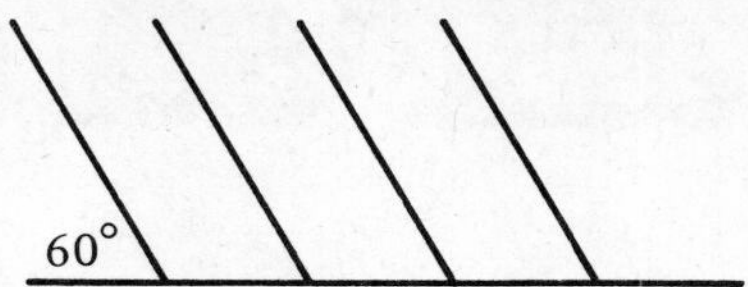

parallel lines intersecting a line at 60°

chapter test

Simplify. Use exponents.

1. $x^4 \cdot x^3$
2. $(2x \cdot x \cdot x)(3 \cdot y \cdot y)$
3. $a^3(-2a^2b^2)(5b)$
4. $(2xz)^3$
5. $(2mn)^2$

Multiply.

6. $-n(n^2 - 2n + 3)$
7. $pq(p^2 - 2pq + 3)$
8. $5x(xy^2 + x^2y)$
9. $2a(3a + 4) + 3a(2a + 3)$
10. $10x(x + 6)$
11. $(t - 5)^2$
12. $(5x + 2)(5x - 2)$
13. $-3a(a^2 + 5a - 3)$
14. $(s - 4)(2s + 3)$
15. $(x - 4)(2x^2 - 9x + 1)$

Express the answer as a polynomial in simplest form.

16. A rectangle has length $2y - 1$ and width $y + 4$. Find the area.
17. A square has sides of length $4z + 2$. Find the area.

Divide. Assume no denominator is 0.

18. $\dfrac{z^5}{z^2}$
19. $\dfrac{-4x^2z}{xz}$
20. $\dfrac{15a^2 + 10a}{5a}$
21. $\dfrac{21y^2 - 12y + 9}{3y}$
22. $\dfrac{m^2 - 8m + 16}{m - 4}$
23. $\dfrac{a^2 - 7a + 10}{a - 5}$

Review of Skills

Name the factors and the greatest common factor.

Sample: 12 and 14 *Solution:* 12: 1, 2, 3, 4, 6, and 12
14: 1, 2, 7, and 14
GCF of 12 and 14 is 2.

1. 6 and 36 **2.** 4 and 8 **3.** 4 and 19

4. 3 and 8 **5.** 10 and 15 **6.** 12 and 16

7. 14 and 35 **8.** 5 and 11 **9.** 7 and 28

Tell whether or not the number is prime.

10. 8 **11.** 13 **12.** 19

13. 35 **14.** 43 **15.** 27

Complete.

Sample: $28 = 2 \cdot 2 \cdot \underline{\ ?\ }$ *Solution:* $28 = 2 \cdot 2 \cdot 7$

16. $35 = 5 \cdot \underline{\ ?\ }$ **17.** $80 = 2 \cdot 2 \cdot 2 \cdot 2 \cdot \underline{\ ?\ }$

18. $106 = \underline{\ ?\ } \cdot 53$ **19.** $50 = \underline{\ ?\ } \cdot 5 \cdot 5$

20. $141 = 3 \cdot \underline{\ ?\ }$ **21.** $27 = 3 \cdot 3 \cdot \underline{\ ?\ }$

Write as the product of prime numbers.

Sample: 45 *Solution:* $45 = 3 \cdot 3 \cdot 5$

22. 42 **23.** 55 **24.** 58

25. 121 **26.** 144 **27.** 100

28. 142 **29.** 120 **30.** 270

Tell whether the statement is *always* true, *never* true, or *sometimes* true.

31. The GCF of two different prime numbers is 1.

32. The GCF of two numbers which are not prime is 1.

33. The product of two prime numbers is also prime.

34. The GCF of two consecutive counting numbers is 1.

Left: Uniformed security guards, 1900.

Right: Central security office at convention center in Chicago.

14 Products and Factoring

14-1 *Factoring Whole Numbers*

OBJECTIVE
Write the prime factorization of a composite number.

A positive number which has exactly two different positive factors, itself and 1, is called a prime number. A number which can be expressed as the product of two or more prime numbers is called a composite number. 1 is neither a prime number nor a composite number.

EXAMPLE 1 15 is a composite number. $15 = 3 \cdot 5$ (primes)

A composite number written as the product of primes is in prime factorization form.

EXAMPLE 2 The prime factorization of 15 is $3 \cdot 5$.

EXAMPLE 3 $42 = 2 \cdot 3 \cdot 7$ (prime factorization of 42)

EXAMPLE 4 $36 = 2 \cdot 2 \cdot 3 \cdot 3 = 2^2 \cdot 3^2$ (prime factorization of 36)

EXERCISES

Tell whether the number is prime or composite.

1. 12	**2.** 17	**3.** 16
4. 7	**5.** 18	**6.** 5
7. 10	**8.** 19	**9.** 11

Written EXERCISES

Name all the factors. Then express the number as the product of primes.

Sample: 6 *Solution:* The factors are 1, 2, 3, and 6.
$6 = 2 \cdot 3$

A

1. 5	**2.** 9	**3.** 4
4. 17	**5.** 21	**6.** 35
7. 45	**8.** 29	**9.** 16
10. 12	**11.** 30	**12.** 49

Complete the prime factorization.

Sample: $28 = 2 \cdot 2 \cdot \underline{\ ?\ } = \underline{\ ?\ }$ *Solution:* $28 = 2 \cdot 2 \cdot 7 = 2^2 \cdot 7$

13. $60 = 2 \cdot 2 \cdot 3 \cdot \underline{\ ?\ } = \underline{\ ?\ }$

14. $20 = 2 \cdot \underline{\ ?\ } \cdot \underline{\ ?\ } = \underline{\ ?\ }$

15. $100 = 2 \cdot 2 \cdot \underline{\ ?\ } \cdot \underline{\ ?\ } = \underline{\ ?\ }$

16. $52 = 2 \cdot \underline{\ ?\ } \cdot \underline{\ ?\ } = \underline{\ ?\ }$

17. $45 = 3 \cdot 3 \cdot \underline{\ ?\ } = \underline{\ ?\ }$

18. $68 = 2 \cdot \underline{\ ?\ } \cdot \underline{\ ?\ } = \underline{\ ?\ }$

19. $141 = 3 \cdot \underline{\ ?\ }$

20. $88 = \underline{\ ?\ } \cdot 11$

Write the prime factorization.

B

21. 125	**22.** 235	**23.** 144
24. 42	**25.** 270	**26.** 625
27. 1000	**28.** 243	**29.** 120
30. 111	**31.** 194	**32.** 57

calculator corner

Here is a calculator race that you can have with one of your friends. The first person to add the whole numbers from 1 to 50 with the calculator wins. One of you can simply add while the other can use a trick from algebra. Add the first and last numbers (1 and 50) and multiply the answer by half of the last number (25). Who won?

You may want to use this method to add the whole numbers from 1 to 1000. Can you see why this method works?

14-2 *Factoring Monomials*

OBJECTIVES

Factor a monomial.

Find the GCF of two monomials.

The monomial $8a^2$ can be written as a product in several ways. A few are shown below. Each is called a **factorization.**

$$2a \cdot 2a \cdot 2 \qquad 8 \cdot a \cdot a \qquad (-2)(-4)a \cdot a \qquad 2 \cdot 2 \cdot 2 \cdot a \cdot a$$

We call $2 \cdot 2 \cdot 2 \cdot a \cdot a$ the **complete factorization** of $8a^2$. None of the factors can be factored any further. We **factor** a monomial by finding its complete factorization.

EXAMPLE 1 $10mn^2 = 2 \cdot 5 \cdot m \cdot n \cdot n$

complete factorization

To find the greatest common factor (GCF) of two monomials, compare their complete factorizations.

EXAMPLE 2 $10mn^2$ and $15mn$

$$10mn^2 = 2 \cdot \boxed{5 \cdot m \cdot n} \cdot n$$
$$15mn = 3 \cdot \boxed{5 \cdot m \cdot n}$$

The GCF of $10mn^2$ and $15mn$ is $5 \cdot m \cdot n = 5mn$.

EXAMPLE 3 $4r^2s$ and $-10s$

$$4r^2s = 2 \cdot \boxed{2} \cdot r \cdot r \cdot \boxed{s}$$
$$-10s = -1 \cdot \boxed{2} \cdot 5 \cdot \boxed{s}$$ ◄ Use -1 as the first factor.

The GCF of $4r^2s$ and $-10s$ is $2s$.

EXAMPLE 4 $8x^3y$ and $6x^2y$

$$8x^3y = \boxed{2} \cdot 2 \cdot 2 \cdot \boxed{x \cdot x} \cdot x \cdot \boxed{y}$$
$$6x^2y = \boxed{2} \cdot 3 \cdot \boxed{x \cdot x} \cdot \boxed{y}$$

The GCF of $8x^3y$ and $6x^2y$ is $2x^2y$.

True or false?

Sample: $4m^2$ is a factor of $12m^2n$. *What you say:* True

1. $3w$ is a factor of $21w^2$.
2. $5t$ is a factor of $5t^2$.
3. $6y$ is a factor of $12x$.
4. bc is a factor of $3bc$.
5. x^2y^2 is a divisor of $-7x^2y^3$.
6. $-2m$ is a divisor of $-10mn$.
7. $-3a$ is a divisor of $9b^2$.
8. $-8y$ is a divisor of $16x^2y$.
9. $3b$ is a common factor of $15ab$ and $7a^2b$.
10. $2n$ is a common factor of $8m$ and $6mn$.
11. x^2 is a common factor of $3x^2y$ and $2x^2$.
12. $2k^3$ is a common factor of $24k^3r$ and $-4k^3t$.

Written EXERCISES

A

Complete.

Sample: $21x^3y = 3x^3(\underline{\ ?\ })$ *Solution:* $21x^3y = 3x^3(7y)$

1. $26y^2 = 2y(\underline{\ ?\ })$
2. $24x^4 = 3x(\underline{\ ?\ })$
3. $12mn = 6(\underline{\ ?\ })$
4. $25s^2t = 5t(\underline{\ ?\ })$
5. $15b^5c^5 = 5b^5(\underline{\ ?\ })$
6. $30x^2y^2 = -6xy(\underline{\ ?\ })$
7. $-15r^3s^5 = -3rs(\underline{\ ?\ })$
8. $-20xz^2 = 2(2)(\underline{\ ?\ })(xz^2)$
9. $36a^2b^3c^4 = -4abc(\underline{\ ?\ })$
10. $-51rst^2 = -3rt(\underline{\ ?\ })$

Write two different factorizations.

Sample: $-18ax^2$ *Solution:* $-9 \cdot 2ax^2$; $3a(-6x^2)$
(Other answers are possible.)

11. $16t$
12. $30x$
13. $12mn$
14. $-20rs$
15. $-18r^2s^2$
16. $50ab^2$
17. $5cd^2$
18. $7m^2n^2$
19. $-3xyz$

Write the complete factorization of each monomial. Then name the GCF.

Sample: $4a^2$ and $6ab^2$ *Solution:* $4a^2 = 2 \cdot 2 \cdot a \cdot a$
$6ab^2 = 2 \cdot 3 \cdot a \cdot b \cdot b$
The GCF is $2a$.

20. $2r^3$ and $8r^2$
21. $5ab$ and $10ab$
22. $3xy^2$ and $12x^2y$
23. $14m^2n$ and $7mn$
24. $12s^2$ and $60st$
25. $18w^2$ and $-3w$
26. $2x^2$ and $6xy^4z$
27. 15 and $3mn$

Name the GCF.

Sample 1: $12r^3$ and $36rs^2t$ *Solution:* $12r$

Sample 2: $4c$, $2ac$, and $3c^2$ *Solution:* c

B

28. $8r^2$ and $16r$
29. $6x^2y$ and $-24y$
30. $3k^2$ and 10
31. $15x^3$ and $5y^3$
32. $3x^2$ and $-6x$
33. $2b$, $3b^2$, $2ab$
34. $14m^2$, $6n$, and 8
35. $4x^2$, $-8x$, and x^3

Write each monomial as a product whose first factor is the GCF of the monomials listed.

Sample: $8m^2n^2$ and $14mn^2$ *Solution:* $8m^2n^2 = (2mn^2)(4m)$
$14mn^2 = (2mn^2)(7)$

C

36. $6axy$ and $2xy^2$
37. $7r^2s$ and $-28r^4s^2$
38. $13x^5y^3$ and x^2y^2
39. $4rst$ and $-2x$
40. $15x^2$, $-10xy$, and $5y$
41. $5s^3$, rs^2, and $5r$

Time out

Andrea and Brian are sister and brother. Andrea is twice as old as Brian was six years ago. Brian's age is one-twelfth Andrea's height in centimeters. Their street number is twice their combined ages and ten less than Brian's weight. The sum of their parents' ages is five times Brian's age. Brian is 14. How old is Andrea? (*Hint:* Read the problem very carefully. Decide how much of the information you really need.)

14-3 *Factoring Polynomials*

OBJECTIVE

Factor polynomials like $6n^2 + 4$ and $16m^3 + 40m^2 - 24m$.

To **factor** a polynomial, we first identify the greatest common factor of its terms. Then we use the distributive property to "factor out" the GCF.

EXAMPLE 1 $6n^2 + 4$

$$6n^2 = 2 \cdot 3 \cdot n \cdot n \qquad 4 = 2 \cdot 2$$

GCF of $6n^2$ and 4 is 2.

$$6n^2 + 4 = 2(3n^2) + 2 \cdot 2 = 2(3n^2 + 2)$$

EXAMPLE 2 $12x^2 - 15xy$ ◄ **GCF is $3x$.**

$$12x^2 - 15xy = 3x(4x) - 3x(5y)$$
$$= 3x(4x - 5y)$$

EXAMPLE 3 $16m^3 + 40m^2 - 24m$ ◄ **GCF is $8m$.**

$$16m^3 + 40m^2 - 24m = 8m(2m^2) + 8m(5m) + 8m(-3)$$
$$= 8m(2m^2 + 5m - 3)$$

It is always a good idea to check the answer by multiplying the factors.

EXAMPLE 4 $7y^2 - 21y = 7y(y) - 7y(3)$

$$= 7y(y - 3)$$

Check: $7y(y - 3) = 7y^2 - 21y$ ✓

Oral EXERCISES

Name the GCF of the terms.

Sample 1: $2ab + 8bc$ *What you say:* GCF is $2b$.

Sample 2: $16n^2 - 5$ *What you say:* GCF is 1.

1. $12x + 3$	**2.** $5a^2b^2 + 2a^2$	**3.** $6n^2 + 12$
4. $7mn + 10m^2$	**5.** $24t^2 - 8t$	**6.** $12y^2 - 3z^2$
7. $3s^2 + 15$	**8.** $3a^2 + 18c^2$	**9.** $3w^2 + 10$
10. $b^4c^3 + b^2c^2$	**11.** $5t^2 - 35r$	**12.** $x^2 + 7$

Written EXERCISES

Complete.

Sample: $21x^2 - 3y^2 = 3(\underline{\ ?\ })$

Solution: $21x^2 - 3y^2 = 3(7x^2 - y^2)$

A

1. $5k^2 + 15 = 5(\underline{\ ?\ })$
2. $3b^2 + 21b = 3b(\underline{\ ?\ })$
3. $28r^2 + 16r = 4r(\underline{\ ?\ })$
4. $24m^3 + 36m^2n = 12m^2(\underline{\ ?\ })$
5. $45b - 9b^2 = 9b(\underline{\ ?\ })$
6. $15xy + 30x^2y^2 = 15xy(\underline{\ ?\ })$
7. $10y^2 + 15y = 5y(\underline{\ ?\ })$
8. $3a^3b^3 + 12b^2 = 3b^2(\underline{\ ?\ })$

Factor and check.

Sample: $4x^2 - 10xy$ *Solution:* $2x(2x - 5y)$

Check: $2x(2x - 5y) = 4x^2 - 10xy$ ✓

9. $5m - 15$
10. $8t^2 + 12$
11. $6a^2 + 7a$
12. $10ab + 30a^2$
13. $ab^2 - a^2b$
14. $3x^3 - 15x$
15. $20a^2b + 3ab^2$
16. $8x^2 + 4x$
17. $9xyz - xy$
18. $3rs^2 + 12r^2s^2$
19. $az^2 - 12awz$
20. $14bxy + 49by^2$
21. $3y^2 - 3y$
22. $by^2 + bx^2$
23. $50mn - 33n^2$

Complete.

24. $aw^2 - 12awz + 36aw = aw(\underline{\ ?\ })$
25. $6m^3 + 3m^2 - 3m = 3m(\underline{\ ?\ })$
26. $14 - 7z - 21z^2 = 7(\underline{\ ?\ })$
27. $t^3 + t - t^2 = t(\underline{\ ?\ })$
28. $4b^3 - 4b^2 - 4b = 4b(\underline{\ ?\ })$
29. $21y^2 + 42x^2y^2 - 14xy^2 = 7y^2(\underline{\ ?\ })$

Factor.

B

30. $15y + 25y^2 - 20$
31. $3x^3 - x^2 + 5x$
32. $2x^2 - 6x - 4$
33. $4t^2 - 28t + 28$
34. $20y^2 + 43xy - 14y$
35. $x^3 + x^2 - x$
36. $y^3 - y^2 + y$
37. $6v^3 + 26v^2 + 8v$
38. $x^2y + 2bx - x^2$
39. $3m^4 - 57m^3 + 111m^2$

14-4 *Factoring Polynomials by Grouping Terms*

OBJECTIVE
Factor polynomials like $ac + ad + 4bc + 4bd$.

Suppose all the terms of a polynomial do not have a common factor. We may be able to group pairs of terms to express the polynomial as one which can be factored by using the distributive property.

EXAMPLE 1 $3rs + 15st + 2r^2 + 10rt$
$= (3rs + 15st) + (2r^2 + 10rt)$ ◀ Group terms.
$= [3s(r + 5t)] + [2r(r + 5t)]$ ◀ Factor in pairs.
$= (3s + 2r)(r + 5t)$ ◀ $(r + 5t)$ is a common factor.

EXAMPLE 2 $xy - 2x + 3y - 6$
$= (xy - 2x) + (3y - 6)$ ◀ Group terms.
$= [x(y - 2)] + [3(y - 2)]$ ◀ Factor in pairs.
$= (x + 3)(y - 2)$ ◀ $(y - 2)$ is a common factor.

EXAMPLE 3 $ac + ad + 4bc + 4bd$
$= (ac + ad) + (4bc + 4bd)$ ◀ Group terms.
$= [a(c + d)] + [4b(c + d)]$ ◀ Factor in pairs.
$= (a + 4b)(c + d)$ ◀ $(c + d)$ is a common factor.

EXAMPLE 4 $mn + 6mt + 6t + n$
$= mn + n + 6mt + 6t$ ◀ Rearrange terms.
$= (mn + n) + (6mt + 6t)$ ◀ Group terms.
$= [n(m + 1)] + [6t(m + 1)]$ ◀ Factor in pairs.
$= (n + 6t)(m + 1)$ ◀ $(m + 1)$ is a common factor.

There is often more than one way to rearrange and group terms. Compare Example 4 and Example 5.

EXAMPLE 5 $mn + 6mt + 6t + n$
$= 6mt + mn + 6t + n$ ◀ Rearrange terms.
$= (6mt + mn) + (6t + n)$ ◀ Group terms.
$= m(6t + n) + 1(6t + n)$ ◀ Factor in pairs.
$= (m + 1)(6t + n)$ ◀ $6t + n$ is a common factor.

Oral EXERCISES

Simplify.

Sample: $m(m + 3) + 6n(m + 3)$

What you say: $m^2 + 3m + 6mn + 18n$

1. $k(k + 2) + t(k + 2)$
2. $3x(y + 2) + 5(y + 2)$
3. $2r(s + 2t) - 4(s + 2t)$
4. $2t(1 + 2s) + s(1 + 2s)$
5. $2a(b + 2) + 5(b + 2)$
6. $n^2(n - 2) + 3(n - 2)$

Written EXERCISES

A

Write the factored form.

Sample: $5y(x + 2) - 4(x + 2)$ *Solution:* $(5y - 4)(x + 2)$

1. $3s(r + 4) + t(r + 4)$
2. $5b(c - 1) + 2a(c - 1)$
3. $x(y + 3) - w(y + 3)$
4. $2p(r + 7) - 4q(r + 7)$
5. $10a(2 + b) + c(2 + b)$
6. $4m(n + 3) - r(n + 3)$
7. $5(b + c) - a(b + c)$
8. $w(y - 5) - 3(y - 5)$
9. $x^2(y + 7) - 5(y + 7)$
10. $(4 - x)3t + (4 - x)r$

Factor.

Sample: $(4rt + 5st) + (4rx + 5sx)$

Solution: $(4rt + 5st) + (4rx + 5sx)$
$= t(4r + 5s) + x(4r + 5s)$
$= (t + x)(4r + 5s)$

11. $(2st + 8t) + (rs + 4r)$
12. $(2ab + 2a) + (bc + c)$
13. $(mn - 3m) + (nr - 3r)$
14. $(5xy + 10x) + (3y + 6)$
15. $(mn + 3n) - (mt + 3t)$
16. $(2x + 2y) - (mx + my)$
17. $(r^2s - 2r^2) + (st^2 - 2t^2)$
18. $(b^2c - 2b^2) - (cd - 2d)$

Factor.

Sample: $2b^2 + 2c - 4bc - b$

Two possible solutions are given.

Solution 1: $2b^2 + 2c - 4bc - b$
$= (2b^2 - b) + (-4bc + 2c)$
$= b(2b - 1) - 2c(2b - 1)$
$= (b - 2c)(2b - 1)$

Solution 2: $2b^2 + 2c - 4bc - b$
$= (2b^2 - 4bc) - 1(b - 2c)$
$= 2b(b - 2c) - 1(b - 2c)$
$= (2b - 1)(b - 2c)$

B

19. $2pq - 3qr + 10ps - 15rs$
20. $5xy + xk - 4k - 20y$
21. $ac - 2d + cd - 2a$
22. $2r - 3st - rt + 6s$
23. $mn^2 + 3n^2 - 3m - 9$
24. $ms - mt - 3s + 3t$

SELF-TEST 1

Be sure you understand these terms.

composite (p. 382)
prime factorization (p. 382)
complete factorization (p. 384)
factor (p. 384)

Write the prime factorization. **Section 14-1, p. 382**

1. 8
2. 18
3. 42

Write the complete factorization. **Section 14-2, p. 384**

4. $35mn$
5. $-12x^2y$
6. $10a^2b^3$

Name the GCF.

7. $8a^2b$ and $4ab$
8. $9xy^3$ and $-3x^2y$

Complete. **Section 14-3, p. 387**

9. $7w^2 + 14 = 7(\underline{\ ?\ })$
10. $20x - 5x^2 = 5x(\underline{\ ?\ })$

Factor. **Section 14-4, p. 389**

11. $x(2 + x) + y(2 + x)$
12. $4n(m - 2) + m(m - 2)$

Check your answers with those printed at the back of the book.

14-5 *Difference of Two Squares*

OBJECTIVE
Factor polynomials like $m^2 - 64$ and $9x^2 - 1$.

Recall the pattern you learned for multiplying an expression like $(x - 4)(x + 4)$. The product of the sum and difference of two numbers is the difference of their squares.

EXAMPLE 1 $(x - 4)(x + 4) = x^2 - 4^2 = x^2 - 16$

To factor a polynomial that is the difference of two squares, we simply reverse the procedure.

EXAMPLE 2 $x^2 - 16 = (x - 4)(x + 4)$

EXAMPLE 3 $m^2 - 64$ ◄ $64 = 8^2$
$m^2 - 64 = (m + 8)(m - 8)$

EXAMPLE 4 $9x^2 - 1$ ◄ $9x^2 = (3x)^2$; $1 = 1^2$
$9x^2 - 1 = (3x - 1)(3x + 1)$

EXAMPLE 5 $3y^2 - 12 = 3(y^2 - 4)$ ◄ 3 is a common factor.
$= 3(y - 2)(y + 2)$ $y^2 - 4$ is a difference of squares.

EXERCISES

Tell whether or not the expression is a square. If it is, name the factors.

Sample: 25 *What you say:* Yes, $25 = 5 \cdot 5$

1. 36
2. m^2
3. t^4
4. 81
5. 20
6. x^3

Multiply.

7. $(y + 7)(y - 7)$
8. $(r - 1)(r + 1)$
9. $(2x + 2)(2x - 2)$
10. $(b - 3)(b + 3)$
11. $(2t + 1)(2t - 1)$
12. $(z - 2)(z + 2)$

Written EXERCISES

Complete.

Sample: $r^2 - 64 = (r + \underline{\ ?\ })(r - \underline{\ ?\ })$

Solution: $r^2 - 64 = (r + 8)(r - 8)$

A

1. $h^2 - 9 = (h + \underline{\ ?\ })(h - \underline{\ ?\ })$
2. $n^2 - 49 = (n + \underline{\ ?\ })(n - \underline{\ ?\ })$
3. $4k^2 - 1 = (2k + \underline{\ ?\ })(2k - \underline{\ ?\ })$
4. $x^2 - 25 = (\underline{\ ?\ } + 5)(\underline{\ ?\ } - 5)$
5. $4 - t^2 = (\underline{\ ?\ } - t)(\underline{\ ?\ } + t)$
6. $81 - y^2 = (\underline{\ ?\ } - y)(\underline{\ ?\ } + y)$

Factor.

Sample: $a^2b^2 - 4$ *Solution:* $a^2b^2 - 4 = (ab + 2)(ab - 2)$

7. $z^2 - 4$
8. $y^2 - 1$
9. $a^2 - 36$
10. $9 - t^2$
11. $r^2 - 900$
12. $16n^2 - 121$
13. $9p^2 - 144$
14. $m^2n^2 - 9$
15. $t^4 - 100$
16. $169 - r^4$
17. $k^4 - 1$
18. $49 - x^2y^4$

Write as the difference of two squares. Then factor.

Sample: $-4 + m^2$ *Solution:* $-4 + m^2 = m^2 - 4$
$= (m + 2)(m - 2)$

19. $-16 + y^2$
20. $-49 + m^4$
21. $-36 + m^2n^2$
22. $-1 + x^2$
23. $-r^2 + 64$
24. $-4n^2 + 25$
25. $-m^2 + n^2$
26. $-x^2y^2 + z^2$
27. $-x^4 + y^4$

Factor completely.

Sample: $3y^2 - 27$ *Solution:* $3y^2 - 27 = 3(y^2 - 9)$
$= 3(y + 3)(y - 3)$

B

28. $6x^2 - 24$
29. $5n^2 - 20$
30. $72 - 2z^2$
31. $3r^2 - 3s^2$
32. $48 - 3r^2$
33. $4 - 4r^2$
34. $5m^2 - 500$
35. $2m^2n^2 - 162$
36. $-36 + 9x^2$
37. $-75 + 3x^2$
38. $xy^2 - xz^2$
39. $\pi x^2 - \pi y^2$

C

40. $x^2 - \frac{1}{4}$
41. $\frac{x^2}{9} - 1$
42. $\frac{n^2}{4} - 25$

14-6 *Factoring Trinomial Squares*

OBJECTIVE
Factor trinomial squares like $m^2 + 4m + 4$ and $9x^2 + 12x + 4$.

Recall the pattern for expanding an expression like $(x + 5)^2$.

$$(x+5)^2 = \underbrace{x^2}_{\text{square of the first term}} + \underbrace{10x}_{\text{twice the product of the terms}} + \underbrace{25}_{\text{square of the second term}}$$

A polynomial such as $x^2 + 10x + 25$ is called a trinomial square. To factor a trinomial square, we reverse the process.

EXAMPLE 1 $m^2 + 4m + 4$ ◄ Think: $m^2 = m \cdot m$, $4 = 2 \cdot 2$, and $4m = 2(m \cdot 2)$. $m^2 + 4m + 4$ is a trinomial square.

$m^2 + 4m + 4 = (m + 2)(m + 2)$

EXAMPLE 2 $9x^2 + 12x + 4 = (3x + 2)(3x + 2)$ ◄ $9x^2 = 3x \cdot 3x$, $4 = 2 \cdot 2$, $12x = 2(3x \cdot 2)$

$= (3x + 2)^2$

EXAMPLE 3 $4s^2 + 28s + 49 = (2s + 7)(2s + 7)$

$= (2s + 7)^2$

EXAMPLE 4 $t^2 + 2st + s^2 = (t + s)(t + s)$

$= (t + s)^2$

EXERCISES

Tell how to complete.

Sample: $4y^2 + 20y + 25 = (2y + \underline{\ ?\ })^2$

What you say: $5^2 = 25$ and $2(2y \cdot 5) = 20y$.
$4y^2 + 20y + 25 = (2y + 5)^2$

1. $4k^2 + 8k + 4 = (2k + \underline{\ ?\ })^2$
2. $25t^2 + 10t + 1 = (\underline{\ ?\ } + 1)^2$
3. $m^2 + 6m + 9 = (\underline{\ ?\ } + 3)^2$
4. $9a^2 + 6a + 1 = (3a + \underline{\ ?\ })^2$
5. $x^2 + 2xy + y^2 = (x + \underline{\ ?\ })^2$

Written EXERCISES

A

Complete.

1. $4x^2 = (\underline{\ ?\ })^2$
2. $m^2 = (\underline{\ ?\ })^2$
3. $m^2n^2 = (\underline{\ ?\ })^2$
4. $r^2t^2 = (\underline{\ ?\ })^2$
5. $100 = (\underline{\ ?\ })^2$
6. $225 = (\underline{\ ?\ })^2$

Name the missing term.

Sample: $n^2 + \underline{\ ?\ } + 9 = (n + 3)^2$ *Solution:* $2(n \cdot 3)$ or $6n$

7. $x^2 + \underline{\ ?\ } + 9 = (x + 3)^2$
8. $r^2 + \underline{\ ?\ } + 16 = (r + 4)^2$
9. $z^2 + \underline{\ ?\ } + 1 = (z + 1)^2$
10. $m^2 + \underline{\ ?\ } + n^2 = (m + n)^2$
11. $9w^2 + \underline{\ ?\ } + 1 = (3w + 1)^2$
12. $16y^2 + \underline{\ ?\ } + 1 = (4y + 1)^2$
13. $4s^2 + \underline{\ ?\ } + t^2 = (2s + t)^2$
14. $4a^2 + \underline{\ ?\ } + 9b^2 = (2a + 3b)^2$

Expand.

15. $(c + 2)^2$
16. $(2d + 1)^2$
17. $(k + 5)^2$
18. $(a + b)^2$
19. $(3n + 4m)^2$
20. $(2b + 5c)^2$

Factor. Check by multiplying.

Sample: $h^2 + 12h + 36$ *Solution:* $(h + 6)^2$

Check: $(h + 6)(h + 6) = h^2 + 12h + 36$

21. $p^2 + 2p + 1$
22. $b^2 + 4b + 4$
23. $t^2 + 10t + 25$
24. $4r^2 + 4r + 1$
25. $m^2 + 4m + 4$
26. $a^2 + 24a + 144$
27. $100 + 20x + x^2$
28. $q^2 + 18q + 81$
29. $y^2 + 16y + 64$
30. $9w^2 + 6w + 1$
31. $z^2 + 30z + 225$
32. $25b^2 + 30b + 9$
33. $16c^2 + 24c + 9$
34. $9m^2 + 42m + 49$

B

35. $m^2n^2 + 2mn + 1$
36. $p^2 + 2pr + r^2$
37. $k^2 + 16kt + 64t^2$
38. $4b^2 + 4bd + d^2$
39. $100x^2 + 20xy + y^2$
40. $144r^2 + 120rs + 25s^2$
41. $9r^2s^2 + 30rst + 25t^2$
42. $25a^2b^2c^2 + 70abc + 49$
43. $9x^2 + 60xy + 100y^2$
44. $16a^2b^2 + 8abc + c^2$

C

45. $x^2 + x + \frac{1}{4}$
46. $m^2 + \frac{2m}{5} + \frac{1}{25}$

14-7 *Square of a Binomial Difference*

OBJECTIVE

Factor trinomial squares like $x^2 - 10x + 25$ and $4x^2 - 12x + 9$.

When a binomial expression such as $(x + 7)^2$ is expanded, all terms in the result are positive. When $(x - 7)^2$ is expanded, the middle term is always **negative.**

$$(x - 7)^2 = \underbrace{x^2}_{\text{square of the first term}} - \underbrace{14x}_{\text{twice the product of the terms}} + \underbrace{49}_{\text{square of the last term}}$$

To factor a trinomial square like $x^2 - 14x + 49$, we reverse this process.

EXAMPLE 1 $x^2 - 10x + 25$ ◄ **Think: $x^2 = x \cdot x$, $25 = 5 \cdot 5$, and $10x = 2(x \cdot 5)$. $x^2 - 10x + 25$ is a trinomial square.**

$$\begin{aligned} x^2 - 10x + 25 &= (x - 5)(x - 5) \\ &= (x - 5)^2 \end{aligned}$$

EXAMPLE 2

$$\begin{aligned} 9t^2 - 12t + 4 &= (3t - 2)(3t - 2) \\ &= (3t - 2)^2 \end{aligned}$$

◄ **$9t^2 = 3t \cdot 3t$, $4 = 2 \cdot 2$, $12t = 2(3t \cdot 2)$**

EXAMPLE 3

$$\begin{aligned} x^2 - 2xy + y^2 &= (x - y)(x - y) \\ &= (x - y)^2 \end{aligned}$$

EXERCISES

Add or multiply as indicated.

Sample: $(-4) + (-4)$ *What you say:* $(-4) + (-4) = -8$
$(-4)(-4)$ $(-4)(-4) = 16$

1. $(-7) + (-7)$
   $(-7)(-7)$
2. $(-3) + (-3)$
   $(-3)(-3)$
3. $(-10) + (-10)$
   $(-10)(-10)$
4. $(-1) + (-1)$
   $(-1)(-1)$
5. $(-x) + (-x)$
   $(-x)(-x)$
6. $(-m) + (-m)$
   $(-m)(-m)$

7. $(-xy) + (-xy)$
$(-xy)(-xy)$

8. $(-2ab) + (-2ab)$
$(-2ab)(-2ab)$

9. $(-3n) + (-3n)$
$(-3n)(-3n)$

10. $(-5m) + (-5m)$
$(-5m)(-5m)$

11. $(-8rs) + (-8rs)$
$(-8rs)(-8rs)$

12. $(-6t) + (-6t)$
$(-6t)(-6t)$

13. $(-2t) + (-2t)$
$(-2t)(-2t)$

14. $(-3ab) + (-3ab)$
$(-3ab)(-3ab)$

15. $(-4z) + (-4z)$
$(-4z)(-4z)$

Written EXERCISES

A

Simplify.

Sample 1: $(-m)(-m)$ *Solution:* m^2

Sample 2: $(-2t)(-2t)$ *Solution:* $4t^2$

1. $(-s)(-s)$
2. $(-b)(-b)$
3. $(-5y)(-5y)$
4. $(-7x)(-7x)$
5. $(-8)(-8)$
6. $(-10)(-10)$
7. $(3x)(3x)$
8. $(4t)(4t)$
9. $(-10k)(-10k)$
10. $(-ab)(-ab)$
11. $(-xy)(-xy)$
12. $(-2xy)(-2xy)$

Complete with positive factors and then with negative factors.

Sample: $x^2 = \underline{\ ?\ } \cdot \underline{\ ?\ } = \underline{\ ?\ } \cdot \underline{\ ?\ }$

Solution: $x^2 = x \cdot x = -x(-x)$

13. $z^2 = \underline{\ ?\ } \cdot \underline{\ ?\ } = \underline{\ ?\ } \cdot \underline{\ ?\ }$
14. $d^2 = \underline{\ ?\ } \cdot \underline{\ ?\ } = \underline{\ ?\ } \cdot \underline{\ ?\ }$
15. $w^2 = \underline{\ ?\ } \cdot \underline{\ ?\ } = \underline{\ ?\ } \cdot \underline{\ ?\ }$
16. $4t^2 = \underline{\ ?\ } \cdot \underline{\ ?\ } = \underline{\ ?\ } \cdot \underline{\ ?\ }$
17. $25y^2 = \underline{\ ?\ } \cdot \underline{\ ?\ } = \underline{\ ?\ } \cdot \underline{\ ?\ }$
18. $b^2c^2 = \underline{\ ?\ } \cdot \underline{\ ?\ } = \underline{\ ?\ } \cdot \underline{\ ?\ }$
19. $x^2y^2 = \underline{\ ?\ } \cdot \underline{\ ?\ } = \underline{\ ?\ } \cdot \underline{\ ?\ }$
20. $9a^2b^2 = \underline{\ ?\ } \cdot \underline{\ ?\ } = \underline{\ ?\ } \cdot \underline{\ ?\ }$

Expand.

21. $(r - 2)^2$
22. $(m - 1)^2$
23. $(k - 5)^2$
24. $(4 - x)^2$
25. $(1 - y)^2$
26. $(2c - 1)^2$
27. $(a - b)^2$
28. $(x - y)^2$
29. $(2x - 3)^2$
30. $(t - 4s)^2$
31. $(2s - y)^2$
32. $(2x - 5y)^2$

Factor. Check by multiplication.

Sample: $m^2 - 6m + 9$

Solution: $(m - 3)^2$

Check: $(m - 3)(m - 3) = m^2 - 6m + 9$

33. $t^2 - 8t + 16$
34. $n^2 - 4n + 4$
35. $s^2 - 10s + 25$
36. $m^2 - 2m + 1$
37. $c^2 - 6c + 9$
38. $25b^2 - 60b + 36$
39. $r^2 - 6r + 9$
40. $9 - 12s + 4s^2$
41. $9k^2 - 6k + 1$
42. $a^2 - 12a + 36$
43. $x^2 - 14x + 49$
44. $4y^2 - 12y + 9$

B

45. $16a^2 - 8ab + b^2$
46. $a^2 - 2ab + b^2$
47. $9m^2 - 6mn + n^2$
48. $4x^2 - 4xy + y^2$
49. $36y^2 - 36yz + 9z^2$
50. $16r^2 - 40rs + 25s^2$

Factor completely.

C

51. $3n^2 - 6n + 3$
52. $20r^2 - 20r + 5$
53. $2m^2 - 20m + 50$
54. $5a^3 - 10a^2 + 5a$
55. $k^2 - k + \frac{1}{4}$
56. $x^2 - 0.2x + 0.01$

Andrija Mohorovičić 1857–1936

Andrija Mohorovičić discovered one of the most important principles of geology while studying wave patterns of a Balkan earthquake in 1909. He found that waves which penetrated deeper into the earth arrived sooner than waves traveling along the surface. He deduced the fact that the earth possessed a layered structure having sharp separations. Attempts to drill through the first layer of the earth's surface were considered in the 1960's. The project, called *Mohole,* was named after Mohorovičić.

Factoring Other Polynomials

14-8 *Product of Binomial Sums or Differences*

OBJECTIVE
Factor trinomials like $x^2 + 7x + 12$ and $x^2 - 10x + 9$.

We are now ready to factor products of binomial sums and binomial differences. First let's review multiplication of binomials. Notice the signs in the result.

$(x + 5)(x + 7) = x^2 + 12x + 35$ ◄ all terms positive
$(x - 2)(x - 3) = x^2 - 5x + 6$ ◄ middle term negative, last term positive

These processes are reversed to factor trinomials that are not squares.

EXAMPLE 1 $x^2 + 6x + 8$ ◄ Product of binomial *sums*
Step 1 $(\quad)(\quad)$ ◄ Set up parentheses.
Step 2 $(x \quad)(x \quad)$ ◄ Factor x^2 as $x \cdot x$.
Step 3 $(x + \quad)(x + \quad)$ ◄ Signs are $+$.
Step 4 $(x + 4)(x + 2)$ ◄ Factor 8 as $4 \cdot 2$. Note that $4 + 2 = 6$.

EXAMPLE 2 $x^2 - 8x + 12$ ◄ Product of binomial *differences*
Step 1 $(\quad)(\quad)$ ◄ Set up parentheses.
Step 2 $(x \quad)(x \quad)$ ◄ Factor x^2 as $x \cdot x$.
Step 3 $(x - \quad)(x - \quad)$ ◄ Signs are $-$.
Step 4 $(x - 6)(x - 2)$ ◄ Factor 12 as $(-6)(-2)$. Note that $(-6) + (-2) = -8$.

EXERCISES

Complete both statements with the same positive numbers.

Sample: $15 = (\underline{?})(\underline{?})$ $8 = (\underline{?}) + (\underline{?})$ *What you say:* $15 = (5)(3)$ $8 = 5 + 3$

1. $10 = (\underline{?})(\underline{?})$
   $7 = (\underline{?}) + (\underline{?})$
2. $6 = (\underline{?})(\underline{?})$
   $5 = (\underline{?}) + (\underline{?})$
3. $9 = (\underline{?})(\underline{?})$
   $6 = (\underline{?}) + (\underline{?})$
4. $9 = (\underline{?})(\underline{?})$
   $10 = (\underline{?}) + (\underline{?})$
5. $12 = (\underline{?})(\underline{?})$
   $8 = (\underline{?}) + (\underline{?})$
6. $20 = (\underline{?})(\underline{?})$
   $9 = (\underline{?}) + (\underline{?})$

Complete both statements with the same negative numbers.

7. $12 = (\underline{?})(\underline{?})$
$-7 = (\underline{?}) + (\underline{?})$

8. $7 = (\underline{?})(\underline{?})$
$-8 = (\underline{?}) + (\underline{?})$

9. $24 = (\underline{?})(\underline{?})$
$-11 = (\underline{?}) + (\underline{?})$

10. $15 = (\underline{?})(\underline{?})$
$-8 = (\underline{?}) + (\underline{?})$

11. $9 = (\underline{?})(\underline{?})$
$-10 = (\underline{?}) + (\underline{?})$

12. $12 = (\underline{?})(\underline{?})$
$-13 = (\underline{?}) + (\underline{?})$

Written EXERCISES

Complete.

Sample: $x^2 + 5x + 6 = (x + \underline{?})(x + \underline{?})$

Solution: $x^2 + 5x + 6 = (x + 2)(x + 3)$

A

1. $x^2 + 6x + 8 = (x + \underline{?})(x + \underline{?})$
2. $n^2 - 3n + 2 = (n - \underline{?})(n - \underline{?})$
3. $t^2 - 10t + 16 = (t - \underline{?})(t - \underline{?})$
4. $a^2 + 9a + 20 = (a + \underline{?})(a + \underline{?})$
5. $w^2 - 14w + 24 = (w - \underline{?})(w - \underline{?})$
6. $x^2 + 12x + 20 = (x + \underline{?})(x + \underline{?})$
7. $b^2 - 14b + 40 = (b - \underline{?})(b - \underline{?})$
8. $c^2 + 12c + 32 = (c + \underline{?})(c + \underline{?})$
9. $s^2 - 11s + 24 = (s - \underline{?})(s - \underline{?})$
10. $x^2 - 14x + 33 = (x - \underline{?})(x - \underline{?})$

Factor.

11. $n^2 + 3n + 2$
12. $y^2 + 5y + 4$
13. $k^2 - 5k + 6$
14. $a^2 - 8a + 15$
15. $x^2 - 9x + 20$
16. $r^2 + 18r + 32$
17. $t^2 - 14t + 24$
18. $d^2 + 9d + 8$
19. $z^2 - 7z + 12$
20. $w^2 + 10w + 21$
21. $c^2 + 11c + 24$
22. $x^2 - 11x + 18$

B

23. $r^2 + 9rs + 20s^2$
24. $b^2 - 3bc + 2c^2$
25. $m^2 + 8mn + 15n^2$
26. $x^2 + 14xy + 13y^2$
27. $16 - 10x + x^2$
28. $48 + 14s + s^2$
29. $4 + 5q + q^2$
30. $30 - 17w + w^2$

C

31. $b^2 + 20 - 12b$
32. $30 + x^2 - 11x$
33. $-6m + m^2 + 8$
34. $-13y + 30 + y^2$

14-9 *More About Factoring Trinomials*

OBJECTIVE

Factor trinomials such as $x^2 + 5x - 14$ and $x^2 - 3x - 18$.

The method for factoring $x^2 + 5x - 14$ is very similar to the factoring of other trinomials. Note that the last term is negative. When you factor it, remember that one factor must be positive and one negative.

EXAMPLE 1 $x^2 + 5x - 14$

Step 1 $(\quad)(\quad)$ ◀ **Set up parentheses.**

Step 2 $(x \quad)(x \quad)$ ◀ **Factor x^2 as $x \cdot x$.**

Step 3 $(x + \quad)(x - \quad)$ ◀ **One factor of -14 must be positive and the other negative.**

Step 4 $(x + 7)(x - 2)$ ◀ **Factor -14 as $(7)(-2)$ since $7 + (-2) = 5$.**

EXAMPLE 2 $x^2 - 3x - 18$

Step 1 $(\quad)(\quad)$ ◀ **Set up parentheses.**

Step 2 $(x \quad)(x \quad)$ ◀ **Factor x^2 as $x \cdot x$.**

Step 3 $(x + \quad)(x - \quad)$ ◀ **One factor of -18 must be positive and the other negative.**

Step 4 $(x + 3)(x - 6)$ ◀ **Factor -18 as $(3)(-6)$ since $3 + (-6) = -3$.**

Complete. Use the same numbers in both statements.

Sample: $-10 = (\underline{?})(\underline{?})$
$-3 = (\underline{?}) + (\underline{?})$

What you say: $-10 = 2(-5)$
$-3 = 2 + (-5)$

1. $-18 = (\underline{?})(\underline{?})$
$7 = (\underline{?}) + (\underline{?})$

2. $-24 = (\underline{?})(\underline{?})$
$5 = (\underline{?}) + (\underline{?})$

3. $-12 = (\underline{?})(\underline{?})$
$-1 = (\underline{?}) + (\underline{?})$

4. $-5 = (\underline{?})(\underline{?})$
$-4 = (\underline{?}) + (\underline{?})$

5. $-12 = (\underline{?})(\underline{?})$
$1 = (\underline{?}) + (\underline{?})$

6. $-14 = (\underline{?})(\underline{?})$
$5 = (\underline{?}) + (\underline{?})$

7. $-14 = (\underline{?})(\underline{?})$
$-5 = (\underline{?}) + (\underline{?})$

8. $-30 = (\underline{?})(\underline{?})$
$1 = (\underline{?}) + (\underline{?})$

Written EXERCISES

Complete and check.

Sample: $x^2 + 2x - 35 = (x + \underline{?})(x - \underline{?})$

Solution: $x^2 + 2x - 35 = (x + 7)(x - 5)$

Check: $(x + 7)(x - 5) = x^2 + 2x - 35$

A

1. $n^2 + 7n - 18 = (n + \underline{?})(n - \underline{?})$
2. $y^2 + 3y - 18 = (y + \underline{?})(y - \underline{?})$
3. $x^2 - x - 42 = (x + \underline{?})(x - \underline{?})$
4. $x^2 + x - 42 = (x - \underline{?})(x + \underline{?})$
5. $a^2 - 2a - 63 = (a - \underline{?})(a + \underline{?})$
6. $m^2 + 3m - 40 = (m + \underline{?})(m - \underline{?})$
7. $m^2 - 3m - 40 = (m + \underline{?})(m - \underline{?})$
8. $w^2 + 7w - 44 = (w + \underline{?})(w - \underline{?})$
9. $z^2 - 7z - 44 = (z - \underline{?})(z + \underline{?})$
10. $s^2 + 11s - 26 = (s + \underline{?})(s - \underline{?})$

Factor.

11. $t^2 + 2t - 63$
12. $x^2 - 3x - 18$
13. $r^2 + 9r - 22$
14. $a^2 - 5a - 14$
15. $s^2 - s - 6$
16. $y^2 - y - 42$
17. $c^2 - c - 56$
18. $m^2 + 4m - 45$
19. $n^2 - 12n - 45$
20. $q^2 + 4q - 32$
21. $w^2 + 2w - 48$
22. $r^2 - 17r - 60$
23. $b^2 + 5b - 36$
24. $s^2 - 9s - 36$
25. $x^2 + 3x - 40$
26. $t^2 + 11t - 42$
27. $b^2 + 16b - 17$
28. $n^2 - 11n - 60$

B

29. $y^2 + 22xy - 23x^2$
30. $m^2n^2 - 21mn - 100$
31. $r^2 + 48ar - 100a^2$
32. $b^2 - 10bc - 75c^2$
33. $y^2z^2 - 16yz - 57$
34. $m^2 + 24mn - 81n^2$
35. $a^2 - 14ac - 72c^2$
36. $p^2 - 13pq - 68q^2$
37. $x^2 + 8xy - 65y^2$
38. $r^2 - 15rs - 54s^2$
39. $b^2 + 17bc - 38c^2$
40. $m^2 - 10ms - 39s^2$

Write in standard form and factor.

C

41. $16xy - 57y^2 + x^2$
42. $-24rs + r^2 - 81s^2$
43. $5z + z^2 - 50$
44. $-8x^2 - 2xy + y^2$
45. $b^2 - 24a^2 + 10ab$
46. $-3bc + b^2 - 10c^2$

SELF-TEST 2

Factor.

1. $b^2 - 9$	2. $x^2 - 25$	Section 14-5, p. 392
3. $z^2 + 10z + 25$	4. $y^2 + 4y + 4$	Section 14-6, p. 394
5. $x^2 - 12x + 36$	6. $m^2 - 18m + 81$	Section 14-7, p. 396
7. $x^2 + 5x + 6$	8. $n^2 - 9n + 14$	Section 14-8, p. 399
9. $c^2 + 2c - 8$	10. $c^2 - 2c - 8$	Section 14-9, p. 401

Check your answers with those printed at the back of the book.

chapter summary

1. A **prime number** has exactly two different positive factors, itself and one.
2. A number which can be expressed as the product of two or more prime numbers is called a **composite number.**
3. The prime factorization of a number is its expression as a product of prime factors.
4. It may be possible to factor a polynomial in one of the following ways:
   a. Factor out the GCF of the terms.
   b. Group terms. Then factor out the GCF.
   c. Identify and factor as the difference of two squares.
   d. Identify and factor as the square of a binomial sum or a binomial difference.
   e. Identify and factor as the product of binomial sums or binomial differences.
   f. Identify and factor as the product of a binomial sum and a binomial difference.

chapter test

Write the prime factorization.

1. 28
2. 30
3. 27

Name the GCF.

4. $14x^2$, $6xy$
5. 10 and $8n$
6. $16x^2y$, $12xy^2$

Factor.

7. $6 + 8n^2$
8. $8x^2 - 8y$
9. $6x^2 + 12x - 10$
10. $10y^2 + 50x$
11. $m^2n + n$
12. $4st^2 - 12st + 4s$

Group terms. Then factor.

13. $xy + 2x + 6 + 3y$
14. $mn + 5n - 10 - 2m$

Factor.

15. $w^2 - 64$
16. $x^2 + 6x + 9$
17. $y^2 - 2y + 1$
18. $t^2 - 36$
19. $r^2 + 10r + 25$
20. $a^2 + 7a + 10$
21. $4m^2 - n^2$
22. $b^2 - 8b + 16$
23. $t^2 - 8t + 15$

Factor. Check by multiplication.

24. $n^2 + 6n - 16$
25. $r^2 - 3r - 18$
26. $c^2 + 6c - 27$
27. $t^2 - 2t - 35$

challenge topics

Similar Triangles

When two triangles have the same shape, we say they are **similar.** In this illustration $\triangle ABC$ is similar to $\triangle PQR$. We use the symbol $\sim$ to mean "is similar to" and write $\triangle ABC \sim \triangle PQR$.

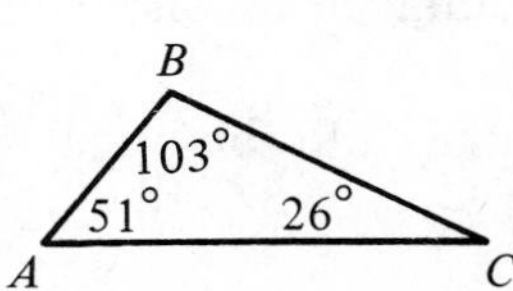

In $\triangle ABC$ and $\triangle PQR$ shown on page 404.

$\overline{AB}$ corresponds to $\overline{PQ}$	$\angle A$ corresponds to $\angle P$
$\overline{AC}$ corresponds to $\overline{PR}$	$\angle B$ corresponds to $\angle Q$
$\overline{BC}$ corresponds to $\overline{QR}$	$\angle C$ corresponds to $\angle R$

When two triangles are similar, the measures of their **corresponding angles** are **equal.**

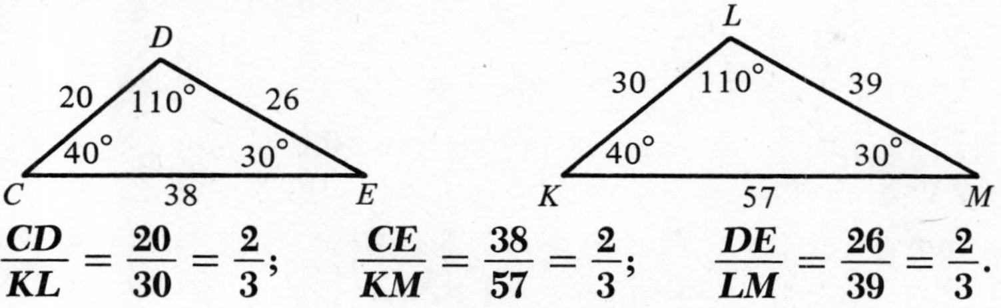

$$\frac{CD}{KL} = \frac{20}{30} = \frac{2}{3}; \quad \frac{CE}{KM} = \frac{38}{57} = \frac{2}{3}; \quad \frac{DE}{LM} = \frac{26}{39} = \frac{2}{3}.$$

For similar triangles, the ratios between the measures of pairs of corresponding sides are equal.

1. If $\triangle KLR \sim \triangle BCD$, what is the length of KL?

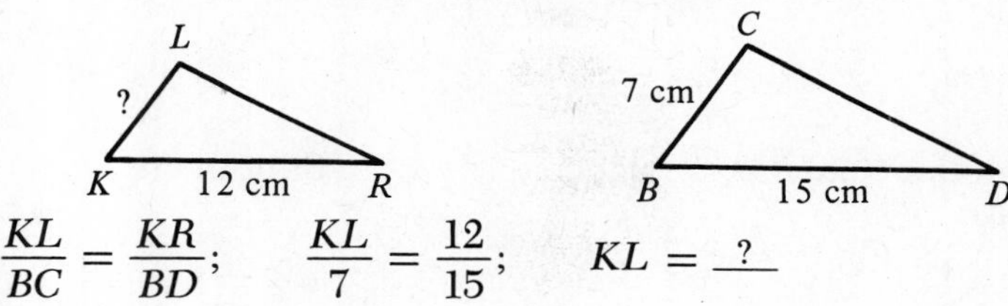

$$\frac{KL}{BC} = \frac{KR}{BD}; \quad \frac{KL}{7} = \frac{12}{15}; \quad KL = \underline{\ ?\ }$$

2. $\triangle XYZ$ and $\triangle BTR$ are similar. What are the measures of $\overline{YZ}$ and $\overline{BR}$?

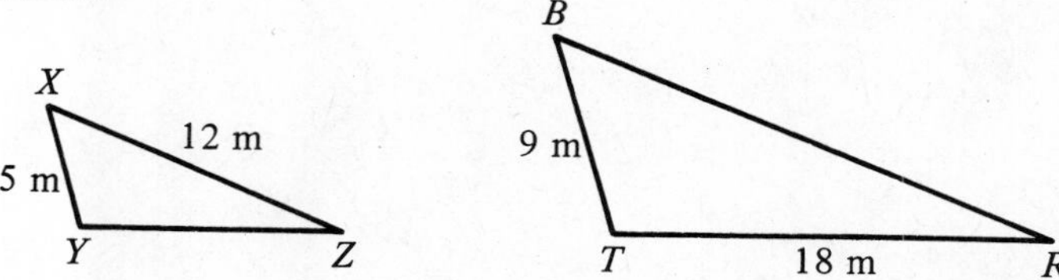

3. $\triangle BGH$ and $\triangle BKT$ are similar. What is the measure of $\angle KTH$? $\angle BHG$? $\angle BKT$? $\angle GKT$? $\angle BGH$?

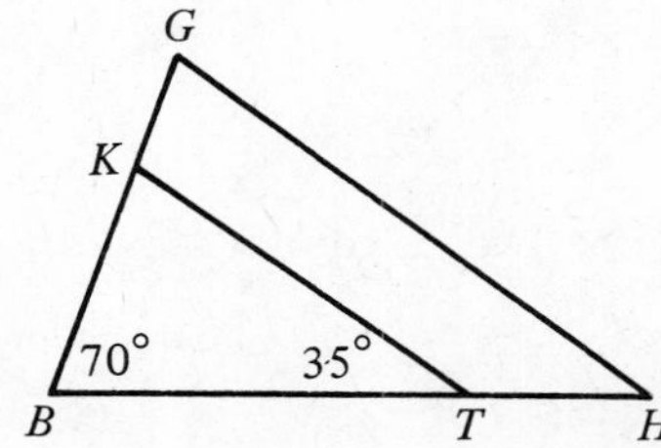

cumulative review

Name the directed number.

1. The positive number 7 units from 0.
2. The negative number 5 units from 0.
3. The negative number 13 units from 0.

Make a number line sketch to show the moves. Tell where you finish.

4. Start at 0. Move 6 units in the negative direction. Then move 4 units in the positive direction.
5. Start at 2 and move 4 units in the negative direction.
6. Start at -1 and move 3 units in the positive direction.

Complete to make a true statement. Use $<$ or $>$.

7. -6 _?_ -10
8. 0.5 _?_ -0.56
9. $\frac{1}{2}$ _?_ $-\frac{3}{2}$
10. 0.4 _?_ 0.47

Write and graph the solution set. The replacement set is {the directed numbers}.

11. $q < 3$
12. $t \geq -3$
13. $s > 0.5$
14. $r \leq 3.7$

Solve.

15. $t = 4 + (-4)$
16. $15 + n = 4$
17. $14 + q = 5$
18. $m + 5 = 15$

Simplify.

19. $-(-7)$
20. $-12 + (-3)$
21. $-(5 + 7)$
22. $-(-4 + 3)$

Complete to make a true statement. Name the property illustrated.

23. $4 = (-2 + 2) +$ _?_
24. $13 +$ _?_ $= 13$
25. _?_ $+ 7 = 7 + 5$
26. $14 + (-14) =$ _?_

Solve. Begin by writing the equivalent addition equation.

27. $15 - (-3) = n$

28. $7 - 20 = d$

29. $3.2 - (-0.2) = g$

30. $-11 - 3 = h$

Complete according to the given function equation.

31. $f(q) = q - (-1)$: $\{(-1, 0), (0, 1), (1, \underline{?}), (2, \underline{?}), (3, \underline{?})\}$

32. $f(t) = 13 - t$: $\{-2, 15), (-1, \underline{?}), (0, \underline{?}), (1, \underline{?}), (2, \underline{?})\}$

Simplify.

33. $4(-11)$

34. $\frac{-52}{4}$

35. $\frac{-21}{7}$

36. $-4(-4)(-4)$

37. $-4(2 + 7)$

38. $a^2 + 2 + 3a^2 + 1$

39. $-48 \div -6$

40. $4 \div \frac{1}{-3}$

41. $\frac{3}{-8} \div \frac{3}{4}$

Solve.

42. $-6x = -18$

43. $4b = -32$

44. $\frac{4}{5}y = -8$

45. $-\frac{1}{y} = 10$

Complete the set of number pairs by using the given function equation.

46. $f(t) = 2t - 6$: $\{(-1, \underline{?}), (0, \underline{?}), (1, \underline{?}), (2, \underline{?})\}$

Solve.

47. $-6 + b = -18$

48. $4x + 3x = -28$

Solve. Use the formula $A = lw$.

49. A table top has area $8m$ and length $4m$. Find the width.

Solve. Graph the solution set.

50. $k - 4 \leq 7$

51. $-2w + 3 > 9$

52. $6r < 30$

53. $\frac{3}{5}s \geq -6$

Tell whether the polynomial is a monomial, a binomial, or a trinomial.

54. $17t + w$ **55.** $q + r - t$ **56.** $2lw$

Write in standard form.

57. $2 + 2x + x^2$

58. $x^3 - x^4 + x + 1$

59. $4x^4 + 2 - x^6$

60. $-10x^3 + 2 + x$

Add.

61.
$$\begin{array}{r} t - 6 \\ \underline{2t + 2} \end{array}$$

62.
$$\begin{array}{l} t^3 + \ \ t^2 + 1 \\ \underline{\qquad 7t^2 \qquad} \end{array}$$

63. $(7k + 3) + (-5k - 2)$

64. $(b + 5) + (4b - 7)$

Subtract the second polynomial from the first.

65.
$$\begin{array}{l} 6k + 2c \\ \underline{4k - 3c} \end{array}$$

66.
$$\begin{array}{l} 7h^2 - 2h \\ \underline{2h^2 - 3h} \end{array}$$

67.
$$\begin{array}{l} 2b^2 + b - 1 \\ \underline{\ \ b^2 - b \qquad} \end{array}$$

68.
$$\begin{array}{l} 4k + 7y \\ \underline{3k + 2y + 5} \end{array}$$

Simplify.

69. $(2t - 3) - (8t - 4)$

70. $(t^2 + 5) - (2t^2 - 8)$

71. $(11t^2 - 3t) - (t + 2)$

72. $(4 + t) - (10 + 3t)$

Write as a polynomial in standard form.

73. The perimeter of a rectangle with length $x^2 + 4$ and width $x^2 - 16$.

Solve and check.

74. $7x + (x - 3) = 13$

75. $10 = 2t - (10 + 3t)$

76. $(4n + 11) + (5 + n) = 21$

77. $0 = (3m + 3) - 2m$

Simplify. Use exponents.

78. $(2 + t)(t + 2)$

79. $-4(q \cdot q \cdot q)(-3)$

80. $-2y(-4)(y)$

81. $(2t^2x)(3t^2x)$

82. $[(-4)^2]^2$

83. $(-3y^2)^2$

Multiply.

84. $-2x(x^2 - 3x + 2)$

85. $t(-t^3 + 2t^2 + 1)$

86. $(x + 2)(x - 3)$

87. $(2r - 4)(r + 3)$

88. $(y + 1)(y^2 + y - 1)$

89. $(2y + 2)(2y + 2)$

90. $(3a - b)(3a - b)$

91. $(t - 3)(t + 3)$

92. $(2t - 4)(2t + 4)$

93. $(7a + 1)(7a - 1)$

Divide. Assume no denominator is 0.

94. $\frac{2ab^2}{ab}$

95. $\frac{6a^2 + 10a}{2a}$

96. $\frac{x^2 - 4x - 12}{x}$

97. $\frac{ab^2 - 2b + 2}{2b}$

98. $\frac{s^2 - 4s + 4}{s - 2}$

99. $\frac{x^2 - 4x - 12}{x - 6}$

Write the prime factorization.

100. 12

101. 72

102. 121

103. 110

104. 98

105. 126

Name the GCF.

106. $3s^3$, $4s^2t$

107. $2ab^2$, $2a^2b$

108. $2rq$, $22r^3q^2$

109. $49x^2$, $7xy$

Factor.

110. $7k^2 - 14k$

111. $39k^4 + 13k - 13$

112. $2q(t + 1) - 3q(t + 1)$

113. $2t + 2s + rt + rs$

114. $(4b^2 + 4b) - (3b + 3)$

115. $25 - b^2$

116. $h^2 + 14h + 49$

117. $4t^2 - 12t + 9$

118. $x^2 + 7x + 10$

119. $x^2 + 11x + 30$

120. $x^2 - 10x + 21$

121. $x^2 - 13x + 22$

122. $x^2 + 6x - 16$

123. $x^2 - 2x - 35$

124. $x^2 + 4x - 77$

125. $x^2 - 5x - 24$

Extra Practice Exercises

For use with Section 1-1.

Simplify.

1. $(5 \times 6) - 8$
2. $18 + 9 + 6$
3. $144 \div 6$
4. $\frac{20}{8 + 12}$
5. $\frac{54 - 34}{2}$
6. $\frac{56}{8}$
7. $64 \div 8$
8. $2^2 + 5$
9. $(3 + 7) + 4$
10. 23×1
11. $(55 - 0) \times 1$
12. $24 - (3 \times 6)$
13. $10 - \frac{15}{3}$
14. $\frac{90}{15}$
15. $4 + \frac{16}{4}$
16. $3^2 + 4^2$
17. $2 \times 3 \times 4$
18. 21×3
19. $6 \times (36 - 24)$
20. $7^2 - (6^2 + 1)$
21. $65 + 0$
22. $\frac{28 + 34}{5^2 + 6}$
23. $(6 \times 7) - 42$
24. $\frac{56 - 24}{8 \times 4}$
25. $(18 - 16) \times 24$
26. $(12 + 9) - 11$
27. $(2^2 + 5^2) - 9$
28. $\frac{52}{20 \cdot 7}$
29. $\frac{3 \times 6}{13 - 4}$
30. $\frac{27}{3} + 18$
31. $200 \div 25$
32. $(34 - 12) + 20$
33. $5 \times 3 \times 4$

For use with Section 1-6.

Solve.

34. $s + 2 = 8$
35. $16 - r = 10$
36. $m + 15 = 30$
37. $n - 12 = 7$
38. $20 + t = 34$
39. $36 = 18 + x$
40. $y = 8 + 9 + 10$
41. $28 - z = 16$
42. $8 + 4 = m$
43. $x - 23 = 7$
44. $46 = t + 19$
45. $h - 13 = 2$
46. $72 + t = 100$
47. $k - 4 = 28$
48. $11 + 22 = r$
49. $33 - y = 17$
50. $q + 15 = 45$
51. $49 - 18 = n$
52. $10 + 8 = 9 + t$
53. $12 - s = 8 + 4$
54. $56 + 49 = 32 + t$
55. $24 + 14 = 46 - m$
56. $3 + h = 4 + 12$
57. $k - 10 = 72 - 47$
58. $21 - 6 = t + 7$
59. $8 + m = 26 - 10$

For use with Section 1-7.

Solve.

1. $r \times 6 = 24$
2. $50 = 25 \times t$
3. $90 = 15 \times m$
4. $\frac{48}{y} = 16$
5. $\frac{56}{r} = 8$
6. $12 \times h = 144$
7. $12 = 4 \times h$
8. $125 = 25 + q$
9. $72 = s \times 12$
10. $\frac{156}{x} = 3$
11. $13 = \frac{169}{r}$
12. $\frac{63}{t} = 9$
13. $k \times 13 = 39$
14. $8 \times h = 88$
15. $12 \times b = 48$
16. $\frac{360}{m} = 60$
17. $24 = \frac{240}{r}$
18. $\frac{425}{k} = 17$
19. $t \times 2 = 666$
20. $8 \times h = 16$
21. $\frac{49}{m} = 7$
22. $4 \times m = 36$
23. $7 \times r = 98$
24. $21 \times s = 84$
25. $\frac{s}{8} = 15$
26. $\frac{55}{r} = 5$
27. $9 = \frac{z}{5}$

For use with Section 3-4.

Write in lowest terms.

28. $\frac{4}{6}$
29. $\frac{10}{50}$
30. $\frac{12}{24}$
31. $\frac{4}{8}$
32. $\frac{16}{24}$
33. $\frac{25}{100}$
34. $\frac{10}{10{,}000}$
35. $\frac{25}{20}$
36. $\frac{8}{12}$
37. $\frac{14}{32}$
38. $\frac{21}{56}$
39. $\frac{12}{16}$
40. $\frac{100}{40}$
41. $\frac{6 \times 3}{42}$
42. $\frac{4 + 3}{35}$
43. $\frac{36}{9}$

Replace the variable to name the equivalent fraction.

44. $\frac{3}{4} = \frac{x}{8}$
45. $\frac{18}{36} = \frac{s}{2}$
46. $\frac{20}{60} = \frac{k}{6}$
47. $\frac{5}{75} = \frac{m}{15}$
48. $\frac{y}{8} = \frac{16}{32}$
49. $\frac{4}{9} = \frac{m}{63}$
50. $\frac{8}{64} = \frac{s}{16}$
51. $\frac{2}{46} = \frac{x}{23}$
52. $\frac{15}{60} = \frac{y}{12}$

For use with Section 3-6.

Write as a decimal.

1. $\frac{1}{2}$	**2.** $\frac{7}{8}$	**3.** $\frac{57}{100}$	**4.** $\frac{1}{5}$
5. $\frac{3}{5}$	**6.** $\frac{3}{3}$	**7.** $\frac{25}{50}$	**8.** $\frac{3}{10}$
9. $\frac{9}{10}$	**10.** $\frac{8}{12}$	**11.** $\frac{5}{8}$	**12.** $\frac{6}{16}$
13. $\frac{4}{25}$	**14.** $\frac{2}{40}$	**15.** $\frac{18}{100}$	**16.** $\frac{16}{60}$

Write as a fraction in lowest terms.

17. 0.2	**18.** 2.6	**19.** 1.8
20. 0.75	**21.** 0.375	**22.** 0.051
23. 2.16	**24.** 0.85	**25.** 3.125
26. 0.15	**27.** 1.01	**28.** 0.90

For use with Section 3-7.

Write as a decimal and as a percent.

29. $\frac{45}{100}$	**30.** $\frac{6}{8}$	**31.** $\frac{3}{10}$	**32.** $\frac{2}{5}$
33. $\frac{12}{12}$	**34.** $\frac{600}{1000}$	**35.** $\frac{2}{16}$	**36.** $\frac{260}{1000}$
37. $\frac{25}{50}$	**38.** $\frac{7}{8}$	**39.** $\frac{6}{10}$	**40.** $\frac{1}{40}$
41. $\frac{8}{25}$	**42.** $\frac{37}{100}$	**43.** $\frac{520}{1000}$	**44.** $\frac{8}{20}$

Write as a fraction in lowest terms.

45. 16%	**46.** 60%	**47.** 24%
48. 80%	**49.** 36%	**50.** 64%
51. 45%	**52.** 72%	**53.** 12%
54. 3%	**55.** 31.5%	**56.** 18%
57. 120%	**58.** 8%	**59.** 64.8%
60. 72.4%	**61.** 420%	**62.** 28.5%

For use with Section 4-1.

Add or subtract. Simplify the result.

1. $\frac{2}{7} + \frac{3}{7}$
2. $\frac{13}{14} - \frac{6}{14}$
3. $\frac{1}{3} + \frac{1}{3}$
4. $\frac{8}{9} - \frac{5}{9}$
5. $\frac{3}{8} + \frac{1}{8} + \frac{2}{8}$
6. $5\frac{3}{4} - \frac{1}{4}$
7. $\frac{7}{12} + \frac{1}{12}$
8. $3\frac{1}{2} - \frac{1}{2}$
9. $\frac{15}{16} - \frac{8}{16}$
10. $4\frac{1}{6} + 1\frac{3}{6}$
11. $9\frac{2}{3} - \frac{1}{3}$
12. $\frac{2}{7} + 5\frac{3}{7}$
13. $5\frac{6}{8} - 4\frac{4}{8}$
14. $6\frac{1}{4} - 6$
15. $3\frac{5}{8} - \frac{5}{8}$

Solve. Simplify the result.

16. $x = \frac{1}{4} + \frac{1}{8}$
17. $t = 2\frac{1}{3} + 3\frac{1}{2}$
18. $\frac{1}{3} + \frac{1}{6} + \frac{1}{6} = h$
19. $4\frac{5}{6} - \frac{1}{3} = h$
20. $\frac{15}{16} - \frac{3}{8} = m$
21. $\frac{5}{7} - \frac{1}{2} = r$
22. $t = \frac{1}{4} + \frac{1}{3}$
23. $h = 6\frac{5}{9} - 4\frac{1}{6}$
24. $s = \frac{5}{6} + \frac{1}{9}$
25. $3\frac{5}{12} + 4\frac{1}{4} = y$
26. $\frac{1}{3} + 1\frac{2}{9} = q$
27. $k = 8\frac{1}{10} - 7\frac{3}{10}$
28. $v = \frac{1}{2} + \frac{4}{9}$
29. $w = 2\frac{3}{7} + 4\frac{1}{3}$
30. $d = \frac{9}{10} - \frac{1}{2}$
31. $1\frac{7}{12} - \frac{1}{4} = m$
32. $\frac{15}{16} - \frac{3}{4} = n$
33. $9\frac{1}{4} - 3\frac{3}{4} = b$

Find the value when $x = 3$, $y = 4$, $z = 2$. Simplify the result.

34. $\frac{1}{x} + \frac{1}{x} + \frac{1}{x}$
35. $\frac{1}{x} - \frac{1}{y}$
36. $\frac{y - x}{z}$
37. $\frac{x}{10} + \frac{z}{10}$
38. $\frac{x + x}{z}$
39. $\frac{2}{x} - \frac{1}{y}$
40. $\frac{y}{7} - \frac{z}{7}$
41. $\frac{z}{x} - \frac{1}{y}$
42. $\frac{y}{5} - \frac{y}{10}$
43. $\frac{x + z}{x + y + z}$
44. $\frac{x}{7} + \frac{1}{z}$
45. $\frac{x}{y} - \frac{z}{x}$

For use with Section 4-2.

Multiply. Simplify the result.

1. $\frac{1}{4} \times \frac{1}{3}$
2. $\frac{2}{3} \times \frac{1}{4}$
3. $\frac{1}{5} \times \frac{5}{6} \times \frac{1}{2}$
4. $2\frac{1}{2} \times 1\frac{1}{3}$
5. $\frac{2}{5} \times \frac{3}{6}$
6. $4\frac{1}{2} \times 2$
7. $\frac{2}{9} \times \frac{3}{9}$
8. $\frac{1}{7} \times \frac{1}{3} \times \frac{2}{3}$
9. $\frac{5}{7} \times \frac{7}{5}$
10. $\frac{3}{4} \times \frac{2}{8}$
11. $1\frac{1}{4} \times 3\frac{1}{5}$
12. $4 \times 2\frac{1}{5}$
13. $\frac{2}{7} \times \frac{1}{2} \times \frac{7}{2}$
14. $\frac{3}{3} \times \frac{4}{9}$
15. $1\frac{3}{8} \times \frac{4}{2}$

Solve. Simplify the result.

16. $x = \frac{1}{2} \div \frac{1}{2}$
17. $y = \frac{3}{4} \div \frac{2}{3}$
18. $a = 1\frac{1}{3} \div 2\frac{1}{6}$
19. $b = \frac{3}{4} \times 4$
20. $d = \frac{4}{5} \div \frac{1}{3}$
21. $2\frac{4}{9} \times 3 = c$
22. $m = 8 \div \frac{1}{2}$
23. $n = \frac{2}{9} \div \frac{2}{9}$
24. $p = 1\frac{3}{8} \times 8$
25. $\frac{3}{8} \div \frac{6}{4} = t$
26. $2\frac{5}{6} \times \frac{2}{4} = s$
27. $k = \frac{4}{3} \div \frac{8}{9}$
28. $h = 3\frac{1}{9} \times \frac{2}{3}$
29. $\frac{5}{8} \div \frac{3}{4} = z$
30. $q = 1\frac{7}{8} \div \frac{3}{16}$
31. $3\frac{5}{6} \times \frac{1}{7} = x$
32. $f = 4\frac{2}{3} \times 1\frac{7}{8}$
33. $\frac{4}{9} \div \frac{8}{3} = m$

Find the value when $s = 1$, $t = 2$, $u = 3$, $v = 5$.

34. $\frac{s}{t} \div \frac{s}{t}$
35. $\frac{t}{u} \times \frac{s}{v}$
36. $\frac{s}{t} \times \frac{t}{u} \times \frac{u}{v}$
37. $\frac{v}{u} \div \frac{u}{t}$
38. $\frac{t}{v} \div v$
39. $\frac{s}{v} \div \frac{t}{v}$
40. $\frac{v}{t} \times \frac{t}{u} \times u$
41. $\frac{v}{s} \times \frac{t}{u}$
42. $\frac{s}{v} \div \frac{u}{t}$
43. $\frac{u}{t} \div t$
44. $\frac{t}{s} \times \frac{u}{v} \times u$
45. $\frac{v}{u} \div \frac{v}{t}$

For use with Section 4-3.

Add or subtract. Estimate to check your work.

1. $1.715 + 2.657$

2. $6.9 - 0.7$

3. $0.01 + 3.328$

4. $23.1 + 0.067 + 9.16$

5. $8.5 - 5.004$

6. $54.08 - 1.76$

7. $3.1 - 0.09$

8. $12.073 + 7.6$

9. $14.96 - 3.002$

10. $200 - 56.8$

11. $18.9 + 6.83$

12. $0.001 + 6.92$

13. $161.02 - 9.88$

14. $27.9 + 30.01 + 0.002$

15. $13.57 - 2.34$

16. $8.997 - 6.899$

Solve.

17. $s = 64.021 - 0.9$

18. $21.7 + 0.02 + 6.89 = t$

19. $115.75 = m + 110.33$

20. $42.006 - k = 21.8$

21. $0.042 - 0.007 = v$

22. $39.62 - 0.07 = h$

For use with Section 4-4.

Solve. Check by estimating the solution.

23. $n = 6.32 \times 0.07$

24. $14.04 \div 12 = s$

25. $63.57 \div 3 = t$

26. $0.506 \times 27.2 = b$

27. $54.02 \times 0.008 = v$

28. $0.168 \div 4 = m$

29. $\frac{1.56}{6} = x$

30. $\frac{14.078}{2} = y$

31. $14.375 \div 5 = k$

32. $74.058 \times 0.03 = p$

Solve.

33. $\$23.96 \times 7 = m$

34. $s = 0.032 \times 14.82$

35. $\$19.05 \div 3 = k$

36. $22\% \times 89 = q$

37. $w = 0.8 \times 17.1 \times 0.02$

38. $48.72 \times 100 = t$

39. $\frac{22.5}{15} = b$

40. $\frac{\$10.24}{8} = r$

For use with Section 4-5.

Simplify.

1. $(5 + 7)(2 + 6)$
2. $[(10 + 4)(2)] \div 7$
3. $(0.01 \times 15.6) \div 3$
4. $15 \div (5 \times 3 \times 10)$
5. $23 + (10.7 - 0.09)$
6. $(144 \div 12) + 13$
7. $(\frac{1}{3} + \frac{1}{6})12$
8. $(1\frac{3}{4} - \frac{1}{2}) + \frac{2}{3}$
9. $[(6)(9)] \div 18$
10. $(12.05 - 8.167) + 0.05$

Solve.

11. $m = 5^2(7 + 3)$
12. $[(15 + 20) \div 5] + 6 \cdot 2^2 = x$
13. $\left(\frac{1}{8} + \frac{3}{4}\right) \div \frac{3}{16} = s$
14. $\frac{(5 + 6 + 10.7)10}{7} = b$
15. $(8 \times 9) + 14.382 = c$
16. $r = 8[9 - (5 + 1 + 2)]$
17. $(12.032 - 0.08) + 1.7 = p$
18. $t = (4^2 + 4.48) - 9.03$
19. $b = (4 \times 3 \times 4) \div 6$
20. $(121 \div 11) + (6.2)(7) = n$

For use with Section 5-2.

Make a table to find the solution set. Use the given replacement set.

21. $4m + (56 \div 7) = 4^2 \quad \{1, 2, 3\}$
22. $6 - k = 24 \div 8 \quad \{3, 5, 7\}$
23. $5.8 + s = 14.23 - 7.15 \quad \{1.28, 6.0, 10\}$
24. $3(t + 9) = 6 \times 7 \quad \{0, 4, 5\}$
25. $\frac{(9 \times 4) - 4}{h} = 2^3 \quad \{2, 4, 6\}$
26. $(18 - 12)5 = b \div 2 \quad \{1, 15, 60\}$
27. $4x = 2 \quad \left\{0, \frac{1}{2}, 1, 2\right\}$
28. $w(4 + 3) = 5w + (100 \div 10) \quad \left\{\frac{1}{4}, 5, 7, 10\right\}$
29. $v^3 - 1 = 13 - 6 \quad \{2, 3, 4\}$
30. $\left(\frac{3}{8} - \frac{1}{4}\right)(8) = \frac{k}{k} \quad \{5, 8\}$
31. $3d + d + 4d = 64 \div 2 \quad \{1.5, 2, 4\}$
32. $(0 \cdot p) + 5 = p - 12 \quad \{3, 6, 7.4, 17\}$

For use with Section 5-3.

Add or subtract the given number to or from both members. Simplify the result.

1. $16 - 8 = 2 + 6$; add 3
2. $10.5 = 4.6 + 5.9$; subtract 0.2
3. $\frac{14.82}{2} = 3 \times 2.47$; subtract 2.39
4. $5 + 8 = 6 + 7$; subtract 0
5. $6 + 8 = 2 \times 7$; subtract 12
6. $14 - 5 = 3 \times 3$; add 3
7. $8 - 7 = 36 \div 36$; add 0.5

Add or subtract. Simplify the result.

8. $k + 8$; subtract 8
9. $15 + m$; subtract 15
10. $t - 5.4$; add 5.4
11. $s - 8.62$; add 8.62
12. $r + 20$; subtract 20
13. $h - 9.2$ add 9.2

For use with Section 5-4.

Multiply or divide both members. Simplify the result.

14. $5 + 3 = 8$; divide by 4
15. $28 = 4 \cdot 7$; divide by 14
16. $24 = 4 \cdot 6$; divide by 3
17. $25 \cdot 2 = 5 \cdot 10$; multiply by 2
18. $10 = 7 + 3$; multiply by 4
19. $3^2 = 9$; multiply by 5
20. $\frac{15}{3} = \frac{25}{5}$; multiply by 6
21. $7 \cdot 8 = 28 \cdot 2$; multiply by $\frac{1}{2}$
22. $4^2 = 32 \div 2$; multiply by 3
23. $11 + 9 = 4 \cdot 5$; divide by 10

To solve, multiply or divide as indicated.

24. $9t = 72$; divide by 9
25. $s \cdot 7 = 63$; divide by 7
26. $\frac{1}{4} \cdot x = 48.6$; multiply by 4
27. $6 = \frac{m}{6}$; multiply by 6
28. $144 = 12k$; divide by 12
29. $n \cdot 8 = 48$; divide by 8
30. $\frac{n}{10} = 12$; multiply by 10
31. $\frac{a}{2} = 64$; multiply by 2
32. $169 = p \cdot 13$; divide by 13
33. $150 = 25c$; divide by 25

For use with Section 5-6.

Solve.

1. A rectangle has width 6.2 cm and length 3.8 cm. Find the area.

2. The diameter of a circle is 14 m. Find the circumference.

3. Find the area of a square whose side measures 14 cm.

4. The lengths of the sides of a triangle are 2.2 m, 0.3 m, and 5.25 m. Find the perimeter.

5. A circle has radius 7 mm. Find the area.

6. A triangle has a base of length 24 cm and height 10 cm. Find the area.

7. A square has a side of length 6.04 m. Find the perimeter.

8. A rectangle has length 9.72 m and width 4.6 m. Find the perimeter.

9. A circle has radius 38.5 cm. Find the circumference.

10. The perimeter of a square is 128 mm. Find the length of each side.

11. A rectangle has length 0.5 m and width 0.4 m. Find the area.

12. A triangle has a base of 0.52 m and a height of 1.5 m. Find the area.

13. The circumference of a circle is 198 cm. Find the diameter.

14. The length of a rectangle is 3.2 m and the width is 1.15 m. Find the perimeter.

15. If the area of a square is 169 cm^2, what is the length of its side?

16. The diameter of a circle is 14 cm. Find the area.

17. The perimeter of a triangle is 90 mm. All three sides are the same length. Find the length of each side.

18. A triangle has base 8 m and height 8 m. What is the area of the triangle?

For use with Section 5-7.

For each member of the replacement set, show whether a true or a false statement results when the variable in the sentence is replaced by the number.

1. $4m < 18$; $\{0, 1, 3, 5\}$

2. $72 \div t > 9$, $\{1, 8, 12\}$

3. $6b - 10 > 3$; $\{2, 4, 7\}$

4. $s^2 > 2s$; $\{1, 2, 3, 4\}$

5. $16 < (x + 8)(0.5)$; $\{4, 8, 30\}$

6. $24.65 - r < 10$; $\{4.65, 14, 20.23\}$

7. $(5 + 3) - n > 2$; $\{0, 4, 7, 8\}$

8. $9 < 6 + b$; $\{0, 2, 6, 30\}$

9. $10k > 5$; $\left\{0, \frac{1}{2}, \frac{1}{5}, 2\right\}$

10. $3 < 18c$; $\left\{\frac{1}{3}, \frac{1}{2}, \frac{1}{9}, \frac{1}{12}\right\}$

For use with Section 5-8.

For each member of the replacement set, show whether a true or a false statement results when the variable is replaced by the number.

11. $k + 8 \geq 12$; $\{2, 4, 6\}$

12. $3p \geq 22$; $\{5, 7, 8, 10\}$

13. $s \leq 16.5$; $\{7, 16, 17\}$

14. $^-7 \leq c$; $\{^-9, ^-7, 0, 1\}$

15. $6r \geq 42$; $\{2, 7, 10, 12\}$

16. $4(8 - n) \neq 32$; $\{0, 2, 5\}$

17. $(27 - k) + 1 \leq 20$; $\{0, 7, 8, 10\}$

18. $y + 14 \leq 36$; $\{10, 22, 30\}$

19. $50h \geq 25$; $\left\{0, \frac{1}{5}, \frac{1}{2}, \frac{4}{5}\right\}$

20. $12 \leq 10 + d$; $\{\frac{1}{2}, 1\frac{1}{2}, 2, 2\frac{1}{2}\}$

For use with Section 7-1.

Combine similar terms to simplify.

21. $15r + 9r$

22. $22t - 10t + 8t$

23. $2(7 - 6m)$

24. $a + b + 2a + 3b$

25. $10vw + 4(vw + 7)$

26. $(9 + 3)(5k - 2)$

27. $(s + 5s) - 2s$

28. $16xy + 7x - 2y - 8xy + 2y$

29. $3(x + 2) + 2(2 + x)$

30. $120 + 80 + 10m - 200 - 10m$

31. $7(a + 3 + 2c) + 6(2c + 1)$

32. $4(4b + b) - b$

33. $14p + 2p - 8p$

34. $28r - 16r - 8r$

35. $6z + 6y + 8y - 3z$

36. $10k + m - 6k + 2 + 3m$

37. $48qr - 3st - 12qr + 5st$

38. $5(6q + 7f) + 2f(6 + 1)$

39. $(7w + 2)8 + (6 + 4w)3$

40. $12a + 3b - 8a + 7b - 6$

41. $f + 2f + g + 5f - g$

42. $4(36c + 10d) - 11d - 46c$

For use with Section 7-2.

Solve. Begin by stating what number should be added to or subtracted from both members.

1. $m + 7 = 15$

2. $0.5 + t = 1.5$

3. $s - 4 = 16$

4. $p - 13 = 23$

5. $\frac{7}{8} = x - 1$

6. $a - \frac{2}{3} = 2$

7. $\frac{4}{7} = k + \frac{2}{7}$

8. $\frac{5}{9} = b - \frac{1}{9}$

Solve and check.

9. $q - 10.5 = 6.4$

10. $17 - m = 9$

11. $14 + k = 43$

12. $23.65 - p = 18.31$

13. $s + 115 = 694$

14. $r + 67 = 81$

15. $96 - d = 42$

16. $w - 18.6 = 2.5$

17. $39 = n + 13$

18. $6.05 = x - 2.38$

For use with Sections 7-3 and 7-4.

Solve. Check your answer.

19. $6r = 30$

20. $0.4t = 1.2$

21. $3q = 42$

22. $\frac{1}{3} = 2m$

23. $\frac{n}{2} = 16$

24. $8t = \frac{8}{9}$

25. $\frac{15y}{3} = 0.25$

26. $7r = 49$

27. $\frac{5b}{6} = 10$

28. $\frac{c}{3} = 5 + 1$

29. $\frac{3}{8}g = \frac{6}{4}$

30. $7 + 2x = 55$

31. $9c - 8 = 46$

32. $\frac{t}{8} = 7$

33. $\frac{k}{100} = 0.05$

34. $\frac{w}{18} = 2$

35. $6v - 13.2 = 11.4$

36. $\frac{4a}{5} = 16$

37. $\frac{f}{81} = 1$

38. $\frac{3}{4}t = \frac{7}{16}$

39. $2.1 + 4x = 3.7$

40. $11z = 121$

41. $8e \div 4 = 4.8$

42. $5j + 21 = 86$

43. $\frac{g}{12} = 168$

44. $\frac{2}{5}h = \frac{16}{25}$

45. $\frac{k}{1.05} = 4.8$

For use with Sections 7-5, 7-6, 7-7.

Write and solve an equation to answer the question.

1. The sum of five times a number and 8 is 38. What is the number?
2. If twelve times a number is decreased by 16, the result is equal to 20. Find the number.
3. If 1.56 is added to four times a number, the result is equal to 3.64. Find the number.
4. The sum of a whole number and a number 3 greater than the first is 19. Find the two numbers.
5. Brandon is 7 cm shorter than Teresa. The sum of their heights is 337 cm. How tall is each person?
6. If half a number is increased by 17, the result is 26. Find the number.
7. Jon worked 1 more hour on his project than Mia. Together they worked 8 hours. How long did each person work?
8. Soap A costs 23¢ more than Soap B. Soap A costs 89¢. How much does Soap B cost?
9. The sum of three consecutive even numbers is 30. What are the three numbers?
10. Vincent has scored 5 more goals than Orlando. Together they have scored 13 goals. How many goals has Vincent scored?
11. April worked 15 more hours this week than last. She worked 27 hours last week. How many hours did she work this week?
12. Two jugs hold a total of 4.8 liters. The large jug holds twice as much as the small jug. How much does each jug hold?
13. A scientist had 9 clean test tubes at the end of an experiment. This was three-fourths of the original number of test tubes. How many test tubes were used?
14. If a number is increased by 27, the result is the same as four times the number. Find the number.
15. The length of a rectangle is 1 cm more than four times the width. The perimeter is 42 cm. Find the length and width.
16. Eight times a number, decreased by four, is the same as 2.5 times the same number increased by 12.5. Find the number.
17. Angela has three more dimes than quarters. She has 27 coins in all. How many dimes does she have?
18. The sum of an even number and the next two consecutive odd numbers is 64. Find the numbers.

For use with Section 9-3.

Solve.

1. $-10 = 2 + t$
2. $m = -(-8 + 37)$
3. $q + 8 = -14$
4. $-7 + (-9) = r$
5. $-[12 + (15 - 2)] = a$
6. $4 + (-3) = s$
7. $11 = 7 + w$
8. $-(15 + 20) = b$
9. $y = -\frac{1}{3} + \frac{1}{4}$
10. $1\frac{1}{2} + (-3\frac{1}{2}) = f$
11. $-3 = k + 10$
12. $-[24 + (-12)] = h$
13. $14 = x + 8.75$
14. $-27 = -5 + u$

For use with Section 9-4.
Simplify.

15. $-10 + 6 + (-17) + 2$
16. $7 + (-3) + (-4) + 7$
17. $3\frac{3}{8} + 2\frac{1}{4} + (-2\frac{1}{4})$
18. $-4\frac{2}{5} + 9\frac{1}{5} + (-9\frac{1}{5})$
19. $27 + (-27) + 3$
20. $-36 + 14 + 7 + (-14) + (-7)$
21. $56 + (-10) + 2 + (-56)$
22. $-12 + 6 + 8 + (-6)$
23. $-11 + (-6) + 24$
24. $5 + 2\frac{7}{9} + (-5) + (-2\frac{7}{9})$

For use with Section 9-5.
Solve.

25. $17 - (-2) = m$
26. $p = 4 - (-14)$
27. $1 - 13 = x$
28. $8 - 9 = k$
29. $6 - (-6) = s$
30. $36 - 27 = r$
31. $38 - 40 = w$
32. $1\frac{3}{4} - (-1\frac{1}{4}) = a$
33. $15 - (-18) = v$
34. $-0.45 - (-0.15) = b$
35. $21 - (-7) = c$
36. $f = 9.4 - (-1.5)$
37. $96 - 13 = k$
38. $c = 25 + (-18)$
39. $7 - 16 = q$
40. $x = 21 - 30$
41. $1\frac{1}{3} - (-\frac{1}{3}) = a$
42. $b = 100 + (-50)$
43. $g = 16 - (-32)$
44. $48 + (-12) = h$
45. $14 - 6 = j$
46. $38 - 56 = s$
47. $61.7 - (-2.3) = w$
48. $x = 17 + (-30)$
49. $-1.65 - (-3.86) = h$
50. $26 - 49 = r$

For use with Section 10-1.

Solve.

1. $(-6 \cdot 3) + (-3 \cdot 6) = x$
2. $8(-6) = p$
3. $-9 \cdot 6 = z$
4. $s = (11)(12)$
5. $a = -0.165(3)$
6. $-155 \cdot 0 = b$
7. $-16 \cdot \frac{7}{8} = f$
8. $-\frac{1}{2} \cdot 50 = g$
9. $h + 3(-4) = 12$
10. $(-5 \cdot 7) + y = 5$
11. $(-5.2)(4) + 1.2 = w$
12. $(-9 \cdot 3) + (-3) = k$
13. $\left(-\frac{4}{5}\right)\left(\frac{15}{4}\right) = d$
14. $\left(\frac{1}{7}\right)\left(-\frac{5}{3}\right) = e$
15. $-2(0.985) = j$
16. $r = (14.83)(1)$
17. $(6 \cdot 0) + 1.05 = n$
18. $27 + (-9 \cdot 2) = m$
19. $\left(\frac{2}{3}\right)(-4) = b$
20. $\left(-\frac{3}{4}\right)\left(\frac{2}{7}\right) = q$
21. $r = (-1)(27)$
22. $-7 \cdot 8 = c$
23. $5(-3) + 3(-2) = a$
24. $f = (-0.54)(3)$

For use with Section 10-3.

Tell whether the expression represented is positive, negative, or zero. Then simplify.

25. $-3 \cdot 2 \cdot 5$
26. $-10 \cdot 1(-6)$
27. $(-4)^2$
28. $-8(-2)(-1)$
29. $0 \cdot 7(-9)$
30. $(-3)^3$
31. $\left(-\frac{1}{2}\right)\left(-\frac{1}{2}\right)\left(\frac{1}{4}\right)$
32. $\frac{2}{3} \cdot \frac{1}{2}(-1)$
33. $\left(-\frac{2}{5}\right)\left(-\frac{1}{7}\right)\left(-\frac{2}{3}\right)$
34. $(-1.5)(-2)(3)$
35. $(-3)(-5)^2$
36. $(2.6)(0.5)(4)$
37. $(4)(-3)(9)$
38. $-7 \cdot 3(-8)$
39. $(-2)6 \cdot 0$

Evaluate. Let $k = -2$, $h = -3$, $m = -1$, $n = 4$, $p = 2$.

40. $k \cdot h \cdot m$
41. $(-n)(-4)$
42. $(-3)h - p$
43. $kn + mp$
44. $(-p) + np$
45. $(k)(-n)(-1)$
46. $\frac{n}{p} + (-n)$
47. $\frac{1}{n}(h)$
48. $\frac{k}{n}(p)$
49. $4 \cdot k \cdot n \cdot p$
50. $h \cdot k + m$
51. $mn \cdot 0$

For use with Section 10-4.

Simplify by combining similar terms.

1. $7x + 3(-2x - 4y)$
2. $3m^2 + m + (-m^2)$
3. $12ab - 4c + (-10ab)$
4. $(5f - 10g)2 + 20g + (-10f)$
5. $\left(\frac{2}{3}m + \frac{2}{5}p\right)15 - (-8m)$
6. $\frac{1}{2}(k + 4h) + (-h)$
7. $6w + (-7u) - 3 + 4u - 2w$
8. $10(pq + 6) - 7pq - 30$
9. $18d + [-12(d - 2)]$
10. $-2s + 7t - 4t + 8s$
11. $3r^2 + 11 + (r \cdot r) - 7$
12. $9mn - n + 3m - 2mn + n$
13. $\frac{7}{8}h - \frac{5}{7}j + \left(-\frac{3}{8}h\right) + \frac{4}{7}j$
14. $\frac{3}{4}(8a + c) + (-3a) + \frac{1}{4}c$
15. $2.5d - 6f + (-0.5d) + 10f$
16. $16x - 10y + 20x + 5y$
17. $-7w + 4(-3w + 6)$
18. $9e^2 + (-e^2) + 15$
19. $\frac{3}{2}(a + b) - \frac{a}{2} + 2\frac{1}{2}b$
20. $\frac{3}{4}s + \frac{5}{6}p - \frac{1}{4}s + \left(-\frac{4}{6}p\right)$

For use with Section 10-5.

Simplify.

21. $-64 \div 8$
22. $-8\overline{)72}$
23. $-32 \div 2$
24. $-12\overline{)132}$
25. $-100 \div 5$
26. $-9\overline{)36}$
27. $\frac{-24}{-8 + 2}$
28. $\frac{35}{-7}$
29. $\frac{-8 + (-7)}{3}$
30. $\frac{-56}{-8}$
31. $\frac{-70}{-1 + (-9)}$
32. $\frac{-40 + (-4)}{16 + (-5)}$

For use with Section 10-6.

Simplify. Use reciprocals.

33. $\frac{-3}{4} \div \frac{1}{8}$
34. $6 \div \frac{1}{-5}$
35. $\frac{2}{3} \div \frac{-8}{9}$
36. $\frac{4}{-7} \div \frac{8}{14}$
37. $\frac{5}{6} \div \frac{-1}{2}$
38. $-28 \div \frac{7}{4}$
39. $\frac{3}{-8} \div \frac{1}{4}$
40. $-36 \div \frac{12}{3}$
41. $\frac{-1}{2} \div \frac{1}{4}$
42. $\frac{-5}{3} \div \frac{1}{6}$
43. $\frac{2}{5} \div \frac{-1}{10}$
44. $-81 \div \frac{9}{2}$

For use with Section 11-1.

Solve and check.

1. $m + 7 = 12$
2. $-56 = u + 7$
3. $-2 - b = 15$
4. $z + (-15) = 24$
5. $-\frac{5}{8} + t = \frac{3}{8}$
6. $c + \frac{3}{5} = -4$
7. $-18 = a + (-14)$
8. $-d - 3.5 = 4.2$
9. $y - \frac{3}{2} = -1$
10. $-f + (-2\frac{3}{8}) = \frac{5}{8}$
11. $g + 3.76 = 5.02$
12. $-15.7 + k = 32.9$
13. $-45 + (-t) = 10$
14. $-87 - e = 6$

For use with Section 11-2.

Solve and check.

15. $9a = 81$
16. $38 = 2b$
17. $-\frac{2}{3}t = -12$
18. $\frac{1}{4}m = -16$
19. $7c = 42.63$
20. $s(-8) = -96$
21. $4k = -11$
22. $-14h = 15.4$
23. $\frac{-5}{8}u = -10$
24. $-16 = \frac{2}{5}w$
25. $36 = 18p$
26. $-48 = 6q$
27. $54.6 = 6f$
28. $g(-7) = 21$

For use with Section 11-3.

Solve and check.

29. $5x + 6x = 121$
30. $16c = 14c + 8$
31. $-4 - (-2m) = -10m$
32. $26a - 11a = -3a + 54$
33. $\frac{2}{3}f + \frac{4}{3}f = -18$
34. $-\frac{4}{5}r + 6 = -\frac{1}{5}r + 4$
35. $6.42s + 3.58s = 160$
36. $7w = -81 - 2w$
37. $\frac{3}{7}(-h) + \left(-\frac{2}{7}\right)h = 15$
38. $-\frac{8}{3} = \frac{1}{3}c + \left(-\frac{5}{3}\right)c$
39. $2d + 4d = 48$
40. $-225 = -42v - 33v$

For use with Section 11-4.

Solve. Use the formula $V = lwh$ (Volume = length × width × height).

1. The volume of a box is 10.5 m^3. The length is 3.5 m and the width is 2 m. Find the height.
2. The dimensions of a carton are as follows: length, 0.75 m; width, 0.5 m; height, 1.5 m. Find the volume.

Solve. Use the formula $I = prt$ (Interest = principal × rate × time).

3. A bank made a two year loan of $1400 at 7% interest to a small business firm. How much interest did the company pay?
4. A couple borrowed money at the rate of 8% for a period of 3 years. The interest charged was $480. What was the amount (principal) of the loan?
5. Randy borrowed $4000 from a local bank. The interest rate was 7.5%. He paid $450 interest. How long did he keep the loan?
6. Gloria borrowed $1560 from the bank for a period of 10 months ($\frac{5}{6}$ year). She paid $117 in interest. What was the rate of interest?

Solve. Use the formula $V = \frac{1}{3}Bh$ (Volume = $\frac{1}{3}$ × area of base × height).

7. The area of the base of a triangular pyramid is 72 cm^2. The height is 14 cm. Find the volume.
8. If the volume of a triangular pyramid is 400 cm^3 and the height is 20 cm, find the area of the base.

Solve. Use the formula $A = lw$ (Area = length × width).

9. The dimensions of a rectangle are as follows: length, 24.5 m and width, 20.6 m. What is the area?
10. A florist wants a garden to cover an area of 192 m^2. The length of the plot is 16 m. Find the width.
11. The length of a frame on a filmstrip is 1.8 cm and the width is 1.5 cm. Find the area of the frame.

Solve. Use the formula Area = $\frac{1}{2}$ × altitude × sum of bases, $A = \frac{1}{2}as$.

12. The measure of the two bases of a trapezoid are 15.3 m and 16.7 m. If the altitude equals 14 m, what is the area?
13. The area of a trapezoid is 86 cm^2. The sum of the two bases is 43 cm. Find the altitude.

For use with Section 12-4.

Add.

1. $\begin{array}{r} 5s + 11 \\ 6s + 5 \\ \hline \end{array}$

2. $\begin{array}{r} 4r^2 + 2m^2 + p^2 \\ 3r^2 - m^2 + 5p^2 \\ \hline \end{array}$

3. $\begin{array}{r} 9x^2 \qquad + 14 \\ 23z - 10 \\ \hline \end{array}$

4. $\begin{array}{r} -7f + 4b - 24 \\ -8f - 3b + 36 \\ \hline \end{array}$

5. $\begin{array}{r} h^3 + 14k^2 - 13 \\ -3h^3 - 2k^2 + 5 \\ \hline \end{array}$

6. $\begin{array}{r} y^3 - z^2 + w - 17 \\ -y^3 + z^2 - w + 17 \\ \hline \end{array}$

7. $\begin{array}{r} 8a + 9c \\ -6a - 7c \\ \hline \end{array}$

8. $\begin{array}{r} -10d - 4e + 6 \\ 3d + 7e - 10 \\ \hline \end{array}$

9. $\begin{array}{r} 8.9y + 1.5x + 2.3 \\ -0.4y - 7.2x + 4.8 \\ \hline \end{array}$

For use with Section 12-7.

Subtract. Check by addition.

10. $\begin{array}{r} 20m + 15n \\ 6m + 9n \\ \hline \end{array}$

11. $\begin{array}{r} -2s^2 + 7s - 19 \\ -5s^2 + 3s - 17 \\ \hline \end{array}$

12. $\begin{array}{r} 16r + 5t - 9 \\ 8r - t + 11 \\ \hline \end{array}$

13. $\begin{array}{r} 3f + 2q^2 \\ -5f + 8q^2 \\ \hline \end{array}$

14. $\begin{array}{r} 4 + e \\ 9 - 2e \\ \hline \end{array}$

15. $\begin{array}{r} -25p + 15q^2 \\ + 8q^2 \\ \hline \end{array}$

16. $\begin{array}{r} -7k + 12j - 6 \\ -4k - 3j + 18 \\ \hline \end{array}$

17. $\begin{array}{r} + w^2 - 18 \\ -40t \qquad + 9 \\ \hline \end{array}$

18. $\begin{array}{r} 6x^3 + z^2 \qquad \\ - x^3 \qquad + 14 \\ \hline \end{array}$

For use with Section 12-8.

Write the answer as a polynomial in standard form.

19. The length of a rectangular pool is $8 - 6p$ and the width is $3 + 2p$. Find the perimeter of the pool.

20. A truck driver drove a distance of $3x^2 + x - 9$. Then he realized he has passed his stop. He retraced a distance of $x^2 - 2x + 8$. What was the actual distance from the beginning point to his destination?

21. A plumber has a length of tubing measuring $7a - 2b + c$. She only needs a piece $-4a + 3b + c$ long. How much should she cut off?

22. A real estate agent purchased two pieces of property. The first had an area of $10w^3 - 14$ and the second an area of $w^3 + 4w^2 + 6w$. Find the combined area.

23. A sports car was using gasoline at the rate of $-2f + 14$ before a tune-up and $12f - 5$ after the tune-up. By how much did the gasoline usage improve?

For use with Section 12-9.

Solve. Check your solution.

1. $48 = (2t + 8) + (4t - 2)$
2. $r + (r - 7) + 5r + 3 = 31$
3. $-(10m + 8) + 14m = 32$
4. $-72 = -q + 3(-1 + 2q) + 1$
5. $x^2 + 6 - (9x + x^2) = -12$
6. $0.4y + 2(10 - 1.3y) = 64$
7. $(3f + 7) - (19 + f) = 0$
8. $50 = (4g - 27) + 2 + 21g$
9. $a - (9 + a) + (3a - 6) = 9$
10. $-(8 + 20b) + 4 = 12(b - 1)$
11. $3(k - 2) - (8 - k) = 14$
12. $-7n + 13 + 2(n - 2) = -16$
13. $-4c - (7 + 2c) = 35 + c$
14. $(8d + 52) - (6d + 8) = 68 - 4d$
15. $2.3 - 9(0.9 + f) = 0.6 - f$
16. $25 = 3p - (8p + 5)$
17. $(x - 5) - (8x + 6) = x + 21$
18. $3r + 4(5 - 2r) = 2r - 1$
19. $17w + 6(8 - 3w) = 2w$
20. $-1.1 + 2(j + 6) = 8.9$

For use with Sections 13-1, 13-2, 13-3.

Simplify.

21. $(x + 3)(x + 3)(x + 3)$
22. $(12 \cdot 6)(b \cdot b)$
23. $-7(14)(z \cdot z \cdot z \cdot z \cdot z)$
24. $s \cdot s(-s) \cdot s(-s)$
25. $3(f \cdot f \cdot f)$
26. $4(-12)(w^2)(w^4)$
27. $b^4 \cdot b \cdot b^3$
28. $(12 \cdot 11)(c - 2)(c - 2)$
29. $(8 \cdot 9)(p \cdot p \cdot 2p)$
30. $2^3 \cdot 2^2 \cdot 2$
31. $(14xyz)(xy)$
32. $(m \cdot m)(m \cdot m \cdot m)$
33. $2(j \cdot j \cdot j)(-3)$
34. $(h^3)(h^2)(-5)$
35. $7(-8y)$
36. $c(d \cdot d^2)(e^3 \cdot e^3)$
37. $(4f \cdot f)(g^2)(g \cdot g^3)$
38. $(0.7qr)(-0.7q^2r^3)$
39. $(-st)(8s^2t^2)(s^3)$
40. $(u^3v)(-4uv^3)(8c)$
41. $(-36i)(2h^2i)(h^3i^4)$
42. $(2.5k^2m)(-0.5km^3)$
43. $\left(\frac{2}{3}pr\right)\left(\frac{1}{7}pr\right)$
44. $\left(\frac{3}{4}x^2yz^3\right)\left(\frac{1}{6}xy^2z\right)$
45. $(4st)^3$
46. $(3f^2g)^4$
47. $(-ab)(6a^2b^5)(-3ac)$
48. $(-5j^3k^2)^3$
49. $(-cd)\left(\frac{1}{3}d^2\right)\left(\frac{5}{2}c^3d^3\right)$
50. $\left(\frac{1}{8}mn^2p^3\right)\left(-\frac{3}{5}m^3np^2\right)$
51. $(e^4)^5$
52. $(7ab)^2 + (2a^3b)(9ab^2)$
53. $c(c^3d^2)^4 + 5(cd)^3$
54. $n^2(m^3n^4) + (mn^2)^3$

For use with Sections 13-4, 13-5.

Simplify.

1. $f(e - f) + 6f(e + f)$
2. $7ab(a + 2b) - 3a(b^2 + 2ab)$
3. $20mn^2(2 + 5m^2n^3 - 6m^3n^5)$
4. $1.6(s^2t - st^3) + s^2(2.4t + t^3)$
5. $-uv\left(\frac{3}{4}u^2 + \frac{1}{5}v\right) + \frac{1}{5}u\left(v^2 + \frac{5}{4}u^2v\right)$
6. $\frac{3}{8}j(2j + 3k) + \frac{1}{4}(-j^2 + k)$
7. $6cd(c^2d + 10) - cd(4 + 2c^2d)$
8. $(xy + 5x)8 - 9x(2xy - 7)$

Multiply. Use either the vertical or horizontal form.

9. $(a + b)(a + b)$
10. $(x + 4)(x - 4)$
11. $(4 + 7n)(3 + 6n)$
12. $(q - r)(2q^2 + qr + r^2)$
13. $(1.2t + 2)(7.4 - 3t)$
14. $(6c + 5)(3c + 8)$
15. $(5f + 9)(5f - 9)$
16. $(d - 1)(2d^2 + d + 4)$

For use with Sections 13-6, 13-8.

Multiply.

17. $(f + 6)^2$
18. $(4q + 7)(4q - 7)$
19. $(eg + eh)^2$
20. $(2uv + 16)(2uv - 16)$
21. $\left(9s + \frac{2}{5}t\right)\left(9s - \frac{2}{5}t\right)$
22. $\left(\frac{1}{2}w + \frac{2}{3}\right)^2$
23. $(z + 3y)^2$
24. $(8b - 6c)^2$
25. $(6 - 2j)(6 + 2j)$
26. $(11ab - cd)(11ab + cd)$

Simplify. Assume no denominator is 0.

27. $\frac{t^5}{t^3}$
28. $\frac{24a^5b^3}{12a^2b}$
29. $\frac{-25m^6}{75m^7}$
30. $\frac{-q^3r^7}{q^5r^4}$
31. $\frac{64x^2y^7z^3}{(-2xyz)^3}$
32. $\frac{0.3kh^4}{1.2k^3h^2j}$
33. $\frac{(-4e^3f^2g)^3}{8e^{10}f^4g}$
34. $\frac{(uv)^5}{u^3v^2}$
35. $\frac{-8a^7b^9c}{56a^2b^5}$
36. $\frac{(6z)^2w^5y^3}{(4w)^3zy}$
37. $\frac{1.44s^4r^3t^5}{1.2sr^5t^3}$
38. $\frac{(5d^2e^3f)^2}{30d^2f^4}$
39. $\frac{(2ij^2)^3}{(-8i^3j)^2}$
40. $\frac{19p^3r^5t^7}{-38p^5r^2t^4}$
41. $\frac{21x^{10}}{14x^6}$

Glossary

absolute value (p. 261). The distance from 0 of a number on the number line. The absolute value of any directed number is always a positive number or zero.
addition property of equality (p. 186). For every number r, every number s, and every number t, if $r = s$, then $r + t = s + t$.
addition property of inequality (p. 305). For all directed numbers r, s, and t, if $r < s$, then $r + t < s + t$; if $r > s$, then $r + t > s + t$.
additive identity element (p. 173). Zero. When you add 0 to any number, the sum is the number that was added to 0.
additive inverse (p. 241). The opposite of a number. *See also* opposite.
additive property of 0 (p. 173). For every number r, $r + 0 = 0 + r = r$.
associative property of addition (p. 162). For every number r, every number s, and every number t, $r + (s + t) = (r + s) + t$.
associative property of multiplication (p. 163). For every number r, every number s, and every number t, $r(st) = (rs)t$.

base (p. 346). A repeating factor in a multiplication expression. For example, in 7^4, 4 is the exponent and 7 is the base.
binomial (p. 316). A polynomial expression having two terms.

centimeter (p. 78). A metric unit of length, 0.01 of a meter.
closure property (p. 157). A set of numbers is closed under an operation if performing the operation on any two numbers of the set results in a member of the set.
coefficient (p. 106). Any factor of an expression can be called the coefficient of the remaining factors.
common factor (p. 59). A number which is a factor of two or more numbers.
common multiple (p. 56). A number which is a multiple of two or more numbers.
commutative property of addition (p. 162). For every number r and every number s, $r + s = s + r$
commutative property of multiplication (p. 162). For every number r and every number s, $r \cdot s = s \cdot r$
complete factorization (p. 384). An expression in which none of the factors can be factored any further.
composite (p. 382). A number which can be expressed as the product of two or more prime numbers.
congruent figures (p. 27). Figures having exactly the same size and shape.
coordinate (p. 31). The number matched with a point on the number line.
coordinate axes (p. 47). Two perpendicular number lines used to graph ordered pairs.
coordinates (p. 47). The numbers in an ordered pair.
counting numbers (p. 56). The numbers 1, 2, 3, 4, 5, 6, 7, and so on.

degree of a polynomial in one variable (p. 318). The greatest exponent of the polynomial.
directed numbers (p. 212). The positive numbers, the negative numbers, and 0.
distributive property (p. 166, 169). For every number r, every number s, and every number t:
1. $r(s + t) = rs + rt$ and $(s + t)r = sr + tr$
2. $r(s - t) = rs - rt$ and $(s - t)r = sr - tr$

division property of equality (p. 189). For every number r, every number s, and every number t except 0, if $r = s$ then $\frac{r}{t} = \frac{s}{t}$.

empty set (p. 30). The set with no members. $\emptyset$

equation (p. 5). A number sentence that consists of two expressions joined by the "is equal to" symbol, $=$.

equivalent equations (p. 250). Equations having the same solution set.

equivalent fractions (p. 65). Fractions that name the same number.

even numbers (p. 62). The numbers in $\{0, 2, 4, 6, 8, 10, 12, \ldots\}$. Numbers that can be expressed in the form $2 \times n$, where n is a whole number.

expand (p. 360). To find the product of the factors of an expression.

exponent (p. 346). The number of times a base is used as a factor. For example, in m^3, m is the base and 3 is the exponent.

exponential notation (p. 312). A simplified way of writing a number with repeating factors. For example, $3 \times 3 \times 3 \times 3 = 3^4$ in exponential notation. 3 is the base, 4 is the exponent.

factorization (p. 106). An indicated multiplication. For example, $2 \cdot 5$ is a factorization of 10.

factors (p. 106). Two or more numbers that are multiplied to name a product.

first coordinate (p. 47). The first number in an ordered pair.

formulas (p. 137). Equations used to solve problems that occur frequently.

fraction (p. 86). A number in form $\frac{a}{b}$, where $b \neq 0$. For example: $\frac{1}{8}$, $\frac{8}{10}$.

function (p. 110). A set of ordered pairs, in which no two different pairs have the same first element.

graph of an equation (p. 124–125). The graph of the equation's solution set.

graph of an inequality (p. 228). The graph of the inequality's solution set.

graph of a number (p. 37). The point on the number line that corresponds to the number.

graph of an ordered pair (p. 47). The point on a graph that corresponds to the ordered pair. Coordinate axes are used to graph ordered pairs.

greatest common factor (GCF) (p. 59). The greatest member of the set of common factors of two or more numbers.

honest (p. 288). In probability, coins (or dice) are honest if all possible outcomes are equally likely when the coins (or dice) are tossed.

identity element for addition (p. 240). *See* additive identity element.

identity element for multiplication (p. 364). *See* multiplicative identity element.

inductive reasoning (p. 233). A method of reasoning by drawing a general conclusion from a particular example.

inequality (p. 120). A number sentence which contains one of the symbols $<$, $>$, $\leq$, $\geq$, or $\neq$.

integers (p. 34). The numbers in $\{\ldots -4, -3, -2, -1, 0, +1, +2, +3, +4 \ldots\}$. The whole numbers (including zero) and their opposites.

inverse operations (p. 276). Operations that "undo" each other, such as addition and subtraction, or multiplication and division.

least common multiple (LCM) (p. 56). The least member of the set of common multiples of two or more numbers.

like fractions (p. 86). Fractions having a common denominator.

like terms (p. 184). *See* similar terms.

lowest terms (p. 65). A fraction is in lowest terms when the greatest common factor of the numerator and denominator is 1.

magnitude (p. 212). The distance between 0 and any number on the number line.
members of an equation (p. 17). The expressions joined by the "is equal to" symbol, =.
meter (p. 78). The basic unit of length in the metric system.
millimeter (p. 78). A metric unit of length, 0.001 of a meter.
monomial (p. 316). A polynomial expression having one term.
multiple of a whole number (p. 56). The product of the whole number and any counting number.
multiplication property of equality (p. 191). For every number r, every number s, and every number t, if $r = s$, then $rt = st$.
multiplication property of inequality (p. 308). For all directed numbers r, s, and t:
(1) If t is positive and $r < s$, $rt < st$.
If t is positive and $r > s$, $rt > st$.
(2) If t is negative and $r < s$, $rt > st$.
If t is negative and $r > s$, $rt < st$.
(3) If $t = 0$ and $r < s$ or $r > s$, then $rt = st = 0$
multiplicative identity element (p. 173). One. When you multiply any number by 1, the product is the number that was multiplied by 1.
multiplicative inverses (p. 364). *See* reciprocals.
multiplicative property of 1. (p. 173). For every number r, $r \cdot 1 = 1 \cdot r = r$.
multiplicative property of 0 (p. 173). For every number r, $r \cdot 0 = 0 \cdot r = r$.

negative numbers (p. 34, 212). The numbers naming points to the left of 0 on the number line. On a vertical number line, the numbers below 0.
negative slope (p. 343). A slope that is downward from left to right.
numbers of arithmetic (p. 127). The numbers in {0 and all numbers to the right of 0 on the number line}.

odd numbers (p. 62). The numbers in {1, 3, 5, 7, 9, 11, 13, . . .}. Numbers that can be expressed in the form $(2 \times n) + 1$, where n is a whole number.
opposite of a sum (p. 243, 246). The opposite of a sum is the sum of the opposites. That is, for all directed numbers r and s, $-(r + s) = -r + (-s)$.
opposites (p. 212). Two different numbers that are the same distance from 0 on the number line. Also called *additive inverses.*
ordered pair (p. 47). A pair of numbers in which the order is important.
origin (p. 30, 47). The point marked "0" on the number line. The point (0, 0) where coordinate axes intersect.
outcome (p. 288). The result of an event.

percent (p. 74). An expression which names the ratio of a number to 100.
polynomial (p. 316). A polynomial in one variable takes the form $ax^m + bx^n + cx^p + \cdots + d$ where a, b, c, and d are directed numbers and m, n, and p are positive integers.
positive numbers (p. 34, 212). The numbers naming points to the right of 0 on the number line. On a vertical number line, the numbers above 0.
positive slope (p. 343). A slope that is upward from left to right.
power of a power (p. 350). An expression of the form $(a^p)^q$ where a is a directed number and p and q are positive integers.
prime factorization (p. 382). A form of a composite number in which the number is written as the product of primes.
prime number (p. 52). A whole number that has exactly two different whole number factors, itself and 1.

ratio (p. 68). A comparison of two quantities or numbers.

reciprocal property (p. 278). For every directed number r except 0, $r \cdot \frac{1}{r} = \frac{1}{r} \cdot r = 1$.

reciprocals (p. 90). Two numbers whose product is 1.

reflexive property of equality (p. 154). For any number r, $r = r$.

replacement set for a variable (p. 104). The set of numbers that the variable may represent.

scientific notation (p. 312). A way of writing a number as the product of a number between 1 and 10 and a power of 10.

second coordinate (p. 47). The second number in an ordered pair.

sign of a product (p. 271). The product of two or more directed numbers is positive if there is an even number of negative factors. The product is negative if there is an odd number of negative factors.

similar figures (p. 404). Figures having the same shape.

similar terms (p. 184). Terms which contain the same variables, or terms which contain no variables.

slope (p. 342–343). The steepness of a non-vertical line defined by the quotient $\frac{\text{difference in second coordinates}}{\text{difference in first coordinates}}$.

solution (p. 124). A member of the replacement set for an open sentence that makes the sentence true.

solution set (p. 124). The set of members of the replacement set for an open sentence that make the sentence true.

standard form of a polynomial (p. 318). A polynomial in one variable is in standard form when the terms are ordered so that the variable in the first term has the greatest exponent, the variable in the second term has the next greatest exponent, and so on. A polynomial with more than one variable is in standard form when the terms are ordered according to the exponents of one of the variables.

substitution principle (p. 157). A numeral may be substituted for any other numeral that names the same number.

subtraction property of equality (p. 186). For every number r, every number s, and every number t, if $r = s$, then $r - t = s - t$.

symmetric property of equality (p. 154). For any numbers r and s, if $r = s$, then $s = r$.

terms (p. 106). The parts of an expression that are separated by a plus or minus sign.

transformations (p. 186). The successive changes made in an equation to produce an equivalent equation in which the variable stands alone as one member.

transitive property of equality (p. 154). For any numbers r, s, and t, if $r = s$ and $s = t$, then $r = t$.

triangular number (p. 151). The nth triangular number is the sum of the first n counting numbers.

trinomial (p. 316). A polynomial expression having three terms.

trinomial square (p. 394). A trinomial obtained by squaring a binomial.

unlike fractions (p. 86). Fractions having different denominators.

unlike terms (p. 184). Terms of an expression that contain different variables or different powers of the same variable.

values of an expression (p. 104). The values the expression takes when members of the replacement set are substituted for the variables.

variable (p. 8). A letter used in algebra to represent one or more numbers.

whole numbers (p. 30). The numbers 0, 1, 2, 3, 4, 5, and so on.

Index

Photo Credits

Page 1. (left) THE BETTMAN ARCHIVE; (right) Tyrone Hall. Page 4. CULVER PICTURES, INC. Page 16. (left) UPI; (right) Patricia Hollander Gross-STOCK, BOSTON. Page 29. (left) THE BETTMAN ARCHIVE; (right) Digital Corporation. Page 55. (left) CULVER PICTURES, INC.; (right) John Hamilton Burke. Page 85. (left) BROWN BROTHERS; (right) Tyrone Hall. Page 89. Tyrone Hall. Page 103. Independent Order of St. Luke. Page 119. (left) THE BETTMAN ARCHIVE; (right) New England Telephone. Page 123. (left) U.S. Department of Labor; (right) Tyrone Hall. Page 136. THE BETTMAN ARCHIVE. Page 153. (left) Paul Thomspon-FREE LANCE PHOTOGRAPHERS GUILD, INC.; (right) DeWYS, INC. Page 161. Tyrone Hall. Page 183. (left) THE BETTMAN ARCHIVE; (right) Michael Kennedy-Harvard College Observatory. Page 211. (left) THE BETTMAN ARCHIVE; (right) Tyrone Hall. Page 215. (both) American Telephone and Telegraph. Page 227. Bryn Mawr College. Page 235. (left) Smithsonian Institute; (right) American Textile Manufacturers Institute. Page 253. (left) Elliot Erwitt-MAGNUM PHOTOS, INC.; (right) Tyrone Hall. Page 263. (left) THE BETTMAN ARCHIVE; (right) UPI. Page 266. SEKAI BUNKA PHOTO. Page 282. Tyrone Hall. Page 291. (left) National Archives; (right) National Weather Service. Page 294. BROWN BROTHERS. Page 315. (right) San Francisco Bay Area Transit Authority. Page 317. THE BETTMAN ARCHIVE. Page 345. (left) University of Louisville Photographic Archives; (right) Ellis Herwig-STOCK, BOSTON. Page 363. (left) Tyrone Hall; (right) UPI. Page 381. (left) Pinkerton's, Inc.; (right) Paul Sequeira-PHOTO RESEARCHERS, INC. Page 398. Courtesy D.S. Halacy from THEY GAVE THEIR NAMES TO SCIENCE by D.S. Halacy, © 1967, G.P. Putnam's Sons.

DEFGHIJ-RM-798

Answers to Odd-Numbered Exercises

Chapter 1. Working with Integers

Pages 3–4 Written Exercises A **1.** 45 **3.** 17 **5.** 0 **7.** 20 **9.** 25 **11.** 23 **13.** 3 **15.** 64 B **17.** 34 **19.** 5 **21.** 49 **23.** 1 **25.** 8, 20, 5 **27.** 2, 4, 12 **29.** 15, 1, 1 C **31.** 4, 13 **33.** 45, 3

Pages 6–7 Written Exercises A **1.** True **3.** False **5.** False **7.** True **9.** False B **11.** False **13.** True **15.** False **17.** 5 **19.** 2 **21.** 20 **23.** 2 **25.** 6 C **27.** 54 **29.** 48 **31.** 16 **33.** 2 **35.** 2 **37.** 3 **39.** 5 **41.** Any whole number **43.** 1

Page 9 Written Exercises A **1.** 36 **3.** 84 **5.** 7 **7.** 3 **9.** 7 **11.** 3 **13.** 13 B **15.** 2 **17.** 35 **19.** 52 **21.** 125 C **23.** 3 **25.** 10 **27.** 625 **29.** Answers may vary. Examples: $m + y + w$, $y^2 + z$
31. Answers may vary. Examples: $(w \times z) + (y \times z)$, $w^2 + m + y$
33. Answers may vary. Examples: $(y \times w) - m$, $z^2 - w - y$

Pages 11–12 Written Exercises A **1.** 92 **3.** 32 **5.** 10,000 **7.** 270 **9.** 8 **11.** 1110 B **13.** 400 **15.** 400 **17.** 256 **19.** 153 **21.** 125 C **23.** 72

Page 12 Problems **1.** 204 **3.** 60 **5.** 15

Page 15 Written Exercises A **1.** The sum of six and nine **3.** Sixteen divided by some number **5.** The difference of some number and six **7.** The product of five and eight **9.** The product of some number and ten **11.** The difference between twenty-five and some number **13.** The sum of ten and some number is equal to forty-two **15.** The difference of thirty-five and some number is equal to nineteen. **17.** The sum of thirty-seven and some number is equal to ninety-five. **19.** Forty-five divided by nine is equal to some number. B **21.** The difference of some number and sixty-eight is equal to fourteen. **23.** Thirty-nine is equal to the sum of some number and ten. **25.** Seventy-five is equal to the difference of ninety-two and some number. **27.** $n + 16 = 17$ **29.** $36 = 6 \times n$ **31.** $\frac{n}{15} = 10$ **33.** $0 + n = 12$

Pages 18–19 Written Exercises A **1.** 12 **3.** 36 **5.** 6 **7.** 8 **9.** 60 **11.** 4 **13.** 12 **15.** 40 **17.** 1 B **19.** 8 **21.** 2 **23.** 5 **25.** 6 **27.** 50 **29.** 9 C **31.** 15 **33.** 29 **35.** 9

Pages 21–22 Written Exercises A **1.** $6 \times n = 30$ **3.** $8 = \frac{32}{n}$ **5.** $42 = 6 \times n$ **7.** 12; 5; 60 **9.** 7; 6; 42 **11.** 17; 153; 9 B **13.** 50 **15.** 5 **17.** 24 **19.** 10 C **21.** 16 **23.** 4 **25.** 20 **27.** 44 **29.** 1

Pages 24–25 Written Exercises A **1.** 16; 25; 36; 49; 64; 81; 100 **3.** 484; 529; 576; 625; 676; 729; 784; 841; 900 **5.** 343; 512; 729; 1000 **7.** $10 \times 10 \times 10$; 1000 **9.** $15 \times 15 \times 15$; 3375 **11.** 28×28; 784 **13.** 19×19; 361 **15.** $4 \times 4 \times 4$; 64 B **17.** 5 **19.** 20 **21.** 24 **23.** 12 **25.** 8 **27.** 9 **29.** 14 C **31.** 5 **33.** 4

Page 28 Review of Skills **1.** $<$ **3.** $<$ **5.** $>$ **7.** Forty-seven hundredths **9.** Three and one hundred twenty-five thousandths **11.** One hundredth **13.** 10.65 **15.** 0.05 **17.** 1343 **19.** $11\frac{4}{5}$ **21.** 269 **23.** $7\frac{3}{4}$ **25.** 5110 **27.** $\frac{3}{10}$ **29.** 17.75 **31.** 8 **33.** $\frac{1}{3}$ **35.** 50

Chapter 2. Positive and Negative Numbers

Pages 32–33 Written Exercises A **1.** 8 **3.** 7 **5.** 4 **7.** 1 **9.** 2 **11.** *Q* **13.** *H* **15.** *M* B **17.** *M* **19.** *B* **21.** {1} **23.** {6, 7} **25.** {0, 1, 2, 3, 4, 5} **27.** {0, 1, 2, 3, 4, 5, 6, 7, 8} C **29.** The whole numbers between 2 and 7 **31.** The whole numbers between 9 and 13 **33.** The whole numbers greater than 6 **35.** The whole numbers greater than 20 **37.** 3 **39.** 8 **41.** 13 **43.** The average of 3 consecutive whole numbers is the middle number. **45.** 13, 14 **47.** 9, 10, 11

Pages 35–36 Written Exercises A **1.** $^{+}4$ **3.** $^{+}7$ **5.** 0 **7.** $^{-}7$ **9.** $^{+}1$ **11.** *X* **13.** *R* **15.** *G* **17.** $^{-}3, ^{-}2, ^{+}2, ^{+}3$ **19.** $^{-}1, 0, ^{+}1, ^{+}2$ **21.** $^{-}2, ^{-}1, 0$ **23.** $0, ^{+}1, ^{+}2$ B **25.** $\{^{-}5, ^{-}4, ^{-}3, ^{-}2, ^{-}1, 0\}$ **27.** $\{^{+}1, ^{+}2, ^{+}3, ^{+}4, ^{+}5, \ldots\}$ **29.** $\{\ldots, ^{-}5, ^{-}4, ^{-}3, ^{-}2, ^{-}1\}$ **31.** {0} **33.** {0} **35.** The integers between $^{-}3$ and $^{+}1$ **37.** The integers between $^{-}2$ and $^{+}2$ C **39.** Negative **41.** Positive

Pages 38–39 Written Exercises A **1.** $\{^{+}1, ^{+}2, ^{+}3, ^{+}4, ^{+}5\}$ **3.** $\{^{-}3, ^{-}2, ^{+}2, ^{+}3\}$ **5.** $\{^{-}6, ^{-}4, ^{-}2\}$

7.  $^{-}5$ $^{-}4$ $^{-}3$ $^{-}2$ $^{-}1$ 0 $^{+}1$ $^{+}2$ $^{+}3$ $^{+}4$ $^{+}5$ **9.** 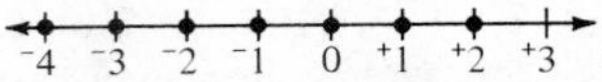 $^{-}4$ $^{-}3$ $^{-}2$ $^{-}1$ 0 $^{+}1$ $^{+}2$ $^{+}3$

11. 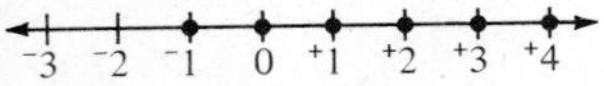 $^{-}3$ $^{-}2$ $^{-}1$ 0 $^{+}1$ $^{+}2$ $^{+}3$ $^{+}4$ B **13.** 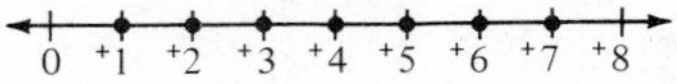 0 $^{+}1$ $^{+}2$ $^{+}3$ $^{+}4$ $^{+}5$ $^{+}6$ $^{+}7$ $^{+}8$ **15.** 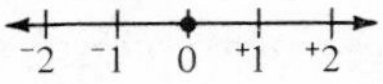 $^{-}2$ $^{-}1$ 0 $^{+}1$ $^{+}2$

17. 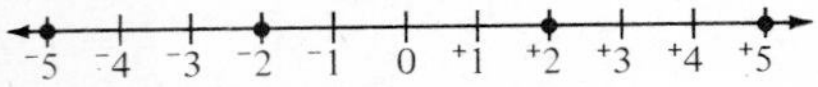 $^{-}5$ $^{-}4$ $^{-}3$ $^{-}2$ $^{-}1$ 0 $^{+}1$ $^{+}2$ $^{+}3$ $^{+}4$ $^{+}5$

C **19.** {the integers greater than $^{+}99$} **21.** {the integers between $^{+}9$ and $^{+}14$} **23.** {the integers less than $^{+}1$} **25.** {the integers between $^{-}5$ and 0} **27.** {the integers between $^{-}10$ and $^{-}7$ and their opposites} **29.** {the even integers between 0 and $^{+}6$ inclusive} **31.** {the integers greater than $^{+}4$}

Pages 42–43 Written Exercises A **1.** $^{-}1\frac{1}{2}$ **3.** $^{+}2\frac{3}{4}$ **5.** $^{-}1\frac{3}{4}$ **7.** $^{-}\frac{3}{4}$ **9.** $^{+}\frac{3}{4}$ **11.** Left, < **13.** Left, < **15.** Left, < **17.** $^{-}7, ^{-}5, 0, ^{+}2, ^{+}8$ **19.** $^{-}6, ^{-}3, ^{-}2, 0, ^{+}1$ **21.** $^{-}6, ^{-}1\frac{1}{2}, 0, ^{+}1, ^{+}5$ **23.** $^{-}7, ^{-}5, ^{-}4, ^{-}3, ^{-}1$ B **25.** $^{-}1\frac{1}{2}, ^{-}\frac{2}{3}, ^{+}\frac{1}{2}, ^{+}\frac{4}{5}$ **27.** $^{-}75, ^{-}\frac{3}{4}, 0, ^{+}1, ^{+}5$

29. 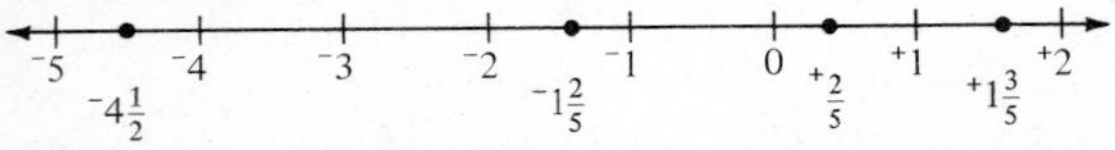 $^{-}5$ $^{-}4$ $^{-}3$ $^{-}2$ $^{-}1$ 0 $^{+}1$ $^{+}2$; $^{-}4\frac{1}{2}$ $^{-}1\frac{2}{5}$ $^{+}\frac{2}{5}$ $^{+}1\frac{3}{5}$ **31.** 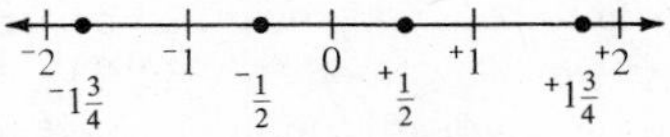 $^{-}2$ $^{-}1$ 0 $^{+}1$ $^{+}2$; $^{-}1\frac{3}{4}$ $^{-}\frac{1}{2}$ $^{+}\frac{1}{2}$ $^{+}1\frac{3}{4}$

33. 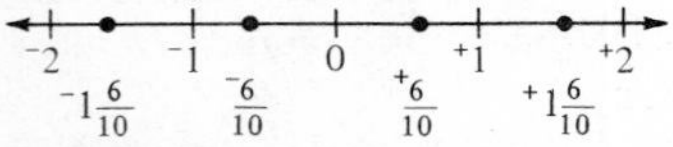 $^{-}2$ $^{-}1$ 0 $^{+}1$ $^{+}2$; $^{-}1\frac{6}{10}$ $^{-}\frac{6}{10}$ $^{+}\frac{6}{10}$ $^{+}1\frac{6}{10}$ **35.** 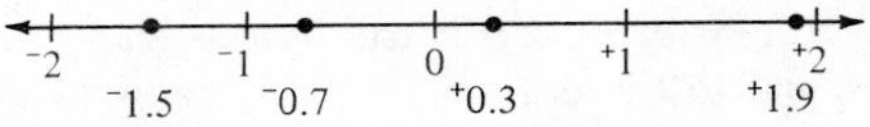 $^{-}2$ $^{-}1$ 0 $^{+}1$ $^{+}2$; $^{-}1.5$ $^{-}0.7$ $^{+}0.3$ $^{+}1.9$

37. 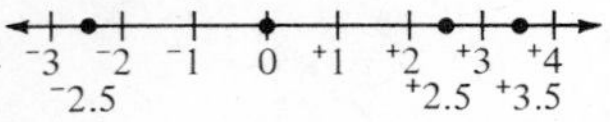 $^{-}3$ $^{-}2$ $^{-}1$ 0 $^{+}1$ $^{+}2$ $^{+}3$ $^{+}4$; $^{-}2.5$ $^{+}2.5$ $^{+}3.5$ **39.** > **41.** <

Pages 45–46 Written Exercises A **1.** 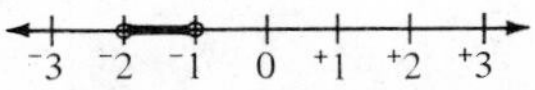 $^{-}3$ 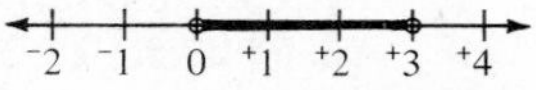 $^{-}2$ $^{-}1$ 0 $^{+}1$ $^{+}2$ $^{+}3$ **3.** $^{-}2$ $^{-}1$ 0 $^{+}1$ $^{+}2$ $^{+}3$ $^{+}4$

5. 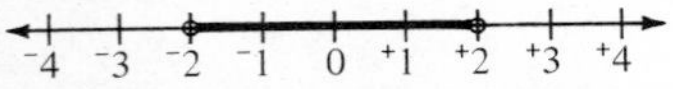 $^{-}4$ $^{-}3$ $^{-}2$ $^{-}1$ 0 $^{+}1$ $^{+}2$ $^{+}3$ $^{+}4$ **7.** 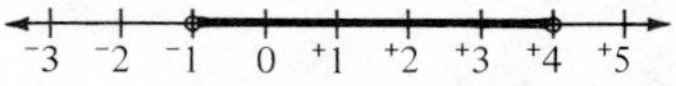 $^{-}3$ $^{-}2$ $^{-}1$ 0 $^{+}1$ $^{+}2$ $^{+}3$ $^{+}4$ $^{+}5$ **9.** $^{+}3$ $^{+}4$ $^{+}5$ $^{+}6$ $^{+}7$ $^{+}8$ $^{+}9$

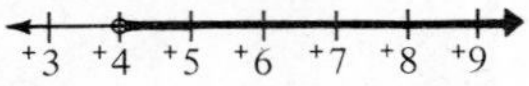

11. 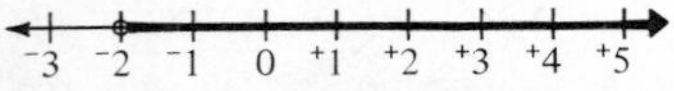 $^{-}3$ $^{-}2$ $^{-}1$ 0 $^{+}1$ $^{+}2$ $^{+}3$ $^{+}4$ $^{+}5$ **13.** 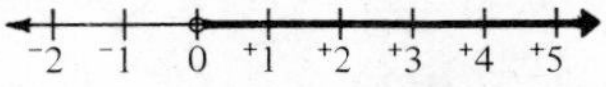 $^{-}2$ $^{-}1$ 0 $^{+}1$ $^{+}2$ $^{+}3$ $^{+}4$ $^{+}5$

15. 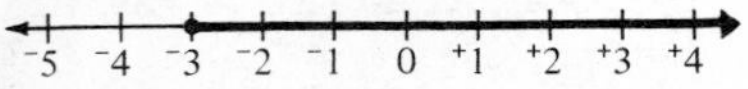 $^{-}5$ $^{-}4$ $^{-}3$ $^{-}2$ $^{-}1$ 0 $^{+}1$ $^{+}2$ $^{+}3$ $^{+}4$ **17.** 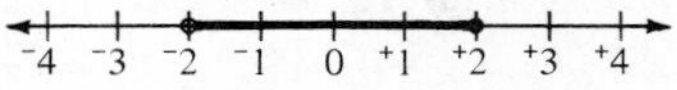 $^{-}4$ $^{-}3$ $^{-}2$ $^{-}1$ 0 $^{+}1$ $^{+}2$ $^{+}3$ $^{+}4$

19. 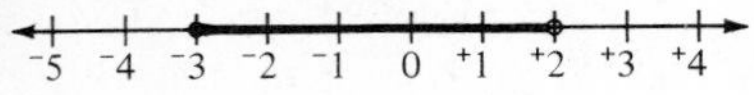 $^{-}5$ $^{-}4$ $^{-}3$ $^{-}2$ $^{-}1$ 0 $^{+}1$ $^{+}2$ $^{+}3$ $^{+}4$ B **21.** 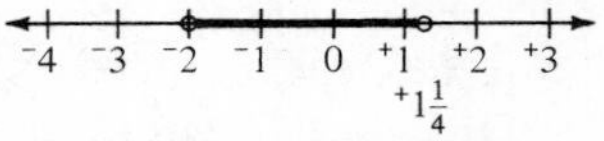 $^{-}4$ $^{-}3$ $^{-}2$ $^{-}1$ 0 $^{+}1$ $^{+}2$ $^{+}3$; $^{+}1\frac{1}{4}$

23. 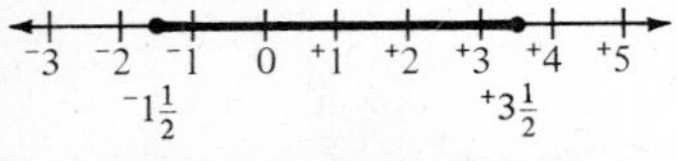 $^{-}3$ $^{-}2$ $^{-}1$ 0 $^{+}1$ $^{+}2$ $^{+}3$ $^{+}4$ $^{+}5$; $^{-}1\frac{1}{2}$ $^{+}3\frac{1}{2}$ **25.** 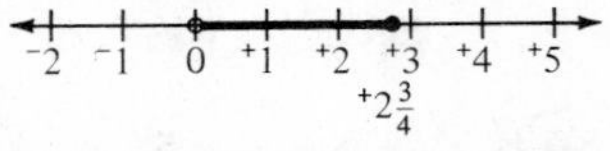 $^{-}2$ $^{-}1$ 0 $^{+}1$ $^{+}2$ $^{+}3$ $^{+}4$ $^{+}5$; $^{+}2\frac{3}{4}$

27. 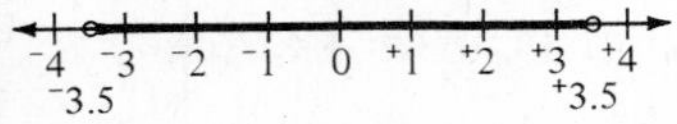 $^{-}4$ $^{-}3$ $^{-}2$ $^{-}1$ 0 $^{+}1$ $^{+}2$ $^{+}3$ $^{+}4$; $^{-}3.5$ $^{+}3.5$ **29.** 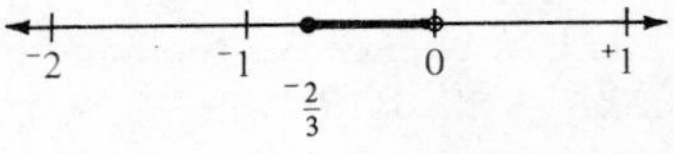 $^{-}2$ $^{-}1$ 0 $^{+}1$; $^{-}\frac{2}{3}$

Pages 48–50 Written Exercises A **1.** B **3.** D **5.** A **7.** $(^+1, {}^+5)$ **9.** $(^-4, 0)$ **11.** $(^+5, 0)$ **13.** $(^-2, {}^-5)$ **15.** $(^+2, {}^-2)$

17.

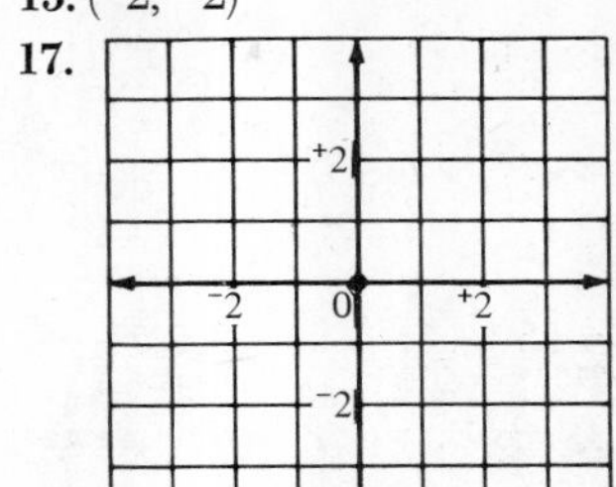

19.

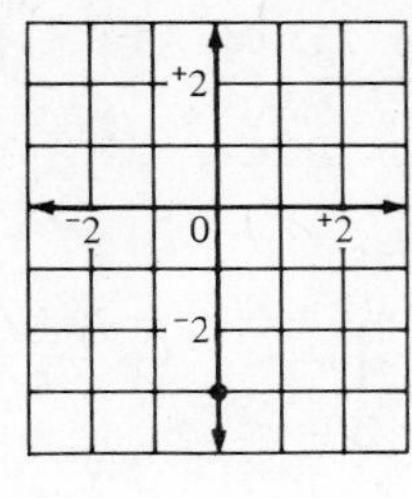

21.

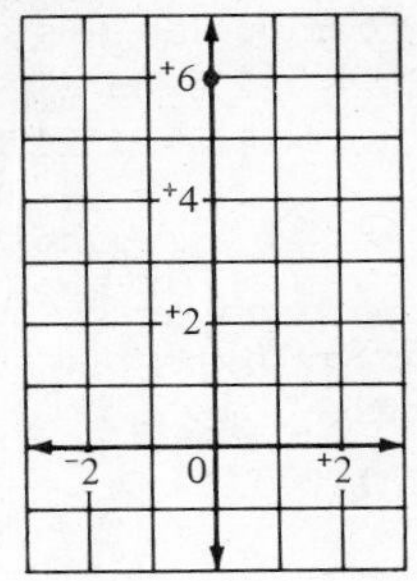

23.

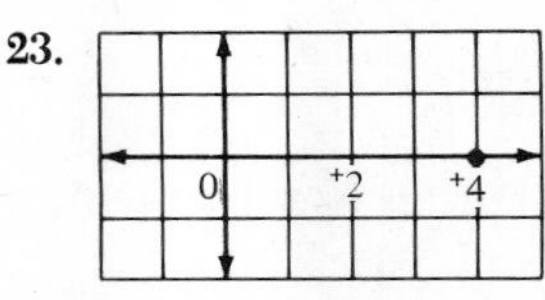

25.

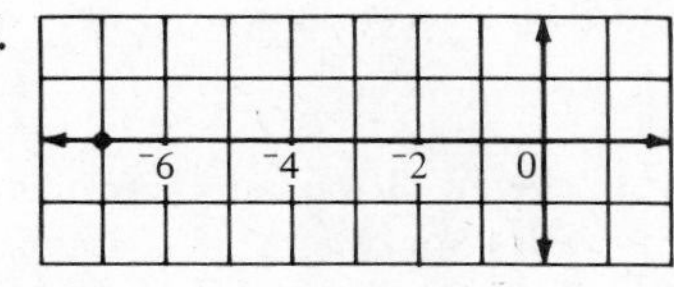

B **27.** $(^+2, 0)$ **29.** $(^-8, {}^+5)$ **31.** $(0, {}^+6)$ **33.** $(0, {}^-6)$ **35.** $(^-3, {}^-3)$, $(^-2, {}^-2)$, $(^-1, {}^-1)$, $(0, 0)$ **37.** $(^-3, 0)$, $(^-2, 0)$, $(^-1, 0)$, $(0, 0)$, $(^+1, 0)$, $(^+2, 0)$

Page 54 Review of Skills **1.** 9 **3.** 4 **5.** 8 **7.** 4 **9.** 4 **11.** hundreds **13.** hundredths **15.** tenths **17.** thousandths **19.** 13 **21.** 19 **23.** 15 **25.** 6 **27.** 2 **29.** 2.5 **31.** 0.6 **33.** 0.5 **35.** 0.25

Chapter 3. Factors and Multiples

Pages 57–58 Written Exercises A **1.** $a = 9$, $h = 18$, $m = 27$, $w = 36$; $\{9, 18, 27, 36, \ldots\}$ **3.** $t = 4$, $r = 8$, $p = 12$, $n = 16$; $\{4, 8, 12, 16, \ldots\}$ **5.** 6 **7.** $\{3, 6, 9, 12, \ldots\}$, $\{4, 8, 12, 16, \ldots\}$, $\{12, 24, 36\}$; 12 **9.** 15 **11.** 12 **13.** 12 **15.** 10 **17.** 16 B **19.** 18 **21.** 60 **23.** 60 **25.** 55 **27.** 10 **29.** 40 **31.** 20 **33.** 40 **35.** 270 **37.** 96 **39.** 80 **41.** 144

Pages 60–61 Written Exercises A **1.** D **3.** A **5.** B **7.** $v = 35$, $w = 7$; $\{1, 5, 7, 35\}$ **9.** $k = 17$; $\{1, 17\}$ **11.** 1, 2, 13, 26 **13.** 1, 2, 7, 14 **15.** 1, 13 **17.** 1, 2, 5, 10, 25, 50 B **19.** $\{1, 2, 4\}$; 4 **21.** $\{1, 2, 4\}$; 4 **23.** $\{1, 3, 9\}$; 9 **25.** $\{1\}$; 1 **27.** 3 **29.** 2 **31.** 1 C **33.** True **35.** True

Pages 63–64 Written Exercises A **1.** 2×7 **3.** Not possible **5.** Not possible **7.** 2×36 **9.** Not possible **11.** Not possible **13.** $(2 \times 11) + 1$ **15.** $(2 \times 20) + 1$ **17.** $(2 \times 27) + 1$ **19.** $6 + 8 = 14$; even + even = even **21.** $4 + 0 = 4$; even + even = even **23.** $7 + 9 = 16$; odd + odd = even **25.** $5 + 1 = 6$; odd + odd = even **27.** $8 + 9 = 17$; even + odd = odd **29.** 5, 7, 9 B **31.** $\{1, 2, 7, 14\}$; 2, 7 **33.** $\{1, 11\}$; 11 **35.** $\{1, 2, 4\}$; 2 **37.** $\{1, 3, 19, 57\}$; 3, 19 **39.** Even **41.** Odd **43.** Even C **45–49.** Answers may vary. Examples: **45.** $3 + 5$ **47.** $31 + 19$ **49.** $97 + 3$

Pages 66–67 Written Exercises A **1.** $\frac{5}{10}$ **3.** $\frac{8}{10}$ **5.** $\frac{1}{8}$ **7.** $\frac{3}{8}$ **9.** 1 **11.** $\frac{3}{4}$ **13.** $\frac{7}{10}$ **15.** $\frac{1}{2}$ **17.** $\frac{3}{5}$ **19.** $\frac{3}{4}$ **21.** $\frac{7}{10}$ **23.** $\frac{1}{5}$ **25.** 21 **27.** 90 **29.** 5 B **31.** $r = 20$, $t = 15$ **33.** $h = 5$, $a = 50$ **35.** $x = 25$, $y = 40$

Page 69 Written Exercises A **1.** $\frac{2}{3}$ **3.** $\frac{19}{100}$ **5.** $\frac{5}{6}$ **7.** $\frac{9}{5}$ **9.** $\frac{1}{4}$ **11.** $\frac{1}{5}$ B **13.** 2, 5 **15.** 3, 5 **17.** 3, 7

Pages 69–70 Problems **1.** $\frac{1}{5}$, $\frac{4}{5}$ **3.** $\frac{7}{3}$, $\frac{10}{7}$ **5.** $\frac{1}{75}$ **7.** $\frac{3}{1}$

Pages 72–73 Written Exercises A **1.** five tenths **3.** twenty-three hundredths **5.** eight and forty hundredths **7.** twenty-five thousandths **9.** eight tenths **11.** twenty and zero hundredths **13.** 0.2 **15.** 0.4 **17.** 0.8 **19.** 0.7 **21.** 0.18 **23.** 0.125 **25.** $\frac{2}{10} = \frac{20}{100} = \frac{200}{1000}$ **27.** $\frac{13}{100} = \frac{130}{1000} = \frac{1300}{10,000}$ **29.** 0.7 = 0.70 = 0.700 = 0.7000 **31.** 0.12 = 0.120 = 0.1200 = 0.12000 **33.** $\frac{2}{5}$ **35.** $\frac{3}{4}$ B **37.** $\frac{7}{8}$ **39.** $\frac{1}{40}$ **41.** $1\frac{1}{20}$ **43.** $0.1\overline{6}$ **45.** $0.\overline{5}$ **47.** $0.8\overline{3}$ **49.** 2.75

Pages 75–76 Written Exercises A **1.** 0.37 = 37% **3.** 0.70 = 70% **5.** 0.25 = 25% **7.** 0.625 = 62.5% **9.** 1.00 = 100% **11.** 0.45 = 45% **13.** $\frac{3}{20}$ **15.** $\frac{1}{10}$ **17.** $\frac{1}{4}$ **19.** $\frac{21}{50}$ **21.** 1 B **23.** 12.5% = 0.125 = $\frac{125}{1000} = \frac{1}{8}$ **25.** 87.5% = 0.875 = $\frac{875}{1000} = \frac{7}{8}$ **27.** 5% = 0.05 = $\frac{5}{100} = \frac{1}{20}$ **29.** 325% = 3.25 = $3\frac{25}{100} = 3\frac{1}{4}$ C **31.** 0.035 **33.** 0.0275 **35.** 0.0075

Pages 76–77 Problems **1.** Boys: $\frac{2}{5}$, girls: $\frac{3}{5}$ **3.** Nonfiction: $\frac{1}{2}$, fiction: $\frac{1}{4}$, reference: $\frac{1}{8}$; nonfiction or fiction: $\frac{3}{4}$

Pages 79–80 Written Exercises A **1.** 9.0 cm **3.** 4.5 cm **5.** 6.7 cm **7.** 9.5 cm B **19.** 0.95 m **21.** 0.6 m **23.** 4 m 9 cm **25.** 5.0 cm **27.** 10.0 cm **29.** 12 cm 5 mm C **31.** 2.6 cm **33.** 94 mm **35.** 6 mm **37.** 0.15 m **39.** 75 cm **41.** 60 cm

Page 84 Review of Skills **1.** $3\frac{1}{2}$ **3.** $4\frac{1}{5}$ **5.** $\frac{7}{3}$ **7.** $\frac{8}{7}$ **9.** 6.367 **11.** 34.5 **13.** 1 **15.** $\frac{1}{7}$ **17.** 52.48 **19.** 17.23 **21.** 1.7 **23.** 230 **25.** 216 **27.** (3, 2) **29.** (5, 4)

Chapter 4. Working with Fractions and Decimals

Pages 87–88 Written Exercises A **1.** $\frac{7}{9}$ **3.** $\frac{3}{4}$ **5.** $\frac{3}{5}$ **7.** $\frac{1}{2}$ **9.** 1 **11.** 4 **13.** $7\frac{7}{10}$ **15.** $\frac{1}{4}$ **17.** $1\frac{1}{2}$ **19.** 4; $t = \frac{5}{8}$ **21.** 2; $m = \frac{1}{2}$ B **23.** $\frac{11}{40}$ **25.** $\frac{1}{4}$ **27.** $2\frac{1}{6}$ **29.** $11\frac{3}{8}$ **31.** 1 **33.** $2\frac{1}{3}$ **35.** $\frac{1}{2}$ **37.** 1 **39.** $\frac{1}{5}$

Pages 91–92 Written Exercises A **1.** $\frac{2}{27}$ **3.** $3\frac{3}{10}$ **5.** $\frac{1}{2}$ **7.** $\frac{3}{20}$ **9.** $\frac{5}{6}$ **11.** $\frac{3}{8}$ **13.** $\frac{5}{6}$ **15.** $\frac{1}{2}$; 3 B **17.** $\frac{1}{8}$ **19.** $\frac{2}{5}$ **21.** 9 **23.** $\frac{1}{7}$ **25.** 1 **27.** $\frac{n}{m}$ **29.** $\frac{5}{a}$ **31.** $1\frac{1}{5}$ **33.** $2\frac{1}{4}$ **35.** 1 **37.** $\frac{6}{7}$ **39.** 2 **41.** $1\frac{7}{10}$ **43.** $\frac{1}{4}$ **45.** $\frac{1}{24}$ **47.** 4

Pages 94–95 Written Exercises A **1.** 19.18 **3.** 57.7 **5.** 0.005 **7.** 11.607 **9.** 4.203 **11.** 48.6 **13.** 10.97 **15.** 6.25 **17.** 6.908 B **19.** 436.28 **21.** 7.404 **23.** 11.396 **25.** 248.77 C **27.** 2.5 **29.** 2.54 **31.** 11.996

Page 95 Problems **1.** \$13.16 **3.** \$6.14 **5.** \$159.80

Pages 97–98 Written Exercises A **1.** 4.6265 **3.** 57.998 **5.** 0.00832 **7.** 11.25 **9.** 43.82 **11.** 3.1 **13.** 33.67 **15.** 1.91 **17.** 18 **19.** 112 B **21.** 11.59 **23.** 2.55 **25.** \$312 **27.** \$968.40 **29.** 13.6 **31.** 768 **33.** 5.0275; 50.275; 502.75; 5027.5 **35.** 34.28; 342.8; 3428; 34,280

Page 98 Problems **1.** \$2700 **3.** 717.01 cm^2 **5.** \$4.73 per kilogram

Pages 101–102 Written Exercises A **1.** 72 **3.** 31 **5.** 32 **7.** 46 **9.** $4\frac{1}{2}$ **11.** $4\frac{1}{3}$ **13.** 5 **15.** 67 B **17.** 210 **19.** 71 **21.** 175 **23.** $5\frac{3}{4}$ **25.** $2\frac{7}{8}$ **27.** 10 **29.** 36 **31.** 30 C **33.** $5\frac{1}{3}$ **35.** $(6 \times 4) - 4 = 20$ **37.** $17 = (3 \times 5) + 2$ **39.** $4 + [(2 \times 3) \times 1] = 10$ **41.** $(12 \div 4) - 3 = 0$ **43.** $8 - (2 \times 3) = 2$

Page 105 Written Exercises A **1.** 11, 13, 15, 17 **3.** 3, 5, 7, 9 **5.** $\frac{1}{2}, \frac{3}{2}, \frac{5}{2}, \frac{7}{2}$ **7.** 3, 9, 15, 21 **9.** 1, 9, 25, 49 **11.** 10, 14, 18, 22 **13.** 16 **15.** 30 **17.** 5 B **19.** 38 **21.** 17 **23.** 5 **25.** 10 C **27.** 37 **29.** 18 **31.** 5

Pages 107–109 Written Exercises A **1.** s, $2s$, $5s$ **3.** $\frac{1}{8}$, $\frac{t}{4}$, $\frac{t}{2}$ **5.** yz, xz, xy **7.** $2m$, m, 2

9. $8k = 8(4) = 32$

$4(2k) = 4(8) = 32$

$2(4k) = 2(16) = 32$

11. $\frac{kt}{3} = \frac{4(6)}{3} = 8$

$\frac{1}{3}(kt) = \frac{1}{3}(24) = 8$

$\frac{t}{3}(k) = 2(4) = 8$

13. $\frac{1}{2}kt = \frac{1}{2}(4)(6) = 12$

$\frac{k}{2} \cdot t = 2 \cdot 6 = 12$

$k \cdot \frac{t}{2} = 4 \cdot 3 = 12$

15. $6x$ **17.** $9ab$ B **19.** $P = 2l + 2w$ **21.** $A = \frac{1}{2}bh$ **23.** $54m^2$ **25.** $\frac{3}{5}bc$ **27.** $\frac{5pq}{2}$

C **29.** $8(rs)$, $8r(s)$, $8s(r)$ **31.** $3rs\left(\frac{1}{t}\right)$, $3r\left(\frac{s}{t}\right)$, $3\left(\frac{rs}{t}\right)$ **33.** $2(d)$, $\frac{1}{2}(4d)$, $6\left(\frac{d}{3}\right)$ **35.** $3t(\frac{1}{10})$, $3\left(\frac{t}{10}\right)$, $\frac{3}{5}\left(\frac{t}{2}\right)$

37. $a\left(\frac{1}{cd}\right)$, $\frac{1}{c}\left(\frac{a}{d}\right)$, $\frac{1}{d}\left(\frac{a}{c}\right)$ **39.** $\frac{4}{5}(cd)$, $4c\left(\frac{d}{5}\right)$, $\frac{d}{5}(4c)$

Page 109 Problems **1.** $2d$ **3.** $6ab$

Pages 112–114 Written Exercises A **1.** (7, 2), (8, 3), (9, 4) **3.** (8, $1\frac{3}{5}$), (12, $2\frac{2}{5}$), (16, $3\frac{1}{5}$), (20, 4), (24, $4\frac{4}{5}$)
5. (2, 4), (3, 9), (6, 36), (7, 49)

7.

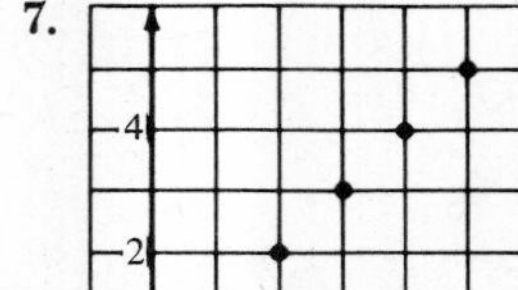

9.

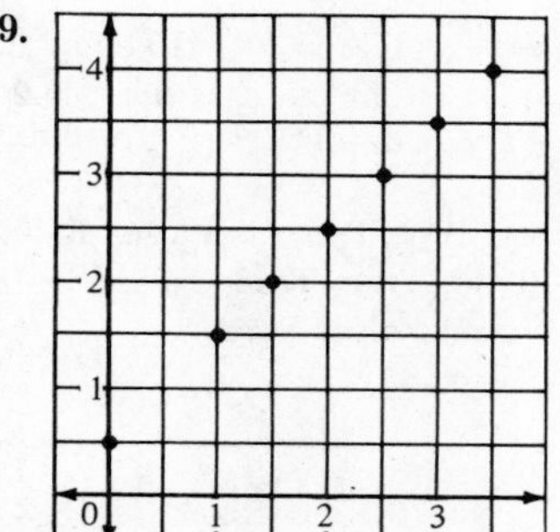

11. C **13.** E B **15.** (0, 0.5) **17.** 2.0; (1.5, 2.0) **19.** 3.0; (2.5, 3.0) **21.** 2; (4, 2) **23.** $3\frac{1}{3}$; (8, $3\frac{1}{3}$)
25. $4\frac{2}{3}$; (12, $4\frac{2}{3}$) C **27.** $\frac{1}{2}x$ **29.** x^2 **31.** $\frac{1}{10}x$

Page 118 Review of Skills **1.** 10^2 **3.** 5^5 **5.** n^3 **7.** 45 **9.** 490 **11.** 0 **13.** 64 **15.** 1008 **17.** True
19. True **21.** 7 **23.** 9 **25.** 8 **27.** $412.38 **29.** $\frac{3}{4}$ **31.** $\frac{1}{4}$ **33.** $\frac{3}{5}$ **35.** $\frac{3}{4}$

Chapter 5. Equations and Inequalities

Pages 121–122 Written Exercises A **1.** C **3.** F **5.** H **7.** B **9.** $n + 8 = 23$ **11.** $3x^3 > 7$
13. $3.4n > 100$ B **15.** $2n^2 > 5$ **17.** $4n + 1 < 20$ **19–25.** Answers may vary.
One example is given for each. **19.** 7 is less than some number minus 2.
21. The sum of 5 squared and s is not equal to 8. **23.** The product of 2 and r added to 3 is less than 11.
25. 3 subtracted from the square of a is greater than 10.

Pages 125–126 Written Exercises A **1.** {12} **3.** {6} **5.** {2} **7.** {3} **9.** {2}

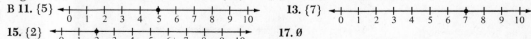

B **11.** {5} 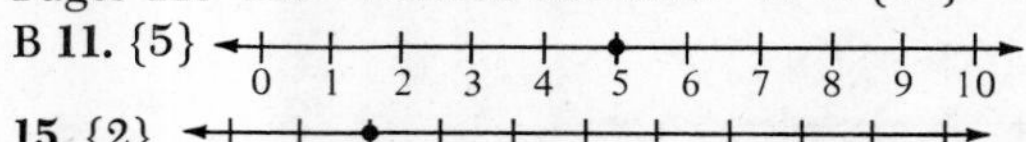

13. {7}

15. {2}

17. ∅

19. {0, 2} 21. {2}

23. {0} 25. ∅

Pages 128–129 Written Exercises A **1.** 13 = 13 **3.** 16 = 16 **5.** 6 = 6 **7.** 7 = 7 **9.** 31 = 31 **11.** 12 = 12 **13.** $x + 10 - 10 = x$ **15.** $n - 17 + 17 = n$ **17.** $10 + z - 10 = z$ **19.** $3.9 + m - 3.9 = m$ **21.** 7 **23.** 30 B **25.** $7\frac{1}{2}$ **27.** 5 **29.** $3\frac{1}{3}$ C **31.** 25; 5 **33.** 36; 6 **35.** 21 **37.** 79 **39.** $6\frac{1}{2}$

Pages 131–133 Written Exercises A **1.** 2 = 2 **3.** 30 = 30 **5.** 4 = 4 **7.** 24 = 24 **9.** 6 = 6 **11.** 8 = 8 **13.** $\frac{8n}{8} = n$ **15.** $\frac{4x}{4} = x$ **17.** $7 \cdot \frac{h}{7} = h$ **19.** 21 **21.** 18 **23.** 294 B **25.** 13 **27.** 400 **29.** 32.5 **31.** 5 **33.** $22\frac{1}{2}$ **35.** 6

Pages 135–136 Written Exercises A **1.** $\frac{2}{3}a$ **3.** $c^2 - 1$ **5.** $\frac{3}{4}m + 2$ **7.** $x - 2$ **9.** $y + 5$ **11.** $\frac{1}{3}z - 1$ or $\frac{z}{3} - 1$ **13.** $10a + 5$ **15.** $t + b$ **17.** $100 - 5r$ **19.** $5n - 2k$ B **21.** $\frac{1}{4}mn$ or $\frac{mn}{4}$ **23.** $n - 2$ **25.** $\frac{a + b + c}{3}$ C **27.** $10d + 5n + p$

Pages 138–139 Written Exercises A **1.** $A = lw$; 115 cm^2 **3.** $A = \frac{1}{2}bh$; 65 cm^2 **5.** $P = a + b + c$; 4.4 m **7.** $P = 4s$; 36 cm **9.** $A = lw$; 336.2 cm^2 B **11.** $C = \pi d$; 21 cm C **13. a.** $C = \pi d$; 80 cm **b.** $C = \pi d$; 80 cm

Pages 141–142 Written Exercises A **1.** True **3.** False **5.** False **7.** False **9.** False; True; True **11.** True; True; True; False **13.** True; True; True; False B **15.** False; False; False; True **17.** True; True; True **19.** True; False; False; True

21. {the numbers of arithmetic < 7}

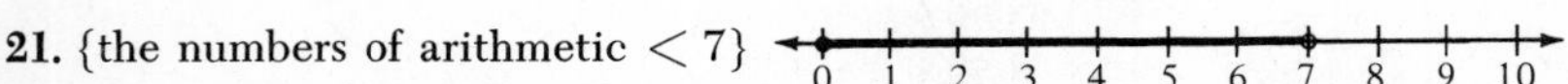

23. {the numbers of arithmetic > 4}

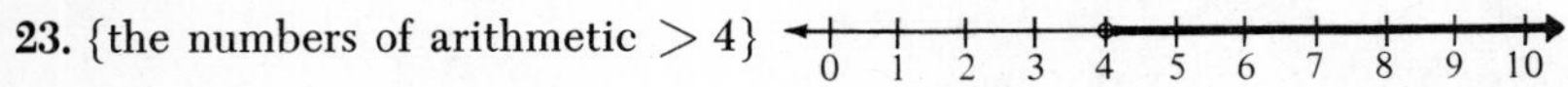

25. {the numbers of arithmetic > 2.5}

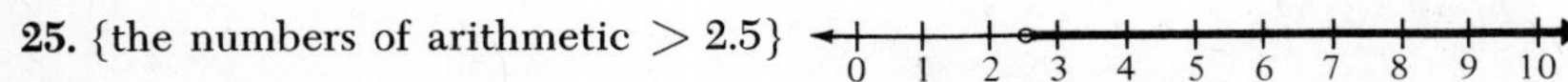

27. {the numbers of arithmetic > 11}

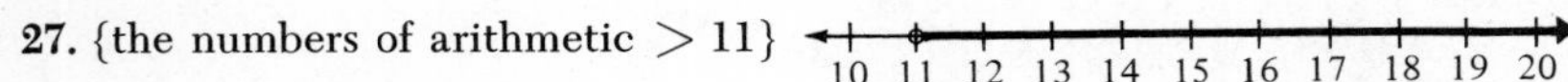

29. {the numbers of arithmetic}

C **31.** {the numbers of arithmetic > 21}

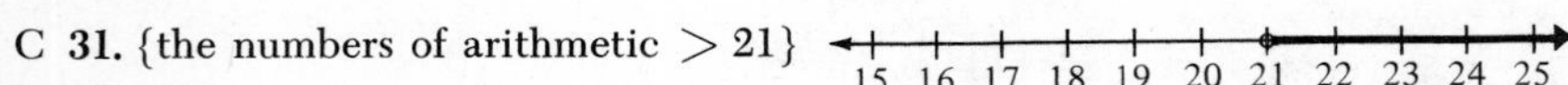

33. {the numbers of arithmetic > 0}

35. {the numbers of arithmetic whose squares are greater than 47}

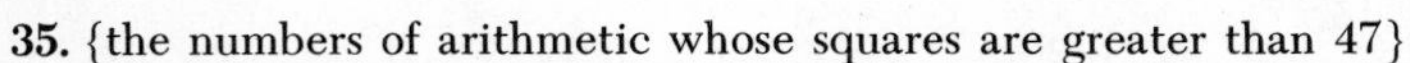

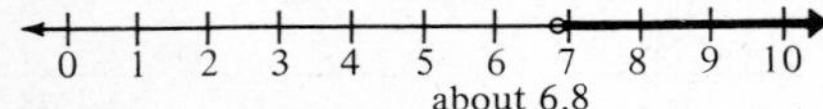

37. {the numbers of arithmetic > 10}

39. {the numbers of arithmetic $> 1\frac{1}{2}$}

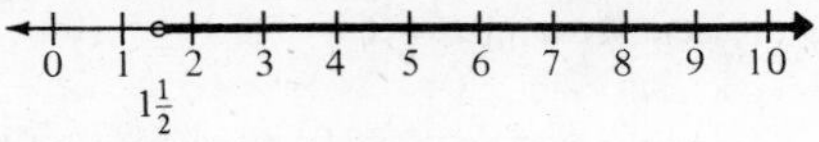

41. {the numbers of arithmetic > 2}

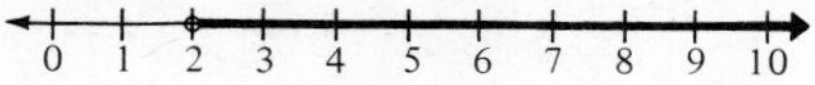

Pages 144–145 Written Exercises A **1.** True; True; False **3.** False; False; True **5.** True; True; True **7.** True; False; False **9.** False; True; True **11.** True; False; False B **13.** True; True; False **15.** False; False; True; True **17.** *B* **19.** *A* **21.** *D* **23.** {the numbers of arithmetic ≥ 1} **25.** {the numbers of arithmetic $\leq 4\frac{1}{2}$} **27.** {the numbers of arithmetic ≤ 5} C **29.** {the numbers on the number line ≤ 0} **31.** {the numbers on the number line $\leq {}^{-}3$} **33.** {the numbers on the number line, except 3}

35. **37.**

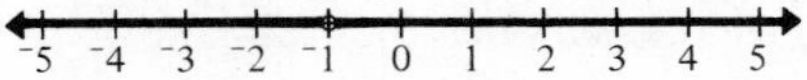

39.

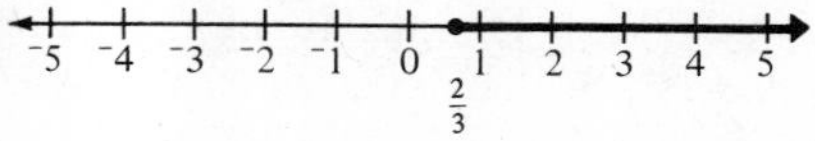

Pages 147–148 Problems A **1.** $4s < 50$; {the numbers of arithmetic $< 12\frac{1}{2}$} **3.** $n \geq 10$ and $n \leq 18$; {the numbers of arithmetic between 10 and 18, inclusive} **5.** $2\frac{1}{3} + n < 14$; {the numbers of arithmetic $< 11\frac{2}{3}$} B **7.** $2l + 2 \cdot 10 \leq 100$; {the numbers of arithmetic ≤ 40} **9.** $\frac{22}{7}d \geq 44$; {the numbers of arithmetic ≥ 14}; $2 \cdot \frac{22}{7}r \geq 44$; {the numbers of arithmetic ≥ 7}

Page 152 Review of Skills **1.** 72 **3.** 210 **5.** $\frac{23}{20}$ or $1\frac{3}{20}$ **7.** 6 **9.** 11 **11.** 125 **13.** 25 **15.** 0 **17.** 33 **19.** True **21.** False **23.** True **25.** True **27.** True **29.** 8 **31.** 0 **33.** 2.5 **35.** 0 **37.** 12 **39.** {0} **41.** {4}

Chapter 6. Axioms and Properties

Pages 155–156 Written Exercises A **1.** $m = m$ **3.** $a + b^3 = a + b^3$ **5.** $10 = m + 4$ **7.** $p = b + 2c$ **9.** $k(k^2 + k + 1) = k^3 + k^2 + k$ **11.** $7 = 5 + 2$ **13.** $48 \div 12 = 2^2$ B **15.** $q = 13$ **17.** $x^2 + 1 = p^3$ **19.** $m = r^2 + t$ C **21.** Symm. Prop.; Trans. Prop. **23.** Trans. Prop.; Trans. Prop. **25.** Symm. Prop.; Trans. Prop. **27.** Trans. Prop; Trans. Prop.

Pages 158–160 Written Exercises A **1.** Closed under add. and mult.; not closed under subtr. and div. **3.** Closed under add. and mult.; not closed under subtr. and div. **5.** Closed under mult.; not closed under add., subtr., and div. **7.** Closed under mult. and div.; not closed under add. and subtr. **9.** Not closed under add., subtr., mult., and div. **11.** 1; $\frac{1}{2}$; 1 **13.** 18, 14; 32 **15.** $\frac{3}{4}$; $1\frac{1}{2}$; $2\frac{1}{2}$ **17.** 6.1; 13.8; 19.4 **19.** $\frac{2}{9}$, $\frac{4}{9}$; $\frac{2}{3}$ **21.** 2, $\frac{1}{2}$; $2\frac{1}{2}$

Pages 164–165 Written Exercises A **1.** 27 = 27; Assoc. Prop. of Add. **3.** 21.2 = 21.2; Comm. Prop. of Add. **5.** $6\frac{1}{6} = 6\frac{1}{6}$; Comm. Prop. of Mult. **7.** $2\frac{1}{4} = 2\frac{1}{4}$; Assoc. Prop. of Add. **9.** 1.83 = 1.83; Comm. Prop. of Mult. B **11.** 1.23 = 1.23; Comm. Prop. of Add. **13.** 5.23 = 5.23; Assoc. Prop. of Add. **15.** 0.156 = 0.156; Comm. Prop. of Mult. **17.** 5.23 = 5.23; Assoc. Prop. of Add. **19.** 0.144 = 0.144; Comm. Prop. of Mult. **21.** Comm. Prop. of Add.; Assoc. Prop. of Add.; Subst. Principle; Subst. Principle **23.** Comm. Prop. of Mult.; Assoc. Prop. of Mult.; Subst. Principle; Subst. Principle **25.** = **27.** = **29.** $\neq$ **31.** = **33.** = **35.** = **37.** =

Pages 167–168 Written Exercises A **1.** 27 = 27 **3.** 104 = 104 **5.** 161 = 161 **7.** 12 = 12
9. 3.18 = 3.18 B **11.** 1836 **13.** 922 **15.** 3708 **17.** 2933 **19.** 12,496 **21.** 37,017
23. Comm. Prop. of Mult.; Subst. Principle; Dist. Prop.; Subst. Principle; Subst. Principle
25. Subst. Principle; Dist. Prop.; Subst. Principle, Comm. Prop. of Add.; Subst. Principle C **27.** True
29. True

Pages 170–171 Written Exercises A **1.** 28 = 28 **3.** 123 = 123 **5.** 165 = 165 **7.** 33.5 = 33.5
9. $19\frac{49}{50} = 19\frac{49}{50}$ B **11.** 117 **13.** 56 **15.** 433 **17.** 71 **19.** 49 **21.** 107 **23.** 53.4 **25.** $79\frac{1}{2}$ **27.** = **29.** ≠

Page 174 Written Exercises A **1.** 1 **3.** 0 **5.** 0 **7.** 0 **9.** 1 **11.** 2 **13.** 0 **15.** 0 B **17.** 0 **19.** 0
21. Every number is a solution. **23.** Every number is a solution **25.** Every number is a solution
27. Every number except 0 is a solution. C **29.** No solution **31.** 2 **33.** 1
35. Every number is a solution **37.** 0

Pages 176–178 Written Exercises A **1.** (0, 0) **3.** (2, 1) **5.** 2; (4, 2) **7.** $(0, \frac{1}{2})$ **9.** $6\frac{1}{2}$; $(6, 6\frac{1}{2})$
11. $12\frac{1}{2}$; $(12, 12\frac{1}{2})$ **13.** (0, 1) **15.** 13; (4, 13) **17.** 31; (10, 31) **19.** 0; (0, 0) **21.** 6; (3, 6) **23.** 30; (6, 30)
B **25.** {(0, 1), (1, 2), (2, 5)}

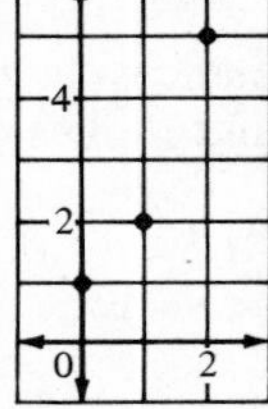

27. $\{(0, \frac{1}{2}), (3, 1\frac{1}{2}), (6, 2\frac{1}{2})\}$

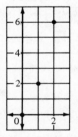

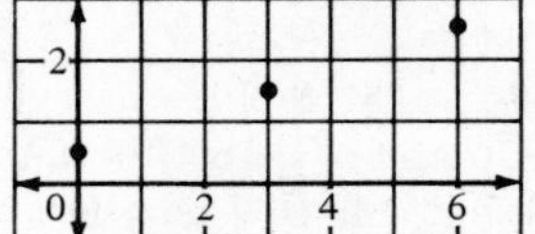

29. $\{(0, \frac{3}{4}), (1, 1), (2, \frac{5}{4}), (3, \frac{3}{2})\}$

31. {(0, 0), (1, 2), (2, 6)}

33. (0, 1); (3, 7); (6, 13); (9, 19) **35.** (2, 0); (5, 21); (8, 60); (11, 117) **37.** (0, 29); (1, 28); (2, 21); (3, 2)
C **39.** 6; 12; 20 **41.** 4; 8; 14; 22 **43.** $9\frac{1}{3}$; $16\frac{1}{4}$; $25\frac{1}{5}$

Page 182 Review of Skills **1.** 40 **3.** $16x + 32$ **5.** $12a + 18$ **7.** $15n + 10$ **9.** $10m$ **11.** $5y$ **13.** $10\frac{5}{8}$
15. $\frac{3}{5}$ **17.** 0.82 **19.** 0 **21.** 30 **23.** 3 **25.** 1 **27.** 2 **29.** 1 **31.** 3 **33.** 8 **35.** 5
37. Every number is a solution. **39.** Every number is a solution. **41.** 2

Chapter 7. Equations and Problem Solving

Page 185 Written Exercises A **1.** $11r$ **3.** $7s$ **5.** $5p + 14$ **7.** $4cd$ **9.** $4t + 5$ **11.** $9k + 12t$ **13.** $5m$
15. $7mn + 8$ B **17.** $11k$ **19.** $4a + 5b$ **21.** $7s + 3$ **23.** $12q$ **25.** $12ab + 14a$ **27.** $11a + 11b$
29. $9k + 9m$ **31.** $46x + 3$ **33.** $42f + 14g$ **35.** $18x + 4y + 32$ C **37.** $32k + 11m$ **39.** $45 + 30c + 66d$
41. $8m^2 + 32m + 10mn + 8n$

Pages 187–188 Written Exercises A **1.** 9 **3.** 6 **5.** $5\frac{1}{3}$ **7.** 26 **9.** 8 **11.** 5 **13.** $3\frac{1}{2}$ **15.** $\frac{4}{5}$ **17.** 67 B **19.** $1\frac{5}{6}$ **21.** $1\frac{1}{2}$ **23.** $\frac{3}{4}$ **25.** 39 **27.** 42 **29.** 74 **31.** 52 **33.** 0.9 **35.** 0.01 C **37.** $\frac{1}{2}$ **39.** $\frac{3}{5}$

Page 190 Written Exercises A **1.** 7 **3.** 4 **5.** $11\frac{1}{2}$ **7.** $6\frac{4}{7}$ **9.** $\frac{1}{20}$ **11.** $\frac{1}{8}$ **13.** 0 **15.** 6 **17.** 8 B **19.** 4 **21.** 11 **23.** 0 **25.** 20 **27.** $5\frac{1}{2}$ C **29.** $1\frac{1}{2}$ **31.** 0.29 **33.** 3.06

Pages 192–193 Written Exercises A **1.** 16 **3.** 2.5 **5.** 0.18 **7.** 4 **9.** $1\frac{3}{5}$ **11.** 51 **13.** $4\frac{1}{2}$ **15.** 6 B **17.** 0.175 **19.** 0.08 **21.** 9 **23.** $4\frac{2}{3}$ **25.** 0.6 **27.** $1\frac{2}{3}$ C **29.** 0.32 **31.** 6 **33.** 0.1 **35.** 2 **37.** 44 **39.** 4

Pages 195–196 Written Exercises A **1.** 7 **3.** 12 **5.** 5 **7.** 2 **9.** 5 **11.** 3 **13.** 6 **15.** 6 B **17.** 6 **19.** 3 **21.** 2 **23.** $3\frac{1}{3}$ **25.** $6\frac{1}{4}$ **27.** 1 **29.** $23\frac{2}{3}$ **31.** 40 C **33.** 5.5 **35.** 1

Pages 196–197 Problems **1.** 4 **3.** 50 **5.** 25 and 26 **7.** Rollie: 150, Maria: 155 **9.** 42 and 44

Pages 199–200 Written Exercises A **1.** \$15 **3.** 8 runs **5.** 79¢ B **7.** 44 pieces **9.** 51, 52, 53 **11.** 36 and 38 C **13.** width: 21, length: 27 **15.** Sam: 9, brother: 2 **17.** 42 km **19.** 26 and 28

Page 202 Written Exercises A **1.** 3 **3.** 7 **5.** 1.9 **7.** 9 **9.** 24 **11.** $\frac{1}{2}$ **13.** 3 **15.** 7 **17.** 4.3 **19.** 2 **21.** 5 B **23.** 2 **25.** $\frac{1}{3}$ **27.** $\frac{1}{2}$ C **29.** 2 **31.** 1 **33.** 11

Pages 202–203 Problems **1.** 15 **3.** 7 **5.** width: 8, length: 15 **7.** 8 nickels

Pages 206–209 Cumulative Review **1.** 5 **3.** 0 **5.** False **7.** 18 **9.** 104 **11.** 17 **13.** 3 **15.** 7 **17.** 3 **19.** $^{-}1$ **21.** $^{+}17$ **23.** $^{-}4$ **25.** 0, 1, 2, 3, 4, 5

27. 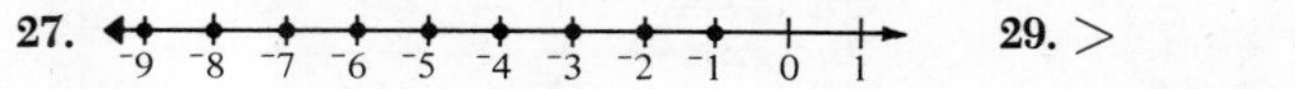

29. $>$

31. 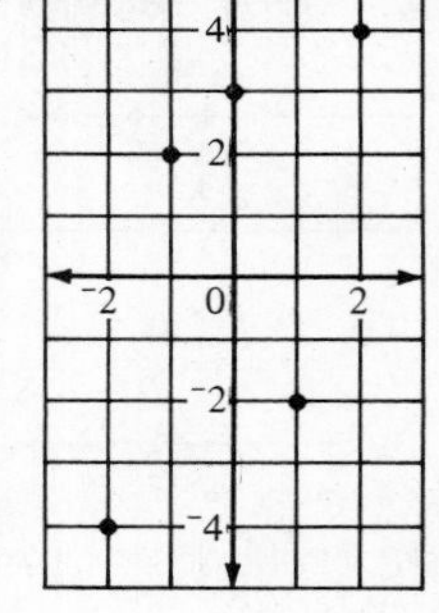

33. LCM = 12, GCF = 3
35. $(2 \times 10) + 1 = 21$ **37.** 12 **39.** $\frac{1}{4}$ **41.** 0.15, 15%
43. 0.99, 99% **45.** 1000 **47.** $\frac{3}{22}$ **49.** $\frac{6}{7}$ **51.** 6 **53.** 1
55. 7.7 **57.** 2 **59.** 14 **61.** {14, 15, 18}
63. $14(lm)$, $7(2lm)$, $2l(7m)$ **65.** $2.7x = 7.1$
67. {the numbers of arithmetic < 4}
69. 14 **71.** 26 **73.** 12 cm^2
75. {the numbers of arithmetic ≥ 3} 0 1 2 3 4 5 6

77. Assoc. Prop. of Addition **79.** Comm. Prop. of Addition
81. Trans. Prop. of Equality
83. Closure Property **85.** Comm. Prop. of Mult. **87.** Distributive Property **89.** Additive Identity
91. Mult. Identity **93.** {(1, 2), (2, 4), (3, 6)} **95.** 38 **97.** 1 **99.** 4 **101.** 9

Page 210 Review of Skills **1.** *H* **3.** *K* **5.** *M* **7.** 5 **9.** $^{-}2$ **11.** 1 **13.** $^{-}5$

Chapter 8. Working with Directed Numbers

Page 214 Written Exercises A **1.** 2 **3.** $^{-}1\frac{1}{4}$ **5.** $1\frac{1}{4}$ **7.** $^{-}1\frac{1}{2}$ **9.** $\frac{1}{4}$ **11.** $^{-}12$ **13.** $^{-}100$ **15.** 22.8 **17.** $^{-}0.1$ **19.** 0 **21.** 5 **23.** 20.9 B **25.** $^{-}15$ **27.** $^{-}45\frac{7}{9}$ **29.** 11 and $^{-}11$ **31.** $5\frac{1}{9}$ and $^{-}5\frac{1}{9}$ C **33.** 1 and 9 **35.** $^{-}10$ and 16

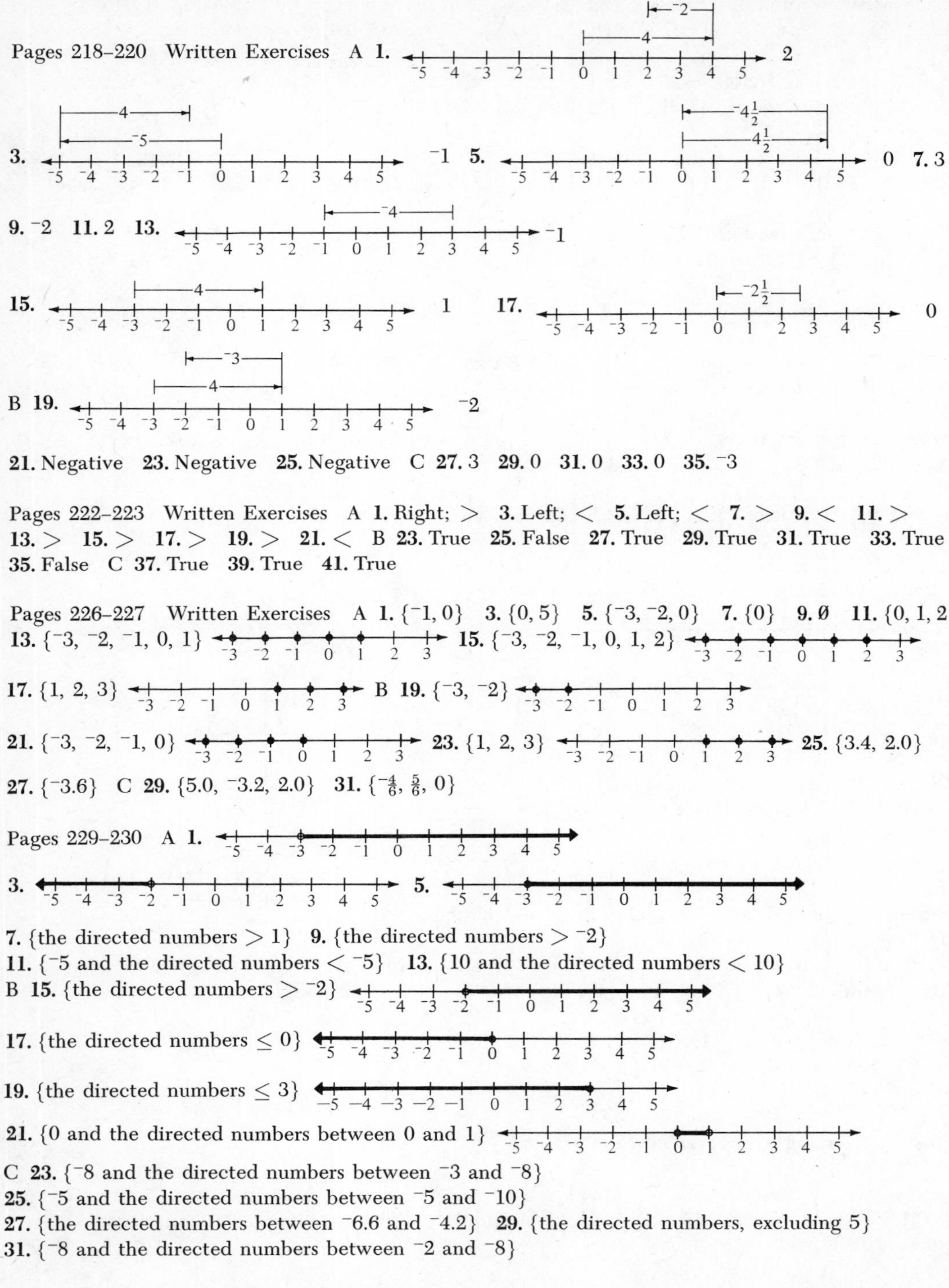

Pages 218–220 Written Exercises A **1.** 2

3. $^{-}1$ **5.** 0 **7.** 3

9. $^{-}2$ **11.** 2 **13.** $^{-}1$

15. 1 **17.** 0

B **19.** $^{-}2$

21. Negative **23.** Negative **25.** Negative C **27.** 3 **29.** 0 **31.** 0 **33.** 0 **35.** $^{-}3$

Pages 222–223 Written Exercises A **1.** Right; > **3.** Left; < **5.** Left; < **7.** > **9.** < **11.** > **13.** > **15.** > **17.** > **19.** > **21.** < B **23.** True **25.** False **27.** True **29.** True **31.** True **33.** True **35.** False C **37.** True **39.** True **41.** True

Pages 226–227 Written Exercises A **1.** {$^{-}1$, 0} **3.** {0, 5} **5.** {$^{-}3$, $^{-}2$, 0} **7.** {0} **9.** Ø **11.** {0, 1, 2} **13.** {$^{-}3$, $^{-}2$, $^{-}1$, 0, 1} **15.** {$^{-}3$, $^{-}2$, $^{-}1$, 0, 1, 2}

17. {1, 2, 3} B **19.** {$^{-}3$, $^{-}2$}

21. {$^{-}3$, $^{-}2$, $^{-}1$, 0} **23.** {1, 2, 3} **25.** {3.4, 2.0}

27. {$^{-}3.6$} C **29.** {5.0, $^{-}3.2$, 2.0} **31.** {$^{-}\frac{4}{6}$, $\frac{5}{6}$, 0}

Pages 229–230 A **1.**

3. **5.**

7. {the directed numbers > 1} **9.** {the directed numbers > $^{-}2$}
11. {$^{-}5$ and the directed numbers < $^{-}5$} **13.** {10 and the directed numbers < 10}
B **15.** {the directed numbers > $^{-}2$}

17. {the directed numbers ≤ 0}

19. {the directed numbers ≤ 3}

21. {0 and the directed numbers between 0 and 1}

C **23.** {$^{-}8$ and the directed numbers between $^{-}3$ and $^{-}8$}
25. {$^{-}5$ and the directed numbers between $^{-}5$ and $^{-}10$}
27. {the directed numbers between $^{-}6.6$ and $^{-}4.2$} **29.** {the directed numbers, excluding 5}
31. {$^{-}8$ and the directed numbers between $^{-}2$ and $^{-}8$}

Page 234 Review of Skills **1.** Fall **3.** South **5.** 0 **7.** 3 **9.** 1 **11.** 15 **13.** $x + 1$ **15.** $R + 8$ **17.** 9 **19.** 11 **21.** 13 **23.** (7, 2), (11, 6), (13, 8)

Chapter 9. Addition and Subtraction of Directed Numbers

Pages 237–238 Written Exercises A **1.** 2 **3.** 3 **5.** 2

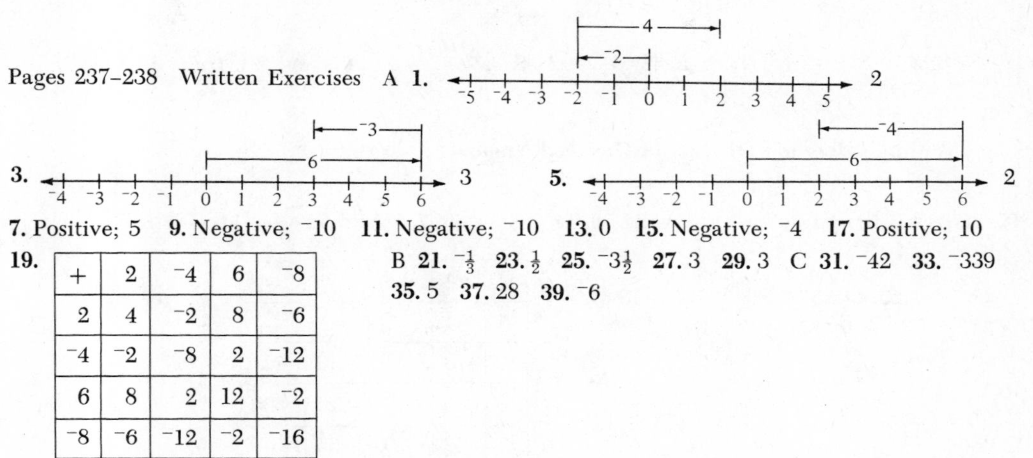

7. Positive; 5 **9.** Negative; $^-10$ **11.** Negative; $^-10$ **13.** 0 **15.** Negative; $^-4$ **17.** Positive; 10

19.

+	2	$^-4$	6	$^-8$
2	4	$^-2$	8	$^-6$
$^-4$	$^-2$	$^-8$	2	$^-12$
6	8	2	12	$^-2$
$^-8$	$^-6$	$^-12$	$^-2$	$^-16$

B **21.** $^-\frac{1}{3}$ **23.** $\frac{1}{2}$ **25.** $^-3\frac{1}{2}$ **27.** 3 **29.** 3 C **31.** $^-42$ **33.** $^-339$ **35.** 5 **37.** 28 **39.** $^-6$

Page 239 Problems **1.** 26 bales **3.** 915 m **5.** Fifth floor **7.** 88 cm **9.** 3270 m

Pages 241–242 Written Exercises A **1.** $-(^-4)$; 4 **3.** -3; $^-3$ **5.** $-(^-16)$; 16 **7.** $-(^-3.4)$; 3.4 **9.** $-(-6.08)$; 6.08 **11.** 5, $^-5$ **13.** 20, $^-20$ **15.** 0, $^-10$ **17.** Yes **19.** No **21.** No **23.** Yes **25.** Yes **27.** 6 B **29.** 3 **31.** 0 **33.** $^-2\frac{2}{3}$ **35.** $\frac{2}{3}$ **37.** 4 **39.** 0 **41.** The opposite of $^-16$; 16 **43.** The opposite of 1.42; $^-1.42$ **45.** The opposite of $^-0.63$; 0.63 C **47.** 3 **49.** $^-3$ **51.** 1.3

Pages 244–245 Written Exercises A **1.** -7 **3.** -39 **5.** -16 **7.** -8 **9.** -1 **11.** 3 **13.** -1

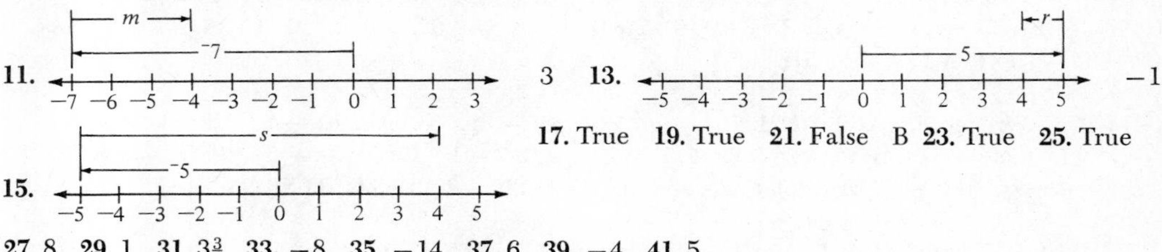

17. True **19.** True **21.** False B **23.** True **25.** True

27. 8 **29.** 1 **31.** $3\frac{3}{4}$ **33.** -8 **35.** -14 **37.** 6 **39.** -4 **41.** 5

Pages 247–249 Written Exercises A **1.** Comm. Prop. **3.** Add. Prop. of Inverses **5.** Add. Prop. of Zero **7.** 16 **9.** 0 **11.** 0 **13.** 7 **15.** 17 **17.** -15 **19.** 7 **21.** -27 **23.** 23 **25.** $3\frac{1}{4}$ **27.** -5 **29.** 33 B **31.** $10 = 10$ **33.** $-8\frac{1}{3} = -8\frac{1}{3}$ **35.** $21 = 21$ **37.** 2 **39.** 7 C **41.** 74 **43.** -71 **45.** 5.7

Pages 251–252 Written Exercises A **1.** 12 **3.** -11 **5.** 17 **7.** 33 **9.** 14 **11.** 14 **13.** 8 **15.** 9 **17.** -5 **19.** -25 **21.** $-4\frac{1}{2}$ **23.** -10 **25.** -17 **27.** 7 **29.** 14 B **31.** -26 **33.** 11 **35.** -42 **37.** -1 C **39.** 20 **41.** -25 **43.** -22 **45.** -15 **47.** 6 **49.** 0

Pages 256–257 Written Exercises A **1.** (2, 4) **3.** (0, 0) **5.** (−2, −4)
7. {(−3, 0), (0, 3), (3, 6), (6, 9), (9, 12)} **9.** {(2, 1), (4, 3), (6, 5), (8, 7)}
11. {(6, −4), (4, −6), (2, −8)} **13.** {(6, 6), (8, 8), (−4, −4), (−6, −6)} **15.** No **17.** Yes B **19.** *B*
21. *A* **23.** *C* **25.** {(5, 7), (10, 12), (15, 17), (20, 22), (25, 27)}
27. {(−21, −28), (−14, −21), (−7, −14), (0, −7), (7, 0), (14, 7), (21, 14)}
C **29.** {($\frac{1}{2}$, $-\frac{1}{2}$), (1, −1), ($1\frac{1}{2}$, $-1\frac{1}{2}$), ($2\frac{3}{4}$, $-2\frac{3}{4}$)} **31.** {($-\frac{1}{2}$, $\frac{1}{2}$), ($-\frac{1}{4}$, $\frac{3}{4}$), (0, 1), ($\frac{1}{4}$, $1\frac{1}{4}$)}
33. {(−1, −3), ($-\frac{1}{2}$, $-2\frac{1}{2}$), ($\frac{1}{2}$, $-1\frac{1}{2}$), (1, −1)}

Page 262 Review of Skills **1.** $\frac{5}{8}$ **3.** $\frac{5}{2}$ **5.** 41 **7.** −12 **9.** 0, −4, −8 **11.** True **13.** True **15.** False
17. $16y$ **19.** $5t + 5n$

Chapter 10. Multiplication and Division of Directed Numbers

Pages 265–266 Written Exercises A **1.** −24 **3.** 143 **5.** −36 **7.** $-5w$ **9.** $\frac{-p}{5}$ **11.** −0.30
13. −0.963 **15.** $\frac{5}{6}$

17.

×	−1	−3	−5	−7
1	−1	−3	−5	−7
3	−3	−9	−15	−21
5	−5	−15	−25	−35
7	−7	−21	−35	−49
9	−9	−27	−45	−63

19. −24 **21.** −6 **23.** 1 **25.** −54 B **27.** −18
29. −15 **31.** 1 **33.** −60 **35.** −17 **37.** −1
C **39.** 3 **41.** 33 **43.** −3

Pages 268–269 Written Exercises A **1.** 15 = 15 **3.** −63 = −63 **5.** −56 = −56 **7.** −24 = −24
9. −1 = −1 **11.** −7 = −7 **13.** −40 = −40 **15.** −9 = −9 **17.** −30 = −30 **19.** −9 = −9
21. −15 = −15 **23.** −35 = −35 B **25.** −9 = −9 **27.** $-\frac{5}{4} = -\frac{5}{4}$ **29.** −5 = −5 **31.** −6 = −6
33. 0 = 0 C **35.** −648 **37.** −112 **39.** −745 **41.** −192 **43.** −1488

Pages 271–272 Written Exercises A **1.** Negative; −18 **3.** Negative; −30 **5.** Positive; 30
7. Negative; −12 **9.** Positive; 21 **11.** Positive; 25 **13.** −6 = −6 **15.** −24 = −24 **17.** 6 = 6
19. $-\frac{5}{2} = -\frac{5}{2}$ **21.** 35 = 35 **23.** 3 = 3 B **25.** 6 **27.** 15 **29.** −11 **31.** −9 **33.** 9 C **35.** −21
37. −30 **39.** −1 **41.** −27 **43.** −512

Pages 274–275 Written Exercises A **1.** $4b - 3a$ **3.** $-9xy - 3p$ **5.** $3m - 6x - 2$ **7.** $2a + 2c + 6$
9. $ab - 5$ **11.** $-2c^2 + 7c$ B **13.** $4x^2 - 2x + 5$ **15.** $ab + 3c + 1$ **17.** $-13s + 6$ **19.** $\frac{3}{5}m - \frac{1}{3}m^2$
C **21.** $7x^2 - 4x + 5$ **23.** $-110a^2 - 80a$ **25.** 150 **27.** −6 **29.** −4 **31.** 14 **33.** 0 **35.** 194.5

Page 277 Written Exercises A **1.** −5 **3.** −12 **5.** −6 **7.** −4 **9.** 7 **11.** 4 **13.** −3 **15.** 5 **17.** −7
19. −0.6 **21.** −0.6 **23.** 0.2 **25.** 0.12 **27.** 0.75 **29.** −0.75 **31.** False **33.** True **35.** True

Pages 280–281 Written Exercises A **1.** 1 **3.** −3 **5.** −1 **7.** $-\frac{1}{2}$ **9.** $-\frac{1}{2}$ **11.** −28 **13.** 1 **15.** −49
17. $\frac{25}{36}$ **19.** −2 **21.** −7 **23.** −5 **25.** 1 **27.** 10 **29.** $\frac{1}{2}$ B **31.** $-\frac{1}{6}$ **33.** −25 **35.** $\frac{1}{21}$ **37.** $-15a$ **39.** $\frac{m}{15}$
41. $\frac{t}{2}$

Page 281 Problems **1.** $-\frac{1}{2}$ **3.** $-\frac{7}{5}$ **5.** $-\frac{7}{5}$ **7.** 8

Pages 284–286 Written Exercises A **1.** 2; $(-1, 2)$ **3.** -4; $(2, -4)$ **5.** $-\frac{2}{3}$; $(1, -\frac{2}{3})$ **7.** $\frac{2}{3}$; $(-1, \frac{2}{3})$ **9.** 2; $(-3, 2)$ **11.** 0; $(0, 0)$ **13.** $\frac{4}{3}$; $(-2, \frac{4}{3})$ **15.** $(0, 0)$, $(1, \frac{1}{3})$ **17.** $(0, 0)$, $(1, -\frac{1}{5})$ **19.** $(-2, \frac{4}{5})$, $(0, 0)$, $(1, -\frac{2}{5})$ B **21.** $\{(-2, 8), (-1, 5), (0, 2), (2, -4), (3, -7), (4, -10)\}$ **23.** $\{(-2, 0), (-1, \frac{1}{2}), (0, 1), (6, 4)\}$ **25.** $\{(-5, -\frac{6}{5}), (-4, -\frac{3}{2}), (-3, -2), (-2, -3), (-1, -6)\}$ **27.** $\{(-4, \frac{7}{4}), (-3, \frac{7}{3}), (-2, \frac{7}{2}), (3, -\frac{7}{3})\}$ **29.** $\{(-2, 20), (-1, 5), (0, 0), (2, 20)\}$

Page 290 Review of Skills **1.** -5 **3.** -12 **5.** -14 **7.** 0 **9.** -15 **11.** -10 **13.** -5 **15.** -9 **17.** 15 **19.** 8 **21.** 33 **23.** $m(8 - 3) = 5m$ **25.** $y(5 + 4) = 9y$ **27.** $<$ **29.** $>$ **31.** $<$ **33.** $<$ **35.** False **37.** True

Chapter 11. Solving Equations and Inequalities

Pages 293–294 Written Exercises A **1.** 0; 25 **3.** $-5\frac{1}{4}$; 0; $2\frac{3}{4}$ **5.** 22 **7.** 22 **9.** 41 **11.** $-5\frac{2}{3}$ **13.** 3 **15.** -14 **17.** 5.1 **19.** $1\frac{1}{2}$ B **21.** $-\frac{1}{6}$ **23.** $\frac{1}{12}$ **25.** 2.6 **27.** $y = z - s$ **29.** $d - b = y$ **31.** $y = -t - r$ C **33.** $z = s + r$ **35.** $m - q = z$ **37.** $z = -h + g$

Pages 296–297 Written Exercises A **1.** 13 **3.** $-\frac{18}{5}$ or $-3\frac{3}{5}$ **5.** 35 **7.** $\frac{23}{4}$ or $5\frac{3}{4}$ **9.** $-\frac{9}{7}$ **11.** $d = \frac{v}{g}$ **13.** $\frac{a}{l} = w$ **15.** $\frac{i}{p} = r$ **17.** $d = \frac{c}{\pi}$ **19.** $\frac{s}{t} = c$ B **21.** -5 **23.** 14 **25.** $-17\frac{6}{7}$ **27.** 0.4 **29.** -0.2 **31.** $\frac{c}{2\pi} = r$ **33.** $\frac{v}{b} = h$ C **35.** $n = \frac{s}{u} = \frac{1}{2}$ **37.** $m = -\frac{r}{u} = \frac{1}{10}$ **39.** $p = -\frac{t}{t} = -1$ **41.** $c = -\frac{s}{t} = -20$

Pages 300–301 Written Exercises A **1.** 4; $\frac{1}{4}$; $\frac{1}{4}$; 3 **3.** $-\frac{2}{4}$; 0; -10 **5.** -18; $-\frac{1}{18}$; $-\frac{1}{18}$; -2 **7.** $z = \dfrac{b}{c + d}$ **9.** $\dfrac{g}{v + r} = q$ **11.** $h = \dfrac{-3}{3 + j}$ **13.** $\frac{13}{7}$ **15.** -7 **17.** 2 **19.** 0.1 **21.** $-\frac{1}{9}$ **23.** 5 **25.** 6 **27.** 1 B **29.** 9 **31.** 3 **33.** -16 **35.** 4 C **37.** $\frac{5}{2}$ **39.** 3 **41.** $-17\frac{1}{3}$

Page 303 Problems **1.** 7 meters **3.** 2 years **5.** \$1500 **7.** 16 cm **9.** 3 cm

Pages 306–307 Written Exercises A **1.** E **3.** A **5.** D **7.** -11; -11; -8

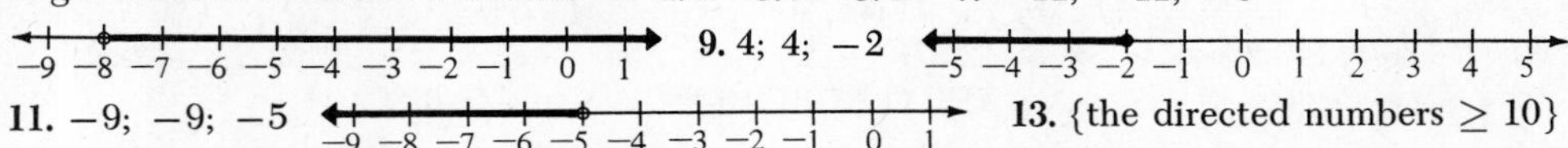

9. 4; 4; -2 **11.** -9; -9; -5 **13.** {the directed numbers ≥ 10} **15.** {the directed numbers > 12} **17.** {the directed numbers > -13} **19.** {the directed numbers ≥ -5} **21.** {the directed numbers < -4} **23.** {the directed numbers ≥ 0} B **25.** {the directed numbers ≤ -16} **27.** {the directed numbers ≤ 4} **29.** {the directed numbers ≥ -13} **31.** {the directed numbers ≥ -8} **33.** {the directed numbers > 12} C **35.** {the directed numbers ≥ 7} **37.** {the directed numbers $\leq -\frac{1}{4}$} **39.** {the directed numbers < 4}

Pages 309–310 Written Exercises A **1.** $-6(-5) > -5(-5)$ **3.** $26 \cdot \frac{1}{13} \geq 13 \cdot \frac{1}{13}$ **5.** $-4 \cdot 4 > -10.4$ **7.** $-2(-3) \leq -5(-3)$ **9.** $-\frac{d}{3}(-3) \leq 7(-3)$

11. $m \geq 3$ −5 −4 −3 −2 −1 0 1 2 3 4 5 **13.** $w \leq 20$ 17 18 19 20 21 22 23 24 25 26 27

15. $d \leq -2$ −5 −4 −3 −2 −1 0 1 2 3 4 5

17. $s > -5$ −5 −4 −3 −2 −1 0 1 2 3 4 5

19. $-3 < b$ −5 −4 −3 −2 −1 0 1 2 3 4 5

21. {the directed numbers $\leq \frac{9}{7}$} **23.** {the directed numbers $< -\frac{1}{2}$}
25. {the directed numbers ≥ -15} **27.** {the directed numbers ≤ -5}
B **29.** {the directed numbers < 28} **31.** {the directed numbers > -32}
33. {the directed numbers > -4} **35.** {the directed numbers > 1}
37. {the directed numbers > -30} **39.** {the directed numbers ≥ 4}
C **41.** {the directed numbers $< 21\frac{1}{2}$}

Page 314 Review of Skills **1.** 10^3 **3.** 10^7 **5.** $6 \cdot 10^3 + 3 \cdot 10^2 + 2 \cdot 10 + 5$ **7.** $8 \cdot 10^4 + 4 \cdot 10^2 + 9 \cdot 10 + 1$ **9.** $11x$ **11.** $-14q$ **13.** 28 **15.** 310 **17.** 7 **19.** 0 **21.** 85 **23.** 76 **25.** 29 **27.** 110 **29.** 0 **31.** 10 **33.** $-\frac{1}{5}$ **35.** $\frac{4}{3}$ **37.** 0 **39.** 3 **41.** $\frac{11}{3}$

Chapter 12. Addition and Subtraction of Polynomials

Page 317 Written Exercises A **1.** Monomial **3.** Binomial **5.** Binomial **7.** Trinomial **9.** Trinomial **11–15** Answers may vary. One example is given. **11.** $3 + c^2 - b^5 + b$ **13.** $b^5 + b + 3$ **15.** $c^2b - c^2 - 3 + b - b^5 + c^2b^5$

Page 319 Written Exercises A **1.** $-7c^5 + c$ **3.** $3k^5 - k^3 + 9k^2 - 5$ **5.** $3n^5 + n^2 - 4n$ **7.** $-8a^7 + 14a^5 + a^3$ **9.** $r^9 + 5r^4 - 2r^2$ B **11.** $-3x^2 + 4xy$ **13.** $7a^6 - 6a^3b + 2a^2b^2$ **15.** $2a^2 + ab + 2b^2$ **17.** $m^4n^2 + m^3n^2 + m^2 + n^3$ **19.** $3m^4 + 0m^3 + 0m^2 + 0m - 1$ **21.** $s^5 + 0s^4 + 0s^3 - 3s^2 + 0s + 2$ **23.** $x^7 + 0x^6 + 0x^5 + x^4 + 0x^3 + 0x^2 + 0x + 0$ **25.** $k^7 + 0k^6 - 2k^5 + 0k^4 + 0k^3 + 0k^2 + k - 19$

Pages 321–322 Written Exercises A **1.** 0 **3.** 0 **5.** 6 **7.** −24 **9.** 7 **11.** 3 **13.** −12 **15.** (−7, 120) **17.** 6; (−1, 6) **19.** 21; (4, 21) **21.** 105; (8, 105)
B **23.** {(−6, −13), (−4, −7), (−2, −1), (0, 5), (2, 11), (4, 17), (6, 23)}
25. {(−3, −17), (−2, 0), (0, 4), (2, 8), (3, 25)} **27.** {(−4, −40), (−2, −2), (0, 12), (2, 2), (4, −32)}
29. {(−2, −9), (−1, −2), (0, −1), (1, 0), (2, 7)} C **31.** {(−0.1, 3.31), (0, 3), (0.1, 2.71)}

Pages 324–325 Written Exercises A **1.** $14w + 9$ **3.** $3a + 9a^3$ **5.** $2n^2$ **7.** $2x^2$ **9.** $-10x^2 + 3xy - 2y^2$ **11.** $5m^2 - 4n^2 - 4p^2$ **13.** $10c - 8$ **15.** $-a - 2b$ **17.** $4x^2 - 5y - 3$ **19.** $2y^2$ **21.** $9.4a + 0.7b + 8$ **23.** $3m^2 - 5m - 3$ **25.** $k^4 - 3k^3 - 5k^2 + 6k + 3$ **27.** $4x^2 + 4y^2$ B **29.** $7b - 5$ **31.** $13a - 2b - 15$ **33.** $-5 - d$ **35.** $4d^3 - 8d^2$ **37.** $1\frac{1}{2}s^3$ **39.** $a - 4b$ **41.** $2.4 + 5ab$ **43.** $20x^4 - 12.2x^2y^2 - 2.2y^4$ **45.** $13x^3 + 2x^2 + x + 3$

Pages 327–328 Written Exercises A **1.** $16 - 2b = 16 - 2b$ **3.** $4b - 10 = 4b - 10$ **5.** $5z^2 - 2z + 3 = 5z^2 - 2z + 3$ **7.** $2m^2 + 5m - 8 = 2m^2 + 5m - 8$ **9.** $a^4 - a^3 + 2a^2 - 9a = a^4 - a^3 + 2a^2 - 9a$ **11.** $2y - 2$; $2y - 2$ **13.** $-8x + 6y$; $-8x + 6y$ **15.** $x^2 + y^2$; $x^2 + y^2$ **17.** −2 **19.** 13 **21.** −3 **23.** 0 **25.** 11.0 **27.** 1 B **29.** 24 = 24 **31.** 137 = 137 **33.** −22 = −22 **35.** $1\frac{1}{2} = 1\frac{1}{2}$

Pages 331–332 Written Exercises A **1.** $-2m^2 + 3m - 15$ **3.** $-\frac{m^2}{10} - \frac{4mn}{2} + \frac{2n^2}{7}$
5. $-12x^9 - 6x^7 - 3x^5 - x - 1$ **7.** $-5x^2 - 3x + 7$ **9.** $-k^6 + 4k^3 + 7k^2 + 2k - 1$
11. $-3y^2 - 13y - 5$ **13.** $x^2 - 4x + 10$ **15.** $2x^3 - 25x^2 + 10$ **17.** $-1.8x^5 + 6.2x^3 + 0.7x - 15$
19. $y^7 - 2y^5 + 6y^3 - y + 2$ B **21.** $4x^2 + 4x$ **23.** 0 **25.** 0 **27.** $-8r^2 + 5s - 6t - 8$ **29.** $\frac{5}{6}x^2 + 1$
C **31.** $-s^3 + 5s^2 - 4s - 8$ **33.** $-a^5 + 2a^2 - 6a + 10$ **35.** $2y^3 - 15y^2 + 3y - 7$
37. $2x^4 + x^3 + x^2 + 5x - 8$

Pages 334–336 Written Exercises A **1.** $r + 9s$ **3.** $7p$ **5.** $4x^2 + 5$ **7.** $2b^2 + 13c - 5$
9. $m^2 + 7m + 4$ **11.** $-2k + 9h^2$ **13.** $k - 10 - 2k - 15$ **15.** $-2y^2 - 4y - y^2 + 3y$
17. $2x - y + 8 - 13x - 4y - 9$ **19.** $-w - 12$ **21.** $6t^2 - 4$ **23.** 0 B **25.** w **27.** $3d - 3c$
29. $4d^2 - 10d - 1$ **31.** $4r^2 + 3r + 11$ **33.** $h^2 - 21h - 13$ **35.** $b^2 + 6b - 2$ **37.** $7x^2 - 32x + 7$
39. $k^2 + 5k - 5$ C **41.** $k - 18$ **43.** $x^2 + 2x + 5$

Pages 337–338 Problems **1.** $a^2 + 6a - 10$ **3.** $a^2 + \frac{5}{6}a - 4$ **5.** $z^2 - 3z + 3$ **7.** $-4a^2 - 5a - 3$
9. $\frac{11}{12}x^3 + 2\frac{1}{4}x^2 + x + 5$

Pages 339–340 Written Exercises A **1.** 1 **3.** 6 **5.** 8 **7.** 17 **9.** -1 **11.** 45 **13.** 12 B **15.** -17
17. $-\frac{17}{3}$ or $-5\frac{2}{3}$ **19.** -6 **21.** 4 **23.** -14 **25.** -1 C **27.** -4 **29.** 5

Page 344 Review of Skills **1.** F **3.** C **5.** B **7.** 16 **9.** 216 **11.** 125 **13.** $12 - 3t$ **15.** $rs - rt$
17. $2mn + 2mp$ **19.** Mult. Prop. of 1 **21.** Comm. Prop. **23.** Assoc. Prop. **25.** 6 **27.** 2 **29.** 7 **31.** 9

Chapter 13. Multiplication and Division of Polynomials

Page 347 Written Exercises A **1.** 4 **3.** 72 **5.** 54 **7.** 36 **9.** 36 **11.** 216 **13.** $12x^2$ **15.** $(x + y + z)^2$
17. $-15h^2$ **19.** $-14z^4$ **21.** $-84y^4$ **23.** $-6x^2$ **25.** $24m^6$ **27.** $-42t^2$ **29.** 2^3 **31.** x^7 **33.** p^5 **35.** $-a^5$
37. y^6 B **39.** 4 **41.** 6 **43.** 2

Page 349 Written Exercises A **1.** $28x^2y^3$ **3.** $48b^3$ **5.** $-60m^3n$ **7.** $-30x^2y$ **9.** $-3a^2b^2$ **11.** $-6s^4r$
13. $-36c^2b$ **15.** $3x^3y^2$ B **17.** $21y^8x^6$ **19.** $-0.4b^7a^5$ **21.** $-35c^8b^3a^3$ **23.** $81n^3m^3$ C **25.** $25x^2y$
27. $-14b^4a^3$ **29.** $20m^4n^2$ **31.** $\frac{1}{2}x^2y^2$ **33.** $-\frac{1}{2}m^3n$ **35.** $2.04a^2b^2c^2$

Page 351 Written Exercises A **1.** $81a^4b^4$ **3.** $81x^4y^4z^4$ **5.** $64m^2n^2$ **7.** $100x^4y^4$ **9.** $-a^3b^3$ **11.** r^8s^8
13. n^{16} **15.** 0 **17.** 1,000,000 **19.** 256 **21.** 729 **23.** 25,000,000 **25.** -125 **27.** 2500 **29.** 400
31. $25x^2y^4$ **33.** $0.04a^2b^4c^6$ **35.** $144a^2b^2c^2$ B **37.** $109a^4b^4$ **39.** $5m^3$ **41.** $-r^7s^9$ C **43.** $1.1a^5t^4$

Pages 353–354 Written Exercises A **1.** $-x^3 - 6x^2 + 7x$ **3.** $5d^2 - 10ad + 5c^2$ **5.** $-d^3 + ad^2 - bd^2$
7. $x^5 + 3x^3 - 7x^2$ **9.** $y^6 - y^5 - y^3$ **11.** $-5x^3 + 10x^2 + 25x$ **13.** $-0.6k^3 + 0.8k^2 + 2k$
15. $4m^4 - m^3n + 2m^2n^2$ **17.** $2x^2 - 3xy$ **19.** $-6m^2 - 8mn$ **21.** $8a^2 + 8ab$ **23.** $18y^2 - 6xy$
25. $-6x^3 + 8x^2w$ **27.** $7x^3y + 2x^2y^3$ B **29.** $60a^2b - 24a^3b^5 + 36a^8b^5 - 6a^2b^{11}$
31. $-\frac{1}{2}a^5b^2 + \frac{1}{2}a^6b^3 - a^4b^3 + a^3b^4$ **33.** $-63x^6y^4 + 84x^5y^5 - 105x^4y^6$ **35.** 11 **37.** -1 **39.** -4 **41.** 16
C **43.** -16 **45.** -13

Pages 354–355 Problems A **1.** $\frac{1}{2}m^2 + m$ **3.** $6x^3 + 15x$ B **5.** $50\pi t + 225\pi$ **7.** $8x^2 + 3x$ **9.** **a.** y^6 **b.** $6y^4$

Pages 357–358 Written Exercises A **1.** $a^2 + 9a + 20$ **3.** $12m^2 + 86m + 52$ **5.** $x^2 + 3x + 2.25$
7. $x^2 - 81$ **9.** $x^2 - 4$ **11.** $24 + 59n + 36n^2$ **13.** $18 - 36y + 16y^2$ **15.** $9 - 3n - 20n^2$ **17.** $25t^2 - 1$

19. $16x^2 + 44x + 10$ **21.** $2x^2 + 5x + 3$ **23.** $2 - 3b - 2b^2$ **25.** $2s^2 + 11s + 12$ **27.** $8q^2 - 82q + 20$
29. $1.5w^2 - w - 2.5$ B **31.** $8 - 32m - 40m^2$ **33.** $4n^2 - m^2$ **35.** $6m^2 + 3.5mn + 0.5n^2$
37. $x^3 - 9x^2 + 25x - 21$ **39.** $s^3 - t^3$ **41.** $36 + 13x^2 + x^4$ **43.** $a^4b^4 + 2a^2b^2 + 1$
45. $42 - 11r - 15r^2 - 2r^3$ **47.** $2x^2 - 2xy + 0.5xz + 8yz - 4y^2 - 3.75z^2$

Page 359 Problems A **1. a.** $2x^2 + 9x + 4$ **b.** $6x + 10$ **3.** $t^2 + t - 30$ B **5. a.** $c^3 - 4c$ **b.** $c^2 - 4$
C **7.** $w^2 + 4w - 40 = w^2 - 4$

Pages 361–362 Written Exercises A **1.** $b^2 + 8b + 16$ **3.** $x^2 - 2ax + a^2$ **5.** $9x^2 - 12cx + 4c^2$
7. $x^2 - y^2$ **9.** $9k^2 - q^2$ **11.** $a^2c^2 + 2abc^2 + b^2c^2$ B **13.** $k^4 + 12k^2 + 36$ **15.** $9x^2 - 30xwy + 25w^2y^2$
17. $9 + 6xy^2 + x^2y^4$ **19.** $16m^2 + 80m + 100$ **21.** $9b^2c^2 + 60ab^2c + 100a^2b^2$ **23.** $16m^2 + 56bm + 49b^2$
25. $324 + 72ab + 4a^2b^2$ **27.** $s^2t^4 - 4st^2 + 4$ **29.** $0.16m^4 + 0.72m^2n + 0.81n^2$ C **31.** $4y^6 - 4y^3 + 1$
33. $z^6 - 2x^3z^3 + x^6$ **35.** $0.04 + 0.2m^2 + 0.25m^4$ **37.** $16k^2 - k + \frac{1}{64}$ **39.** $6\frac{1}{4}p^2 - p + \frac{1}{25}$

Page 362 Problems **1.** $9x^2 + 48x + 64$ **3.** 15 cm **5.** 20; 21 **7.** 35; 36

Pages 366–367 Written Exercises A **1.** $\frac{a - b}{bm}$ **3.** $\frac{a - b}{m - b}$ **5.** $\frac{(x + 1)^2}{x^2 + 2x + 1}$ **7.** $\frac{4}{3(a + b^2)}$
9. $a^3b - ab^3 = a^3b - ab^3$ **11.** $40mnx + 32mny = 40mnx + 32mny$
B **13.** $b^2x - 0.25a^2x = b^2x - 0.25a^2x$ **15.** $3x^3 + 2x^2 - 3x - 2 = 3x^3 + 2x^2 - 3x - 2$ C **17.** $4y^7 - 4y^3$
19. $x^3y + x^2y^2 + xy^3$ **21.** $\frac{1}{8}m^3n^2p^3$ **23.** $4.6x^5 + 1.15x^3$ **25.** $\frac{25}{4}n^2 - \frac{1}{9}$ **27.** $3t^3 - 0.2t^2 - 0.05t$
29. $3s^2 - 5s$

Page 370 Written Exercises A **1.** x^4 **3.** $\frac{1}{(rs)^5}$ **5.** $-\frac{1}{2m^5}$ **7.** $\frac{q^2}{5}$ **9.** $\frac{4}{3x^2z}$ **11.** $\frac{5n}{3m}$ **13.** $\frac{2y}{3x}$ **15.** $\frac{2a}{3b^2}$
B **17.** $-\frac{1}{xyz}$ **19.** $\frac{3}{xyz}$ **21.** $\frac{3xy^2}{z}$ **23.** $\frac{10b}{3d}$ **25.** $21x^3y$ **27.** $-2r^4$ **29.** $\frac{2p}{3m^3n}$ C **31.** $\frac{a^2b}{0.9}$ or $\frac{10a^2b}{9}$
33. $\frac{y^4}{0.7x^{10}}$ or $\frac{10y^4}{7x^{10}}$ **35.** $\frac{-8x^{p-q}}{y^{p-q}}$ **37.** $\frac{(-69)^r}{23^r}$ or $(-3)^r$

Pages 372–373 Written Exercises A **1.** $4x - 3$ **3.** $-7b - 4$ **5.** $-6x^2 - 12$ **7.** $-2a^2 - 2a - 3$
9. $y - 2$ **11.** $k + 9a$ **13.** $2q + 9q^2$ **15.** $3 + 4b^2$ **17.** $-3m^3 - 7$ **19.** $2b - 4$ B **21.** $\frac{t^2}{s} + st + \frac{1}{s}$
23. $y^2 - xy + x^2$ **25.** $2t^2 - 8t - 5$ **27.** $s^2 - s + 27$ **29.** $mx + n + ax^2$ **31.** $\frac{4y^3}{x} + \frac{8y^2}{x^2}$

Pages 375–376 Written Exercises A **1.** $x + 3$ **3.** $b - 2$ **5.** $y - 2$ **7.** $m + 5$ **9.** $p + 9$ **11.** $3x + 2$
13. $3c - 3$ B **15.** $a - b$ **17.** $2b - c$ **19.** $s + 2$ **21.** $3t + 3$ **23.** $2a + 1$ **25.** $3b - 1$ **27.** $x + a$
29. $5a - 4b$ C **31.** $y^2 + 2$ **33.** $t + 2$ **35.** $3b - 2$ **37.** $x^2 + 1$

Page 380 Review of Skills **1.** 6: 1, 2, 3, 6; 36: 1, 2, 3, 4, 6, 9, 12, 18, 36; GCF: 6
3. 4: 1, 2, 4; 19: 1, 19; GCF: 1 **5.** 10: 1, 2, 5, 10; 15: 1, 3, 5, 15; GCF: 5
7. 14: 1, 2, 7, 14; 35: 1, 5, 7, 35; GCF: 7 **9.** 7: 1, 7; 28: 1, 2, 4, 7, 14, 28; GCF: 7 **11.** Prime
13. Not Prime **15.** Not Prime **17.** 5 **19.** 2 **21.** 3 **23.** $5 \cdot 11$ **25.** $11 \cdot 11$ **27.** $2 \cdot 2 \cdot 5 \cdot 5$
29. $2 \cdot 2 \cdot 2 \cdot 3 \cdot 5$ **31.** Always **33.** Never

Chapter 14. Products and Factoring

Page 383 Written Exercises A **1.** 1, 5; not possible **3.** 1, 2, 4; $2 \cdot 2$ **5.** 1, 3, 7, 21; $3 \cdot 7$

7. 1, 3, 5, 9, 15, 45; $3 \cdot 3 \cdot 5$ **9.** 1, 2, 4, 8, 16; $2 \cdot 2 \cdot 2 \cdot 2$ **11.** 1, 2, 3, 5, 6, 10, 15, 30; $2 \cdot 3 \cdot 5$ **13.** 5; $2^2 \cdot 3 \cdot 5$ **15.** 5; 5; $2^2 \cdot 5^2$ **17.** 5; $3^2 \cdot 5$ **19.** 47 B **21.** 5^3 **23.** $2^4 \cdot 3^2$ **25.** $2 \cdot 3^3 \cdot 5$ **27.** $2^3 \cdot 5^3$ **29.** $2^3 \cdot 3 \cdot 5$ **31.** $2 \cdot 97$

Pages 385–386 Written Exercises A **1.** $13y$ **3.** $2mn$ **5.** $3c^5$ **7.** $5r^2s^4$ **9.** $-9ab^2c^3$ **11–19.** Answers may vary. Two examples are given for each. **11.** $4 \cdot 4t$; $2 \cdot 8t$ **13.** $2m(6n)$; $(3m)(4n)$ **15.** $-9rs \cdot 2rs$; $-6r \cdot 3rs^2$ **17.** $(-5c)(-d^2)$; $5d \cdot cd$ **19.** $(-x)(3yz)$; $-3z \cdot xy$ **21.** $5ab$: $5 \cdot a \cdot b$; $10ab$: $2 \cdot 5 \cdot a \cdot b$; GCF: $5ab$ **23.** $14m^2n$: $2 \cdot 7 \cdot m \cdot m \cdot n$; $7mn$: $7 \cdot m \cdot n$; GCF: $7mn$ **25.** $18w^2$: $2 \cdot 3 \cdot 3 \cdot w \cdot w$; $-3w$: $-1 \cdot 3 \cdot w$; GCF: $3w$ **27.** 15: $3 \cdot 5$; $3mn$: $3 \cdot m \cdot n$; GCF: 3 B **29.** $6y$ **31.** 5 **33.** b **35.** x C **37.** $7r^2s(1)$; $7r^2s(-4r^2s)$ **39.** $2(2rst)$; $2(-x)$ **41.** $1 \cdot 5s^3$; $1 \cdot rs^2$; $1 \cdot 5r$

Page 388 Written Exercises A **1.** $k^2 + 3$ **3.** $7r + 4$ **5.** $5 - b$ **7.** $2y + 3$ **9.** $5(m - 3)$ **11.** $a(6a + 7)$ **13.** $ab(b - a)$ **15.** $ab(20a + 3b)$ **17.** $xy(9z - 1)$ **19.** $az(z - 12w)$ **21.** $3y(y - 1)$ **23.** $n(50m - 33n)$ **25.** $2m^2 + m - 1$ **27.** $t^2 + 1 - t$ **29.** $3 + 6x^2 - 2x$ B **31.** $x(3x^2 - x + 5)$ **33.** $4(t^2 - 7t + 7)$ **35.** $x(x^2 + x - 1)$ **37.** $2v(3v^2 + 13v + 4)$ **39.** $3m^2(m^2 - 19m + 37)$

Pages 390–391 Written Exercises A **1.** $(3s + t)(r + 4)$ **3.** $(x - w)(y + 3)$ **5.** $(10a + c)(2 + b)$ **7.** $(5 - a)(b + c)$ **9.** $(x^2 - 5)(y + 7)$ **11.** $(2t + r)(s + 4)$ **13.** $(m + r)(n - 3)$ **15.** $(n - t)(m + 3)$ **17.** $(r^2 + t^2)(s - 2)$ B **19.** $(2p - 3r)(q + 5s)$ **21.** $(c - 2)(a + d)$ **23.** $(n^2 - 3)(m + 3)$

Page 393 Written Exercises A **1.** 3; 3 **3.** 1; 1 **5.** 2; 2 **7.** $(z + 2)(z - 2)$ **9.** $(a + 6)(a - 6)$ **11.** $(r + 30)(r - 30)$ **13.** $(3p + 12)(3p - 12)$ **15.** $(t^2 + 10)(t^2 - 10)$ **17.** $(k^2 + 1)(k^2 - 1)$ **19.** $(y + 4)(y - 4)$ **21.** $(mn - 6)(mn + 6)$ **23.** $(8 + r)(8 - r)$ **25.** $(n + m)(n - m)$ **27.** $(y^2 - x^2)(y^2 + x^2)$ B **29.** $5(n + 2)(n - 2)$ **31.** $3(r + s)(r - s)$ **33.** $4(1 + r)(1 - r)$ **35.** $2(mn + 9)(mn - 9)$ **37.** $3(x + 5)(x - 5)$ **39.** $\pi(x + y)(x - y)$ C **41.** $\left(\frac{x}{3} + 1\right)\left(\frac{x}{3} - 1\right)$

Page 395 Written Exercises A **1.** $2x$ **3.** mn **5.** 10 **7.** $6x$ **9.** $2z$ **11.** $6w$ **13.** $4st$ **15.** $c^2 + 4c + 4$ **17.** $k^2 + 10k + 25$ **19.** $9n^2 + 24mn + 16m^2$ **21.** $(p + 1)^2$ **23.** $(t + 5)^2$ **25.** $(m + 2)^2$ **27.** $(10 + x)^2$ **29.** $(y + 8)^2$ **31.** $(z + 15)^2$ **33.** $(4c + 3)^2$ B **35.** $(mn + 1)^2$ **37.** $(k + 8t)^2$ **39.** $(10x + y)^2$ **41.** $(3rs + 5t)^2$ **43.** $(3x + 10y)^2$ C **45.** $(x + \frac{1}{2})^2$

Pages 397–398 Written Exercises A **1.** s^2 **3.** $25y^2$ **5.** 64 **7.** $9x^2$ **9.** $100k^2$ **11.** x^2y^2 **13.** $z \cdot z$; $-z(-z)$ **15.** $w \cdot w$; $-w(-w)$ **17.** $5y \cdot 5y$; $-5y(-5y)$ **19.** $xy \cdot xy$; $-xy(-xy)$ **21.** $r^2 - 4r + 4$ **23.** $k^2 - 10k + 25$ **25.** $1 - 2y + y^2$ **27.** $a^2 - 2ab + b^2$ **29.** $4x^2 - 12x + 9$ **31.** $4s^2 - 4sy + y^2$ **33.** $(t - 4)^2$ **35.** $(s - 5)^2$ **37.** $(c - 3)^2$ **39.** $(r - 3)^2$ **41.** $(3k - 1)^2$ **43.** $(x - 7)^2$ B **45.** $(4a - b)^2$ **47.** $(3m - n)^2$ **49.** $(6y - 3z)^2$ C **51.** $3(n - 1)(n - 1)$ **53.** $2(m - 5)(m - 5)$ **55.** $(k - \frac{1}{2})(k - \frac{1}{2})$

Page 400 Written Exercises A **1.** 2; 4 **3.** 8; 2 **5.** 12; 2 **7.** 4; 10 **9.** 8; 3 **11.** $(n + 2)(n + 1)$ **13.** $(k - 3)(k - 2)$ **15.** $(x - 5)(x - 4)$ **17.** $(t - 12)(t - 2)$ **19.** $(z - 4)(z - 3)$ **21.** $(c + 8)(c + 3)$ B **23.** $(r + 5s)(r + 4s)$ **25.** $(m + 5n)(m + 3n)$ **27.** $(8 - x)(2 - x)$ **29.** $(4 + q)(1 + q)$ C **31.** $(b - 10)(b - 2)$ **33.** $(m - 4)(m - 2)$

Page 402 Written Exercises A **1.** 9; 2 **3.** 6; 7 **5.** 9; 7 **7.** 5; 8 **9.** 11; 4 **11.** $(t + 9)(t - 7)$ **13.** $(r + 11)(r - 2)$ **15.** $(s - 3)(s + 2)$ **17.** $(c - 8)(c + 7)$ **19.** $(n - 15)(n + 3)$ **21.** $(w + 8)(w - 6)$ **23.** $(b + 9)(b - 4)$ **25.** $(x + 8)(x - 5)$ **27.** $(b + 17)(b - 1)$ B **29.** $(y + 23x)(y - x)$ **31.** $(r + 50a)(r - 2a)$ **33.** $(yz - 19)(yz + 3)$ **35.** $(a - 18c)(a + 4c)$ **37.** $(x + 13y)(x - 5y)$ **39.** $(b + 19c)(b - 2c)$ C **41.** $(x + 19y)(x - 3y)$ **43.** $(z + 10)(z - 5)$ **45.** $(b + 12a)(b - 2a)$

Pages 406–409 Cumulative Review **1.** 7 **3.** -13

5. -2

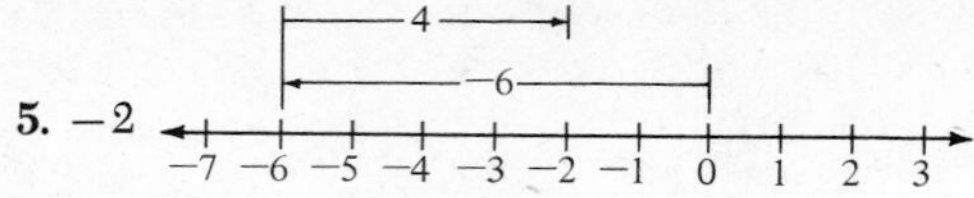

7. $>$ **9.** $>$ **11.** {the directed numbers < 3}

13 {the directed numbers > 0.5} **15.** 0 **17.** -9 **19.** 7

21. -12 **23.** 4; Add. Prop. of Opp. **25.** 5; Comm. Prop. **27.** 18 **29.** 3.4 **31.** 2; 3; 4 **33.** -44
35. -3 **37.** -36 **39.** 8 **41.** $-\frac{1}{2}$ **43.** -8 **45.** $-\frac{1}{10}$ **47.** -12 **49.** 2

51. $w < -3$

53. $s \geq -10$

55. Trinomial **57.** $x^2 + 2x + 2$ **59.** $-x^6 + 4x^4 + 2$ **61.** $3t - 4$ **63.** $2k + 1$ **65.** $2k + 5c$
67. $b^2 + 2b - 1$ **69.** $-6t + 1$ **71.** $11t^2 - 4t - 2$ **73.** $4x^2 - 24$ **75.** -20 **77.** -3 **79.** $12q^3$ **81.** $6t^4x^2$
83. $9y^4$ **85.** $-t^4 + 2t^3 + t$ **87.** $2r^2 + 2r - 12$ **89.** $4y^2 + 8y + 4$ **91.** $t^2 - 9$ **93.** $49a^2 - 1$
95. $3a + 5$ **97.** $\frac{ab}{2} - 1 + \frac{1}{b}$ **99.** $x + z$ **101.** $2^3 \cdot 3^2$ **103.** $2 \cdot 5 \cdot 11$ **105.** $2 \cdot 7 \cdot 3^2$ **107.** $2ab$ **109.** $7x$
111. $13(3k^4 + k - 1)$ **113.** $(2 + r)(t + s)$ **115.** $(5 + b)(5 - b)$ **117.** $(2t - 3)(2t - 3)$
119. $(x + 6)(x + 5)$ **121.** $(x - 11)(x - 2)$ **123.** $(x - 7)(x + 5)$ **125.** $(x - 8)(x + 3)$

Extra Practice Exercises

Page 410 **1.** 22 **3.** 24 **5.** 10 **7.** 8 **9.** 14 **11.** 55 **13.** 5 **15.** 8 **17.** 24 **19.** 72 **21.** 65 **23.** 0 **25.** 48
27. 20 **29.** 2 **31.** 8 **33.** 60 **35.** 6 **37.** 19 **39.** 18 **41.** 12 **43.** 30 **45.** 15 **47.** 32 **49.** 16 **51.** 31 **53.** 0
55. 8 **57.** 35 **59.** 8

Page 411 **1.** 4 **3.** 6 **5.** 7 **7.** 3 **9.** 6 **11.** 13 **13.** 3 **15.** 4 **17.** 10 **19.** 333 **21.** 7 **23.** 14 **25.** 120
27. 45 **29.** $\frac{1}{5}$ **31.** $\frac{1}{2}$ **33.** $\frac{1}{4}$ **35.** $\frac{5}{4}$ or $1\frac{1}{4}$ **37.** $\frac{7}{16}$ **39.** $\frac{3}{4}$ **41.** $\frac{3}{7}$ **43.** 4 **45.** 1 **47.** 1 **49.** 28 **51.** 1

Page 412 **1.** 0.5 **3.** 0.57 **5.** 0.6 **7.** 0.5 **9.** 0.9 **11.** 0.625 **13.** 0.16 **15.** 0.18 **17.** $\frac{1}{5}$ **19.** $1\frac{4}{5}$ **21.** $\frac{3}{8}$
23. $2\frac{4}{25}$ **25.** $3\frac{1}{8}$ **27.** $1\frac{1}{100}$ **29.** 0.45; 45% **31.** 0.3; 30% **33.** 1; 100% **35.** 0.125; 12.5% **37.** 0.50; 50%
39. 0.6; 60% **41.** 0.32; 32% **43.** 0.52; 52% **45.** $\frac{4}{25}$ **47.** $\frac{6}{25}$ **49.** $\frac{9}{25}$ **51.** $\frac{9}{20}$ **53.** $\frac{3}{25}$ **55.** $\frac{63}{200}$ **57.** $1\frac{1}{5}$ **59.** $\frac{81}{125}$
61. $4\frac{1}{5}$

Page 413 **1.** $\frac{5}{7}$ **3.** $\frac{2}{3}$ **5.** $\frac{3}{4}$ **7.** $\frac{2}{3}$ **9.** $\frac{7}{16}$ **11.** $9\frac{1}{3}$ **13.** $\frac{1}{4}$ **15.** 3 **17.** $5\frac{5}{6}$ **19.** $4\frac{1}{2}$ **21.** $\frac{3}{14}$ **23.** $2\frac{7}{18}$ **25.** $7\frac{2}{3}$
27. $\frac{4}{5}$ **29.** $6\frac{16}{21}$ **31.** $1\frac{1}{3}$ **33.** $5\frac{1}{2}$ **35.** $\frac{1}{12}$ **37.** $\frac{1}{2}$ **39.** $\frac{5}{12}$ **41.** $\frac{5}{12}$ **43.** $\frac{5}{9}$ **45.** $\frac{2}{3}$

Page 414 **1.** $\frac{1}{12}$ **3.** $\frac{1}{12}$ **5.** $\frac{1}{5}$ **7.** $\frac{2}{27}$ **9.** 1 **11.** 4 **13.** $\frac{1}{2}$ **15.** $2\frac{3}{4}$ **17.** $1\frac{1}{8}$ **19.** 3 **21.** $7\frac{1}{3}$ **23.** 1 **25.** $\frac{1}{4}$ **27.** $1\frac{1}{2}$
29. $\frac{5}{6}$ **31.** $\frac{23}{42}$ **33.** $\frac{1}{6}$ **35.** $\frac{2}{15}$ **37.** $1\frac{1}{9}$ **39.** $\frac{1}{2}$ **41.** $3\frac{1}{3}$ **43.** $\frac{3}{4}$ **45.** $\frac{2}{3}$

Page 415 **1.** 4.372 **3.** 3.338 **5.** 3.496 **7.** 3.01 **9.** 11.958 **11.** 25.73 **13.** 151.14 **15.** 11.23 **17.** 63.121
19. 5.42 **21.** 0.035 **23.** 0.4424 **25.** 21.19 **27.** 0.43216 **29.** 0.26 **31.** 2.875 **33.** $167.72 **35.** $6.35
37. 0.2736 **39.** 1.5

Page 416 **1.** 96 **3.** 0.052 **5.** 33.61 **7.** 6 **9.** 3 **11.** 250 **13.** $4\frac{2}{3}$ **15.** 86.382 **17.** 13.652 **19.** 8 **21.** {2}
23. {1.28} **25.** {4} **27.** $\{\frac{1}{2}\}$ **29.** {2} **31.** {4}

Page 417 **1.** $11 = 11$ **3.** $5.02 = 5.02$ **5.** $2 = 2$ **7.** $1.5 = 1.5$ **9.** m **11.** s **13.** h **15.** $2 = 2$ **17.** $100 = 100$ **19.** $45 = 45$ **21.** $28 = 28$ **23.** $2 = 2$ **25.** 9 **27.** 36 **29.** 6 **31.** 128 **33.** 6

Page 418 **1.** 23.56 cm^2 **3.** 196 cm^2 **5.** 154 mm^2 **7.** 24.16 m **9.** 242 cm **11.** 0.2 m^2 **13.** 63 cm **15.** 13 cm **17.** 30 mm

Page 419 **1.** 0, true; 1, true; 3, true; 5, false **3.** 2, false; 4, true; 7, true **5.** 4, false; 8, false; 30, true **7.** 0, true; 4, true; 7, false; 8, false **9.** 0, false; $\frac{1}{2}$, false; $\frac{1}{5}$, false; 2, true **11.** 2, false; 4, true; 6, true **13.** 7, true; 16, true; 17, false **15.** 2, false; 7, true; 10, true; 12, true **17.** 0, false; 7, false; 8, true; 10, true **19.** 0, false; $\frac{1}{5}$, false; $\frac{1}{2}$, true; $\frac{4}{5}$, true **21.** $24r$ **23.** $14 - 12m$ **25.** $14vw + 28$ **27.** $4s$ **29.** $5x + 10$ **31.** $7a + 27 + 26c$ **33.** $8p$ **35.** $3z + 14y$ **37.** $36qr + 2st$ **39.** $68w + 34$ **41.** $8f$

Page 420 **1.** Subtract 7; $m = 8$ **3.** Add 4; $s = 20$ **5.** Add 1; $x = 1\frac{7}{8}$ **7.** Subtract $\frac{2}{7}$; $k = \frac{2}{7}$ **9.** 16.9 **11.** 29 **13.** 579 **15.** 54 **17.** 26 **19.** 5 **21.** 14 **23.** 32 **25.** 0.05 **27.** 12 **29.** 4 **31.** 6 **33.** 5 **35.** 4.1 **37.** 81 **39.** 0.4 **41.** 2.4 **43.** 2016 **45.** 5.04

Page 421 **1.** 6 **3.** 0.52 **5.** Teresa: 172 cm, Brandon: 165 cm **7.** Mia: $3\frac{1}{2}$ hours, Jon: $4\frac{1}{2}$ hours **9.** 8, 10, 12 **11.** 42 **13.** 3 **15.** Width: 4 cm, length: 17 cm **17.** 15 dimes

Page 422 **1.** -12 **3.** -22 **5.** -25 **7.** 4 **9.** $-\frac{1}{12}$ **11.** -13 **13.** 5.25 **15.** -19 **17.** $3\frac{3}{8}$ **19.** 3 **21.** -8 **23.** 7 **25.** 19 **27.** -12 **29.** 12 **31.** -2 **33.** 33 **35.** 28 **37.** 83 **39.** -9 **41.** $1\frac{2}{3}$ **43.** 48 **45.** 8 **47.** 64 **49.** 2.21

Page 423 **1.** -36 **3.** -54 **5.** -0.495 **7.** -14 **9.** 24 **11.** -19.6 **13.** -3 **15.** -1.97 **17.** 1.05 **19.** $-2\frac{2}{3}$ **21.** -27 **23.** -21 **25.** -30 **27.** 16 **29.** 0 **31.** $\frac{1}{16}$ **33.** $-\frac{4}{105}$ **35.** -75 **37.** -108 **39.** 0 **41.** 16 **43.** -10 **45.** -8 **47.** $-\frac{3}{4}$ **49.** -64 **51.** 0

Page 424 **1.** $x - 12y$ **3.** $2ab - 4c$ **5.** $18m + 6p$ **7.** $4w - 3u - 3$ **9.** $6d + 24$ **11.** $4r^2 + 4$ **13.** $\dfrac{h}{2} - \dfrac{j}{7}$ **15.** $2d + 4f$ **17.** $24 - 19w$ **19.** $a + 4b$ **21.** -8 **23.** -16 **25.** -20 **27.** 4 **29.** -5 **31.** 7 **33.** -6 **35.** $-\frac{3}{4}$ **37.** $-\frac{5}{3}$ **39.** $-\frac{3}{2}$ **41.** -2 **43.** -4

Page 425 **1.** 5 **3.** -17 **5.** 1 **7.** -4 **9.** $\frac{1}{2}$ **11.** 1.26 **13.** -55 **15.** 9 **17.** 18 **19.** 6.09 **21.** $-\frac{11}{4}$ **23.** 16 **25.** 2 **27.** 9.1 **29.** 11 **31.** $\frac{1}{3}$ **33.** -9 **35.** 16 **37.** -21 **39.** 8

Page 426 **1.** 1.5 m **3.** \$196 **5.** $1\frac{1}{2}$ years **7.** 336 cm^3 **9.** 504.7 m^2 **11.** 2.7 cm^2 **13.** 4 cm

Page 427 **1.** $11s + 16$ **3.** $9x^2 + 23z + 4$ **5.** $-2h^3 + 12k^2 - 8$ **7.** $2a + 2c$ **9.** $8.5y - 5.7x + 7.1$ **11.** $3s^2 + 4s - 2$ **13.** $8f - 6q^2$ **15.** $-25p + 7q^2$ **17.** $40t + w^2 - 27$ **19.** $22 - 8p$ **21.** $11a - 5b$ **23.** $14f - 19$

Page 428 **1.** 7 **3.** 10 **5.** 2 **7.** 6 **9.** 8 **11.** 7 **13.** -6 **15.** -0.8 **17.** -4 **19.** 16 **21.** $(x + 3)^3$ **23.** $-98z^5$ **25.** $3f^3$ **27.** b^8 **29.** $144p^3$ **31.** $14x^2y^2z$ **33.** $-6j^3$ **35.** $-56y$ **37.** $4f^2q^6$ **39.** $-8s^6t^3$ **41.** $-72h^5i^6$ **43.** $\frac{2}{21}p^2r^2$ **45.** $64s^3t^3$ **47.** $18a^4b^6c$ **49.** $-\frac{5}{6}c^4d^6$ **51.** e^{20} **53.** $c^{13}d^8 + 5c^3d^3$

Page 429 **1.** $7ef + 5f^2$ **3.** $40mn^2 + 100m^3n^5 - 120m^4n^7$ **5.** $-\frac{1}{2}u^3v$ **7.** $4c^3d^2 + 56cd$ **9.** $a^2 + 2ab + b^2$ **11.** $12 + 45n + 42n^2$ **13.** $14.8 - 2.88t - 3.6t^2$ **15.** $25f^2 - 81$ **17.** $f^2 + 12f + 36$ **19.** $e^2g^2 + 2e^2gh + e^2h^2$ **21.** $81s^2 - \frac{4}{25}t^2$ **23.** $z^2 + 6yz + 9y^2$ **25.** $36 - 4j^2$ **27.** t^2 **29.** $-\dfrac{1}{3m}$ **31.** $-\dfrac{8y^4}{x}$ **33.** $-\dfrac{8f^2g^2}{e}$ **35.** $-\dfrac{a^5b^4c}{7}$ **37.** $\dfrac{1.2s^3t^2}{r^2}$ **39.** $\dfrac{j^4}{8i^3}$ **41.** $\dfrac{3x^4}{2}$

Answers to Self-Tests

Chapter 1

Page 13 **1.** 14 **2.** 2 **3.** False **4.** True **5.** 8 **6.** 4 **7.** 20 **8.** 12

Page 25 **1.** The product of three and some number is equal to twenty-one. **2.** $n + 12 = 48$ **3.** 24 **4.** 11 **5.** 11 **6.** 3 **7.** 4 **8.** 3

Chapter 2

Page 39 **1.** 794, 795, 796, 797 **2.** 0; 5; 1; 9; 7 **3.** $^{-}1$, $^{+}1$; $^{-}4$, $^{+}4$; $^{+}2$, $^{-}2$; $^{+}4$, $^{-}4$; $^{-}2$, $^{+}2$ **4.** $^{-}8$, $^{-}7$, $^{-}6$ **5.** $\{^{-}1, 0, ^{+}1, ^{+}2\}$ **6.** {the integers between $^{+}2$ and $^{+}7$}

Page 50 **1.** $^{-}\frac{3}{4}$; $^{+}3\frac{1}{4}$; $^{+}2\frac{1}{4}$; $^{+}1\frac{1}{2}$; $^{-}2$ **2.** $<$ **3.** $^{-}5$, $^{-}2\frac{3}{4}$, $^{+}\frac{1}{2}$, $^{+}\frac{9}{10}$, $^{+}1$ **4.** **5.** $^{-}3$, $^{+}3$; $^{+}1$, $^{-}2$; $^{+}2$, $^{+}2$; $^{-}1$, $^{-}2$ **6.**

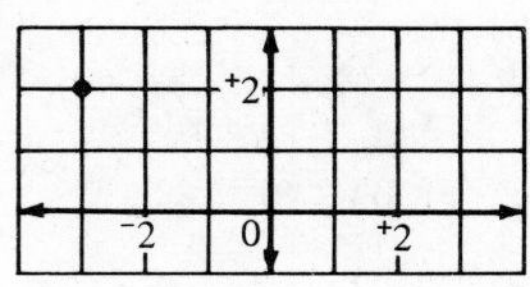

Chapter 3

Page 64 **1.** $r = 7$, $s = 14$, $t = 21$; {7, 14, 21, . . .} **2.** $d = 3$, $e = 6$, $f = 9$; {3, 6, 9, . . .} **3.** 77 **4.** {1, 2, 5, 10} **5.** {1, 3}; 3 **6.** $18 = 2 \times 9$ **7.** $15 = (2 \times 7) + 1$

Page 77 **1.** $x = 30$ **2.** $\frac{2}{23}$ **3.** $\frac{4}{7}$ **4.** seven eighths; 0.875 **5.** $2.06 = 2.060 = 2.0600$ **6.** $0.4 = 40\%$ **7.** $0.20 = 20\%$

Page 80 **1.** 5 m 90 cm **2.** 0.87 m **3.** 3 cm 9 mm **4.** 72.0 cm

Chapter 4

Page 99 **1.** $\frac{1}{2}$ **2.** $\frac{9}{10}$ **3.** $\frac{6}{55}$ **4.** $\frac{12}{7}$ **5.** 10.842 **6.** \$7.81 **7.** 9.541 **8.** 34.52 **9.** 6

Page 114 **1.** 15 **2.** $3(14) = 42$; $6(7) = 42$ **3.** 28 **4.** $2s$, s, 2 **5.** $6xy$ **6.** (1, 8), (2, 9), (3, 10), (4, 11), (5, 12), (6, 13) **7.**

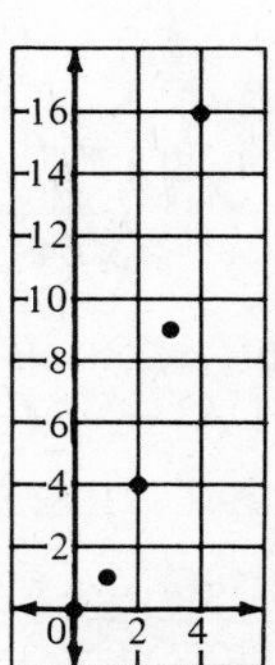

Chapter 5

Page 133 **1.** $k + 2 < 14$ **2.** $r \cdot 7 > 5$
3. Answers may vary. Example: The product of 3 and m is greater than 1.
4. Answers may vary. Example: 4 multiplied by n minus 3 is less than 10. **5.** {8} **6.** {5} **7.** $x = 4.5$
8. $y = 10$ **9.** $r = 12$ **10.** $s = 8$

Page 139 **1.** $4k - 1.3$ **2.** $m - 7$, $m + 7$ **3.** $P = 2l + 2w$; 46 cm **4.** $A = s^2$; 56.25 m

Pages 148–149 **1.** True; True; False **2.** 0 1 2 3 4 5 6 7 8 9 10 **3.** False; False; True
4. $^-5$ $^-4$ $^-3$ $^-2$ $^-1$ 0 1 2 3 4 5 **5.** $8l \leq 120$; {the numbers of arithmetic ≤ 15}
6. $7 + 2n < 19$; {the numbers of arithmetic < 6}

Chapter 6

Page 160 **1.** $6 + x$ **2.** $m(n + 3)$ **3.** $9 = 4 + a$ **4.** $z = x^2 \cdot 6$ **5.** $3 - k = m \cdot 5$ **6.** $k + 3 = m$
7. Closed under addition and subtraction; not closed under subtraction and division
8. Closed under multiplication and division; not closed under addition and subtraction **9.** 13; 21; 30
10. $\frac{1}{2}$; $\frac{2}{5}$; $\frac{1}{15}$

Page 172 **1.** Commutative property of multiplication **2.** Commutative property of addition
3. Commutative property of multiplication **4.** Associative property of multiplication
5. Distributive property **6.** Distributive property **7.** 1264 **8.** 534 **9.** 244 **10.** 123

Page 178 **1.** 0 **2.** Every number is a solution. **3.** No solution
4. Every number except 0 is a solution. **5.** $\{(0, 3), (\frac{1}{2}, 3\frac{1}{2}), (1, 4), (1\frac{1}{2}, 4\frac{1}{2})\}$
6. $\{(2, 0), (3, 1), (4, 2)\}$

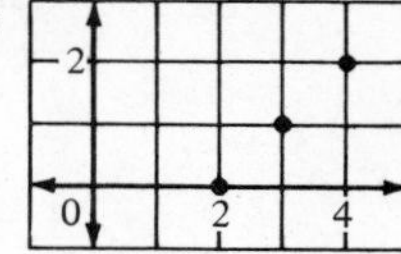

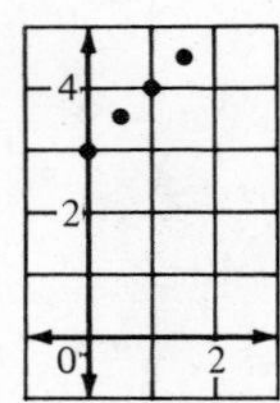

Chapter 7

Page 193 **1.** $7a$ **2.** $r + 2s$ **3.** $4t + 5$ **4.** $4mn + 4m$ **5.** 25 **6.** 8.3 **7.** 8 **8.** 0.9 **9.** 15 **10.** 1.6

Page 203 **1.** 2 **2.** 1.6 **3.** 8 **4.** 8 **5.** 16 **6.** 11 **7.** 37, 39 **8.** 8 **9.** 3 **10.** 8 **11.** 12

Chapter 8

Page 224 **1.** 2 **2.** $^-5$ **3.** 3 **4.** $^-5$

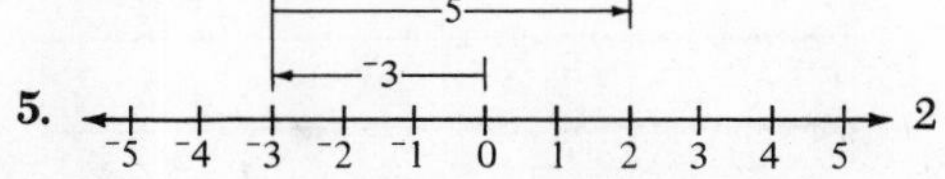

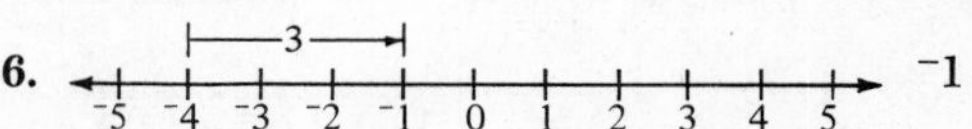

7. Right; > **8.** Right; > **9.** True **10.** False **11.** False

Page 231 **1.** {1} **2.** {$^-1$, 0, 1} **3.** {$^-1$, 0, 1} **4.** {$^-1$, 0, 1}
5. {the directed numbers < 2}
6. {the directed numbers > 1}
7. {$^-3$ and the directed numbers > $^-3$}
8. {the directed numbers between $^-2$ and $^-1$}

Chapter 9

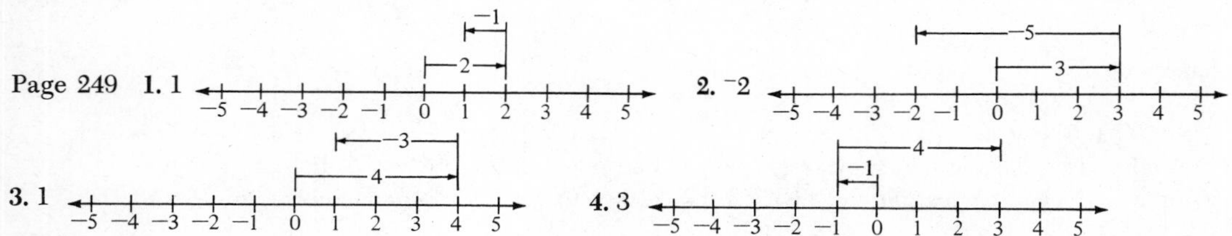

5. Negative five; $^-5$ **6.** The opposite of negative 6; 6 **7.** 0 **8.** 0 **9.** $^-7$ **10.** 4 **11.** -9 **12.** -7 **13.** 3
14. -5 **15.** Additive property of inverses **16.** Associative property
17. Property of the opposite of a sum **18.** Commutative property

Page 258 **1.** 5 **2.** -2 **3.** -9 **4.** 1 **5.** 32 **6.** 9 **7.** 20 **8.** 10 **9.** {(3, 1), (2, 0), (-2, -4), (0, -2)}
10. {(4, 0), (3, -1), (-1, -5), (4, 0)}

Chapter 10

Page 275 **1.** -12 **2.** -40 **3.** 0 **4.** 1 **5.** -10 **6.** -2 **7.** Commutative property
8. Commutative property **9.** Distributive property **10.** Positive; 24 **11.** Negative; -120
12. $-4(-6) + (-4)2$; $16 = 16$ **13.** $-8(-9) + (-8)(-14)$; $184 = 184$ **14.** $-8m + 4n$ **15.** $-21k + 2$

Pages 286–287 **1.** -9 **2.** 3 **3.** -4 **4.** $\frac{7}{3}$ **5.** 1 **6.** 49 **7.** -24 **8.** $-\frac{16}{9}$ **9.** -9 **10.** 8 **11.** 7 **12.** -2
13. {(0, 0), (-4, 2), (4, -2), (-5, $\frac{5}{2}$)}

Chapter 11

Page 304 **1.** 5 **2.** -5 **3.** -5 **4.** -3 **5.** $-\frac{1}{2}$ **6.** 4 **7.** $6\frac{1}{2}$ meters **8.** 11 meters

Page 311
1. $x > 3$
2. $t \leq -1$
3. $-3 \leq t$
4. $m < 3$

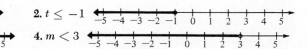

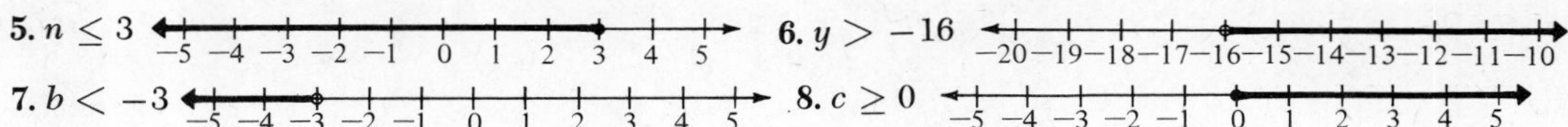

Chapter 12

Page 329 **1.** Binomial **2.** Binomial **3.** Trinomial **4.** Monomial **5.** $9x^2 + 2x + 5$ **6.** $m^3 + m^2 + 2$ **7.** $x^2y + xy^2 + 1$ or $xy^2 + x^2y + 1$ **8.** $y^5 + 2y + 1$ **9.** 4 **10.** -4 **11.** $12a - 9$ **12.** $5a^2 + ab + b^2$ **13.** Associative property **14.** Commutative property

Page 336 **1.** 0 **2.** $7x^2 - 1$ **3.** $2y^3 + 3y^2 - y$ **4.** $-z^3 - 11z$ **5.** $6m - 1$ **6.** $t + 3$ **7.** $-2x^2 - 2x$ **8.** $n^2 + 13$

Page 340 **1.** $9ab - 1$ **2.** $16x + 8$ **3.** $2x^2 - 9$ **4.** 4 **5.** 6 **6.** 3 **7.** 3

Chapter 13

Page 355 **1.** $-10x^3$ **2.** $-3n^3$ **3.** 4^5 **4.** z^{11} **5.** $-6t^3s^3$ **6.** $-8m^3n$ **7.** $8x^3y^3$ **8.** a^4 **9.** 256 **10.** 729 **11.** $-3x^3 - x^2 + 5x$ **12.** $4a^2 + 12ab + b^2$

Page 367 **1.** $b^2 - b - 6$ **2.** $n^2 - 4n - 5$ **3.** $6t^2 + 19t - 7$ **4.** $4x^3 + 5x^2 + 3x + 2$ **5.** $n^2 - 8n + 16$ **6.** $4b^2 + 24b + 36$ **7.** $n^2 - 16$ **8.** $4b^2 - 36$
9. Distributive property; associative property; commutative property; Reciprocal Property

Page 376 **1.** x^4 **2.** $2n^2$ **3.** $-\frac{3}{zx^2}$ **4.** $\frac{5}{x}$ **5.** $2z + 4$ **6.** $3b - \frac{6}{b}$ **7.** $-4n + 2$ **8.** $c + d$ **9.** $m + 3$ **10.** $2n - 5$

Chapter 14

Page 391 **1.** 2^3 **2.** $2 \cdot 3^2$ **3.** $2 \cdot 3 \cdot 7$ **4.** $5 \cdot 7 \cdot m \cdot n$ **5.** $-2 \cdot 2 \cdot 3 \cdot x \cdot x \cdot y$ **6.** $2 \cdot 5 \cdot a \cdot a \cdot b \cdot b \cdot b$ **7.** $4ab$ **8.** $3xy$ **9.** $w^2 + 2$ **10.** $4 - x$ **11.** $(x + y)(2 + x)$ **12.** $(4n + m)(m - 2)$

Page 403 **1.** $(b + 3)(b - 3)$ **2.** $(x + 5)(x - 5)$ **3.** $(z + 5)(z + 5)$ **4.** $(y + 2)(y + 2)$ **5.** $(x - 6)(x - 6)$ **6.** $(m - 9)(m - 9)$ **7.** $(x + 3)(x + 2)$ **8.** $(n - 7)(n - 2)$ **9.** $(c + 4)(c - 2)$ **10.** $(c - 4)(c + 2)$